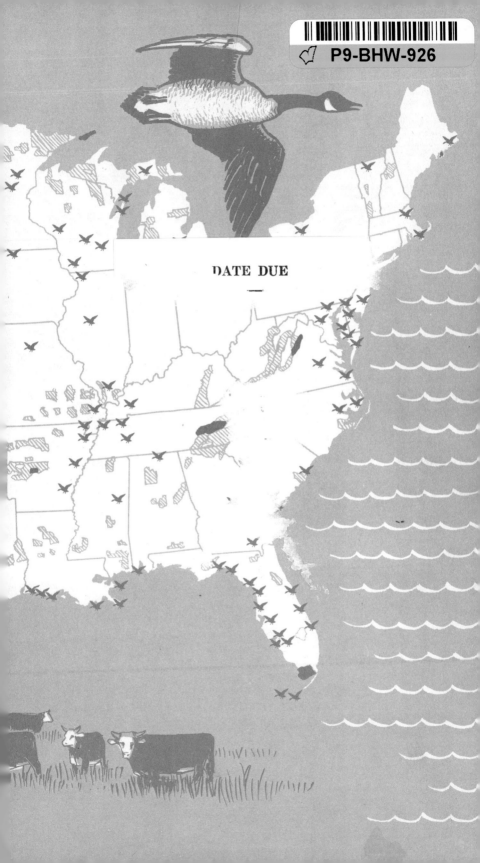

DATE DUE

85TH CONGRESS, 2D SESSION, HOUSE DOCUMENT NO. 280

The

Yearbook of

Agriculture

1958

THE UNITED STATES

GOVERNMENT PRINTING OFFICE

LAND

the yearbook of agriculture 1958

THE UNITED STATES DEPARTMENT

OF AGRICULTURE, WASHINGTON, D. C.

A foreword by the Secretary of Agriculture.

Science has ushered in the Atomic and Space Age. Man has launched satellites and is now planning with a degree of confidence on reaching the moon. These thoughts and plans stir us. They are an index of the strength of human aspirations, imagination, and genius.

But with all our Space Age planning, we still live close to the land. Many of us make our living from it. Many others derive pleasure from the recreation that the forests, fields, and streams afford. For each of us the land provides living space and is the source of our food, clothing, and housing.

Land, indeed, is part and parcel of our growth as a Nation—of our history and our national attitudes toward freedom and democracy. Ours is a choice land, blessed of Heaven.

As citizens, then, we should know more about land. We should get a panoramic view of the makeup of our country—cropland, grazing and forest lands, city land, lakes, deserts, and mountains, all of which form the natural resources base of our Nation.

Worthwhile also is the knowledge we gain when we travel the land and see the variations in topography, soil, plant cover, and climate; the ownership and management of land; and the practices of farmers and ranchers. All reflect the forces of environment on man and the patterns of settlement.

From the technical viewpoint, we need to look ahead to the requirements of coming generations for food, fiber, and timber and for urban and rural development.

Such an inventory and projection can tell us what we must do to husband our God-given resources and how we must deal with problems of land use and conservation. It will remind us of the ways in which we have been careless, unaware, and indifferent to our heritage. It will also indicate some accomplishments in the wiser use of our land. Finally, it demonstrates again how much we have for which we must be thankful to the Creator of all.

This book will stimulate thought about our land and its use. It will provide much material for discussion. This is as it should be, for discussion often strikes the spark to ignite inspired thoughts that guide us into a better future. By *Ezra Taft Benson*.

A preface by the

editor. We make a survey in this book of the land Americans have, use, and need. We discuss the land that was here when the colonists came, its importance in our history and growth, the use and management of public and private lands, the income and valuation of land, resources and prospective needs, and emerging problems of ownership and control.

We consider the profound changes these later days have brought, and we try to see what they mean in relation to our land resources: The growth of population and cities; the growth of the size of farms and the decline of the farm population (for land, used by people for people, has meaning only in terms of people); the use of millions of acres for highways, airports, factories, and subdivisions; the expanding number of part-time and residential "farms" of those who want to live two lives in the country and the city; the difficulties of getting started in farming; the need for more group action as the problems exceed the scope of individuals.

A broad subject—one worthy of our best effort; one that demands sharp thinking, deep wisdom, and courage to face up to the Nation's problems. Of the reader it asks the same and is worthy of his close attention, for our future will depend greatly on what we do with our land.

We present no ready program, no easy solution, and no definite policy. That is not our intention or our province; policies and programs are made by the people and their elected representatives. The suggestions presented here are personal, individual ones and are not necessarily those of the Department of Agriculture or any unit of the Government. Because the men who wrote the chapters were given no orders as to what they were to say, there are conflicts and contradictions. That is all to the good, however, because of the nature of the subject, which arouses strong opinions, depending (as one writer says) on whose ox is gored, and because of our purpose, which is to spur us to forward-looking action.

The members of the 1958 Yearbook Committee, which planned the scope and made the outline, are:

Sherman E. Johnson, Agricultural Research Service, Chairman
Ernst H. Wiecking, Agricultural Research Service, Secretary
Joseph Ackerman, Farm Foundation
Carleton P. Barnes, Agricultural Research Service
John B. Bennett, Department of the Interior

Howard E. Conklin, Cornell University
Virgil D. Gilman, Federal Extension Service
Carl P. Heisig, Agricultural Research Service
James M. Hunt, Agricultural Conservation Program Service
H. R. Josephson, Forest Service
Charles E. Kellogg, Soil Conservation Service
Edward F. Mynatt, Office of the General Counsel
Lewis B. Nelson, Agricultural Research Service
Harold E. Pinches, Agricultural Research Service
D. Harper Simms, Soil Conservation Service
Harry A. Steele, Agricultural Research Service
Charles L. Stewart, University of Illinois
John F. Timmons, Iowa State College

To them are due thanks for much hard work and unstinted effort, time, and thought.

If it were our policy to dedicate a Yearbook of Agriculture to an individual, this Yearbook would be dedicated to Charles L. Stewart, professor of agricultural economics in the University of Illinois, for his active interest in this book and this subject and for his devoted, conspicuously successful teaching of others to appreciate its scope and importance. By *Alfred Stefferud*, Office of Information.

Contents:

ix

Some financial aspects

of land use.

Rights, ownership,

and tenure.

Taking care of what

we have.

LAND

Forever the land:
A section of pictures. An account of what
the fathers found; the winning of the West; the growth of
people and the Nation; the development of scientific agriculture;
problems of this later day; what of the future?

The help of Robert B. Branstead of the Soil Conservation Service, Leland J. Prater of the Forest Service, and a committee, headed by Joseph D. Tonkin, of the Federal Extension Service in preparing this section of pictures is gratefully acknowledged.

Among the photographers are Mr. Prater; Mr. Branstead; Lloyd F. Ryan, Bluford W. Muir, J. L. Averell, Daniel O. Todd, J. G. Jack, K. D. Swan, Paul S. Bieler, George S. Griffith, Paul Fair, W. E. Seibel, Fred E. Dunham, William E. Hallen, and Roy M. Filloon, Forest Service; Hermann Postlethwaite and Ed Hunton, Office of Information; B. C. McClean, Gordon Smith, R. J. Wagner, Sam Cole, C. A. Rechenthin, and E. Cole, Soil Conservation Service; and photographers of the State Extension Services and land-grant colleges. The prints are from the Collections of the Library of Congress.

Some of the photographs were made later than the time to which we apply them, but because they typify the time, place, and event, the faults of anachronism and anachorism may not be serious.

Land where my fathers died,
Land of the pilgrim's pride:
Of thee I sing.

These the fathers found: Forests primeval,
boundless, untrod by feudal foot.   [Wisconsin]

In them were fuel for the home fires,
wood for the homes that were coming,
meat for the body, and peace for the soul.   [Michigan]

Clear ran the streams:
Unsullied, pure, and
teeming with bass,
trout, and salmon.
[Washington]

Creeks, swamps, marshes, potholes:
All were part of Nature's design;
each, in its way, a purposeful blessing.   [South Carolina]

Prairies were to the westward,
with grass belly-high to a horse.   [Oklahoma]

Far beyond the world the fathers knew
were mountains, majestic and awesome
and holders of wealth for the future.   [Washington]

The desert, remote and waiting for man to disclose its resources and values of space, beauty, quiet.   [Arizona]

In this land, this diverse, unspoiled land that knew not despot and serfdom, the fathers planted their seed.   [North Carolina]

They built.   When need was, they defended
their homes and their futures.

Some built stately mansions.   [South Carolina]

Many moved westward.   Hope and adventure were stronger than terrors and hardships of trackless expanses.

Before them went scouts and explorers, men who extended frontiers and saw new horizons.   [Hayden Expedition, 1870]

Men lifted their eyes to the hills
for the gold and the wisdom they found there.

EMIGRATION

UP THE MISSISSIPPI RIVER.

The attention of Emigrants and the Public generally, is called to the now rapidly improving

TERRITORY OF MINNESOTA,

Containing a population of 150,000, and goes into the Union as a State during the present year. According to an act of Congress passed last February, the State is munificently endowed with Lands for Public Schools and State Universities, also granting five per cent. on all sales of U. S. Lands for Internal Improvements. On the 3d March, 1857, grants of Land from Congress was made to the leading Trunk Railroads in Minnesota, so that in a short time the trip from New Orleans to any part of the State will be made in from two and a half to three days. The

CITY OF NININGER,

Situated on the Mississippi River, 35 miles below St. Paul, is now a prominent point for a large Commercial Town, being backed by an extensive Agricultural, Grazing and Farming Country; has fine streams in the interior, well adapted for Milling in all its branches; and Manufacturing **WATER POWER** to any extent.

Mr. JOHN NININGER, (a Gentleman of large means, ideas and liberality, speaking the various languages,) is the principal Proprietor of **Nininger**. He laid it out on such principles as to encourage all **MECHANICS**, Merchants, or Professions of all kinds, on the same equality and footing: the consequence is, the place has gone ahead with such rapidity that it is now an established City, and will annually double in population for years to come.

Persons arriving by Ship or otherwise, can be transferred without expense to Steamers going to Saint Louis; or stop at Cairo, and take Railroad to Dunleith (on the Mississippi). Steamboats leave Saint Louis and Dunleith daily for **NININGER**, and make the trip from Dunleith in 36 to 48 hours.

NOTICES.

1. All Railroads and Steamboats giving this card a conspicuous place, or *gratuitous insertion* in their cards, AIDS THE EMIGRANT and forwards their own interest.

2. For authentic documents, reliable information, and all particulars in regard to Occupations, Wages, Preëmpting Lands (in neighborhood), Lumber, Price of Lots, Expenses, &c., apply to

THOMAS B. WINSTON, 27 Camp street, New Orleans.
ROBERT CAMPBELL, St. Louis.
JOSEPH B. FORBES, Dunleith.

The people grew. The Nation grew.

Lanes became roads. The roads became highways.

Railroads linked ocean and ocean.

The winning of the West meant primitive sod huts.

The winning of a new country meant drudgery and hard work.

It meant the few, forgotten comforts from the crossroads store.

For many, who failed to understand that methods of farming in the East would not succeed in the West, it meant poverty.

It meant despair, failure—or a new start, new hope.

Some sought other homes in a kinder place.

But life had its pleasures, too,
like driving to town on Saturday afternoon.

And always there was faith in God, in themselves,
and in the future of their Nation.   [North Carolina]

A new day came to American farming when men of vision
founded State colleges of agriculture [Pennsylvania]

and the countrywide system of county agents,
dedicated men who showed them new methods

and expounded the principles of balanced farming.

Their sons and daughters joined 4–H Clubs.

In the West,
and later
in the East,
they began to
irrigate fields
for larger and
more certain
harvests. [Utah]

The land yielded its bounty of hay,
[Lolo National Forest, Montana]

and pasture, [Idaho]

and corn, [Ohio]

and wheat—and much, much more.   [North Dakota]

Electric power brought conveniences and greater efficiency
to millions of remote farms.

So the fathers conquered a continent
and learned much about land and themselves.   And the sons?
The sons, for quick profits and heedless of sons to come,
cut over and let burn many forests.   [Oregon]

Logging at an end, towns died.   [California]

They let the streams be polluted.   [Ohio]

Silt from denuded watersheds choked reservoirs,
led to floods, and wasted water,
which was becoming more and more precious.   [California]

People plowed land that should be grassland,
and saw how duststorms [Colorado]

could despoil the prairies.   [Oklahoma]

They overgrazed and uncovered the slopes
and paid the price in erosion, [Alabama]

in the forced sales of homes and farms, [Georgia]

and poverty.

Now we are at
a crossroads.
At this moment
in history, when
our population
is growing,
the demand for
many products
of fields and
forest mounts,
and the face
of the land
is changing,
we can choose,
perhaps for the
last time,
what we are
to do with
our land,
our country.
[New York]

We see how cities grow out into farmlands
and orchards.   [California]

We see how highways, airports, factories,
and other developments, however necessary they may be,
take over acres for all time.   [Virginia]

For the future that we can build, we have the
lessons of the past. We have the knowledge, from research
and experience, of how to manage forests and keep them
productive. [Lassen National Forest, California]

We have learned about the need to plant trees
to protect some hillsides and how to do it
and which trees to plant.   [Mississippi]

We have new kinds of grasses
and knowledge of their management.   [Texas]

We have a heightened appreciation of the beauty of our land
and the growing need of people for recreation.
[Ouachita National Forest, Arkansas]

[Pisgah National Forest, North Carolina]

We have learned a good deal about irrigation,
contour tillage, stripcropping, and other improvements
that help prevent erosion. [Idaho]

Farmers, like those in this picture
of a father and his son going over their partnership records,
know more about the economics of farming.

Research is giving us a growing body of
scientific knowledge, of importance to all of us.   [Hawaii]

[Studies of the effect of cutting on water supplies in
Fraser Experimental Forest, Colorado]

[Coweeta Hydrologic Laboratory, Pisgah National Forest, North Carolina]

[National Tillage Machinery Laboratory, Auburn, Alabama]

Our young people
are eager to learn,
confident,
responsive.

Of this land
and these people
I sing:
O beautiful
for spacious skies
And waving fields
of grain
[Wisconsin]

Their purple mountains' majesty
Above the fruited plain.
[Mt. Baker National Forest, Washington]

Our heritage
of land —Land and the growth of the Nation—Our wealth
of land resources—How we acquired our landed estate—Land
and our economic development—The heritage of our public
lands—The uses to which we put our land

Land and the growth of the Nation.

We have two main problems with respect to land: How should it be used? How should rights in land be distributed? Our success in answering them will reflect our success in anticipating the changing conditions of the future. But the voice of the future is heard only feebly over the din of the market place, and the public has a responsibility to speak on behalf of future citizens. By *Walter E. Chryst* and *William C. Pendleton, Jr.*, Farm Economics Research Division.

LAND IS MANY THINGS to many persons—to the farmer, livelihood; to the townsman, space or a place to build his house; to the child, a playground; to the poet, a theme; to the patriot, a symbol.

To the economist, land is the soil under his feet, the materials in that soil, the slope that determines the ease of cultivation, the rain and sunlight that plants need.

To him, land also is the bays and inlets along the coasts; the fall of the streams, which permits the hydraulic generation of electricity; the rivers on which are carried grain and industrial products to the seaports.

It is the deposits of iron ore in Minnesota, the coal in West Virginia, the oil in Texas.

It is the soil and climate that make timber in the Pacific Northwest, corn in Iowa and Illinois, wheat in the Great Plains, cotton in the South, citrus fruits in Florida, pastures in Wisconsin and New York.

Land, in the economic sense, is our entire natural environment—all the forces or the opportunities that exist independently of man's activity.

LAND has much to do with our needs and the way we fulfill them.

Much of our activity we devote to getting the basic items of food, shelter, and clothing; other items—furniture, telephones, automobiles, highways, washing machines, bathtubs, refrigerators, picture windows, soap, newspapers—that make life more comfortable; and items that make life more stimulating—recreation, movies, and radio, concerts, education, books, libraries.

We want many things. It is likely that if we had all that we could list, new wants would arise tomorrow, and again we would be faced with the problem of how to satisfy them.

Four types of resources are available to each generation of Americans.

First, each generation has some legacy of capital goods from previous generations—tools, factories, railroads, canals, buildings, livestock, fences, wells, and so on. Some of them, such as canals and wells, are durable; they may serve for a century with little attention. Others require considerable maintenance and early replacement.

Second, each generation has energy and the ability to do physical labor, to plant, shape, and mold.

Third, each has some ingenuity—to plan, measure, evaluate, and direct.

Fourth, all generations have the natural environment—the fertility of the soil, the iron ore in the mountains, the fall of the rivers, the water of the bays, the deposits of petroleum, and the variations in climate.

Our success in providing a good level of living, educating the young, preserving freedom and liberty, and leaving a physical and cultural legacy for our children depends fundamentally on how well we use the four factors of inherited capital, human energy, ingenuity, and natural resources.

It is not meaningful to discuss which of them is most important.

Some progress in the satisfaction of wants conceivably would be possible without tools inherited from the previous generation. No progress can be made if no labor is applied, if labor is applied without intelligence, or if natural resources with which to work do not exist. Each of these items can limit the goods produced to satisfy wants. In time, however, the restrictive effect of many of these limitations can be lessened: Labor can become skilled; tools can be accumulated; better methods of combining labor, tools, and land can be devised; and land can be utilized more fully. But the area of land, as we think of it here, cannot be increased. Land remains the final restricting factor.

We learn more about the importance of land by looking at the economic development of other countries. Farmers elsewhere have applied their energies with as much diligence as American farmers. Industrial laborers have skills equal to those of American laborers. Inventors in other countries also have developed new, ingenious techniques. In terms of total production, however, the results have not been the same. The difference may be attributed largely to the more generous physical environment in which American economic life is conducted.

The United States has been fortunate in its endowment of natural resources, but this fact is apparent: In terms of what we want, we do not have as much of some types of land as we could use. We do not have, for instance, as much Class I farmland as we could use, or it would not sell for more than 400 dollars an acre in Indiana; not as much petroleum as we could use, or crude oil would not command a price while lying beneath the waters of the Gulf of Mexico; and not as much space as we want, or land on Chicago's Michigan Avenue and New York's Fifth Avenue would not be priced at thousands of dollars a foot.

If we had as much farmland as we could use, it would have no price—like air and sunlight, it would be free for the asking. But land is not free. The value of agricultural land (including buildings) is estimated at 10 times the annual net income of agriculture. We have no satisfactory estimates of the value of nonagricultural land, but it can be expected to exceed the value of farmland severalfold. Most of the types of land that we want are in scarce supply. It is this scarcity that creates the economic problem of land.

MUCH OF OUR LAND can contribute in more than one way to the satisfaction of our wants.

When we approach a familiar city after a year's absence, we now expect to see suburban housing developments on land that may have been farmed for a century.

We observe that old but serviceable buildings are being demolished to permit construction of expressways in Chicago and in Baltimore, turnpikes and interchanges are being built on the fertile farmlands of New Jersey, new railroad sidings and chemical industries are filling valleys in West Virginia and Tennessee, and bottom land is inundated as dams are made so that power can be generated in Arkansas. Ranchers in Oklahoma, Kansas, and Nebraska can use their land to produce wheat or to pasture beef cattle; farmers in Iowa can substitute soybeans for corn; producers in Minnesota can raise oats or flax; and farmers in Georgia can grow cotton or peanuts.

Little of our land is limited to the output of one commodity or service.

If we had unlimited land, we could devote land to every use in such quantity that an additional acre in any use would not increase the output by a single pound, bushel, or kilowatt.

Because we are not that wealthy, we must apportion our limited resources among the different uses in which they may be employed. We must decide whether to use a tract for a homesite or for crops; whether to use a valley to produce corn or to produce electricity; whether to use the Missouri River bottom land between Kansas City, Mo., and Kansas City, Kans., for tomatoes and cabbage or for an airport.

Determining which acreages to employ in each use and whether the land should be used now or later are the basic economic problems that are associated with the use of natural resources.

How can we determine how much land to use for wheat, pasture, homesites, or any other of the services that land can supply? Of the land that can be used to grow wheat or to grow grass for beef—how much should be used for wheat and how much for beef? In order to decide, we must know something of the ability of the land to satisfy wants when it is used for wheat and when it is used for pasture, or its productivity in each use.

To determine the productivity of land, we have to distinguish between physical productivity and economic productivity and between the productivity of the land itself and that of the labor, capital, and other resources combined with it.

Consider an acre of wheatland that yields 30 bushels. Those 30 bushels measure the total physical productivity of all the resources used in producing wheat on that acre.

In order to get the idea of the economic productivity, however, we must make use of an economic measure— the price the wheat will bring when it is sold. If the price is 2 dollars a bushel, the economic productivity of all the inputs used is 60 dollars an acre. But before we can measure the contribution of land to this total, we must make allowance for the costs of labor, gasoline, fertilizer, wear and tear on machinery, and so on. If these other costs amount to 55 dollars an acre, the economic productivity of the acre is 5 dollars.

That is quite different from the 30 bushels we started with, but it is a more useful figure. This 5-dollar measure of productivity takes account of the values consumers place on flour, bread, macaroni, cake mixes, and other products made from wheat, because these valuations have a big part in determining the 2-dollar price of wheat. It also takes into account the efficiency of the grower, as reflected in his choice of machinery, seeding rates, amount of fertilizer, and so on. Finally it takes into account the amounts and costs of the resources that must be combined with land in the production of wheat.

We need a figure like this if we are to use our land resources most effectively. The farmer needs it when he decides to sow his land to wheat or when he decides to buy or sell land. The economist needs it when he tries to appraise patterns of land use. The legislator needs it when he works on farm programs and legislation that affect land use. They need it because an efficient use of land can be achieved only through comparisons of the economic productivity of land in its various uses.

If this particular acre would yield a net return of 6 dollars when it is devoted to the production of beef, it should be grazed, rather than planted to wheat. Likewise, when hilly, eroded land would yield 2 dollars' worth of timber an acre a year, as compared to the dollar it yields in farming, a shift to trees is indicated. The same forces operate when highly productive dairy farms in New York are sold to builders because the economic productivity of the land as building lots is higher than when it is producing butter, milk, and cream.

The general principle is this: Each acre should be devoted to the use in which its economic productivity is highest. Only by allocating land (or any other resource) according to productivity can we expect it to reach its highest efficiency in the satisfying of our wants.

ANOTHER PRINCIPLE of land use that is implicit in the examples we have given is that all land with any economic productivity should be used. The validity of this principle is clearer when we observe that a given output may be obtained from several different combinations of land, labor, and capital. Let us say, for example, that 1 million bushels of wheat can be obtained from 70 thousand acres of land, 200 man-years of labor, and 500 thousand dollars' worth of equipment, seed, and fertilizer. Let us say also that 1 million bushels of wheat could be had from 100 thousand acres of land, 150 man-years of labor, and 400 thousand dollars' worth of equipment, seed, and fertilizer. In this example, 30 thousand acres can be substituted to some degree for 50 man-years of labor and 100 thousand dollars in capital.

The implication of this principle is clear—to the extent that land can be used to free labor and capital for other types of production, land should be used. The failure to use land (when it is available) as a substitute for labor and capital results in a waste of human energy and the tools of production or in an output of the national economy that is less than the one that might be achieved if all resources were used.

The allocation of land and other resources is accomplished in an enterprise system such as ours largely in response to changes in relative prices—prices of the products and services the land can help produce, prices of the resources combined with the land, and the price of land itself.

When the price of beef goes up relative to the price of wheat, for example, some farmers who have a choice will shift into beef. When the wages of hired labor rise rapidly, the signal is given to farmers to mechanize. When paper companies can offer 30 dollars an acre for land that is worth no more

than 20 dollars to farmers, a shift is indicated. Many other examples might be listed to underscore the principle: Relative prices and changes in relative prices are major factors in our decisions as to the use of land.

The responsibility for the decisions rests mostly with individual citizens.

The decisions involve a tremendous number of possibilities, for there are dozens of basic types of land and millions of farms. If only three decisions as to the use of land were made on each farm, more than 10 million decisions that affect land use would have to be made in agriculture each year.

The framework of the decisions is a tenure system which is based on the principle of private property and through which the control of the various tracts of land and their earnings are identified with individuals.

THUS THE RESPONSIBILITY for the decisions is tied to the consequences of the decisions.

If the person in control of land decides to use it to produce the items the consuming public prefers, his income is increased.

If he insists on not using the land or on using it to produce something the public does not want, he can expect little or no income from the land.

If a piece of land has a higher economic productivity in pasture than in wheat, he will be able to claim more of the total output of commodities and services if he devotes the land to pasture.

If the land has a higher economic productivity when it supports three-bedroom houses than when it is in corn or watermelons, the landowner's economic welfare will be improved if he permits the land to be used for building sites.

If he insists on growing watermelons in the center of a big subdivision, he will pay a price in terms of the goods and services that he must forego. The same incentive is applicable for each pair of crops, each pair of business uses, each pair of livestock enterprises—in general, each pair of uses in which land can be employed.

The land-tenure system also determines the distribution of the income the land earns. People receive income, in general, because the resources they control contribute to production.

Some people receive income for the physical or mental work they perform; some from the use of their tools, machines, livestock, and other instruments of production; some from the natural resources they control; and some from various combinations of the three.

The size of a person's income depends on the worth of the resources he contributes; it measures the value society places on the things his labor, land, and capital produce.

Because land can contribute in so many ways to the satisfaction of wants, it earns an income—often extraordinarily high—and therefore ownership of land is instrumental in determining how the output of the national economy is distributed.

If the landownership is unequal, the distribution of income from land is correspondingly unequal. If a policy of encouraging small holdings is followed, the distribution of income presents a different picture.

How much inequality in the distribution of income is desirable and how this distribution affects efficiency in production are questions that have been the subject of debate and public concern for centuries.

Those are questions that we cannot try to answer here. But it is clear that our economic system operates on the assumption that an individual who uses his land to get from it the maximum income uses it as efficiently as possible and that in this way his land makes the largest possible contribution to the output of the economy. Thus individuals, while acting in their own best interests, are assumed to act in the best interests of the public.

BUT THE INTERESTS of the individual are not necessarily the interests of the public, and the mechanism of leaving decisions as to the use of land to the individual does not always result in the use the public wants.

The individual is concerned with how to use his own resources within the span of his lifetime and the lifetime of his immediate heirs. The public is concerned with the use of all resources over a longer period. These differences in expectations and orientation give rise to public intervention in decisions involving the use of land.

The need for public intervention will be observed when it is noted that each landowner uses his land within a much larger physical environment. The cost of cropping practices that increase the rate of runoff in the upper Mississippi Valley, for example, is not borne entirely by those who use those practices; it is borne partly by those downstream whose properties might be flooded by the practices. Similarly, the cost of producing wheat on land susceptible to wind erosion is borne partly by those who must live and work in areas affected by duststorms. The cost of chemical production may not be paid entirely by the producer who dumps his waste into a stream; it is paid partly by the downstream users of water who must install a more elaborate purification mechanism to eliminate the health hazard created by the presence of the waste.

Conversely, the least expensive way of eliminating a flood or erosion hazard on one farm may be to erect a dam on a farm higher up the slope. But the first farmer has no right to use the land of the other for this purpose, and the second has no incentive to provide this protection, as he does not participate in the benefits. Many similar examples might be cited, but it is evident that frequently, when there is an off-site benefit or cost for any land-use activity, there is need for public intervention if all of the land is to be used most effectively.

The foregoing examples pertain to the separation of benefits and costs of land-use practices in space.

A similar situation exists when the benefits and costs of a land-use practice are separated in time. The present landowner gets the benefit of a cropping system that leaves the land impaired in terms of its future ability to produce, but the cost must be borne by later generations, who either must have fewer agricultural products or must substitute labor and capital for the wasted land resource—labor and capital that could be used to produce something else. So, also, the use of timber, coal, oil, gas, or subsurface water can be excessive at one point in time if future needs are not taken properly into account.

The voice of the future is heard only feebly over the din of the market place, and the public has a responsibility to speak on behalf of future citizens.

MANY USES OF LAND are socially desirable, but they cannot be left to individual decision. We need land for parks, playgrounds, roads, streets, airports, schools, hospitals, military encampments, and testing grounds. This land is needed for long periods and may require elaborate structures. Decisions with respect to the use of such land must be made by the public, if long tenures are to be achieved and the facilities are to be located to provide a maximum advantage to the population.

The public also has an interest in developments that are too large or too risky for individuals to attempt or that must be coordinated with other activities. A levee along the Ohio River is economically feasible if the increased productivity resulting from its construction is greater than the expected productivity of the needed labor and capital in any other use.

The variability in income from such a project, however, might place any private group or corporation in too dangerous a financial position, but the public, with its command over large quantities of resources, would be able to absorb the risk.

The public has a greater ability to absorb risks, can command more re-sources, and can wait longer for results than an individual can. When an economically feasible project cannot be handled by an individual or group of individuals because they cannot assemble the resources, cannot stand the risk, or want an early return, the public must act if the best use of our resources is to be achieved.

SUPPLEMENTING these public actions in the interest of more efficient land use are a number of policies that deal with the question of distribution. In general, as a Nation we have favored a policy of widespread distribution of rights in land. This policy has been shown in several ways, such as the sale of the public domain in small tracts at prices within the means of small farmers, recognition of the claims of the small farmer who had "preempted" unregistered public lands, and the 160-acre limitation on homestead lands.

Several measures have been used to insure the position of the family farm in agriculture. The agricultural experiment stations, the State agricultural colleges, and the State extension services have contributed to the development and dissemination of the scientific knowledge needed to keep the family farmer in a competitive position. The Federal Land Bank System and the Farmers Home Administration were established to provide credit on favorable terms to the operators of small farms.

Two basic problems, however, continue to exist with respect to the distribution of the rights to land.

First, means must be devised so that qualified youths, regardless of the circumstances of birth, have opportunity to compete for the use of our natural resources.

Second, tenure must not result in a distribution of income that contributes to economic and political instability.

The first problem must be solved if our resources are to be controlled by the most competent farm operators and used efficiently. Progress has been made toward this end through vocational training and by making necessary credit available.

The second problem rarely has been serious in the United States, largely because of the availability of land during our early history, the more recent developments in techniques and communication, and constant attention to land policies designed to foster a widespread distribution of rights to natural resources.

THUS WE HAVE two main problems with respect to land—how land should be used and how rights to land should be distributed. Both problems are met in the first instance by individuals who make decisions through the price and tenure systems. Both demand more or less public action. They cannot be solved once and for all. Their solutions change with the changing times—as the population swells or recedes, as new skills are developed, as we change the values we attach to the things we consume. We must find solutions that can be adapted to changing conditions. Our success in doing so will reflect largely our success in anticipating the changing conditions of the future.

THE IMPORTANCE OF LAND in the future will reflect three factors: What we want; the extent to which we create additional machines, factories, buildings, transportation, and similar tools to facilitate production; and our ability to devise new techniques of increasing output.

What we will want will depend upon how many of us there will be and our tastes with respect to the items we consume. If we may look to the past to see the shape of coming events, we anticipate that many more people will want many more things in the year 2000. A century ago there were 31 million people in the United States. There are about 175 million in 1958. Population experts predict that the number of our fellow citizens will reach 300 million by 2000. Thus, on the basis of numbers alone, assuming no change in the quantities of goods and services the

individual desires, our wants will increase nearly twofold in this period.

The magnitudes of the wants of the population, however, cannot be predicted on the basis of increasing numbers only. As we cannot say today that we would exchange our present comforts and conveniences for the world of 1913—the magnetotelephone; the cereal-heavy diet; the unreliable but expensive automobile; the drafty framehouse; the 60-hour week; the one-room country school; the limited medical and health facilities; the horse-drawn, wheat-shocking, corn-shucking, kerosene-lighted farm life of that day—so will our son's son utter a small prayer of appreciation that he did not have to survive the hardships of life in the 1950's. He will want to eat and dress better than we do today. He will want more spacious housing, more travel, and more recreation. He will spend a larger part of his life in school preparing for his vocation or profession. He will probably drive larger automobiles that go faster and take more room to park than those we use today. We want more than our grandfathers, and Americans four decades hence will want more than we want now.

What are the prospects that the increasing wants of this increasing population will be met? It depends partly on what we accumulate in the way of tools of production—ships, warehouses, office buildings, railroads, planting and harvesting machinery—devices that multiply the effectiveness of labor. It also depends partly on what we learn about the way the things that we want go together—production processes in factories; the feeding, care, and mating of plants and animals; and the ways they come apart, such as developments in mining and earth-moving techniques, the conversion of sea water, and atomic fission, for example. If the wants of the 300 million citizens of the United States in the year 2000 are to be fulfilled reasonably successfully, we are going to have to know a great deal more about the technical aspects of production than is known now, when our economy is functioning reasonably well and the wants of 175 million persons are not fully satisfied.

GAINS in techniques will be essential, but the uses made of natural resources will continue to be of paramount importance. The 31 million people of a century ago were served by about 1.9 billion acres of land. The 175 million people today have about 1.9 billion acres. The 300 million in 2000 will probably still be living on the same 1.9 billion acres. The fall of our streams will not change, and it is unlikely that rainfall will increase. Therefore our potential hydroelectric capacity will remain unchanged. We will have less coal, less topsoil, less iron ore, less petroleum, and probably less timber. Any failure of technological development to keep pace with the expanding population will result in greater demands on our natural resources, with a corresponding increase in the care that must be exercised in determining their use and rate of exploitation.

It is likely that the gains in technology will not be important enough to eliminate the vital place of land in determining how well the wants of the population are satisfied in decades to come.

Great gains in the arts of production have been achieved in the past century, but our welfare today depends partly upon how well we allocate our land resources among its alternative uses and how well we substitute land for labor and capital wherever such a substitution is economically feasible.

Great gains in the arts of production can be expected in the next century, but the basic question of land use will remain, and the welfare of generations to come will depend upon how well they succeed in getting each acre of land into its most economic use and how successful they are in arriving at the most economic combinations of land and other productive resources. To the extent that future generations fail to allocate and substitute resources properly in the production process,

they must pay a cost for this failure by accepting a level of living lower than the highest attainable.

As the future appears to hold for us an increasing population, increasing wants on the part of individuals, unknown advances in the techniques of production, and new and competing uses for many of our land resources, we anticipate that our land problems will be with us for many years to come.

Constant surveillance of the way we use our natural resources will be needed. As the way land is used affects our welfare in a general way through its effect on the level of output of the economy, the distribution of claims to land affects our welfare in a specific way by determining our individual claims to that output. As laws bearing upon this use and these claims are passed or modified with regularity, it is in the interest of each of us to be in a position to vote intelligently on questions that involve land.

Land has served us well in the past. It was virtually the only resource available to our ancestors at the end of the Revolutionary War. Proceeds from the sale of land were used to provide funds to launch the fledgling Nation. More importantly, our land was productive enough so that through the release of labor and the sale of agricultural products abroad, extensive capital formation was made possible which facilitated the rapid industrialization of our economy. Sales of land have financed some of our communications—canals, railroads, and the National Pike. The setting aside of public lands has been particularly helpful in educating the young—for example, the land-grant college system. In a larger but immeasurable sense, land may have been responsible for much of our political and economic freedom.

LAND CAN MAKE the contribution to our welfare in the future that it has made in the past only if we have full knowledge of its potential capacity and if we take thought about its best use and how we can achieve it.

Our wealth of land

resources. The Sahara contains as much land as our 48 States, but land to be good for crop production must have enough water, retentive soils, and not too steep slopes. Sometimes we are apt to forget that our land resources are not inexhaustible. A challenge of our time is to use our land with skill and consideration for the greatest good of people and the land itself. By *Carleton P. Barnes,* research coordinator, Agricultural Research Service, and *F. J. Marschner,* collaborator, Farm Economics Research Division.

WE HAVE 1,903,800,000 acres of land in the 48 States, but the figure tells us almost nothing about the extent of our land resource. The Sahara has as many acres, such as they are.

Because land must have water to be of much value for agriculture, forestry, or almost any other use, the value of our land depends directly on our resources of water, primarily rainfall.

Nearly one-third of our land (about 600 million acres) is thought to have characteristics favorable for crop production—enough moisture, soils sufficiently deep and moisture retentive, and level enough to allow the use of laborsaving machinery.

We use about 400 million acres for crops each year. We could till much more than the 600 million favorable acres if we had to, but more hand labor would be required than is practical in our country and great care would be needed to prevent erosion.

We consider here the resources of land for producing farm and forest products—not those we devote to manufacturing, transportation, stores, residences, and so on, except as such uses may affect the extent of resources of agricultural land.

The extent is not fixed. It changes as new techniques are discovered and as the needs and wants of people change. Before we had large machines to produce and harvest wheat in the Great Plains, for instance, it was impractical for a worker to produce enough on these low-acre-yield lands to give him a living. Inexpensive fertilizers have made land with infertile but physically favorable soils more valuable than it was before.

Better pumps and sources of power have made irrigation practical in places where formerly it was impractical. The great increase in our need for paper has given value to land that otherwise might have little value.

On the other hand, land resources can be lost through erosion and such other causes as the waterlogging and alkalinization of irrigated land.

Differences in productive capacity are tremendous—on the deserts we can produce almost nothing; on some lands that have plentiful water, productive soils, and good location in relation to markets, we can produce several thousand dollars' worth of products from an acre in a single year.

We have land so cold most of the year that we can grow only a few kinds of crops on it. We have lands on which we grow vegetables in midwinter.

When we consider the extent of our

land resources, we look for land that can produce abundant plant material.

Plants are the basis of all agriculture, although some types of farming are possible on land where no plants grow. Near Los Angeles, for example, are dairy farmers who grow no crops; they buy all their feed. But somewhere there has to be land to produce the feed for the cows.

First of all, land must have plenty of moisture from precipitation or irrigation to produce plants. But irrigation requires precipitation, somewhere, to provide the water. Plenty of moisture can be had only in or from the humid areas—areas 1–6 on the accompanying map. They cover all of the United States east of the Great Plains, or approximately that part east of the 97th meridian; the coastal parts of Washington, Oregon, and northern California; and the higher mountains in the rest of the West.

Irrigation in the dry parts of the West is possible mainly because of the mountains, which are the humid areas of the West. Winds passing over them are forced upward, cooled, and caused to precipitate their moisture as rain and snow, which in due season provide water for irrigating the land.

Our western mountains therefore are just as essential to most of the important irrigated areas as are the lands on which the irrigated crops are grown and are just as valuable a land resource. Without the mountains, we would have little irrigated farming, and the great cities of Los Angeles and San Francisco would not exist, for they also depend on the mountains for their water. That is why we must manage the forests on the mountains so as to husband the water supplies that originate on them.

Humid lands make up a little more than half of our total area.

Precipitation alone is not enough to make land a valuable agricultural resource: Not all our humid areas are highly productive farmlands. All humid areas contribute to our water supply, however, whether to grow crops or forest on the land where the rain falls or to increase streamflow or ground water that can be withdrawn for use elsewhere.

Productive land for plants must also have soils that will take in, hold, and supply the water to the plants in the amounts they need. Rock outcrops, soils that have bedrock or other dense layers close to the surface, and deep sand generally cannot hold enough water for abundant plant growth.

Slopes also affect the supply of moisture. Often much of the moisture that falls on steep slopes runs off too fast and is therefore not available for plant growth on such slopes.

Soils whose physical characteristics prevent plants from getting proper amounts of water usually are more unfavorable for crops than are infertile soils that can take in, store, and supply moisture to the crop. Deficiencies in fertility can be overcome by fertilization, but often there is no practical way to overcome such physical shortcomings as lack of moisture-storing ability.

Finally, productive agricultural land in our country must permit the use of machines for planting, cultivating, and harvesting crops. Land that is steep, rocky, or irregular in surface can produce crops only with much hand labor. Such land has disadvantages in that the returns to hand labor are apt to be small.

Our humid areas have a high percentage of land that combines these three favorable characteristics—good moisture supply; deep, moisture-retentive soils; and gentle slopes.

A LARGE AREA of this kind—area 1 on the map—lies south and west of the Great Lakes. It is one of the largest bodies of highly favored agricultural land on earth. Nearly all of its rural land is farmed. Most of it is used to produce feed. Parts of it originally were poorly drained but are now drained with tile and ditches and are highly productive, because these nearly level lands tend to withstand drought better and suffer little or no erosion.

Furthermore, its central location and access to the Great Lakes put within this great region the center of our network of rail and inland water transportation. The Great Lakes give access to the populous markets of the Northeast and Europe and to industrial raw materials. In and around it are great industrial developments, based on easy assembly of coal, petroleum, natural gas, limestone, iron ore, and water. The population supported by this industry gives market advantages that enhance the value of the farmlands. Industry helps the region support public services that could hardly be afforded were the region entirely dependent on agriculture.

OTHER PARTS of our humid areas are only slightly less favored.

In the section we designate as area 2 on the map, nearly level and naturally poorly drained land predominates. It is our main area where the problem of too much water tends to be greater than the problem of too little water. The productiveness of the land depends mainly on the control of water by drainage or flood control, or both, so as to keep the soils from being wet at times when wetness is not wanted. The parts of the area that have such water control include some of our most productive farmlands, but some sections lack water control and are used for forest.

The soils here have a wide range of physical properties and fertility, but the ease of controlling water tends to overshadow other soil characteristics and to determine use potentialities. Even in the localities that mostly are poorly drained are soils that are too wet at some seasons and too dry at others.

One advantage of poorly drained lands is that a system of ditches, gates, and pumps makes it possible in many places to maintain the soil-water level at desired heights—to lower it when the soil is too wet and (by closing outlets or reverse pumping) to raise it when the soil is too dry. Not much land in the United States has such control of water, however.

This area contains a large reserve of potential cropland for use when our national needs require it. We cannot safely predict the rate at which it may be economically developed or designate the parts most favorable to development because those factors depend on the cost and returns of providing control of water, which in turn reflect in each place the special circumstances of the sources of floods, the groundwater levels, drainage outlets, the soils, and pumping requirements.

Area 2 (like the southern part of area 3) has a long frost-free season.

AREA 3 has soils and surface relief predominantly less favorable than those in area 1, but its moisture supply generally is as good.

In many places in area 3 are lands that have steep slopes, poor soils, or both, and the area therefore contains a much higher percentage of forest land except in the "prairie" parts (in Illinois, Missouri, Kansas, and Texas). It contains much of our best forest land.

The long frost-free season in parts of area 3 permits the growing of cotton, citrus fruits, and other subtropical crops; vegetables at seasons when northern areas cannot produce them; peanuts, pecans, and so on. This advantage of being able to produce products that the rest of the humid areas cannot produce has offset in some places in Florida the disadvantage of soils that are both infertile and poorly retentive of moisture.

The Pacific Northwest Coastal Belt, the less mountainous parts of which we put in area 3, is our only area of marine climate. Winters are mild and summers are cool. This climate is especially suited to the production of forage and to raising livestock. Were it not for the high proportion of soils that retain moisture poorly and nearly rainless periods in July and August, the Pacific Northwest part of area 3 would be among the most productive of our humid areas.

Although the climate in the warmer parts of area 3 permits a wide variety of crops, much of the land that could produce crops remains in forest: Apparently our national needs of peanuts, tobacco, pecans, vegetables, and fruits can be supplied from relatively few acres. Cotton, the most widely grown cash crop in the warm part of area 3, could be grown on far more land than it is. Our national need for livestock products has not required that we use for feed or forage most of the potentially productive cropland of areas 2 and 3 not needed for cotton, tobacco, fruits, and vegetables.

Most of our remaining reserve of land favorable for crop production is in the southeastern quarter of the country. Nearly three-fourths of the 105 million acres of woodland that the Soil Conservation Service has estimated to be physically capable of crop production is in the 14 Southeastern States. Most of this is in areas 2 and 3.

The qualities that make this land favorable for other crops tend also to make it advantageous for forests— ample precipitation, deep and retentive soils, and slopes that are not too steep. The costs of forest production are less where the terrain permits mechanized operation. A network of roads facilitates the transport of logs and pulpwood in areas 2 and 3. In them, therefore, we can expect competition between the use of land for crops and its use for timber as our national growth requires.

The forest land resources of area 3 also include many millions of acres not especially well suited to crops and not likely to be needed for them unless our needs increase greatly. This land is scattered throughout most of the area in bodies too small to be shown on the map.

Larger areas that have similarly unfavorable characteristics as to soil and topography appear as areas 4 and 5.

AREA 5 mainly has steeply sloping land, land with bedrock close to the surface, or a rock outcrop with almost no soil. It includes nearly all our mountains, except the mountains in the arid areas that are too low to trap enough rain and snow to support forests.

We said that in the West our mountains are valuable resources because they catch the moisture that makes possible our irrigated agriculture and cities: Mountains in the generally humid East also comb the clouds for water—water that we need to store and use.

Mountains have many other uses. Most of them produce forests, which help regulate the flow of water off and out of the mountains and keep it freer of sediment. Forests provide lumber and pulpwood. Millions of Americans find recreation in mountain forests. Mountain lands in some sections provide summer grazing for livestock when the lower and hotter lands are without forage.

Many mountain lands can be managed to provide several of these benefits together, but excessive devotion to one may prevent others from being enjoyed. The management of mountain lands needs to be devoted therefore to achieving the greatest benefit for the most people.

Measured by ability to satisfy human needs, our humid mountain lands (area 5) are among our scarcest and most valuable resources.

SCATTERED THROUGH the humid region are places unsuitable for crops, not because the slopes are steep or the soils are shallow over bedrock but because the soils have other poor physical characteristics that affect the moisture supply of plants. The largest are shown on the map as area 4. The smaller ones cannot be shown on so small a map.

The larger swamps and marshes, generally wetter than are the poorly drained lands of area 2, are shown as area 6. It may be physically possible to reclaim them, but the need appears remote because we have many other resources for other crop production.

Too little moisture is a handicap to

the use of land resources in the sub-humid and arid areas.

Drought occurs even in the humid areas. In the subhumid and arid areas, however, one can expect drought more frequently, and in the drier of these areas drought can be considered to be normal.

The transition from humid to sub-humid climate in the middle of the United States occurs gradually in a broad zone as we travel westward.

On the map we have to draw a line to show the western edge of the humid region. We draw it to separate the region with an index of precipitation effectiveness normally of 48 or more (humid) from that with less, as shown in *Atlas of Climatic Types in the United States, 1900-1939*, by C. W. Thorn-thwaite.

All land west of this line we consider subhumid or arid, except the coastal part of Oregon, Washington, and northern California and the mountains with enough moisture to support forest of stature greater than pinyon-juniper woodland or chaparral.

WITHIN THESE DRIER AREAS, our most productive agricultural land resources are those that have water for irrigation. Most of the water comes from humid mountain areas (area 5) within or near the dry areas.

Water pumped out of the ground irrigates some lands. Water from the humid mountains helps replenish some of this ground water, but some is re-plenished only by rain passing down into the water-bearing layer in the subhumid and arid sections themselves. In either instance, the withdrawal must be balanced by the recharge, or pump-ing eventually will become too costly. We are pumping out ground water in some dry areas faster than it is replen-ished. In some places water is used up that took centuries to accumulate. As we said, the productivity of the land depends on the quantity and depend-ability of a water supply; water makes the land resource.

Acre for acre, irrigated lands are among our most productive, because on them we can control the water ac-cording to the needs of the plants and we do not have to rely on the more un-certain timing of rains.

Our 25 million acres of irrigated land in the West contribute a greater share of our total production than their per-centage of total cropland. Even so, irrigated land ranges widely in pro-ductivity. Some, like that in the Im-perial Valley of California, can pro-duce crops the year round. Some at high elevations can produce little but forage. Some has productive soil, while some has poor drainage, an injurious concentration of salt, or poor physical characteristics. It is wrong to think, as some persons do, that water is all that land in the West needs in order to produce well.

Scarce as water is in the arid and subhumid regions, more land could be irrigated there. But the costs of im-pounding and transporting the water tend to be high. The less costly irriga-tion projects were developed years ago. The costs of obtaining an additional quantity of farm products by irri-gating more cropland in the dry areas appear to be much greater than the costs of obtaining an equal quantity from the uncultivated but productive soils of the humid region, where water is more plentiful.

An equivalent contribution to pro-duction at less cost could probably be made by more efficient use of the water in existing irrigation projects.

More than half the water in many irrigation projects is lost before it reaches the crop it is intended for. Often the water is not applied at the right time or rate for highest production.

The growing urban populations in the dry areas in the Southwest will re-quire that a larger part of the West's scarce water supply be used for non-agricultural purposes.

CROPS CAN BE GROWN in the moister parts of the nonhumid areas without irrigation, particularly in places where the soils and surface relief favor the conservation of moisture. These sub-humid sections (area 7) are particularly characteristic of the eastern part of the Great Plains. The choice of crops is smaller than in humid areas, and the possibilities of increasing production by heavier fertilization and other techniques are limited more sharply because of too little moisture.

Land in the progressively drier areas becomes correspondingly less productive. Average yields are lower. More land is needed to support a family. On many of the drier croplands, farmers often follow a year of wheat with a year of fallow so the soil can accumulate moisture to crop the land again.

SOILS IN THE SUBHUMID AREAS that are shallow over tight layers or are of deep sand cannot store enough moisture for crops and are used for grazing. So are strongly sloping lands that tend to let too much rainfall run off—not into—the soil. They and extensive sections that do not get enough rain for crops but furnish a moderate amount of forage are shown as area 8. Such land supports fewer people than that of area 7.

Land in area 8 that gets enough water for stock and for irrigating small acreages of feed crops supports an extensive livestock industry, but recurrent droughts often impair the feed supply to the point that herds must be reduced or additional feed must be shipped in.

AREA 9 is even drier. Except for occasional irrigated land, the land there supports only a sparse population, and grazing land has low carrying capacity. It is not a desert, although parts of it locally are called "desert." It has some water and forage, but most of the livestock must rely on forage from area 5 or 8 part of the year or on feed from irrigated land.

We have relatively little desert, if we consider desert as land that has little or no vegetation. The salt deserts of Utah and Nevada and the Mojave and Colorado River Deserts of south-eastern California, southwestern Arizona, and southern Nevada are so lacking in water that we can properly call them desert (area 10). They have almost no agricultural value.

The nearly barren lands of the alpine zone above timberline are not of this character. They are valuable because they provide water.

ALTHOUGH WATER fixes the use potentials of land so completely that land without it is almost always valueless, other features of climate, especially temperature, affect the utility of our land resources.

We have within our borders most kinds of climate except the tropical: Sections with a long frost-free season, mild winters, and hot summers; sections with an equally long frost-free season, mild winters, and cool summers; sections with a short frost-free season, cold winters, and cool summers; and sections with a short frost-free season, cold winters, and hot summers. All of these climates affect the range and choice of crops and farm enterprises.

The distribution of areas with long and short frost-free seasons is indicated on the map by lines (marked 260) separating areas averaging more from those averaging less than a 260-day, frost-free season; lines (marked 200) separating areas that average more than 200 days in the frost-free season from those that average less; and lines (marked 140) that separate areas that average more than 140 days in the frost-free season from those that average less.

In the eastern half of the United States, where differences in elevation are smaller, the differences in frost-free seasons depend mainly on the distance north and south. In the West, where differences in elevation are great, places with short seasons may exist anywhere at high elevations.

Temperatures in the coastal parts of the Pacific States are affected further by prevailing winds that blow inland off the Pacific and keep the coast relatively mild in winter and cool in summer, because the offshore water of the ocean is cold relative to land in summer and warm in winter. These areas therefore have types of climate not found elsewhere in our country and advantages in some kinds of enterprises.

Winds predominantly blow seaward on our eastern seaboard, so the marine influence on its climate is much less than it is along the Pacific coast. Climate over most of the country is of a continental type, and the range in temperatures from summer to winter is wide.

Long frost-free seasons give some advantages to areas so favored. Areas with short frost-free seasons, say fewer than 140 days, have a shorter list of enterprises, the growth of forests there tends to be slower, the pasture season is shorter, more expensive housing for livestock is needed, and more feed and forage has to be prepared and stored for winter use.

But we must not suppose that the long-season sections can produce everything the shorter-season sections can. It is not that simple, especially if the long-season areas have hot summers, as they do everywhere except along the Pacific coast. Apples do not do well in localities that have hot summers. Milk production in long, hot summers faces difficulties not encountered in areas with long frost-free seasons and cool summers (like the coastal areas of Washington, Oregon, and California), which favor the abundant production

of feed and forage and good physiologic functioning of dairy cows.

It is our good fortune that our great region of low moisture supply extends across all of our major temperature zones and does not coincide with one or a few of them, as it does in some countries. So we have humid lands in every temperature zone and a source of the farm products that are suited to each.

So far we have stressed the value of land for producing crops. Much of our land is valuable also for grazing or forest.

Grazing is merely a way of harvesting by having animals eat the growing plants. Plants for grazing have requirements of moisture, soils, and relief as do plants harvested in other ways.

Grazing generally can be done on steeper slopes than can be safely or economically used for crops, however, because less machine operation usually is required. Some land can be too steep for grazing, because of the danger of erosion and because of the need on most grazing land to control weeds or revegetate the land, operations that are done economically by machines.

Grazing also is practical on the dry lands of our arid and semiarid areas where crop production is impractical because the cost of planting and harvesting crops would exceed the returns from the small yields.

Forests generally are restricted to more humid climates. Mechanized tim-

GENERALIZED LAND RESOURCE AREAS

Our land exhibits a wide range in productive capacity. Climate, surface relief, and soil are the major factors that, through various combinations, have produced the great diversity in the use potentiality of the land. Of these factors, climate is the most important because moisture supply controls land use. The land resource areas delimited here are therefore first divided according to moisture differences.

The country is divided into a humid East and a drier West, in which only the higher mountains and the North Pacific coastal region receive enough precipitation to bring them in the humid category. The line drawn to separate the humid East from the drier West, running almost north and south across the middle of the country, represents no abrupt change, but is placed in the zone of transition between moist and dry. It approximates a line that separates the area where average annual precipitation exceeds average potential evapotranspiration from those where the reverse is true.

Broad belts differentiated according to length of frost-free season are used to give some indication of differences in temperature that affect potentialities of land resources. Among the humid areas, differences in surface relief, soils, and drainage account for the different classes of areas shown. Among the subhumid and arid areas, different degrees of aridity overshadow differences in surface relief or soil in all but the moister areas and therefore mainly account for the different classes of drier areas.

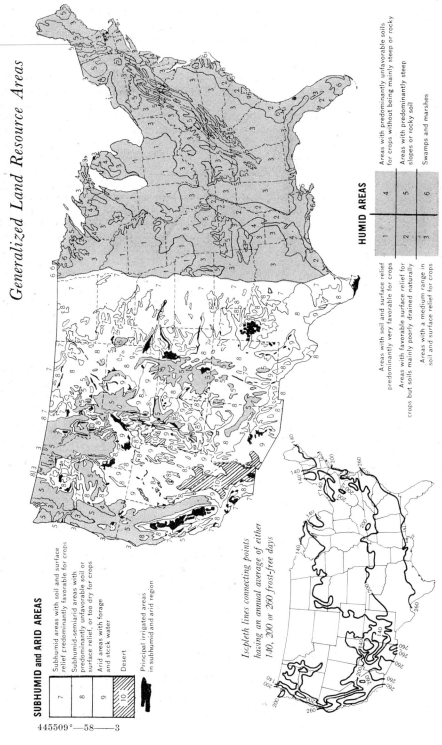

Generalized Land Resource Areas

HUMID AREAS

1		4
2		5
3		6

Areas with soil and surface relief predominantly very favorable for crops

Areas with favorable surface relief for crops but soils mainly poorly drained naturally

Areas with a medium range in soil and surface relief for crops

Areas with predominantly unfavorable soils for crops without being mainly steep or rocky

Areas with predominantly steep slopes or rocky soil

Swamps and marshes

SUBHUMID and ARID AREAS

7	Subhumid areas with soil and surface relief predominantly favorable for crops
8	Subhumid-semiarid areas with predominantly unfavorable soil or surface relief, or too dry for crops
9	Arid areas with forage and stock water
10	Desert
	Principal irrigated areas in subhumid and arid region

Isopleth lines connecting points having an annual average of either 140, 200 or 260 frost-free days

445509°—58——3

ber harvest is possible on fairly steep slopes, on which erosion can be controlled with proper logging methods. Gentle slopes are an advantage, however, in forest management and in building access roads to stands of timber.

Because forestry and grazing are feasible on some lands not suitable for crops, they have tended to be residual uses on land not needed for crops.

BECAUSE AN ABUNDANT WATER supply underlies a productive agriculture and the industry and other activities that support urban populations, the heaviest farm production and the heaviest concentration of consuming population exist in or near the humid areas. In them also we can look for the greatest development of land resources.

The dry areas have not yet used all the water that originates in the adjacent humid mountains of the West, but the limits on agricultural development based on this water are more closely approached now (and will be reached sooner) than in the humid East.

We have more land resources than we now need to use to produce the farm products we consume. As population grows, the greater supply that will be needed will be achieved by producing more on the present acreage or by putting more acres into crops. That we can do by applying more generally the good practices we already know about, discovering new and better practices, and converting some forest land to cropland—although a survey in 1955 by the Forest Service indicated that we may need nearly all of our forest land to produce wood.

In our complex system of needs and satisfactions, land is needed for a greater number of uses than formerly. The abundance of our resources for some of these needs is not so evident as it is for food. Outdoor recreation is an example. A survey by the National Park Service showed that beaches of the Atlantic and gulf coasts rapidly are being brought into private use in a way that nearly excludes public use of most of them.

We need food, but the luxury element in food consumption, which includes our waste of food, is less important to health and happiness than, say, swimming, sailing, and fishing. Some production of food therefore may be less essential than outdoor recreation, the preservation of wildlife, and other supposedly less important needs.

It comes down to this: We have a wealth of land resources, but they are not inexhaustible. As we become more numerous, we shall not necessarily have enough land to satisfy all of our increasingly varied wants. A great challenge of our time is to use our land with skill and consideration for the greatest good, and in the knowledge that man cannot live by bread alone.

OUR POPULATION now increases at a rate that will give us 700 million people in 100 years and 2,800 million in 200 years. If we took 500 million acres of our best cropland and used it as intensively as the Japanese use their cropland, we could feed almost 2 billion people—assuming that these acres are as productive as the average Japanese cropland acres and that we consumed the cropland products directly rather than as animal products.

Perhaps we shall not need to feed this many people, but this gives us some idea of our capabilities if we should really be pressed. Probably we shall run into shortages of resources for other things we want more quickly than we shall for cropland resources. And perhaps our greatest problem will be in having enough land merely for living space. Many persons, if they had to choose, would rather have some space around their homes than to have beefsteak.

A national population of 2 billion would have less than 1 acre per person for all its wants—food, clothing, shelter, paper, factories, stores, roads, airports, and space for living and recreation. Actually there would be even less, since we have so many acres that lack water and so are unsuited to filling any of these needs.

How we acquired our landed estate.

How we got our land is the core of our history, beginning with the Thirteen Colonies and continuing with the Louisiana Purchase (4 cents an acre for 529,911,680 acres), Florida, the Northwest Territory, Alaska, Texas, the Pacific Southwest, the Gadsden Purchase, and others—until the national domain extended from sea to shining sea and beyond the seas. By *Karl S. Landstrom,* lands officer, Bureau of Land Management, Department of the Interior.

THE LANDED ESTATE of the American people is the resource base on which the American economy functions. How it was acquired is the core of our history.

The national domain is all land, public and private.

The public domain is the remaining portion of lands originally acquired by our Government.

THE PUBLIC DOMAIN, at its broadest extent, consisted of three-fourths of the continental United States and nearly all of Alaska, a total of 1,807 million acres.

The public domain was acquired by cessions from the Thirteen Original States, 1781 to 1802; the Louisiana Purchase, 1803; the Spanish Cession of Florida, 1819; the Oregon Compromise, 1846; the Mexican Cession, 1848; the Texas Purchase, 1850; and the Gadsden Purchase, 1807. Alaska was purchased from Russia in 1867.

THE THIRTEEN ORIGINAL STATES made up the area of the United States at the close of the Revolutionary War. The boundaries of the new Republic were established by treaty with Great Britain. The western boundaries of the Original States were ill defined. There had been overlapping and rival claims, based on conflicting crown grants.

Six of the States had clearly defined boundaries in the sense that they were bounded by the claims of other States to westward. The other seven—New York, Virginia, North Carolina, South Carolina, Georgia, Massachusetts, and Connecticut—held claims to "wilderness" to the west. The claims extended to the Mississippi River.

The attention of the Government of the newly formed Confederation was early drawn to the problem of the western land claims of the States. The States having no western claims contended that the western claims of the other States should be ceded to the Confederation.

Maryland contended that the unsettled domain to the west had been wrested by "common blood and treasury" and should be made their common property. Future unequal representation was feared as the larger States would grow with westward migration.

The Articles of Confederation had left the sale and disposition of western lands to the exclusive control of the States owning them. Some States had opened land offices, made private grants, granted land bounties, or otherwise disposed of portions of their domain.

The Continental Congress in 1779 passed a compromise resolution recommending that the States withhold further grants of western lands for the duration of the War. Eight States voted for the resolution, and three voted against it.

New York tendered her claims to western land to the Congress without reservation in 1780 to alleviate dissatisfaction of the smaller States. The Congress adopted a resolution "earnestly" requesting other States to do the same.

New York had claimed an area of undefined and unsettled lands west of Pennsylvania and north of the Ohio River. These lands, ceded in 1781, are now in Erie County in Pennsylvania.

Virginia's western possessions north of the Ohio River were ceded in 1784. The present State of Kentucky was ceded directly to that State. Kentucky accordingly is one of the States that never contained public domain of the United States.

Massachusetts succeeded to the ownership of its vacant lands and became proprietor of unoccupied lands in Maine. These lands were disposed of under State laws.

To the United States in 1785 were ceded claims to western lands that overlapped Virginia's claims in what is now Pennsylvania, Illinois, Wisconsin, and Michigan.

Maine took charge of her own lands and made no cession to the United States.

South Carolina in 1787 ceded a strip of land that now lies in the northern parts of Georgia, Alabama, and Mississippi.

North Carolina ceded her western lands forming what is now the State of Tennessee, in 1790.

Connecticut's claim to western unoccupied lands, except to a tract known as the Western Reserve, in Ohio, was relinquished to the United States in 1880.

Georgia completed the cessions of the original States in 1802 by ceding lands that now are part of Alabama and Mississippi. Payment for this transfer was made by the United States of 6,200,000 dollars, which was approximately 11 cents an acre.

Pennsylvania, Rhode Island, and Vermont made no cessions.

Delaware, Maryland, and New Jersey had no western lands to cede.

These cessions gave the United States title to 236,825,600 acres of land and water area, as computed in 1912 by a committee representing the General Land Office, Geological Survey, Bureau of Statistics, and Bureau of the Census. This was the nucleus of the land to be known as the public domain. The Government of the United States assumed the role of proprietor of these lands and trustee for the people.

By events listed thus far, citizens of the United States and the Nation by 1802 had acquired title to lands west to the Mississippi River. At that time, Florida was claimed by Spain, and Louisiana was claimed by France.

LOUISIANA, which included the Mississippi Valley, was early recognized as having geographic and economic importance on the American continent. The Ohio and Mississippi Rivers and their tributaries afforded an avenue to the sea, but the mouth of the Mississippi River was under the control of foreign powers.

France's claim to territory in the Mississippi Valley and along the Gulf of Mexico was based on LaSalle's voyage and proclamation of 1682. The eastward boundary of Louisiana thus claimed was the "River Palms." This is identified as a river in what is now Florida; it empties into Palm Sound, now called Sarasota Bay.

France's Louisiana Territory was ceded to Spain in 1762. The area was described as "the whole country known under the name of Louisiana, together with New Orleans and the island on which that city stands."

By treaty in 1763, France and Spain ceded to Great Britain all of Louisiana east of the Mississippi. Twenty years later, in boundary settlements at the close of the Revolutionary War, the United States took over from Great Britain all that part of the original Louisiana ceded to it by France.

Spain in 1800 ceded back to France the Louisiana Territory less the part east of the Mississippi and north of latitude 31°, which had been acquired by the United States in 1783 from Great Britain. Before that time, the ministers of the United States in Europe had been instructed to prevent, if possible, the return of Louisiana to Spain. France was urged to consent to the sale of the City and Province of New Orleans to the United States. The urgency of purchase was heightened by the temporary closure of the port of New Orleans to the United States in October 1802.

President Thomas Jefferson, in December 1802, obtained the consent of the Congress to negotiate for the purchase of New Orleans from France. Negotiations were conducted by James Monroe and others. France agreed to the sale for a price of 80 million francs.

It is said that when Napoleon Bonaparte instructed his minister of treasury regarding the Louisiana sale he ventured the forecast that the country that would hold the Mississippi Valley would eventually become the most powerful country on earth.

The boundaries of Louisiana as purchased from France were indefinite. Definite boundaries were established later by a treaty with Spain and a series of treaties, concluded in 1871, with Great Britain.

The cost of 529,911,680 acres of land and water surface acquired in the Louisiana Purchase was 23,213,568 dollars, or about 4 cents an acre.

FLORIDA was claimed by Spain by discovery and exploration.

Spain ceded Florida to Great Britain in 1736, but in 1783, after the conclusion of the treaty between the United States and Great Britain, Florida was ceded back to Spain. The boundaries of Florida were in dispute between Spain and the United States.

President James Madison issued a proclamation in 1810 taking possession of the east bank of the Mississippi River under the authority of the treaty of purchase with France. The proclamation left the question of ownership for future settlement. After a series of incidents, John Quincy Adams for the United States and Don Luis de Onis for Spain signed a treaty of cession of Florida to the United States in 1819.

The Florida purchase cost the United States 6,674,057 dollars for 46,144,640 acres of public domain—about 14 cents an acre.

THE NORTHWEST TERRITORY was established as part of the United States by the treaty with Great Britain in 1846.

Long before the purchase of Louisiana, the interests of the United States had been directed toward the unknown interior country west of the Mississippi. Several overland journeys were begun, but none was brought to a conclusion.

The northwestern coasts had been visited by ships of several countries. Captain Robert Gray, an American, discovered the mouth of the Columbia River and sailed many miles upstream.

The American claim to "Oregon Territory" was based upon Captain Gray's discovery and later expeditions by land and water.

President Jefferson asked the Congress in 1803 to appropriate 2,500,000 dollars for an overland expedition, which was begun the next year by Meriwether Lewis and William Clark. Furtherance of the American claim was the prime motive of the expedition. Exploration of the newly purchased Louisiana Territory was also an objective.

The Lewis and Clark expedition began by water from the mouth of Wood River on the Illinois bank of the Mississippi, opposite the mouth of the Missouri River. The party reached an Indian village at Mandan by October 26. There, on the north bank of the Missouri, a fort, called Fort Mandan, was erected.

The route followed in 1805 passed through the lofty Bitter Root Range, down the Clearwater River to its junction with the Snake River, and down the Snake to the Columbia River.

Captain Clark wrote that on November 7, 1805, they saw for the first time "the object of all our labors, the reward of all our anxieties," the waters of the Pacific Ocean.

After the winter of 1805–1806 at Fort Clatsop, the party arrived at St. Louis on September 23, 1806.

The report, "Brief Account of the Lewis and Clark Expedition," published in 1905 and reissued by the Bureau of Land Management, characterizes it as influencing greatly subsequent political acts that affected the ownership of the Oregon Territory.

Russia at that time had an undefined claim to territory in what is now Alaska. By treaty in 1824, the United States recognized Russian sovereignty over the northwestern coast from latitude 54°40′ north to the North Pole. Great Britain later confirmed with Russia by treaty in 1825 that Russian sovereignty extended northward from latitude 54°40′. The eastward extent of Russian sovereignty was defined with Great Britain as the present eastern line of Alaska.

Sovereignty over the land south of latitude 54°40′ was hotly disputed by the United States and Great Britain. Disputed territory was occupied by both countries.

The northern boundary of the United States was placed by treaty in 1846 at the 49th parallel extended to the middle of a channel that separates Vancouver Island from the mainland, thence southerly along the center of the channel and of the Strait of San Juan de Fuca to the Pacific Ocean. The exact location of the channel referred to was in dispute from 1846 to 1872. An exact location was determined in 1872 by Wilhelm I, Emperor of Germany, who was arbitrator without appeal, agreed upon by the two countries.

The Oregon Compromise established 183,386,240 acres as public domain of the United States. No payment of moneys was involved.

TEXAS, annexed in 1845, was originally included in French and Spanish possessions. The treaty of purchase of Florida contained recognition by the United States of the present eastern boundary of Texas as the eastern boundary of Spanish possessions.

Mexico obtained her independence from Spain in 1821.

Secretary of State Martin Van Buren in 1829 instructed the United States Minister to Mexico to offer to buy the part of Texas east of the Nueces River. Mexico refused. The Republic of Texas was proclaimed in 1836 and was recognized by the United States in 1837.

Admission of Texas to the United States was soon urged. It became a political issue. A joint resolution for annexation was adopted by the Congress and was signed by President John Tyler in 1845.

The State of Texas succeeded to the ownership of all lands of the former Republic east of the Rio Grande that were included in a region bounded on the east by the Spanish-American boundary as established under the Florida treaty of 1819. These boundaries had been confirmed by a treaty with Mexico in 1828, but they were indefinite. Persons living at Santa Fe, in what is now New Mexico, denied that they were within the State of Texas.

During the Mexican War in 1847, General Stephen W. Kearney, under War Department orders, captured the Mexican province of New Mexico. As military governor, he published a series of laws for the government of the province.

An organic law for the government of the Territory of New Mexico was enacted after 3 years of military government. The law defined the eastern boundary of the Territory at the present eastern line of New Mexico, reducing thus the extent of the claim of Texas. By the act of September 9, 1850, the United States proposed the purchase from the State of Texas of its claim to lands north of latitude 36° 30′ and west of the 100th meridian and those north of latitude 32° and west of the 103d meridian. The State accepted, and the purchased property became public domain of the United States.

The lands added by this purchase consisted of 78,926,720 acres of land and water surface, costing 15,496,448 dollars, or approximately 20 cents an acre. These lands are now parts of Kansas, Colorado, New Mexico, and Oklahoma.

THE PACIFIC SOUTHWEST, especially the coast of California, was early a matter of jealous attention by several rival countries.

Russians occupied a part of the California coast in 1812 by permission of Spain. A military governor was in command.

President Andrew Jackson proposed in 1835 to Mexico that the Pacific Southwest be sold to the United States. Negotiations failed. John Charles Fremont's overland expedition and Charles Wilkes' voyage under auspices of the United States added information about this area.

After the terms of the Texas annexation had been accepted by the Republic of Texas, President James K. Polk in 1845 ordered the United States Army to occupy and hold the western part of the Texas claim. Steps were taken to offer to the Mexican Government terms for the acquisition of the disputed western Texas Territory and lands to the west, including the bay and harbor of San Francisco.

War was declared with Mexico on May 13, 1846. After repeated failure of negotiations and resumption of hostilities, a treaty was completed by Commissioner Nicholas P. Trist, on behalf of the United States, at the city of Guadalupe Hidalgo, Mexico, on February 2, 1848. President Polk proclaimed the treaty on July 4, 1848.

This action resulted in recognition of the western boundaries of Texas and added to the public domain the lands bounded on the east by the Rio Grande River and a meridian extending north, on the north by the 42d parallel, on the west by the Pacific Ocean, and on the south by the national boundary established by the treaty. The area of public domain acquired was given by the Federal Interagency Committee in 1912 as 338,680,960 acres. The cost was 16,295,149 dollars, or approximately 5 cents an acre.

THE GADSDEN PURCHASE was completed in 1853, when Franklin Pierce was President.

James Gadsden, the United States Minister to Mexico, entered into the treaty of purchase on behalf of the United States for the purpose of defining more correctly the boundary and making a more regular line between the United States and Mexico.

The boundaries given were the Gila River on the north, the Rio Grande on the east, and a point 20 miles below the mouth of the Gila River, on the Colorado River, on the west. The area of public domain added was 18,988,-800 acres (land and water surface). The cost was 10 million dollars, or approximately 53 cents an acre.

THREE PARCELS OF TERRITORY, now securely parts of the United States, had been collectively omitted by the various formal treaties of cession or purchase.

One of these areas is what is now western Louisiana, west of the Mississippi River drainage. It was relinquished by Spain in 1819.

Another is an extensive area in Minnesota and the Dakotas. It drains northward through the Red River. It was relinquished by Britain in 1818.

The third area is in central Colorado. It was not included in the Louisiana or Texas Purchases but was covered by a treaty with the Ute Indians in 1868.

The total of original public domain acquired in continental United States from 1781 to 1867 was given by the Federal Interagency Committee in 1912 as 1,462,466,560 acres (land and water area). The aggregate cost was 77,879,222 dollars, or approximately 5 cents an acre.

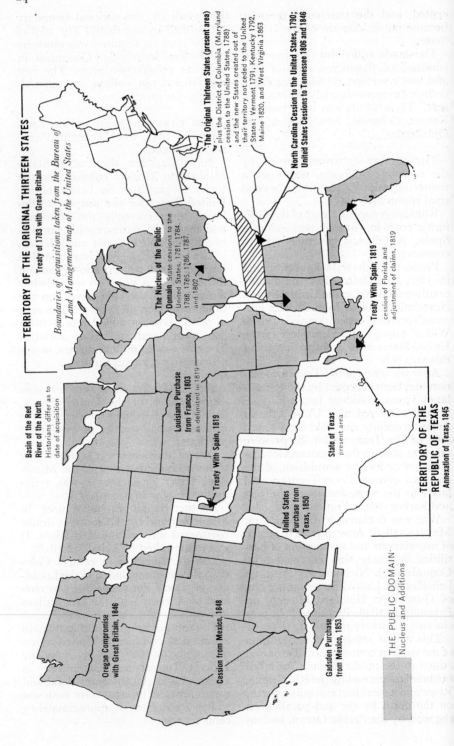

THE PUBLIC DOMAIN · Nucleus and Additions

TERRITORY OF THE ORIGINAL THIRTEEN STATES
Treaty of 1783 with Great Britain

Boundaries of acquisitions taken from the Bureau of Land Management map of the United States

Basin of the Red River of the North
Historians differ as to date of acquisition

The Nucleus of the Public Domain State cessions to the United States, 1781, 1784, 1785, 1786, 1787, 1788, and 1802.

The Original Thirteen States (present area)
plus the District of Columbia (Maryland cession to the United States, 1788) and the new States created out of their territory not ceded to the United States: Vermont 1791, Kentucky 1792, Maine 1820, and West Virginia 1863

North Carolina Cession to the United States, 1790; United States Cessions to Tennessee 1806 and 1846

Treaty With Spain, 1819
cession of Florida and adjustment of claims, 1819

Louisiana Purchase from France, 1803
as delimited in 1819

Treaty With Spain, 1819

Oregon Compromise with Great Britain, 1846

Cession from Mexico, 1848

United States Purchase from Texas, 1850

State of Texas
present area

TERRITORY OF THE REPUBLIC OF TEXAS
Annexation of Texas, 1845

Gadsden Purchase from Mexico, 1853

AMERICAN INDIANS or Indian tribes originally occupied or claimed most of the lands embraced in the treaties and purchases of the United States. At the time of acquisition from other powers, Indians were largely in possession.

In the later stages of westward migration, Indian claims to land were customarily settled by means of treaties with the tribal authorities. The treaties usually provided for areas to be reserved to Indian possession.

The total cost of Indian land claims is unknown, but it is known that it far exceeds the cost of payments to other countries. Several lawsuits against the United States on account of Indian land claims have been settled in recent years. Other large claims were pending in 1958.

AN EXAMPLE of an Indian land claim is that of the *Alcea Band of Tillamooks, et al.* v. *The United States*, involving 2,772,580 acres. The lands are located in the coastal areas of Oregon. Suit was brought under the Act of August 26, 1935 (49 Stat. 801), which gave the Court of Claims jurisdiction over this class of cases.

The court had decided on April 2, 1945 (103 C. Cls. 494), and it had been affirmed by the United States Supreme Court (329 U. S. 40) that four of the tribes had proved their original Indian title and that the taking of the lands by the United States had been involuntary and uncompensated. Judgment was entered on January 3, 1950, for the tribes under the provisions of the Fifth Amendment to the Constitution of the United States (115 C. Cls. 463). The amount awarded was measured by the appraised value of the lands as of the date they had been taken, plus reasonable interest, offset by the value of the tribes' interests in the reservation lands allotted to them as of the date the lands were taken and less the equivalent of gratuities from the United States to the tribes over the years to the latest date of accounting.

The court set the value of the lands taken at 1.20 dollars an acre as of November 9, 1855. The rate of interest on the amount due was fixed at 4 percent from 1855 to 1934 and 5 percent thereafter.

The total amount due the four tribes, with interest, less offsets, was fixed by the Court of Claims at 16,515,604.77 dollars, to which certain additional interest was to be added until the date of payment.

On reversal by the United States Supreme Court (341 U. S. 48), final judgment was entered by the Court of Claims on May 1, 1951 (119 C. Cls. 835) at 2,259,986.80 dollars.

ALASKA was claimed by Russia on the basis of voyages by Vitus Bering in 1728 and 1741. After Bering's second voyage, Russian fur traders advanced along the Aleutian Islands. A Russian trading corporation, the Russian-American Company, took domination over Russian America in 1799 under a series of 20-year concessions.

During the Crimean War in 1855, Russia feared that Great Britain might seize Russian America. The area was offered to the United States, but the offer was refused.

The legislature of the Territory of Washington memorialized President Andrew Johnson in 1866 to acquire the Russian territory in Alaska. A treaty of purchase was signed in 1867 by Secretary of State William H. Seward for the United States and Baron de Stoeckl for Russia. The purchase price was 7,200,000 dollars, or approximately 2 cents an acre, for 375,296,000 acres of public domain.

Formal transfer was made at Sitka to Major General L. H. Rousseau, the United States Commissioner, on October 18, 1867.

The early progress made by Russians in Alaska may be traced today by viewing the remaining Russian Orthodox church buildings, wooden framed and turnip topped. These monuments are found at Unalaska, eastward along the Aleutians, in the Kodiak-Afgonak Island group, and at Sitka, which was the last capital of Russian America.

Thus was completed, in 1867, the acquisition of public lands of the United States.

The public domain did not include lands within American insular possessions. The Territory of Hawaii, Puerto Rico, the Virgin Islands, Guam, American Samoa, the Trust Territory of the Pacific Islands, and other islands in the central Pacific have laws for the administration and disposition of their public lands.

ACQUIRED LANDS are distinguished from public domain in that they have been acquired by the United States by purchase or gift or condemnation from individual landowners or from the States in individual transactions not embodied in the major acquisitions of public domain.

The desirability of Federal purchase of privately owned lands to supplement public domain reserved in national forests first arose about 1901. The subject was debated in the Congress beginning in 1909. Advocates stressed the importance of forest management in the control of runoff and hence control of floods and navigation resources. Purchases were proposed in Eastern States where there was no public domain. Opposition was based on such grounds as interference with private ownership, cost, and constitutional authority. An authorizing act, known as the Weeks Act, was adopted in 1911. Purchases under this act were limited to lands necessary to the protection of the flow of navigable streams.

The act established a National Forest Reservation Commission, consisting of the Secretaries of War, Interior, and Agriculture, and two members each of the House and the Senate. The commission approves the price and acreage of all tracts acquired under the authority of this act.

The Clarke-McNary Act of 1924 broadened the authority to include purchase of land in the watersheds of navigable streams for timber production as well as for regulation of streamflow.

The United States Forest Service, as of June 30, 1956, administered 27,960,-067 acres of acquired lands of the United States. Much of this area is in States from Texas eastward to Virginia, including Missouri and Kentucky and States south of them. Some of these acquired forest lands are in New Hampshire, Vermont, Pennsylvania, Michigan, Minnesota, and Wisconsin. Purchases of forest lands in the Western States are small in relation to the area of national forest consisting of reserved public domain.

An important acquisition of Federal lands was that of the revested Oregon and California Railroad lands, known as the O & C lands. Title to almost 3 million acres of forested lands was revested to the United States by an act of the Congress in 1916. The railroad company was paid a price of 2.50 dollars an acre for the lands on the basis that it had been the intention of the Congress in the prior land grant to have given the company a grant of that amount.

A different form of Federal land purchase consisted of purchase of farmlands in submarginal uses during the 1930's. Purchases were made under various funds established by the emergency relief acts, the Agricultural Adjustment Act, and later the Bankhead-Jones Farm Tenant Act of 1937. The purchases under this group of programs included some 11 million acres. Nearly half of these lands were in the northern part of the Great Plains.

A SPECIAL FORM of land purchase requirement is that for military purposes. Such purchases during the Second World War aggregated some 7 million acres. Other lands were leased.

The Department of Defense, for military purposes, held for the United States 7,675,275 acres of acquired lands as of June 30, 1956. For civil functions of the Corps of Engineers, the area of acquired lands held on that date was 3,647,999 acres.

FEW PURCHASES of privately owned lands were made to provide lands for

Indian use before 1934. The Indian Reorganization Act, adopted in 1934, provided funds for land purchase and authorized the use of Indian tribal funds for that purpose. More than 1 million acres have been purchased for the use of Indians. The Bureau of Indian Affairs, on June 30, 1956, held 594,807 acres of Indian lands acquired by purchase, donation, and transfer.

Privately owned lands have been acquired as national parks or national monuments, or to round out public domain areas set aside as national parks or monuments. The National Park Service administered 3,501,969 acres of acquired lands as of June 30, 1956.

WILDLIFE REFUGES have been established or augmented by condemnations and purchases, as well as by reservation or withdrawal of public lands. The first purchase of land for a wildlife refuge was for a bison range on the Flathead Indian Reservation in 1909. General purchase authority was granted by the Congress in the Norbeck-Andersen Act of 1929. Extensive areas were added in the 1930's from lands purchased as submarginal lands.

Acquired lands administered by the Fish and Wildlife Service as of June 30, 1956, aggregated 2,770,646 acres. These lands for the most part are considered incapable of sustained use as cropland because of wetness, dryness, or accelerated erosion.

Lands acquired under the reclamation program and administered by the Bureau of Reclamation totaled 1,538,-016 acres as of June 30, 1956. The Atomic Energy Commission administered 667,926 acres and the Tennessee Valley Authority held 740,030 acres as of June 30, 1956.

All lands acquired by Federal agencies by purchase, donation, or transfer amounted to 50,082,229 acres throughout the world as of June 30, 1956, compared with 724,504,778 acres of public domain (reserved and unreserved) held on that date in continental United States and Alaska.

Federally owned real property out-

side the continental United States as of the same date totaled 365,082,217 acres. Defense agencies held 2,676,538 acres of this property. Civil agencies held the remaining 362,405,679 acres. The Department of Defense did not report the locations of its acreage throughout the world. However, for civil agencies, outside of Alaska, Federal holdings were as follows: North America, 405,868 acres; South America, 52 acres; Europe, 798 acres; Africa, 932 acres; Asia, 1,272 acres; Australasia, 743 acres; Pacific Islands, 17,000 acres; Hawaii, 197,359 acres; and Wake Island, 2,600 acres.

IN FOREIGN COUNTRIES, civil agencies of the United States held 5,150 acres, including Department of State, 2,008 acres; United States Information Agency, 1,949 acres; and General Services Administration, 1,187 acres. These lands were used for office building locations, 300 acres; harbor and port terminals, 56 acres; and housing, 1,360 acres. Other land and vacant land totaled 3,434 acres.

CENTRALIZED RECORDS of public domain of the United States are maintained by the Bureau of Land Management of the Department of the Interior. Records of acquired lands are maintained by the various acquiring or administering agencies. Inventory reports of federally owned real estate are prepared annually as of the end of each fiscal year and are issued early in each session of the Congress. The General Services Administration, in collaboration with the General Accounting Office, develops and supervises agency procedures for the maintenance of real property accounts and the reporting of inventory data.

By means of inventory reports and exchange of information, Federal agencies are able to avoid unnecessary acquisitions, effect economies through joint uses, facilitate transfers or exchanges of administration, and return surplus federally acquired lands to private ownership.

Land and our economic development.

Land was a magnet that drew the first colonists. It shaped the pattern of growth and development; as the slow, painful process of creating a Nation unfolded, the land and its control and use became the main focus of national concern, as expressed in many laws, acts, and policies. Finally it became clear that the agricultural economy was still under the stewardship of family farmers. By *Joe R. Motheral,* formerly of the Farm Economics Research Division; later agricultural adviser to the National Planning Board of Pakistan.

LAND and the promise of its bounty attracted the colonists to this continent. They came first in a trickle of adventurers and seekers after religious liberty. Then, as the Colonies became a Nation and expanded westward, came wave after wave of land-hungry, space-hungry, freedom-hungry refugees from crowded Europe.

The land sustained the colonists until they could build on it. The land was to be the incentive for the network of transportation and communication that bound the Republic together. It was the land that became the basis of the American educational system and a paramount factor in economic, political, and industrial development.

The land and its waters shaped the pattern of settlement and growth. Soil, topography, vegetation, minerals, the animal life the land supported, and the course of streams ordained in large measure where the settlers would pause. If they remained, it was to reap the produce of good land. If they moved on, it was in response to the lure of other land that was richer or more abundant.

Concentrations of people occurred—in conformity with an ancient principle—at the decisive breaks in the natural features of the land and water. Cities grew where the mode of transportation had to be altered—on the seacoasts, lakes, and rivers; at the terminals of canals, railroads, and stagecoaches; at mountain passes; and between woods and plains.

Farmers were able to thrive in large numbers on relatively small tracts when soil and climate were good, but the massing of people in integrated centers reflected the handling and processing of goods in transit.

The first immigrants included Scotch-Irish, Germans, Dutch, Welsh, Swedes, and Frenchmen, but most came from England. Among them were a few artisans, mechanics, sailors, fishermen, merchants, soldiers, and country squires. The majority, though, were farm laborers and tenants. English agriculture was undergoing changes that made life hard for those at the bottom of the manorial system. A rapid growth of population and the enclosure movement were making the growing number of surplus farmworkers restless. By 1607 they were ripe for the venture to the New World.

From the time of the first settlement at Jamestown in 1607 until independence was achieved, colonial history was marked by conflicting land claims and struggles over methods of settlement. England, France, Spain, Portugal, Sweden, and Holland contested for su-

28

premacy of territorial claims. Triumph of one or another would have meaningful consequences. As each failed, leaving England dominant, the pattern of control of land resources that began to evolve has affected ever since our economy and political philosophy.

MANY FORCES motivated the English colonists, but above all they sought liberation from a feudalistic system that was dying too slowly in their homeland. In the coin of the times, this goal translated roughly into family dominion over an area of productive land.

The goal was not easily attained.

Among the techniques England used for shifting the control of land into the hands of the actual farmers—always through the good offices of favored explorers and grantees—three systems stand out.

In the first system of land disposition, the friends of the King received large grants under terms designed to transplant medieval feudalism to America.

Parcels of these landed estates were transferred eventually to the farmers through feudal payments, called quitrents, which relieved the landholder of further payments, dues, and personal services. Having fled from the indignities of this system at home, the immigrant farmers resisted it in America and weakened or destroyed it whenever they could.

Another system of land disposition in the New England Colonies was prophetic of a type of democratic community action that proved to be a significant feature of rural life in the United States into the 20th century. Trading companies became governing bodies for land settlement. Abetted by Puritan concepts of equity and individual participation in group decisions, the New England system at once encouraged independence and cooperation among the farmers. It assured against the creation of class structure in agriculture wherever its impact was felt.

The Virginia Company provided the third important method for disposing of the virgin lands in colonial America.

It involved the use of headrights, and later treasure rights, which entitled the holder to 50 acres of unoccupied land in the vast Commonwealth of Virginia. The individual was free to choose his own holding. Those who came first claimed the best locations and soils. Sea captains and merchants in time assumed headrights for their sailors, servants, and slaves, and plantations were created along the coastal lands, where the early agriculture required a large labor force. Free men, who relied on their own labor, meanwhile were pushed on toward the interior to develop their small holdings. Often they were isolated, and always they were in dread of forays by Indians.

These systems of land settlement set the stage for later struggles over land policy. The increase and movement of population brought different sets of rules into conflict.

The Colonies were deemed to start at the Atlantic coast and to extend westward endlessly. Such infinite horizons brought more and more settlers to the new country, and they spread in every landward direction. From an estimated 28 thousand settlers in the English Colonies in 1640, the population rose to 85 thousand in 1660, 214 thousand in 1690, and 2,205 thousand in 1770. About 9 in 10 families were farm families at the time of the Revolutionary War.

The land was vital in the Revolution: The colonists' positive staying force in their war with the mother country was their knowledge that freedom was possible—had they not had a treasured experience as freeholders, as free men? Militarily, their chances of success were absurd. Ideologically, they could not and would not lose.

As THE SLOW, painful process of creating a Nation unfolded, the land and its control and use became the main focus of national concern.

The fledgling country was blessed with astute leadership. Men of vision and intellect were almost everywhere, it seemed, when their skills were most needed. Foremost, besides the first President himself, were the men in Washington's Cabinet, and none was more forceful and enlightened than were Thomas Jefferson and Alexander Hamilton.

In the sharply different personalities of Jefferson and Hamilton the great public issues were joined. Each device of communication then available was used by Jefferson and Hamilton and their adherents to advance their opposing causes—public debate, newspapers, pamphlets, letters, and persuasion within the Cabinet.

Hamilton's position favored banking, commerce, and industry. Jefferson was the spokesman for agrarian interests. The destiny of the land and landsmen was at stake. Resolution of the contest was to condition American history for centuries.

A somewhat closer look at the central issue is warranted.

Jefferson loved farming, and he spoke of it tenderly: "I have often thought that if heaven had given me choice of my position and calling, it should have been on a rich spot of earth, well watered, and near a good market for the productions of the garden. No occupation is so delightful to me as the culture of the earth. . . ."

Jefferson was the carrier of an ancient tradition, a tradition that prompted Aristotle to exclaim, "Husbandry is the mother and nurse of the other arts," and other philosophers, statesmen, and poets to apostrophize it and the miracles of Nature and life processes.

Jefferson had a down-to-earth motive for championing agriculture. A politician, he was aware that about 90 percent of the voters in the new United States were farmers. He was convinced that the last oppressive vestige of feudalism must be destroyed in the new country if the novel plan of government called democracy were to have a chance. He reasoned that ownership of property makes for responsible citizenship. As the principal kind of property, land must be distributed among all of the people in some form of unrestricted

ownership. A country of yeomen, Jefferson held, would assure the survival of the dream and the substance of the democratic state.

That was the family-farm ideal. Although it was imperfectly defined, the concept of the family farm nevertheless had power and meaning for the pioneers. Then, as now, it meant that the family worked and managed its own productive resources—resources sufficient to assure an independent living but not so great as to bring cleavage between management and labor. It was to pervade and inspire the minds of Americans in the tumultuous years to follow and to affect the land policies of the country and the whole economic, social, and political climate as well.

He had formidable opposition. The brilliant Hamilton and his adherents held that the future of the United States lay in the direction of rapid industrial growth. To the Hamiltonians, or Federalists, this meant a powerful central government to guide economic development. These were men of comparative wealth—bankers, merchants, manufacturers, land jobbers—in the main, a creditor class.

Jefferson's anti-Federalists were the farmers. Most of them were debtors. The differences spread over a broad ideological front, but the central issue was one of property rights and the proper role of government in protecting them.

Hamilton, as the Secretary of State, commanded a wide audience for his proposals. He issued remarkable reports on public credit, taxation, banking, coinage, manufacturing, and public lands. He questioned the thesis that agriculture is "the most beneficial and productive object of human industry," arguing for the greater productivity of manufacturing, commerce, and trade. His position on the public lands favored its disposition in large tracts that would give the land jobbers an advantage.

A considerable part of the Federalist program was fulfilled. The Funding Act of 1790 provided for assumption of the debts of the various States by the National Government. It promoted confidence by foreign investors in the United States, and their capital flowed into the country when it was needed most.

A base for financing the Federal Government was established in 1791 with the voting of excise taxes on rum and whisky. The first protective tariff followed in 1816. The Bank of the United States was created. The currency was standardized. The Jay Treaty freed American shipping from English domination. By 1803, nearly half of the American issues of stocks and bonds were held by foreign investors, the only source—besides the produce of the land—for financing early industrial development.

If the Jeffersonians meanwhile were suffering setbacks in their opposition to financial power, they nonetheless struck telling blows against a feudalistic land policy. The Revolution itself caused a violent reaction against the Tories who held the manorial estates. The big landed holdings were confiscated one by one and subdivided into small farms. Quitrents were abolished. The principle known as entail, under which a land title resided permanently in the same family, was declared illegal in 1786 in all except two States. Another of the trappings of feudalism, primogeniture—the exclusive right of inheritance by the firstborn—was cast out in 1791.

As the country's land area was extended and the population rose by the millions, one compromise after another was effected between those who shared Hamilton's philosophy and those who followed Jefferson.

Marred though the period often was by extremism, speculation, waste, and at times by corruption, the people continued to settle the West as freeholders who substantially achieved the democratic ideal of the family farm. The Nation managed to adopt most of the useful features of two conflicting sets of policies. While the United States was becoming a great industrial power, family farmers were exercising their independence to assure survival of a responsive, popular government.

Daniel Webster summarized it thus: "Our New England ancestors brought thither no great capitals from Europe; and if they had, there was nothing productive in which they could have been invested. They left behind them the whole feudal policy of the other continent. They came to a new country. There were as yet no lands yielding rent, and no tenants rendering service.

"The whole soil was unreclaimed from barbarism. They were themselves either from their original condition, or from the necessity of their common interest, nearly on a level in respect to property. Their situation demanded a parceling out and division of the land, and it may fairly be said that this necessary act *fixed the future frame and form of their government.* The character of their political institutions was determined by the fundamental laws respecting property. The consequence of all these causes has been a great subdivision of the soil and a great equality of condition; the true basis, most certainly, of popular government."

THE SUCCESSION OF LAWS governing the disposition of public lands in the United States indicates at once the magnitude and pace of settlement and the range of policy adjustments underlying it. To the nucleus of the Thirteen Original Colonies, more than 1,300 million acres were added to the public domain between 1781 and 1853.

Differences arose from the outset over the method of transferring public land to the persons who were to occupy it. One view was that the Government sorely needed revenue and that the land should be sold to the settlers. Another view was that the land should be free. A middle ground was reached before it was over, and most public land acquired by individuals was sold to them, but at a very low price.

First among the measures used to dispose of public land was the military bounty, a practice nearly as old as war.

Designed to encourage enlistments during wartimes and to reward faithful soldiers afterward, the free land was offered initially to volunteers by the Continental Congress during the Revolution. Although the practice was recurrent through the First World War, it never was highly important in terms of the land area involved. Bounties were again used in the War of 1812 and in the Mexican War. General land policies had been so liberalized by the time of the Civil War as to make unnecessary special legislation favoring soldiers. Bounty land warrants accounted for about 61 million acres of the public domain.

The first legislation of wide significance after the Revolution was the Land Ordinance of 1785. It was filled with compromises between farming and speculative interests, but the ordinance nevertheless established several principles that were to endure and to serve the objective of orderly economic development. It required that surveys of the extent, value, and ownership precede the sale of land; that sales were to be completed township by township in order to solidify settlement; and that at least 2 of each 36 sections in a township were to be dedicated to the support of public schools. It prohibited the purchase of land by political favorites. As a deterrent to land jobbers, half of the parcels were to be sold in sections and half in townships at a minimum price of a dollar an acre in cash.

The Ordinance of 1785 was a combination of the New England and Virginia systems. It soon drew protests from the settlers. Some of the land companies that sprang up were more concerned with quick profits than with legitimate settlement. By the time a million acres had been disposed of, the Congress began to enact a series of laws that were more in keeping with the wishes of the frontier "radicals." The drift of the legislation was toward smaller parcels, lower prices, and liberal credit terms.

Although the minimum price of federally owned land was raised to 2 dollars an acre in 1796, competitive selling by the States and by individuals with large holdings eventually forced a reduction. A credit feature was introduced in 1800 whereby a purchaser could pay a fourth down and the balance in four annual installments. Interest charges were eliminated except in cases of delinquency. The Congress was listening to the voice of the West.

The credit system was not wholly successful. About one-fourth of the 19 million acres sold between 1800 and 1820 reverted to the Government for lack of payment. Many farmers who held on were heavily in debt. Advocates of family-sized units in 1820 won a victory when the minimum size was dropped to 80 acres and the price to 1.25 dollars an acre, a figure that remained in effect for most lands for a century. For 100 dollars, then, a farmer could go into business free of land debt, usually on a tract of manageable size. Title to 75 million acres of public land passed into the hands of the settlers within 20 years. More than a third of this land was sold in Ohio, Illinois, and Indiana. Many transactions were made in the then Far Western States of Missouri and Iowa.

The settlers approached the Great Plains warily and determinedly. The Plains were among the last to be subdued. They were passed over early in the rush toward the Pacific in the search for gold. Formidable tribes of Indians lived in the region. It was difficult to apply conventional agricultural tools and to cope with the moisture deficiency of the Plains. Thus permanent settlement was thwarted there for years.

Walter Prescott Webb credits the invention of the Colt revolver, the windmill, and barbed wire with making possible the eventual conquest of this rugged environment. To these innovations must be added the steel plow which afforded mastery of the heavy sod that covered the land beyond the wooded areas of the East, and in time the McCormick reaper, the threshing machine, seeders, harrows, binders, and many other laborsaving devices.

A MAJOR CHANGE in land policy was made in 1841 when the Pre-emption Act was passed. In effect, it sanctioned the rights of squatters on unsurveyed land. It was another triumph for the restless westerners.

Some observers regarded preemption as mere legalization of a fact, or of "squatter sovereignty," as thousands of pioneers already had staked out their personal claims on public land in the form of cabin homes and plowed fields.

In the existing political atmosphere, there was little expectation that they would relinquish these "rights" without a struggle.

The act called for the filing of a declaration to purchase as much as 320 acres within 3 months after settlement, or after filing of the survey plat, and payment within 18 months thereafter. Payments, at 1.25 dollars an acre, could be made in cash, military bounty warrants, or agricultural college scrip.

From its inception to its repeal in 1891, the act was criticized by a succession of Commissioners of the General Land Office. Their grounds for condemning it included fraudulent filing by the exploiters who were interested mainly in timber, mineral, or water rights and who gave no thought to rational economic development. The act reinforced the property rights of many bona fide settlers, however, and it may be fairly regarded as one of a sequence of reassertions of the family-farm ideal.

The Nation moved gradually toward a completely free land policy. An eloquent spokesman for such a policy was Senator Thomas Hart Benton, who shouted on the Senate floor, "I . . . contend that no country under the sun was ever paid for in gold and silver before it could be settled and cultivated." Senator Benton was reflecting the sentiment of his growing western constituency.

The migration from Europe after 1800 began to reach the proportions of a human tide, which fed the sprawling flow of population across the country to the West. A quarter of a million immigrants were arriving in the United States each year by 1850. During the 60 years from the first census in 1790 to 1850, the national population rose from 4 million to 23 million. The frontier moved to Texas in the south and lay along an irregular line bordering the 100th meridian to Minnesota in the north.

Great cities came into being, especially along the waterways. Cleveland by 1860 had a population of 43 thousand and Chicago had 100 thousand. Around them, as around the eastern cities, land values rose, and agriculture was intensified to meet the urban demand for fresh vegetables, meat, and milk. The Northeastern States, hard pressed to compete with the mounting production from the fertile western lands, turned more and more to the manufacture of industrial goods. The southern Cotton Belt moved steadily westward, absorbing the cattle ranges and pushing the livestock industry ahead of it. In a few years, under the impetus of extensive land grants, the railroads were to crisscross the country.

Senator Benton's westerners were voters, and they were becoming numerous. Their first strenuous drive for free land met with partial success in 1854 with the passage of the Graduation Act, when they overrode the eastern argument for converting public land into public revenue. This law related the price of land to the actual demand for it. A tract that remained unsold for 10 years was reduced to 1 dollar an acre; if unsold for 15 years, to 75 cents; in 20 years, to 50 cents; in 25 years, to 25 cents; and in 30 or more years, to 12.5 cents.

There was economic logic in this change despite many objections from eastern Congressmen. A uniform price for land of greatly different quality hardly conformed to the realities of the situation, as subsequent events were to prove. Eight times as much land was sold in the year following passage of the Graduation Act as in the average year preceding it. Almost 26 million acres were sold at these lower prices.

Perhaps only the clamor for wholly free land prevented the extension of this principle to all of the western domain.

Free land became a reality in 1862, when the Homestead Act was passed. The slavery question held up formal acceptance of the doctrine for a time, but with the onslaught of the Civil War all doubts were removed, and the bill was passed. Except for a small filing fee, settlers could become owners of 160 acres literally at no cost. The only reservation, made in the interest of permanent settlement, was the requirement that 5 years must pass before the occupant could become an owner.

THE HOMESTEAD ACT marked a turnabout in the land policy. It threw open for settlement all the lands of the West to anyone who would claim them. The homestead policy was imperfect in many respects and was the subject of one amendment after another as the Congress reacted to the demands of the western settlers. Most of the changes tended toward further liberalization. They dealt mainly with adaptations of a law written for the humid areas to the exigencies of subhumid areas. Residence requirements were reduced to the equivalent of 21 months.

The Kinkaid Act upgraded the definition of "homestead" to 640 acres in western Nebraska. The Enlarged Homestead Act, with amendments, in 1909 and 1910 brought a dozen Far Western States under a 320-acre provision. The commutation privilege, which allowed for attainment of ownership by cash payment at the preemption rate of 1.25 or 2.50 dollars an acre, was adjusted repeatedly to discourage land speculators. The coal and mineral rights were reserved by the Government in the Stock-Raising Homestead Act of 1916. Legislative relief was provided for homesteaders at various times to aid them in withstanding crop failures, drought, destruction by grasshoppers, and forest and prairie fires.

Homesteading frequently was a subject of abuse by opportunists of one type or another. Dummy settlement and trick resales were common, but not common enough to defeat the broad purposes of the law. These purposes were directed toward covering the West with free Americans who held the resources to survive and who were loyal to the Union. More than 200 million acres were settled by about 1.5 million farmers under the Homestead Act.

Benjamin H. Hibbard, a leading authority on the public-land policies, praised the act but criticized it for its lack of adaptability to subhumid areas and for playing into the hands of the timber merchants. He also expressed concern over the mounting rate of farm tenancy in homesteaded areas.

Concern over the wanton destruction of forest land was first manifested by the Federal Government in 1873 when the Timber-Culture Act was passed—"An act to encourage the growth of timber on western prairies." A quarter section might be acquired by anyone who would plant and protect 40 acres of timber for 10 years. The Government was trying to defeat by legislation what Nature had deemed appropriate for the Plains. After numerous amendments, the Timber-Culture Act was pronounced a failure in 1891 and was repealed. Nearly 10 million acres received final entry before the law was set aside.

Other attempts were made to adapt the Homestead Act to the unique character of the areas of low rainfall.

"Land must be held in larger quantities," President Grant said in 1875, "to justify the expense of conducting water upon it to make it fruitful or to justify using it as pasturage."

Two years later the first Desert Land Act became law. Under it, a settler in any of 11 Western States and territories could become owner of 640 acres at a cost of 1.25 dollars an acre, provided he irrigate the land within 3 years after filing. The law was not clear about the amount of water that is necessary to constitute "irrigation," and absentee buyers took advantage of its lax provisions to acquire large acreages in the West by illegal means. Slowly the view prevailed that the Government itself should assume some responsibility for irrigation projects. A variety of modifications were introduced in the meantime. The most significant, in 1891, permitted the establishment of irrigation associations and banned nonresident ownership.

Strong pressure was exerted for ceding public lands to the States. The Carey Act in 1894 formalized this aim by giving consent to the donation of an area not to exceed a million acres to each of several Western States. It brought into creation the 160-acre limitation on land reclamation, cultivation, and settlement that was to become a slogan for small farmers and a byword of controversy for years to come. State boards were authorized to administer the affairs of irrigation districts, and the Department of the Interior had to contend with the artifices of promoters eager to take over the half dollar an acre advanced by the settlers. Failure of the enterprise led to Federal participation in reclamation.

THE RECLAMATION ACT of 1902 was a significant move toward a national policy of conservation. It established a reclamation fund from the money received from sale of land and was later augmented by a percentage of the royalties from oil and mineral leases on lands of the United States and collections of "cost-of-construction" payments that settlers were obliged to make within 10 years after taking over a tract of land. The 160-acre limitation again was imposed, this time by restricting water rights to any one person to a quarter section. Sales to nonresidents were prohibited.

Since the passage of the Reclamation Act, the Reclamation Service (now Bureau) has developed 77 irrigation projects that involve more than 7 million acres. The costs and the benefits of these projects have greatly exceeded the expectations of the early sponsors of the legislation.

Other serious problems, according to the Commissioner of the General Land Office, included monopolization by some individuals of the available water supply on desert land that could not be irrigated artificially. That many settlers were disappointed is indicated by the fact that of some 42 million acres originally entered under the different desert land laws up to 1956, patents were obtained on only about 11 million acres.

Whether the high costs of the development of desert land can be justified in the public interest is still a subject of debate. Critics of the policy regard it as a form of regional discrimination and argue that much land in more humid areas can be reclaimed by drainage and other measures at considerably lower cost. It is also contended that American agriculture has demonstrated a capacity to overproduce on land that is already developed and that more farmland is not needed.

The defenders of the policy generally emphasize the human values concerned and hold that nearly 4 dollars of enhanced land valuation have been created for each dollar spent by the Government on irrigation.

Regardless of the merits of this issue, one alternative—promotion of the drainage of swampland in the public domain—was a complete failure. The method adopted under the Swamp Land Acts of 1849 and 1850 was to grant title to the States of the federally owned land which, in the absence of levees or the erection of drainage facilities, was thought to be worthless.

This program miscarried from the start. Classification of land subject to these acts was unsatisfactory. Fraud became commonplace in most of the 15 States that were subject to the law. Overlapping claims piled up in a mass that was not straightened out for years. When claims were resolved, it was usually at the expense of the Federal Government in payment of indemnities to the States or aggrieved persons.

Very little drainage was accomplished. The States realized only small returns for their participation. Of the 65 million acres finally alienated under the Swamp Land Acts, an unknown but apparently helpful part of the funds found its way into educational grants.

The handling of mineral rights in the public domain posed a special problem that has not yet been solved entirely. Should the Federal Government withhold title to a totally unpredictable source of wealth lying under its huge landholdings? The Ordinance of 1785 cautiously reserved rights to the Government of all gold and silver discovered, but it was more an evidence of hopefulness than an enunciation of policy. When a gold strike happened at Coloma, Calif., in 1848, the country was unprepared to deal with the question of ownership of extremely valuable minerals. The Congress had occupied itself between these dates with laws that affected deposits of salt, coal, lead, iron, and copper. It amounted mostly to passing title to the miners at an elevated price. There was no consistent policy for separating surface and subsurface rights.

Beginning with a series of acts after the Civil War, the Congress granted free exploration rights on public lands to all citizens and prospective citizens. It fixed a price on the title to placer lands at 2.50 dollars an acre and on lode claims at 5 dollars an acre. Oil and saline lands were brought under the placer mining rule in 1897 and 1901, respectively. Under President Lincoln's urging, a minimum of 25 dollars an acre was placed on coal lands in 1864. This charge was later reduced to 10 or 15 dollars, depending on the distance of the site from the nearest railroad.

Coal was a strategic factor in the developmental era of the 19th century. It received particular attention from the lawmakers. Provision was made for the withdrawal of all valuable coal lands from private entry, first by order of the President and finally, in 1910, by act of the Congress. Surface and subsurface rights were separated in the same year. The latter were reserved to the Government, with provision for reimbursement of a settler on land not already withdrawn whose surface operations were damaged by discovery and removal of coal. The withdrawal policy was abridged in 1920, when the Mineral Leasing Act was passed and a plan of competitive bidding was established. Meanwhile 35 million acres of coal land, 2.5 million acres of phosphate land, and 6.5 million acres of oil land had been withdrawn from private entry.

Of all the riches of the public domain, none was dissipated more rapidly or with less benefit to the general public than the forest resources. Not until 1817 was legislation related to public forest lands passed. From then until the Timber and Stone Act of 1878, neither the laws nor their administration were adequate to prevent the wholesale slashing of timber in the public domain. Settlers who moved into forested areas under the Homestead Act, or preemption, or with no legal sanction, tended to regard timber as a free good, as did various lumber companies that were raiding the forests. For lack of effective administrative machinery, it was almost impossible for one to buy timber on public lands even if there had been the desire. Many westerners complained that they were forced by circumstances to become trespassers, as timber was essential in mining and many other activities.

THE TIMBER CUTTING ACT and the Timber and Stone Act came in 1878.

The first authorized timber cutting for "mining and domestic purposes." It was an effort to recognize the legitimate needs of settlers in the Far Western States. Instead of reducing violations of the law, however, it is generally credited with having accelerated unlawful depredations.

The Timber and Stone Act originally applied only to California, Oregon, and Nevada and to the Washington Territory. It was extended to all public-land States 15 years later. It set a minimum price of 2.50 dollars an acre on lands valued chiefly for timber and stone and a limit of 160 acres that could be acquired by one person. It forbade purchases by dummy buyers.

For the next 30 years, the 2.50-dollar minimum was in practice virtually the maximum selling price, although some of the land bought under the act was reported by the Land Office to have an actual worth of 100 dollars an acre. Fraudulent entries were commonplace.

The law failed of its purpose to "give the homemaker a timber lot to be used in conjunction with his homestead." It resulted in the alienation of more than 13 million acres of public forest land at an average price of about 2.75 dollars an acre. Possibly its most notable contribution was in strengthening the public resolve to conserve what was left of its forest reserves.

A closely related problem was to protect the public grazing lands from misuse. During the first 100 years after the United States became a Nation, free range was taken for granted on the public lands of the West. When barbed wire became available at low cost, however, cattlemen began fencing in huge areas of the public domain. Some of the tracts covered a million acres each. Considerable land suitable for cultivation was engrossed along with the rest. The maze of fences impeded even such essential travel as that of mail carriers.

The Government in 1885 took a hand by outlawing enclosure of public lands and prescribing punishment for offenders. Most of the fences were removed within 5 years, and the free range was restored.

There ensued an interval of private compacts among livestock producers, who divided up the territory and made their own rules. These agreements were not always kept. Cattlemen and sheepmen collided so frequently and so violently that their armed battles became a colorful item of the country's literature. Worse for the future productiveness of the land, however, was the over-grazing. The Public Lands Commission reported in 1904 that the "general lack of control . . . has resulted in the ruin of millions of acres of otherwise valuable grazing territory." The homestead laws, with their 640-acre limitation on holdings, furnished no relief in regions so arid that as many as 40 thousand acres might be required to support a family.

Such were the conditions on the open range. But by 1900, in the forest reserves that were established in 1891, a system of grazing permits had been set up. It soon proved effective in adjusting livestock numbers to the carrying capacity of the land. Within a few years, these regulations resulted in an actual increase in the numbers of stock that could be grazed in national forests.

Within two decades, the 161 million acres in national-forest lands were supporting under paid permit nearly 2 million cattle, 6.5 million sheep, and thousands of horses, goats, and hogs.

Such advocates of conservation as President Theodore Roosevelt immediately saw the need to extend range-management practices to other parts of the public domain.

Range management soon was to become a feature of a broad national program of conservation that began to evolve after the turn of the century.

If many acts of public-land disposal seemed to lack conscious national purpose, that was never quite the case with the granting of the country's great land wealth to promote internal improvements and education. Most Americans almost from the start accepted the principle that conversion of an abundant public property into vital public facilities and services was in the national interest. Questions of constitutionality delayed positive action for a time, but not for long.

A few early grants from the public domain were made to individuals and States as an aid in building wagon roads. Then in 1823 Ohio received 1,142,000 acres for roadbuilding. That precedent was applied in 1841 to make large grants to 17 other States so that they might use the funds from sale of the land on "roads, railways, bridges, canals, and improvement of watercourses and draining of swamps." All of these first grants, which amounted to less than 10 million acres, ultimately were to be counted in the 137 million acres that were to represent the Federal Government's contribution toward the building of a transportation system.

Grants were made to some States for penitentiaries, fish hatcheries, hospitals, schools, colleges, and a miscellany of special-purpose uses while a policy was being oriented toward transportation. About 3.25 million acres were transferred to the States between 1823 and 1869 for building wagon roads.

Enthusiasm for canals reached a peak between 1825 and 1850, and 4.5 million acres went to augment State bond issues and sundry financing of canals.

Much of the interest in this type of waterway was stimulated by the success of the Erie Canal, which, located as it was in a strategic and highly industrialized area, emerged as about the only self-supporting canal.

Three grants, which add to 2.25 million acres, were made to Alabama, Wisconsin, and Iowa for the development of rivers.

THE RAILROADS received the largest proportion of the public domain allocated for internal improvement.

Railroads, unlike canals and roads, were privately owned, and the policy of encouraging construction of them through public-land grants did not receive immediate acceptance. The need for railroads became urgent only when settlement spread far beyond the Mississippi and other navigable rivers and lakes. The only real concession made to railroads until 1850 was the right-of-way privilege through public lands, but gaining headway was the argument that railroads would increase materially the value of the Government's holdings wherever they were built.

The Illinois Central land grant of 1850 precipitated 21 years of generous subsidy that speeded up western settlement and brought the country into strongly interconnected physical unity. It also set the pattern for the dozen other major railroad grants to be extended later. The main line of the Illinois Central was to be laid from Chicago to Mobile, Ala., and from Dubuque, Iowa, to the mouth of the Ohio River. Except for the transfers of title made through the legislatures of the States affected—Illinois, Alabama, and Mississippi—instead of passing directly to the company, the conditions of the Illinois Central grant became an approximate model of later railroad grants. The States, and through them the railroad, were given alternate sections of land for 6 miles on each side of the line. Wherever this land was already sold, "lieu" lands in alternate sections within 15 miles were substituted. Sections lying between the railroad lands were to be sold for not less than 2.50 dollars an acre.

As the West was the chief beneficiary of railroad grants, many southern and eastern interests resisted this type of grant program. They were only partly successful, however, and after the Civil War began and the political voice of the South was stilled, eastern investments in the railroads increased to such an extent that the interests of the East and West were joined, and an enormous outpouring of railroad grants was underway.

The Union Pacific and the Central Pacific in 1862 were given alternate sections for 20 miles on each side of their proposed routes to the west coast. Similar grants were made later to the Northern Pacific, the Southern Pacific, and the Atlantic & Pacific (later renamed the Atchison, Topeka & Santa Fe). Use of the States as intervening parties in the transfer or sale of the grants was abandoned. Before long, stories of bribery and speculative manipulation were rife, and railroad grants ended in 1871.

In the construction of railroads, people had more control over the natural features of the land than was true in the development of waterways, the exploitation of timber and mineral resources, and agricultural uses of the soil. Although they were restricted by topography to some degree, the railroads could determine the location of terminals, junctions, and way stations. More than one great family fortune was founded on knowledge of where railroad centers were to be laid down and consequently where cities and land values would rise.

Whatever its abuses, the development of railroads offered proof of man's ascending mastery over his environment and hastened a desirable geographical allotment of the population at a rate without parallel in history.

Conflicts between the power of the railroads and the aspirations of the settlers were inevitable. Preemption and railroad grants did not mix readily. In the long struggle between the two, the Congress usually was compelled to act in behalf of the farmers who expressed their resentment in a succession of agrarian upheavals, which included the "railroad monopoly" as a target. The Panic of 1873 confirmed the farmers' worst fears and gave an impetus to the Populist movement, which lost its momentum only in 1896 with the defeat of William Jennings Bryan for President.

Before it ended, the policy of railroad grants removed 128 million acres of land from the public domain—70 percent of it directly and the rest through allocations made through 12 of the States. Its redistribution to farmers and other occupants was pushed by selling campaigns of ingenious proportions. Railroad companies established land divisions that flooded this country and parts of western Europe with advertisements that extolled the virtues of life on the prairies and in the forests along the rights-of-way. Most of the companies held much of the choice land off the market by advance pricing, but at the same time it was to their economic advantage to cover the countryside with producing farmers, and they did that to a remarkable degree. Railroads obtained an estimated average of slightly less than 5 dollars an acre in their first 20 years of land sales.

THE EDUCATIONAL GOALS were among the first that were honored by the immigrants from Europe. Land was the basis of implementation, as so often it was in the new country. The colonists, led by the persevering New Englanders, began to utilize land and its values to support schools as soon as town and colony could be organized. The Virginia Colony was the first to set aside portions of its lands for free schools in 1621. Massachusetts endowed the first college in America in 1636, when Harvard College, with 500 acres for its maintenance, came into existence. The College of William and Mary in Virginia, Yale, and Dartmouth were other early recipients of land.

For the youth of the future, "Section Number 16 in every township" acquired a distinctive meaning in 1802, when the Congress, acting under the Ordinance of 1787, admitted Ohio to the Union and marked one section in each township for the use of schools.

Section 16 became identified with educational support in scores of bills throughout the years, and if section 16 were already occupied, indemnity or substitute lands were provided. Some kind of school grant has been included as a standard clause in almost all land legislation of consequence until recent times. The saline grants, swampland funds, the half-million acre, and "five and three percent" grants were no exceptions. Common schools benefited to the extent of more than 77 million acres as State after State entered the Union under agreements permitting reservation of land for school purposes.

Agitation began in 1850 to establish institutions for the advancement of agriculture and the mechanic arts, their support to be provided by appropriations from the public domain. Impatient for Federal action, Michigan authorized an agricultural college in 1855, and it was built 2 years later east of Lansing. Massachusetts, Maryland, Pennsylvania, and Iowa followed quickly. They and other States began to petition the Congress for national financing of their new colleges.

Here was an American creation. It placed strong emphasis on practical education, a product of the hard lessons of the frontier. Equality of opportunity to learn rang of democratic conviction. The demand for public land to activate the plan was in keeping with the American philosophy of turning the general wealth to the general good. Classical studies were not excluded from the curricula of the proposed institutions; rather, they were placed in a framework of workaday realism. If anything in the idea was imported, it was scarcely more than a yearning for knowledge, a trait too universal for national identity.

Representative Justin S. Morrill of Vermont was the author of the bill that finally passed in 1862. The Morrill bill granted public lands to the States for establishing colleges to teach agriculture and the mechanic arts, the amount to equal 30 thousand acres for each Senator and Representative from a State under the census of 1860.

The older States that lacked sufficient public land received negotiable scrip for land elsewhere. A maximum of 10 percent of the funds raised from the sale of the granted land or scrip could be spent for college and experimental farms; the rest must be invested in safe stocks, which would constitute a perpetual fund. Dollar appropriations were made in amending legislation to assure a minimum fund of 25 thousand dollars for each college, regardless of the sum raised by sales of land. This was enough to enable most States to establish land-grant colleges within a few years. Individual States received between 90 thousand acres (Wyoming) and 780 thousand acres (Pennsylvania) of free land under the act. From sales of the land they soon had receipts ranging from 55 thousand dollars (Wyoming) to 6,779,700 dollars (New York).

The grants for common schools and other institutional allocations brought the total expenditure of public-domain lands for education to approximately 99 million acres—surely one of the most notable applications of America's landed heritage.

IN THE VIEW of Frederick Jackson Turner and other students of American history, the frontier ceased to exist about 1890. This is doubtlessly true in a physical sense. By that date much of the most productive public land had passed into private ownership; large-scale immigration into the United States was coming to an end; the population had risen to 63 million; and there was an air of permanence about settlements in city and country. The restlessness that had been so characteristic of the winning of the West was subsiding. The Nation was consolidating its gains.

It was a time for thoughtful men to assert themselves. In a conservation vacuum, land resources had been exploited to an extent that threatened permanent and irreparable damage to the national economy. Timber, minerals, and the soil were dissipated at an alarming rate. What had begun as a laissez faire approach to land development had deteriorated into a costly lack of restraint.

A few voices had been raised in protest as far back as 1878, when Maj. J. W. Powell made his famous report on the arid lands. Creation of the United States Geological Survey in 1879 marked the beginning of a systematic effort to classify the public resources. Scientific and professional organizations, such as the American Association for the Advancement of Science, directed attention persistently to the need for conservation measures. A large area was withdrawn from the disposable public domain in 1891, when the forest reserves (later called national forests) were established. The big drive came later.

Sparked by such men as Theodore Roosevelt and Gifford Pinchot, an effective conservation movement got underway in 1907, when the indefatigable Roosevelt called a conference of governors and others to consider means of calling a halt to the wastage of natural resources. The conference, which was followed by others, helped to awaken the public to the urgency of the problem. It led to the organization of the National Conservation Association. Eventually it brought about a series of laws and administrative actions that together comprised a far more enlightened conservation policy.

Conservation of forest land received the first and most intensive treatment. The functions of the Forest Service were extended gradually to include a comprehensive program of fire protection, assistance in reforestation of denuded areas, and general responsibility for promoting wise forest management.

Soil erosion was among the last of the serious land problems to receive national attention. When it did, action was hastened by dramatic duststorms in the West in 1933 and 1934. Programs of the Soil Conservation Service and the Agricultural Adjustment Administration were set in motion with State and local participation to provide technical and financial help to millions of farmers.

Awareness of the need for conserving the national landed heritage presaged the end of an epoch of frenzied development. What were the advantages and disadvantages of early land policies? How do they square with the fundamentals of sound husbandry on the one hand, and the fundamentals of democratic principles, on the other?

A balanced appraisal of the land policies of the United States must reserve a place for error, for human frailty, and for wanton exploitation of the natural endowments of land. These things aside, it must be conceded that under these policies the West was settled; the coasts were bound together; despite a divisive war, men learned to live in harmony; a working balance was struck among competing interests; and the economic system that emerged

from the turbulence had no match in history for its productivity. Perhaps these gains could not have been achieved with such incredible dispatch except under a system of towering incentives. Certainly, they could not have been maintained without the strength of family farms.

Family farmers bespoke their discontent when they were in jeopardy, and they clung fiercely to the Jeffersonian model of democracy. Their influence welled over into industrial development and served to restrain the ambitions of greedy or shortsighted men. Their contribution to the Nation's progress may be seen in the formative years of the Industrial Revolution. Starting with a paltry 33 million dollars' worth of agricultural exports set down in the records of 1802–1803, farmers—most of them on family farms—surpassed 2 billion dollars' worth of exports during the Second World War.

The trend is meaningful. As a percentage of total national exports, farm products reached their zenith early in the 19th century, at 80 percent or more of all exports, when industry most needed foreign currency for expansion. The proportional decline to a low of 8.8 percent in 1940–1941 was inversely keyed to the rise of the United States as a manufacturing country.

At times, it has appeared that the practical values associated with the family farm were about to be lost, as the rates of tenancy and land prices have mounted. In the 50 years between 1900 and 1950, the total value of farm real estate in the country rose from 16.6 to 75.3 billion dollars, while mortgage indebtedness stood at variable but discouraging levels. In 1880, the percentage of farmers who were tenants was 25.6. By 1930, it had climbed to a peak of 42.4. The stepped-up demand for farm products in wartime, however, enabled many farmers to achieve solvency. As indebtedness and tenancy rates declined, it became clear that the agricultural economy was still under the stewardship of family farmers.

The heritage of our public lands.

Almost one-fourth of the land area of continental United States is in Federal ownership. Why? The question and the answer are important because the policy for more than 100 years was to transfer the public domain to private ownership as fast as it could. The public lands include forests, rangeland, some farmland, and Indian lands. They have many values. By *John B. Bennett*, director, Technical Review Staff, the Department of the Interior; *H. R. Josephson*, chief, Division of Forest Economics Research, Forest Service; and *Hugh H. Wooten*, Farm Economics Research Division.

ABOUT 358.5 million acres of public domain, not counting land held in trust for Indians, are owned by American citizens through their Government. Land acquired by the Federal Government for various purposes—national forests and parks, military areas, and other uses—total almost 50 million acres. The United States therefore owns outright about 408.2 million acres in the 48 States.

That is an area four times the size of California and equal to six of the 11 Western States. If you would drive fast in a car—at the rate of 500 miles a day, say—it would take you 30 days or more to visit all the principal tracts. Some blocks of public land are large, but many of them are widely scattered in different regions of the country.

People, especially those who become aware for the first time of the extent of Federal holdings, often ask: "Why, in a country that is dominated by private enterprise and in which the efforts of the Government for more than a century were to dispose of its lands, almost one-fourth the land area of continental United States is still in Federal ownership?"

The answer rests on three points:

The absence of private demand for the lower grade public domain; the public interest in retaining some types of public domain in public ownership; and laws unsuited to private acquisition of some types of public domain.

The question and the answer are all the more significant because transfer of the public domain to private ownership as fast as possible was a primary policy of the Federal Government for more than a century—a policy designed to provide revenue to the Federal Treasury, provide farms and homes for settlers, and promote internal improvements, education, and other elements for strengthening the national economy.

Altogether, the title to more than a billion acres of the original public domain has been alienated since disposal began in 1785. With certain exceptions (national forests in the Lake States, Arkansas, and Florida), all the public domain within the great eastern forest region and the central prairie region has been alienated.

The residual public domain in continental United States, except Alaska, lies almost entirely in the desert, semidesert, and mountain areas of the 11

Western States. The disposal of public land went on at a high rate until about 1922, when the rate began to diminish. Disposal is now at the rate of a few hundred thousand acres a year.

Many areas in the national forests, the national parks, and certain other holdings that were withdrawn from entry before settlement began or that have been blocked out by Federal purchase are in compact blocks.

Many other Federal lands are in small and scattered holdings, including the residual unappropriated public domain. The objective of private selection of public lands was the blocking out of economic units for private use. For years no thought was given to retention of economic sizes and shapes of units for public management. In many areas, therefore, public management is complicated by a crazy-quilt pattern of Federal, State, railroad, and individual private ownerships. In some of the older public-land States, such as Arkansas, Mississippi, and Minnesota, for example, many tracts of public domain are isolated and sometimes are miles away from other Federal land.

INDIVIDUALS ORDINARILY are not interested in acquiring title to land unless they can obtain a return greater than the costs of ownership.

The productive agricultural lands and the lands suitable for residence, trade, or industry are nearly all in private ownership in the United States and in other countries. The lands of a low utility—the swamps, jungles, sandy deserts, rocky mountaintops, and Arctic barrens—usually are in public ownership. No individual can use such lands (with minor exceptions) intensively enough to justify his owning them.

It always has been difficult under the public-land laws for individuals to acquire large acreages of public land directly. As certain uses of land, such as grazing in the semiarid and arid West, required large areas for the support of an individual family enter-prise, stockmen assembled economic units only by buying from a number of homesteaders in the areas where the land was attractive to homesteaders. In sections in which the land was not productive enough to be worth the time of homesteaders, there was seldom any legal means through which a stockman could gain title to an economic grazing unit. If he controlled waterholes of other strategic areas, there was no need to acquire surrounding public domain.

An important reason for retaining large areas of land in Federal ownership is the public interest in Federal management of land for the essential public purposes—to achieve military aims, conserve and develop natural resources, and discharge our treaty obligations with the Indians.

Although public lands generally are of lower value per acre than privately owned lands in the United States, in the aggregate they contain enormous values in essential resources—forests, ranges, minerals, wildlife habitat, and scenic treasures.

THE COMMERCIAL FORESTS—about 92 million acres—comprised about one-fourth of the Federal lands in 1955. They produce or are able to produce commercial crops of timber.

The forest lands of noncommercial character in Federal holdings in the continental United States comprised about 81 million acres. They included such types as pinyon pine-juniper, chaparral, and oak woodland; subalpine forests; and unproductive stands in swampy areas. They included some productive forest lands that are reserved for recreational or other purposes. The noncommercial forests support some type of forest cover, but they are valuable chiefly for such other purposes as production of water, grazing, and general recreational use.

The Federal lands classed as commercial forests contain a substantial part of the Nation's timber resources. The total volume of sawtimber on Federal lands in 1955 in continental United

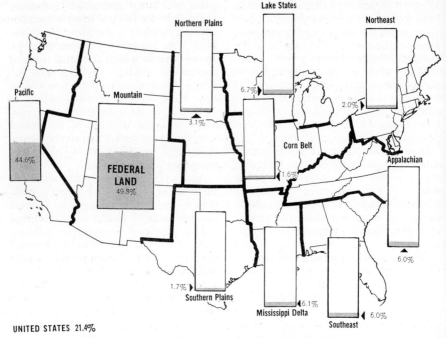

Proportion of land area in Federal ownership, 1956.

States amounted to about 767 billion board-feet—39 percent of our total sawtimber supply. The Indian lands included an additional 45 billion board-feet of sawtimber, or roughly 2 percent of the total supply of sawtimber.

Federally owned timber resources are of significantly larger importance than is indicated by either the percentage of total forest area in 1955 or the percentage of total timber volume that is in Federal landholdings.

Most of the Federal timber in national forests and other holdings is made up of softwoods, which are preferred for lumber, woodpulp, plywood, and other timber products. Most of the timber on Federal lands is old growth of relatively large size and high quality. Timber of this kind represents unusually high values; it also provides a major part of the present resource base for the various forest industries that produce lumber and other products.

Various reasons account for the concentration of a major part of the Na-

tion's remaining supply of sawtimber, particularly old-growth timber, on Federal lands. For many years after the national forests were established in the West, most of the timber harvested for lumber and other forest products was cut on private lands in the Northeast, the Lake States, and the South. As forest industries spread to the Western States, logging operations in the West also were centered largely in private stands. They generally were more accessible and contained timber of higher quality than the parts of the public domain that the Government had retained in national forests or other reserved areas.

In the national forests in the West, for example, most of the timber stands are on remote mountains. They were the last areas to be reached in the process of harvesting old-growth timber. Most national-forest timber and other Federal timber was beyond the economic reach of logging operators because of a lack of access roads.

Private timber supplies, furthermore, were more than adequate to meet market demands, and there was little demand for Federal timber. In fact, during the depression years of the 1930's, it was thought by many that Federal timber should be withheld from a market that was already oversupplied with privately owned timber.

Most of the Federal forest lands in the Eastern States were acquired for national forests, watershed protection, and timber production. Most had been cut over and heavily burned. Until they were built up over a period of years by intensified protection and management, they offered limited opportunity for commercial timber sales.

THE RANGELAND AREAS in the West are roughly three-eighths federally owned. About 212 million acres of Federal land are predominantly suitable for grazing, including both grasslands and desert shrublands. Except for some well-watered mountain meadows, chiefly in the national forests, the lands have a relatively low carrying capacity—sometimes as much as 100 acres are needed to support one cow or horse or five sheep yearlong.

Probably about a third of the western stockmen use the public ranges, usually to supplement their base properties, which supply supplementary range or harvested hay or grain. The public ranges may be used throughout the year in a few localities of favorable climate. More commonly they are used seasonally for summer, spring and fall, or winter grazing.

About 5 million acres of Federal land used for grazing in the West is in special-use areas, where grazing is permitted only when it does not conflict with the purposes for which the areas were set aside. Many of the Federal lands in the East, such as national forests, also are grazed by domestic livestock frequently under management practices that are designed to produce both timber and livestock.

CROPS ARE GROWN on only minor areas of Federal land. The Government owns farmland only under special circumstances. Most of the 1,430,000 acres of Federal land used for crops in 1954 was not needed temporarily for the special public uses for which it was set aside and was leased out for farming purposes. Some of it was used to produce feed for wildlife in wildlife refuges. Experimental and institutional farms make up a small proportion of the total Federal area used for farming. The timber, range, and cropland produce substantial incomes and indirect benefits to communities and the country.

In the West, a major part of the precipitation falls on Federal lands. More than 3 thousand communities in the West depend directly—and others depend indirectly—on water supplied from Federal holdings. The irrigation economy of the West, city populations, and industry could not flourish without adequate supplies of usable water drawn in large measure from Federal watersheds.

Most of the scenic and scientific treasures in the West were reserved from the public domain in advance of settlement and are now included in the national-park system. Many scenic areas and historical sites in the East were acquired by purchase or gift.

A major part of the big game in the West is in the national forests. Management for wildlife habitats is a major use of Federal lands in all parts of the country.

MUCH OF THE MINERAL VALUE of public land was transferred to private ownership during the settlement period of the past century. Public-domain lands bearing iron ore in Minnesota and Michigan were disposed of as farmlands. That the public lands were underlain with oil and gas was not known when the Midwest was settled, and they also were disposed of as agricultural lands.

When gold was discovered in California in 1848, the Federal Government had no organization on the

FEDERAL LAND AREA IN STATES AND PERCENTAGE OF TOTAL LAND AREA, 1956

State and region	Land area Million acres	Federal land Million acres	Percentage of total land area in Federal ownership
Pacific States:			
California	100. 3	46. 9	46. 8
Oregon	61. 6	31. 6	51. 3
Washington	42. 8	12. 7	29. 7
Total	204. 7	91. 2	44. 6
Southern Mountain States:			
Arizona	72. 7	32. 1	44. 2
Colorado	66. 5	24. 1	36. 2
Nevada	70. 3	61. 2	87. 1
New Mexico	77. 8	26. 5	34. 1
Utah	52. 7	37. 0	70. 2
Total	340. 0	180. 9	53. 2
Northern Mountain States:			
Idaho	53. 0	34. 6	65. 3
Montana	93. 3	28. 1	30. 1
Wyoming	62. 4	29. 9	47. 9
Total	208. 7	92. 6	44. 4
Great Plains States:			
Kansas	52. 5	0. 3	0. 6
Nebraska	49. 1	0. 7	1. 4
North Dakota	44. 8	1. 9	4. 2
South Dakota	49. 0	3. 2	6. 5
Oklahoma	44. 2	1. 0	2. 3
Texas	168. 6	2. 6	1. 5
Total	408. 2	9. 7	2. 4
Total 17 Western States	1, 161. 6	374. 4	32. 2
Total 31 Eastern States	742. 2	33. 8	4. 6
United States	1, 903. 8	408. 2	21. 4

ground competent to deal with the situation that was created. The miners themselves had to develop a system of establishing and maintaining claims against private competitors, with little thought of the Government's interests. The mining laws of 1868 and 1872 merely gave Federal sanction to this system, which permits any individual to file a claim to a discovery of a metallic mineral on lands having public-domain status. Practically no known reserves of these minerals consequently exist in public ownership on the public domain.

There are substantial reserves on the public domain of those minerals, including coal, oil and gas, sodium, potassium, phosphates, and sulfur, that were later placed under a leasing system.

The Federal Government owns about 20 percent of the known deposits of coal (chiefly subbituminous and lignite) in the United States and perhaps as much as 10 percent of the known reserves of oil and gas.

PURCHASES or other acquisitions for conservation, military purposes, or other specified uses from time to time have supplemented the Federal holdings of reserved public-domain lands.

Fifty million acres of such acquired lands were administered by various Federal departments in 1956. They represented about 12 percent of all Federal lands. Most of the acquired lands were bought, but some were obtained through donation, condemnation, or land exchanges.

About a third of the acquired lands—18.4 million acres—was bought or was otherwise acquired by the Department of Agriculture for national forests.

About 7 million acres were acquired in submarginal farming areas for land-utilization projects.

The Department of Defense acquired somewhat fewer than 8 million acres for military purposes.

Roughly 4 million acres were obtained in connection with programs to control floods. The remaining 9.6 million acres of acquired Federal lands are in national parks, wildlife refuges, reclamation areas, and other Federal holdings. Most of the acquired Federal lands are in the East.

THE ESTABLISHMENT of forest reserves, or national forests, was the first major conservation action by the Federal Government. The President was empowered under the law of March 3, 1891, to set apart in reserves "public land bearing forests, in any part of the public lands wholly or in part covered with timber or undergrowth, whether of commercial value or not, as public reservations . . . ."

The purposes for which the national forests were to be administered were stated by the Congress in the act of June 4, 1897: ". . . To improve and protect the forests within the reservation, or for the purpose of securing favorable conditions of waterflows, and to furnish a continuous supply of timber for use and necessities of citizens of the United States."

Subsequent legislation has extended and broadened those objectives to include the management and use of forage, recreation, and wildlife resources as well as research and demonstration.

Following passage of the act, forest lands were reserved from the public domain by successive Presidents, until in 1910 the national forests comprised about 160 million acres of public-domain land.

Under the Weeks law of 1911, additional lands were acquired by purchase for the national forests. The Congress also provided in 1922 and in 1925 for other additions to the national forests through exchanges of public land or timber for private forest lands. Donations of land for national forests were authorized in 1924.

Under these authorizations, additions were steadily made to the national forests, but sizable areas of public domain also were eliminated from the forests. The acreage of national-forest lands in 1956 was slightly less than 160 million acres in 41 States.

National-forest lands withdrawn from the original public domain, excluding land obtained in exchange for public-domain land and timber, total 133.5 million acres, or 85 percent of the total area of national forests. Purchases have totaled 18.5 million acres. About 6.6 million acres have been acquired by exchange of national-forest land or timber. About 1.7 million acres have been transferred from other Federal agencies or were donated.

Much of the land acquired for national forests was obtained in the 1930's. Those acquisitions served the basic purposes of protecting watersheds and producing timber, and often were designed to help owners of forest land, minimize tax delinquency, and stabilize the management of cutover and depleted forests. The acreage of land in the national-forest system has been relatively stable since then.

THE BANKHEAD-JONES TITLE III LANDS in 1956 amounted to about 7 million acres. These lands are administered by the Forest Service. The Government acquired them under authority of the Bankhead-Jones Farm Tenant Act of 1937, which directed the Secre-

FEDERAL DISPOSALS OF PUBLIC DOMAIN IN CONTINENTAL UNITED STATES TO 1956 [1]

	Million acres	Percentage
Disposals:		
Homesteads, sales, and grants chiefly to private individuals......	715. 8	49. 6
Granted to railroads to aid in construction of railways..........	91. 3	6. 3
Granted to States for education and public improvements......	223. 8	15. 5
Total disposals.......................................	1, 030. 9	71. 4
Indian tribal and trust lands.................................	52. 8	3. 7
Reserved for public purposes:		
National forests, parks, wildlife refuges, reclamation, power, and national-defense areas.................................	187. 8	13. 0
Unreserved and unappropriated public domain:		
Within grazing districts..................................	142. 6	9. 9
Outside grazing districts.................................	28. 1	2. 0
Total..	170. 7	11. 9
Total Federal...	358. 5	24. 9
Grand total original public domain [2]......................	1, 442. 2	100. 0

[1] U. S. Department of the Interior, Report of the Director of the Bureau of Land Management, Statistical Appendix, June 30, 1956; U. S. Senate, Doc. 25, 85th Cong., 1st sess., *Inventory Report on Real Property Owned by the United States* . . ., as of June 30, 1956, and U. S. Senate, Doc. 100, 84th Cong., 2d sess., *Inventory Report on Federal Real Property in the United States*, as of June 30, 1955, prepared by General Services Administration.

[2] The total area of the original public domain is given as computed in 1912 by a committee representing the General Land Office, the Geological Survey, and the Bureau of the Census. (See U. S. Department of the Interior, Office of the Secretary, *Areas of Acquisitions to the Territory of the United States* . . .) The total has not been adjusted for recomputation of the area of the United States which was done for the 1950 Decennial Census.

THE VARIOUS KINDS OF USES OF FEDERAL LAND [1]

	Total Federal land	Public domain land		Acquired land	
	Million acres	Million acres	Percentage	Million acres	Percentage
National resource lands:					
National forests and related areas......	[2] 167. 2	[3] 139. 3	83. 3	27. 9	16. 7
Grazing districts, and unreserved and unappropriated lands, plus certain reserved areas used partly for grazing....	178. 6	178. 3	99. 8	. 3	. 2
Reclamation and water supply, flood control and power areas.............	16. 0	9. 4	58. 8	6. 6	41. 2
National parks and historic sites........	15. 4	12. 1	78. 6	3. 3	21. 4
Wildlife refuges and game ranges........	8. 1	5. 3	65. 4	2. 8	34. 6
Institutional and other areas...........	1. 4	. 4	28. 6	1. 0	71. 4
Total.............................	386. 7	344. 8	89. 2	41. 9	10. 8
National defense......................	21. 5	13. 7	63. 7	7. 8	36. 3
United States total.................	408. 2	358. 5	87. 8	49. 7	12. 2

[1] U. S. Department of the Interior, Report of the Director of the Bureau of Land Management, Statistical Appendix, June 30, 1956; U. S. Senate, Doc. 25, 85th Cong., 1st sess., *Inventory Report on Real Property Owned by the United States* . . ., June 30, 1956; and U. S. Senate, Doc. 100, 84th Cong., 2d sess., *Inventory Report on Federal Real Property in the United States*, as of June 30, 1955, prepared by General Services Administration.

[2] Includes Bankhead-Jones Title III or Land Utilization Project lands.

[3] Includes land received in exchange for public-domain land.

tary of Agriculture "to develop a program of land conservation and land utilization, including the retirement of lands which are submarginal or not primarily suitable for cultivation in order thereby to correct maladjustments of land use . . . ."

Lands so acquired were obtained largely by purchase during the 1930's. They were supplemented by transfers from the public domain and some exchanges of land. The land-utilization project lands that remain under Federal administration are in 28 States. Their acreages range from 465 acres in Maine to nearly 2 million acres in Montana.

GRAZING DISTRICTS and unappropriated public land make up the largest block of public lands in the United States. They and certain withdrawn areas are administered by the Bureau of Land Management in the Department of the Interior. They aggregated nearly 179 million acres in 1956. They include some of the more valuable mineral lands and a few limited areas with high value for special purposes, but generally they are the public lands of low surface utility and are valuable primarily for extensive grazing. They (except the withdrawn areas) are open to entry under various land laws at the discretion of the Secretary of the Interior.

Information on how to get public-domain lands is available from the Bureau of Land Management, Department of the Interior, Washington 25, D. C.

THE NATIONAL-PARK SYSTEM includes 177 units of national parks, monuments, and parkways, a national seashore recreation area, the National Capital Parks, and several categories of historic sites. The National Park Service also administers four recreational areas around reservoirs for the Bureau of Reclamation.

At least one unit of the system is in each of 40 States and in Alaska, Hawaii, Puerto Rico, and the Virgin Islands.

445509°—58——5

Units of the national-park system were established by separate acts of the Congress or by Executive action under general enabling legislation.

Of the 15.4 million acres of the system in 1956 in continental United States, 12.1 million acres were reserved from the public domain and 3.3 million acres were acquired by Federal purchase or by donation from States, local governments, or individuals.

AREAS FOR RECLAMATION, water supply, flood control, and power totaled 16 million acres, of which more than 9 million acres have been reserved from the public domain. Nearly all of the reclamation and power reservations are in 17 Western States. Some of them are parts of (or held for) reclamation projects works. Others are reserved for opening as reclamation homesteads when water is available for irrigation. Still other areas, relatively small, were leased for the production of crops during a development period.

WILDLIFE REFUGES and game ranges comprised slightly more than 8 million acres in 1956.

Federal wildlife refuges are located along the migratory waterfowl flyways in connection with treaty obligations of the United States with Canada and Mexico to preserve and protect waterfowl migrating from one of the countries to another.

Refuges for upland game and ranges, largely for protection of big game, include several large tracts in Arizona, Montana, Nevada, Oregon, and other Western States. Slightly more than 5 million acres of refuges and ranges have been reserved from the public domain. In the wildlife refuge system are 264 separate units, which extend into 45 States.

INDIAN TRUST and tribal lands totaled about 53 million acres. The United States holds title in trust to them for various Indian tribes and individual Indians.

Most of the Indian trust lands are in

the 17 Western States. Most of them are suitable only for extensive grazing. Some are productive croplands and timberlands, and oil and gas have been discovered in many localities. About 4 million acres of land owned outright by the Federal Government are managed for the benefit of Indians.

OTHER FEDERAL LANDS set apart for special purposes totaled about 21.5 million acres. They included Army posts, airfields, housing, and storage areas, atomic energy installations, and mineral, manufacturing, and experimental areas.

About 1.4 million additional acres were used for farm and range experiment stations, institutions, hospitals, schools, prisons, public buildings, and other special purposes. About two-thirds of the military and atomic energy locations were public-domain lands; one-third was purchased or otherwise acquired.

The public domain is a large proprietary enterprise. Its acquisition by the United States was necessary in connection with the extension and maintenance of the Nation's sovereignty. Its custodianship, management, and disposal have constituted probably the largest real-estate operation in the world. A sovereign function of government seldom is undertaken for profit, but it is well to consider how the operation of the public domain has fared as a proprietary enterprise.

It would be difficult and costly to calculate the costs and returns from the public-domain enterprise, because old records are inexact or lacking, but some rough calculations, derived from statistics in annual reports of Federal agencies, indicate that the enterprise has been profitable, although the greater part of the land was given away or sold at prices under the market value.

The original cost was high for the early days of the Republic, but in modern terms it would be considered fairly low. The cash cost of purchases and cessions, including Alaska, was 85

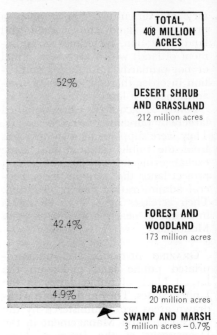

Principal vegetative cover types on Federal land.

million dollars. Associated costs, primarily those incurred in compensating and caring for the Indians, whose rights to the public domain were extinguished, undoubtedly have been much greater than the direct costs of acquisition from foreign governments or the Thirteen Original States. They may have exceeded 1 billion dollars. Costs of administration have been substantial.

The public domain began to produce revenue for the Treasury a few years after the original cession. By 1837, with the help of sales from the public domain acquired to that time, the original public debt of the United States had been paid in full. Receipts from the public domain had exceeded 200 million dollars by 1880. In later years, especially since the Mineral Leasing Act was adopted in 1920, receipts have increased rapidly. They may have totaled about 2 billion dollars.

An estimate prepared for the Committee on Government Operations of the House of Representatives put the "real estate" value of the remaining public domain, including subsurface values, at about 14 billion dollars.

ALL THE STATES have held title to large acreages at some time in their history. The Thirteen Original States and Texas took title to all land within their boundaries that had not already passed into private ownership under prior governments. As the country acquired territory by purchase and treaty, the unoccupied lands became the property of the Federal Government. In the disposition of the public domain, however, the Federal Government made large grants of land, and scrip exchangeable for land, to State governments to promote settlement and to encourage development of educational and other institutions, transportation and communication facilities, and land improvements and reclamation. Altogether, 223.8 million acres of public domain were granted to the States, and 8.2 million acres were reserved to satisfy State claims under English grants.

Some States have retained title to a large part of their State-grant land. The States have retained about 20 percent of that land—approximately 52 million acres in 1956. All States also have bought land for specific public purposes. Some acquired land through tax foreclosures.

The States owned more than 80 million acres of land, of which 27 million acres were reserved for such public uses as parks, wildlife refuges, forests, and institutional purposes. The remaining 53 million acres were not classified with reference to use, but much of this land was leased to farmers, ranchers, miners, and oil companies.

All of the States own land. Some have only a few tracts, which are used for State buildings, institutions, small parks, historic monuments, and the like. Others have large holdings set aside for parks, wildlife refuges, and forests. Some States also have large acreages that are kept as a source of revenue and are leased to farmers and ranchers for farming and grazing. Several States own valuable mineral and oil lands; when they are leased for those purposes, they yield large revenues. A few States own revenue-yielding timber lands.

About three-fourths of the State-owned land is in the 17 Western States. Most of the State-owned farming, grazing, and mineral lands also are in the West.

The land that is leased to farmers and ranchers consists largely of State-grant lands, mainly certain numbered sections, particularly sections 16 and 36, in each township. These are chiefly the remnants of lands that were granted to the Western States from the Federal public domain to help finance public services, schools, and improvements.

In the States that have offered their grant lands for sale, the farmland and better grades of rangeland have been sold, and the land that remains in State ownership is of relatively poor quality and cannot be sold so readily.

In the States that have held their grant lands as a source of income, however, much of the State-owned farm and ranch land is similar in quality to nearby lands in private ownership. On the average, the quality of the State-owned land is below that of farm and ranch land in private ownership, but much of it is better than that of the unreserved land in Federal ownership. Land (except some special areas) that remains in State ownership is usually land that has not attracted buyers because of price and quality.

State-owned grazing and farming land leased to farmers and ranchers for grazing and farming in the Western States comprised about 45.8 million acres in 1954, or about 5 percent of the land used for farming and grazing in that year. The greater part of this acreage—44 million acres—was dry range. The rest was farming land. It is estimated that State-owned rangeland supplies about 7 million animal-unit months of grazing annually.

State-owned grant tracts often are widely scattered. The State-owned range in some States may also include former low-grade farms or other lands, which have reverted for taxes, or land acquired by foreclosure on loans from State funds, or repossessed land that was sold on contract and not paid for.

Much of the State-owned range is located in areas that are marginal for dry farming. The checkerboard location of State lands also has added to the problem of management.

States obtain considerable revenue from their land. Retention of a share of the mineral rights for land sold has added considerably to the public income in several States, notably Louisiana, Texas, New Mexico, California, and Wyoming. A total of 260 million dollars in rents, royalties, and sales of timber and other property was reported by the Bureau of the Census as collected by the States in 1956.

State, county, and municipal forests aggregated about 23.7 million acres in 1956. State forests and related areas totaled 19.3 million acres, and county and other forests 4.4 million acres. Most of the State forest was classified as commercial timber-producing land. Nearly 5 million other acres of forest land were in parks, and 5 million acres were in scattered forest lands and woodland tracts.

State, county, and community forest lands are managed to serve a variety of purposes. Some areas, especially the smaller ones near population centers, are devoted almost wholly to parks and recreational use. Some are wildlife preserves. Others are hunting grounds. In some, protection of watersheds and water supply is paramount. The chief use of others is timber production.

Many of the States own forest land, but a few have gone further than others in the development of State forest land for various uses. Five of the States held nearly three-fourths of all the State forest acreage. Minnesota reported more than 5.5 million acres; Michigan, about 3.6 million acres; New York, 2.1 million acres; Pennsylvania, about 1.8 million acres; Washington, 1.5 million acres; and other States in various parts of the country,

5.0 million acres—a total of 19.3 million acres of State forest land.

Many counties, cities, towns, townships, school districts, and other units maintain local public forests. There were in 1956 more than 3 thousand of these community forests, which covered about 4.4 million acres. County and community forests are especially important in number and acreage in Minnesota, Wisconsin, and the New England States. A number of the community forests date from colonial days.

Several large State forests in the Lake States were formed from tax-reverted cutover lands. Forests in the Western States were set aside from public-domain grant lands as well as from tax-reverted forest lands. Forests in other States were acquired by purchase and gift.

State parks and wildlife preserves covered about 10 million acres in 1955. From 1950 to 1955, the number of park areas rose from 1,725 to 2,034, an increase of 18 percent, and the total acreage rose from 4.7 million to 5.1 million acres.

New York had 2,627,000 acres in State parks in 1957; California, 563 thousand; Maine, 207 thousand; Michigan, 177 thousand; and Pennsylvania, 150 thousand. South Dakota, Michigan, and Minnesota also have large acreages in State parks.

The several hundred State wildlife preserves comprised nearly 5 million acres of land. Like State parks, the wildlife areas have been growing in number and in importance as places of scenic beauty and recreation.

State institutions, such as some colleges and universities, experiment stations, hospitals, and prisons and their related grounds, service areas, and farms occupied more than a million acres. Much of this is land of high value. Miscellaneous other State-land areas were estimated at 8 million acres. In contrast to some of the areas of specific uses, the latter category includes much rough or barren land, open swamp, and unclassified land of low surface value.

The uses to which we put our land.

One of the biggest achievements in history was the clearing of more than 300 million acres of virgin forest and the plowing of about 300 million acres of virgin grassland by American pioneer farmers. Another outstanding development was the increase in American farm production in 1947–1956, which was more rapid than in any period since 1890–1900, when the breaking of the prairies was ending. By *Hugh H. Wooten* and *James R. Anderson*, agricultural economists, Farm Economics Research Division.

FORESTS originally covered about half of the land in the United States. Two-fifths grew grass and herbaceous plants. The rest—about a tenth—was mostly arid and barren.

Most of the humid East was then in relatively compact forests.

Few grasslands existed east of the Mississippi—the prairies in what we now call the Corn Belt and the Lake States, the black-belt lands of Mississippi and Alabama, the Florida Everglades, and other small areas.

West, beyond the Great Plains, were smaller, scattered forests in mountains interspersed with dry valleys and basins. The West had less than a fifth of the original forests of a commercial quality.

Tall grasses extended into the Great Plains. Farther west, short and desert grasses grew—about half the forage there was made up of short and other grasses associated with limited rainfall. Areas of shrub vegetation were associated with scant rainfall and high temperatures.

TODAY the forest area is only 66 percent of the original forest. More than half of the forest land in the East has been cleared and is used for cropland, pasture, urban areas, and other purposes. The commercial forests of the West have been reduced by about 25 percent.

Most of the original tall-grass land has been converted to cropland and improved pasture. The tall-grass prairies of the Central States now comprise one of our best farming regions. The better lands of the short-grass regions farther west are used for irrigated or dry-farm crops, and the rest is used for grazing. Areas covered with shrub vegetation have changed less. Relatively small tracts have been irrigated. Shrub-type plants have replaced short grasses and bunch grass in some areas, and thus have extended the acreage covered with shrub vegetation.

In 1790 agricultural settlement was almost confined to the Atlantic slope from southern Maine to eastern Georgia. But west of the Appalachian Mountains settlement was expanding. The newly born Nation was preparing for one of the most stupendous achievements in the history of the world—the clearing of more than 300 million acres of virgin forest and plowing of about 300 million acres of virgin grass—much of which was accomplished during the 19th century. For the first 50 years of that century, settlement was confined mostly to forested lands.

53

By 1850 agriculture was spreading to the prairie lands of Illinois, Iowa, Kansas, and Texas. A number of courageous pioneers from the Eastern States had settled in Oregon, Utah, and California, and were just learning how to irrigate and farm the land. The improved crop and pasture land of the Nation totaled about 110 million acres. The acreage was about five times that in 1790.

By 1900 the waves of farm settlers had reached the barriers of aridity all along the 100th meridian from central North Dakota to west-central Texas. Only Indian Territory remained with its original grass and forest cover. During the preceding 50 years the Corn Belt had become the agricultural heart of the country, while irrigation and dry farming had expanded the area of cropland, particularly in the Pacific Coast States. The improved cropland and pastureland now totaled about 405 million acres. This was nearly four times the acreage of half a century earlier.

The conquest of the arid, semiarid, and wet lands continued into the 20th century. The irrigated acreage increased from 7.5 million acres in 1900 to nearly 30 million acres in 1954. Drainage enterprises in 1954 included more than 100 million acres. The improved cropland and pasture in 1954 exceeded 600 million acres.

The decade 1947 to 1956 has been in many ways the most extraordinary period in American agriculture. Agricultural production increased more rapidly than in any period since 1890 to 1900, when the agricultural occupation of the prairies approached completion, yet it was done without a great increase in cropland and pasture.

Five factors, some new, and some of greatly increased importance, help to account for this unusual situation: Use of automobiles, tractors, and trucks, which caused a decline since the Second World War of more than 8 million in the number of horses and mules on farms, with resultant release of 20 million to 25 million acres of crops for other purposes; increasing production of crops per acre in several regions; increasing production of animal products per unit of feed consumed; shifts from the less productive areas toward the more productive cropland; and improvement of land for crops and pastures by drainage, irrigation, flood control, and clearing.

AN INVENTORY of major uses of land in the United States in 1954 showed that one-fourth of it was cropland, one-half was pasture and grazing land, and one-sixth was unpastured forest. The rest was in service and miscellaneous other uses. The acreage of cropland used for domestic production was a little more than 2 acres per capita. Open or nonforested pasture totaled about 4 acres per capita.

The major uses of land in 1954 were: Cropland, including 66 million acres of cropland used only for pasture, 465 million acres; pasture and grazing land, 934 million acres, of which 633 million acres were open grassland and 301 million acres were woodland and forest land; forest not pastured, 314 million acres; special uses, such as urban areas, highways, parks, and other public facilities, 110 million acres; and miscellaneous other land, 81 million acres.

All of the cropland was in farms. About 62 percent, or 581 million acres, of pasture and grazing land was in farms, and 353 million acres were not in farms. Nearly a third, or 197 million acres, of woodland and forest was in farms. Much of this acreage was scattered among many farms in woodlots and small tracts. Other farm areas—36 million acres in all—included farmsteads, feedlots, storage yards, lanes, ditches, small orchards, and gardens for home use.

Other land not in farms—155 million acres—included urban and town areas, highway and railroad rights-of-way, parks, wildlife refuges, military areas, flood-control areas, and other special-use areas. Special-use and miscellaneous unaccounted-for areas included marshes, bare rock areas, sand dunes, and deserts—110 million acres in special-use areas and 81 million acres in miscellaneous other land.

Nearly 88 percent of the feed supply obtained from pasture was produced on pasture in farms; 12 percent was produced on grazing land not in farms. A third of the pasture feed was furnished by rotation or cropland pasture. Open permanent pasture in farms supplied more than 40 percent. Woodland pasture in farms furnished 8 percent of the pasture forage and aftermath pasture 8 percent. Of the total of 1,904 million acres, 1,158 million acres were in farms in 1954 and 746 million acres were not in farms.

Our estimates of major uses of land in continental United States are based on data assembled by the Farm Economics Research Division in 1955; reports of the 1954 Census of Agriculture; and reports and records of the Federal and State land-management and conservation agencies.

Cropland occupies almost half of the total land area of the Corn Belt and Northern Plain States.

In the northeastern, Appalachian, and southeastern regions, forest land accounts for more than half of the area.

Nearly half of the total area in the Pacific and Lake States is in forests.

Pasture and grazing land accounts for well over half of the total area in the Mountain States.

Nearly half of the land area in the Great Plains States is used for pasture and grazing.

Special uses occupy the highest proportion of the land area in the Northeastern, Pacific, and Lake States. Some of the uses have expanded rapidly there and in other regions. Urban areas and highways have absorbed a sizable acreage, particularly near large cities. Reservoirs are also a special use of land, but since the total area of land is reduced as reservoirs are established, their occupation of land is not reflected in the map on the next page.

The distribution of urban areas, highways, railroads, airports, farm-steads, farm roads, and other special uses is closely related to the distribution of population and farms. Many of the large areas in such special uses as parks, wildlife areas, and military areas are located in the less populous parts of the country.

Miscellaneous areas occupy about 2 to 8 percent of the land area in the different regions. Considerable acreages of desert land, marshland, sand dunes, and beaches are included in some areas in national-defense areas, parks, wildlife areas, and similar special uses. Most of this land has little value for agriculture or forestry. Some of it has mineral and other subsurface value.

OFFSHORE PARTS of the United States—Alaska, Hawaii, Puerto Rico, the Virgin Islands, Guam, American Samoa, and eight smaller inhabited islands—have more than 372 million acres, or about a fifth as much as continental America. The Territories were estimated to have about 2 million acres of improved cropland, 1.5 million acres of farm pasture, and 1.5 million acres of woodland and other land in farms, or a total in 1954 of about 5 million acres of farmland.

Cropland and pasture in 1950 made up a small part of the land area of Alaska. Land not in farms was largely undeveloped forest, tundra, and grass.

In Hawaii, cropland in 1950 accounted for about a tenth; grassland and brushland pasture comprised a fifth; and forest and woodland made up three-tenths of the total area. Other land included a considerable acreage of nonvegetated lava flows and unusable palis, gulches, and streambeds.

Cropland accounted for more than three-fifths of the land area in Puerto Rico. About half of it was used for crops, and the rest was pasture. Grassland and brushland pasture and forest and woodland each accounted for about a tenth of the total area. Other land, including that occupied by buildings, roads, cities and towns, and wasteland, comprised the remaining fifth.

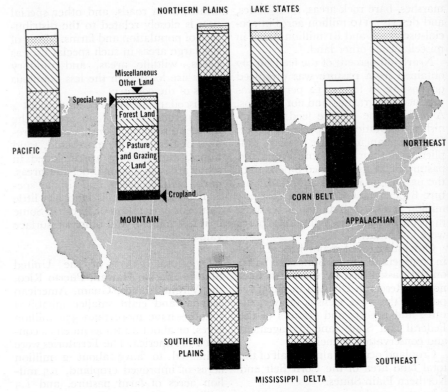

Major uses of all land as compared with total land area, 1954.

American Samoa, Guam, and the Virgin Islands are small tropical islands with relatively little commercial agriculture, except that some sugarcane is grown in the Virgins.

All cropland in the continental United States amounted to 465 million acres in 1954. Cropland used for crops totaled 380 million acres, of which 338 million acres had crops that were harvested, 29 million acres were cultivated summer fallow, and 13 million acres had crop failures. Also included were 19 million acres of cropland in soil-improvement crops or idle and 66 million acres of cropland used only for pasture.

Cropland used for crops averaged 380 million acres in 1950–1954 and 376 million acres in 1945–1949. Since the Second World War, the acreage of cropland has fluctuated between 360

million acres (in 1957) and 386 million acres (in 1949). Cropland used only for crops in 1957 totaled only 360 million acres, according to preliminary estimates. Over a longer period, cropland has remained relatively stable. Since the end of the First World War, fluctuation, rather than progressive change, has characterized the period.

The cropland averaged 4 million acres more in 1950–1954 than in 1945–1949, but the acreage from which crops were harvested averaged 7 million acres less in 1950–1954 than for 1945–1949. The yearly average in 1950–1954 was 339 million acres and 346 million acres in 1945–1949. The preliminary estimate of cropland harvested in 1957 was 319 million acres the lowest since 1936. Thus the increase in the acreage of cropland used for crops is accounted for by increases in crop failure and fallow, which more than offset the decline in harvested area.

Several factors account for the decline in the acreage of cropland harvested. Acreage allotments—part of a program to bring acreage and production into line with market demands—in effect for certain crops in some years from 1950 to 1954 affected the acreage of cropland harvested. Diversion of acreage in wheat, cotton, and corn to other crops accounted for much of the acreage on which allotments applied. Some of this diversion, however, was to such uses as rotation pasture, soil-improving crops, and idle cropland.

Availability of employment in cities has been a factor in the decline in cropland harvested in areas where industry is well developed. Urban and industrial expansion into rural areas is also taking cropland out of production in some sections. Shifts in type of farming, with greater emphasis on livestock and less on cotton, have accounted for reductions in the acreage of cropland harvested in some parts of the South. Reversion of cropland to brush and forest is also taking place in some localities.

THE AVERAGE of crop failure was 13 million acres in 1950–1954 and 9 million acres in 1945–1949. The preliminary estimate of crop failure in 1957 was 12 million acres.

Most of the crop failure occurs in the 14 Great Plains and Mountain States, in which nearly three-fourths of the total estimated crop failure occurred in 1950–1954. Drought is the chief cause of crop failure for the country as a whole, but floods, frost, hail, grasshoppers and other insects, and plant diseases may at times cause significant losses in some areas.

CULTIVATED SUMMER FALLOW has increased appreciably since 1944. The practice is widespread in subhumid and semiarid regions when small grains are produced without irrigation. Rainfall there may be insufficient for a crop each year, and experience has proved

that increases in yields result from fallowing land before small grains are planted. Fallowed land ordinarily is considered to be a part of the cropland used for crops.

Cultivated summer fallow reported in the 1954 Census of Agriculture amounted to 29 million acres. Annual estimates show an average of 28 million acres in 1950–1954 and 21 million acres in 1945–1949.

The high price of wheat led farmers to plow permanent grasslands in high-risk areas for production of wheat in the war and postwar years. An increase in fallowed cropland accompanied the plowing. The acreage of cultivated summer fallow remained high in later years, when acreage allotments for wheat were in effect, partly because yields of wheat are higher on fallowed than on other cropland.

ACREAGES IN PRINCIPAL CROPS harvested, as reported by the Department of Agriculture, plus estimated acreages in fruits, tree nuts, and farm gardens, averaged 347 million acres in 1951–1953 and amounted to 346 million acres in 1954 and 340 million in 1955.

Feed grains and hay crops occupied 213 of the 347 million acres in 1951–1953, 225 million acres in 1954, and 229 million acres in 1955.

Food crops averaged 102 million acres in 1951–1953 but totaled only 93 million and 87 million acres, respectively, in 1954 and 1955. Cotton, flaxseed, tobacco, and a few minor crops accounted for the remaining acreage.

Significant shifts in the acreage of several crops occurred between 1951–1953 and 1954–1955. The shifts may have reflected the influence of acreage allotments for wheat and cotton, which were in effect in 1954 and 1955 but not in 1951–1953. The acreages of wheat and cotton declined sharply. Most of the acreage diverted from those crops was used for sorghums, barley, oats, soybeans, and flaxseed.

THE TOTAL of acres in crops declined from 478 million to 465 million between 1949 and 1954. Acreage allotments in effect in 1954 encouraged the diversion of much of the cropland used for wheat, cotton, and corn to nonallotment crops, but part of the acreage was diverted to pasture and part of it remained idle and fallow.

A decline of 3 million acres in cropland used only for pasture between 1949 and 1954 may be explained partly by the fact that in 1949 cropland used only for pasture that was not actually in rotation with crops was more frequently reported as cropland than in 1954. This shift was particularly evident in parts of the South, where the seeding of pasture on cropland taken out of crop production proceeded rapidly after the Second World War. Much of this cropland, which had been seeded for only a short time when the 1950 Census of Agriculture was taken, has remained in pasture; by 1954, it was generally considered to be permanent grassland pasture.

PASTURE AND GRAZING LAND totaled nearly a billion acres in continental United States in 1954. It included 699 million acres in grassland pasture and grazing land, and some 301 million acres of woodland and forest grazed during part of the year. The grassland pasture included 66 million acres of cropland used only for pasture; such land often is considered to be land available for crops.

Grassland, to which 699 million acres were devoted in 1954, includes all land used primarily for pasture and grazing, exclusive of woodland and forest pastured or grazed. It includes the shrub and brushland types of pasture and grazing land, such as sagebrush, scattered mesquite and some other shrub types in the West and some scattered brushland pasture in the East, and all tame and wild or native grasses and legumes and other forage used for pasture or grazing.

Some 80 million to 90 million acres in planted fields are pastured for short periods each year. These include fall and winter pasturage of small grain

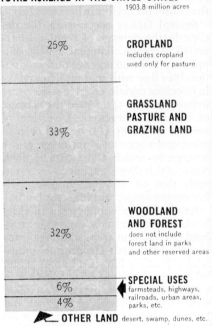

TOTAL ACREAGE IN THE UNITED STATES
1903.8 million acres

25% CROPLAND
includes cropland
used only for pasture

33% GRASSLAND
PASTURE AND
GRAZING LAND

32% WOODLAND
AND FOREST
does not include
forest land in parks
and other reserved areas

6% SPECIAL USES
farmsteads, highways,
railroads, urban areas,
4% parks, etc.

OTHER LAND desert, swamp, dunes, etc.

Major uses of land in the United States (1954).

and after-harvest pasturage of wheat, hay, and cornstalk and stubble fields. The acreage of crops pastured and the acreage of pasture and grazing land vary from year to year, depending on the weather and the available forage. More than 90 percent of all pasture and grazing land is grazed for some period each year.

More than a third of the feed for livestock comes from pasture and grazing land. The average acre yield for unimproved grazing land is low compared with that from cropland. Large acreages of this land furnish pasture for only a few weeks in some seasons. Much of it can be used only for grazing; it is not suitable for cultivated crops or for other intensive uses. Pasture and grazing lands have been improved by seeding and other practices, but the increase in production from pasture has been less rapid than that from cropland.

Exclusive of cropland pasture, there were about 934 million acres of pasture and grazing land in 1954. About 62 percent was in farms and ranches. The rest was largely public land and large privately owned forest tracts not in farms. More than half of the farm and ranch pasture and nearly 80 percent of the grazing land not in farms is in the western range region, or roughly west of the 100th meridian.

More than half of the pasture and grazing land (56.5 percent), exclusive of cropland pasture, is in the 11 Western States. Here about 70 percent of the land area is devoted to this use. Pasture and grazing lands occupy slightly less than half the land area in the 14 Southern States from Virginia to Texas and Oklahoma. About one-fourth of the land in the Northern States is used for pasture and grazing.

Most of the forest and woodland suitable for grazing is in the Southern and Western States. More than half of the woodland and forest area in these regions has some forage of value for grazing. More than 40 percent of the grazed forest and woodland in the country lies in the Western States. Only in some of the Southern States, however, does woodland used for grazing make up as much as half or more of the total pastured acreage.

IMPROVED PASTURE was estimated to total 215 million acres. This included 56 million acres of cropland used only for pasture. Improved pasture also included other grassland pasture in farms generally in tame grasses and legumes, whether seeded or natural growth, but may include native forage land that has been improved. All classes have had two or more improvement or conservation practices applied, such as weed and brush control, artificial or natural seeding or reseeding, fertilization, drainage, irrigation, or similar practices that improve yields.

The acreage of improved pasture increased from an estimated 175 million acres in 1939 to 215 million acres in 1954, an increase of 40 million acres, or an average of about 2.7 million acres a year. The acreage of improved pasture in 1954 represented nearly a third of the entire grassland or non-forested pasture and grazing land area of 699 million acres. An indication of the greater interest in improved pasture is the large number of farmers and ranchers who have carried out pasture-improvement work.

A larger acreage of improved pasture could be attained without reducing the acreage of cropland or forest. The greatest opportunity for increasing production of forage is through improvement of the acreage now used for pasture. Old, neglected pastures can be renovated and production increased. The inclusion of additional pasture in the regular cropland rotation has aided the improvement and production of pasture.

Improvement of pasture and grazing land offers opportunities and presents problems in all regions. Much of this land cannot be used successfully for crops without expensive improvement. Much of the grazing land in the West is range on which yields of forage are low because of limited rainfall. Large areas grazed in the South are made up of brush, woodland, and depleted cropland.

UNIMPROVED GRAZING LAND consists mainly of undeveloped land. Because of rough topography, poor or unsuitable soil, insufficient precipitation, lack of irrigation water, or for other reasons, it cannot be used successfully for crops and improved pastures without considerable improvement. This land is suitable for grazing by domestic livestock. It can support uncultivated and unfertilized forage, primarily native grasses.

Unimproved grazing land generally is considered to include forage-producing forest land economically suitable for grazing by domestic livestock. To this extent, grazing and forest lands overlap. Grazing land excludes large blocks of forest land on which forage is insufficient for domestic livestock, even though such areas are near areas suitable for grazing.

The principal native or unimproved

grazing lands are in the West and the lower South. In the West, they are predominantly grasslands or desert shrublands too dry for arable farming, although mountain woodland, which is moist enough for trees but generally is too rough for tillage, is also important. In the South, they are mainly forested grazing lands in the Coastal Plains and wet plains and marshes.

Much of the depleted, unimproved grazing land can be restored to a higher productivity more economically through management than tillage.

Control and limitation of grazing in accordance with carrying capacity, allowance of growth for natural seeding, artificial reseeding of open areas and abandoned fields, and removal of competing brush are among the chief methods of restoring grazing land.

Abandoned fields that are submarginal for crop production and are used for grazing even though they need reseeding to grass are classified as grazing land. About 785 million acres of unimproved land (including forested areas) were used for grazing in 1954 to 1958.

Income enters strongly into the question of whether or not arable pasture or grazing land can best be used for native pasture, tame pasture, cultivated crops, or other purposes. Costs and returns also enter into the problem of the degree to which the grazing resources of nonarable rangelands should be shared among livestock, wildlife, recreation, and watershed interests.

Just where the line should be drawn between unimproved grazing lands suitable for grazing and low-capacity lands, such as deserts, on which grazing of domestic livestock is not feasible, often is a problem. Such low-capacity land is not usually considered grazing land.

Classification of land as range has long been questioned on the grounds that it does not always provide a lower limit of usefulness as natural pasture—a limit below which the land would not be regarded as range. Some land is so arid, so rocky, so inaccessible, so steep, or otherwise so inherently unproductive that although it does provide some native pasturage, the amount is so small that to term it "range" is misleading. To graze it with domestic livestock may be uneconomic. From a stockman's viewpoint, it may better be called wasteland than rangeland. This lower limit fluctuates with the seasonal precipitation and the water supply. It varies also with economic conditions and with the type of ranching operations carried on.

THE FOREST AND WOODLAND area in continental United States classified by the Timber Resource Review in 1955 is 648 million acres. Of this, 484 million acres are commercial and 164 million are noncommercial.

By definition of forest land, 42 million acres of nonstocked and other open or nonforested areas were included in the area classified as commercial forest land. Much of this acreage was cropland, pasture, and closely cutover land, apparently idle or not used for any other purpose that was thought to be suitable and available for producing timber at the time the field surveys were made. Of the acreage classified as nonstocked forest land, approximately 17 million acres were in the Northern States, 16 million acres in the Southern States, and 9 million acres in the Western States.

The forest area also included 15 million acres of productive timberlands and 11 million acres of nonproductive reserved lands in national and State parks, monuments and wilderness areas, and other special uses. These lands were set aside by statute, ordinance, or administrative order for public purposes. Deducting these special public-use areas from the total forest land area left 622 million acres available primarily for growing timber and related uses.

An additional 7 million acres of forest land overlapped other land use reported by the agricultural census in 1954 and other land-use surveys. Thus the estimated net forest and woodland area was 615 million acres, whose main use was for forestry. Difference

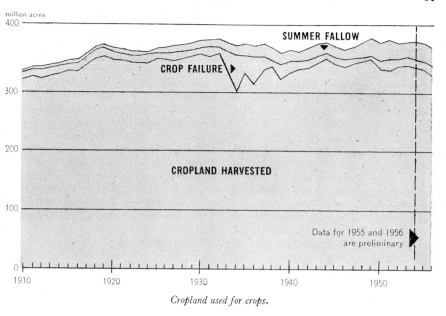

million acres

Cropland used for crops.

in definition of forest land in the timber-resource survey and in the agricultural census and other surveys account for much of this overlap.

Nearly half—301 million acres—of the woodland and forest was estimated to have been grazed at some time during the year or to have forage of significant value for pasturage.

SPECIAL USES of land are many—for urban areas, highways, railroads, airports, parks, national-defense areas, wildlife refuges, farmsteads, and farm roads and lanes. These uses are mostly nonagricultural.

A question often is asked about them: Is it desirable to use good agricultural land for urban sites and other similar purposes when less desirable agricultural land suitable for such uses is available? Competing demands for the use of land are particularly acute in good farming areas where urban and industrial expansion has been rapid.

The acreage occupied by the special-use land totaled 110 million acres in 1954. Urban and transportation areas accounted for about two-fifths of the total land area occupied by these spe-

cial uses. Parks and wildlife areas occupied about a fourth of the total area in special uses. National-defense installations, flood-control areas, and State-owned institutional and related sites accounted for another fourth. The remaining tenth was in farmsteads and farm roads and lanes.

Urban and transportation areas ordinarily are most directly in competition with agriculture for the use of level and fertile land. Other special uses, for which separate estimates have not been made, also compete frequently with agriculture for land. Examples of such areas are industrial, nonfarm residential, and commercial sites in rural areas; mining areas; clay, sand, and stone quarry sites; cemeteries; and golf courses.

Reservoir areas are deducted from the land area when they are completed and hence are not included among the special uses of land. Artificial reservoirs in 1954 occupied about 7 million acres.

The acreage of land in urban areas, highways, airports, and reservoirs increased an average of about 831 thousand acres a year from 1945 to 1954.

The increase in urban areas accounted for 395 thousand acres of this average annual increase, reservoir areas accounted for 360 thousand acres, highways for 78 thousand acres, and airports for 5 thousand acres. The area occupied by railroads decreased by about 7 thousand acres annually during this period. Not all of the land occupied by these nonagricultural uses was tillable land. Besides the changes in area used for the specific purposes we mentioned, increases occurred in the area occupied by parks, wildlife areas, and military sites.

OTHER MISCELLANEOUS unaccounted-for areas included deserts, sand dunes, bare-rock areas, and marshes. Their total acreage amounted to about 81 million acres in 1954. Land with these physical characteristics that was used for such things as military areas, parks, and wildlife refuges was not included in this total.

The many types and classes of rural lands and the varying local conditions, customs, needs, and practices necessarily have led to multiple uses of the same areas. This diversity has meant variations in management governing the main agricultural uses. Management of cultivated cropland and improved pasture differs from that of unimproved range and forests in such elements as intensity of use and degree of investment. Accordingly, these uses tend to restrict cropland and improved grazing land to a single primary use, with possibly one or more limited supplemental uses. Because of their cover and their less intensive use and management, unimproved grazing land, woodland, and forest often have several multiple uses that are almost equal in value to their primary uses.

In some areas, in addition to timber and wood, for example, forests and woodlands produce forage that is of considerable value to livestock growers. Much forest grazing supplements existing farm pastures at certain seasons. Proper grazing produces a significant supplemental income and also reduces fire hazards. The income from grazing often enables a woodland owner to carry his timber crop to an age most suitable for profitable marketing.

Recreation and production of wildlife are important multiple uses of forest and grazing lands and, to a more limited extent, of cropland and pasture.

The influence of forest and grazing lands goes beyond the production of timber, livestock, wildlife, and recreation. A far-reaching benefit of these lands to agriculture, other industries, and the whole economy lies in watershed services.

Some 25 million acres of land are irrigated with water from watersheds that are chiefly in forest and grassland. Most western streams have their sources in forest or grassland areas. They supply a large part of the water for irrigated areas, as well as water for domestic and industrial uses and for power. The services of forested watersheds in the Central and Eastern States are needed increasingly for domestic and industrial water supplies, for navigation, and for power.

How we use and manage
public lands—A report on the public domain—The
management of State lands—Getting and using land in time of
war—The management of tribal lands

A report on the public domain.

We hear solemn pronouncements now and then that the once great acreage of public domain, nearly 2 billion acres at its peak, is no longer a significant factor in American life. The fact is, though, that annual receipts from operations on the public domain now amount to about 239 million dollars. That is more of a land-office business than at any time in the past. By *Harold R. Hochmuth*, lands staff officer, Bureau of Land Management, and *Robert K. Coote*, Technical Review Staff, Office of the Secretary of the Interior.

THE PUBLIC DOMAIN of nearly 180 million acres in continental United States (plus the outer Continental Shelf and the public lands in Alaska) is a small remnant of the once vast Federal holdings, but still it is larger than the area of 13 Eastern States.

It is a remnant, both in quality and quantity—in general, the leavings of a selective process that has been going on for more than 150 years. Yet each time that it has been declared of little or no value in terms of contemporary uses, some turn of events has focused attention on these lands and made them in demand.

The atomic age meant that barren areas of public domain on the Colorado Plateau became the major source of our uranium supplies. Large vacant areas elsewhere proved to be an invaluable asset for the development and testing of new weapons. Industries seeking isolation from crowded urban centers are moving to remote places. Modern pioneers by the thousands are establishing themselves on tracts of the public domain of 5 acres or less. The American public, with greater leisure and the means to enjoy it, is looking to the more accessible public domain for outdoor recreation.

In the light of what has happened, we predict that the future will see more of these lands ripen into higher use.

In the meantime, the public domain, or the greater part of it, will continue to be used for a multiplicity of purposes.

Historically, the predominant uses have been for the grazing of livestock, the production of timber and other products of the surface, and the extraction of minerals. The public lands of the West also are contributors to our river systems and are highly important in any scheme of watershed protection and development.

There will continue to be selective disposal of these lands into private ownership under the public-land laws.

THE HISTORY OF THE PUBLIC DOMAIN roughly divides into three periods—acquisition, disposal, management.

Acquisition started with the beginning of the Nation when the first States ceded their western lands to the Federal Government. At its greatest extent, there were approximately 1 billion, 442 million acres of public domain in the United States and 365 million acres in Alaska.

Beginning as early as 1785, with a system of land sales, the Federal Government started to dispose of these holdings. Pursuant to a policy of trans ferring public-domain lands as rapidly as possible to private ownership, more than 1 billion acres of the original public domain were involved in sales and grants to war veterans, to States for education and internal improvements, to railroads, to homesteaders, and others.

Between 1862 and the passage of the Taylor Grazing Act in 1934, the Congress enacted a great number of public-land laws. The General Mining Law in 1872 opened up the public lands to prospecting and the extracting of hard-rock minerals. The Desert Land Act of 1877 recognized the aridity of the western lands by permitting homesteading on lands susceptible to irrigation with local water supplies.

Various laws of the early 1900's provided for the leasing of minerals not of the metalliferous or hard-rock variety. As gas, oil, and other mineral fuels came into general use, the Congress enacted the Mineral Leasing Act of 1920. It permitted the leasing of public-domain lands containing deposits of coal, phosphate, oil, oil shale, gas, and sodium.

Many of the public-land laws that were adopted between 1862 and 1934 are still in operation and are administered by the Bureau of Land Management of the Department of the Interior. This Bureau came into being on July 16, 1946, when the Grazing Service and the General Land Office were consolidated under provisions of the Reorganization Act of December 20, 1945. The General Land Office, established in 1812, had been primarily a land disposal and lands records agency. The Grazing Service was formed in 1934 to administer the range resources on the public domain.

Selective disposal of the public domain continues, but our Government long ago recognized the need to conserve some of our public domain and began setting aside large areas having unique scenic and recreation features and areas for forests, parks, and other public uses.

Altogether, there were withdrawn

from the public domain and reserved for specific public purposes about 229 million acres. These lands, together with lands later acquired by purchase, gift, or exchange, comprise the 269 million acres of "reserved" lands now in our national forests, national parks and monuments, wildlife refuges, and other Federal management areas.

The remaining lands serve as a bank account of lands from which various Federal agencies may make temporary withdrawals for specific purposes. When the temporary need expires, the lands are redeposited. That is, they are restored to the unappropriated public domain. The military agencies make extensive use of this arrangement in times of national emergency.

A TURNING POINT came in 1934 with the passage of the Taylor Grazing Act. Misuse and lack of management had so deteriorated the lands that, despite the same vigorous opposition that had been arrayed against establishment of the forest reserves, the Congress passed regulatory legislation.

In hearings on the proposed legislation, the Secretary of the Interior characterized the public domain as "a vast empire over which there is at this time no adequate supervision or regulation, and which is rapidly becoming a no-man's land through erosion and deterioration from unregulated use." The Representative from Colorado, for whom the act was named, said, "These lands are arid, and only fit for grazing and poor grazing at that."

The act changed the pattern of use and disposal for more than 180 million acres. It provided for establishing grazing districts and leasing for grazing of the remaining public domain not otherwise permanently reserved for other uses or purposes.

More than 158 million acres of public lands administered by the Bureau of Land Management are included in 59 grazing districts in 10 Western States. Grazing privileges are granted on these lands under annual licenses or permits. Another 18 million acres of public domain outside the grazing districts, largely in 11 Western States, are under grazing leases.

More than 8.5 million head of livestock use Federal grazing-district land. More than 2.5 million head graze on the public domain outside of grazing districts. It is estimated that a million big-game animals also subsist during some part of each year on grazing-district lands.

The management of grazing districts is designed to protect and improve the condition of the Federal range. A balance is sought between grazing use—including use by game animals—on the range and its grazing capacity. The number of livestock and the period of grazing accorded to each applicant for a grazing privilege depend on several factors, which relate to ownership or control of base property, prior use of the range, availability of range and forage, and proper season of use.

Advisory boards of representatives of the range users and wildlife interests make recommendations to the administrative officers concerning all phases of operating the grazing districts.

Multiple-use management is employed in administration of the public ranges. Concurrent uses consistent with conservation of land and resources obtain the greatest use and value from the lands. Provisions are made for proper grazing, range improvement, conservation of soil and moisture, weed control, fire control, management of forest and woodland, wildlife, and recreation. Management plans are based on studies conducted to determine the effect of past and present use on the condition of the range.

Range improvements—particularly fences and watering places for stock—facilitate uniform utilization of range forage and livestock handling. Much of the cost of federally constructed range improvements is paid on a cooperative basis by the range users; many such projects are placed on public lands entirely at their expense.

Conservation programs try to reduce soil erosion and to improve the vegetation on the public ranges. They include reseeding, contour furrowing, soil pitting, controlling brush, insects, and rodents, and building detention dams and water-spreading dikes.

Public land is a sizable part of the drainage areas of the great rivers of the West—the Missouri, Columbia, Colorado, and Rio Grande. The condition of the land affects the quality and quantity of water entering each of these river systems. Much of the sediment the rivers carry comes from the public domain.

A 20-year conservation program was started in 1955 to hasten the recovery of the eroded lands and to enable them better to resist erosion in the future. The work was planned on a watershed basis. Immediate work units are community watersheds, within which all needed conservation work is completed on all lands, irrespective of ownership. The sequence of treatment is based on the severity of erosion and susceptibility of the land to recovery. The completion of the program will place the western watersheds in a stable condition and restore productivity. More forage and a cleaner water will be produced. Further destruction of land, water-storage facilities, and the other properties will be forestalled.

HALOGETON, an annual weed poisonous to livestock, has infested more than 11 million acres of the western rangelands. It affects sheep oftener than cattle, perhaps because sheep eat it more readily, but sheep and cattle usually avoid it if they can get palatable forage. The solution is to improve the forage where halogeton exists. Various projects have been undertaken, principally reseeding to perennial grasses and fencing to control use by livestock. Direct chemical treatment has proved effective in controlling halogeton along rights-of-way, livestock trails, and other concentrations of infestation.

Several other poisonous plants and noxious weeds are controlled to some degree on the public range. These efforts are limited to cooperation with livestock operators on the range and with farmers and weed-control agencies in places where agricultural land adjacent to public range is being treated.

Fire-control organizations are maintained by Bureau of Land Management field offices. Fire presuppression and suppression is a cooperative undertaking of Federal and State agencies, farmers, stockmen, and others who live on or near strategic areas of public lands.

The acreage burned on public-domain lands has been reduced to less than 100 thousand acres a year, as compared to an average of 250 thousand acres a few years ago. This favorable trend can be attributed to better fire-fighting organizations, techniques, and equipment and to a wider understanding of the need to safeguard the lands.

TIMBER AND WOODLAND MANAGEMENT on the public domain had its beginning with the Taylor Grazing Act. The Executive orders of 1934 and 1935, which withdrew the unappropriated and unreserved public land in the United States, laid the groundwork for forestry on the public domain.

An inventory of the commercial forest resources on the public domain has been started to get more exact information about the volume of usable timber, capacity to grow timber, and reforestation needs and other data pertaining to more intensive protection and management of timber, water, and recreational resources.

The management program in 1958 consisted of practices to protect forests against damage by fire, insects, and other causes and to convert the overmature forests to thrifty stands of younger timber. The lands have an estimated productive capacity of 220 million board-feet of sawtimber a year. Annual sales have reached a level of 110 million board-feet, valued at 2.3 million dollars. Management, protec-

tion, and development cost about 1.5 million dollars in 1958.

THE OREGON AND CALIFORNIA Revested Railroad grant lands in western Oregon, a special category of public lands, are managed for commercial timber production. The lands include 75 thousand acres remaining from another revested land grant, known as the Coos Bay Wagon Road Lands Grant. They are not public-domain lands in the usual sense, because special acts of the Congress control their administration, and they are generally not subject to disposal under the public-land laws.

The O & C lands originally were lands in alternate sections, which were granted in a strip 20 miles wide on each side of the railroad right-of-way running on a north-south axis in western Oregon. The railroad defaulted on its grant, and in 1916 the title to the unsold portions was revested in the United States.

The lands, about 2 million acres in 1937, were permanently reserved for the production of timber on a sustained-yield basis. The checkerboard tracts have been consolidated in part by a series of exchanges with other types of ownership, including national forest, in order to facilitate their management.

Modern forest practices on O & C lands provide for fire protection, reforestation, watershed protection, and recreation development. Timber is sold through competitive bidding.

The successful bidder must reforest immediately after logging and must protect the soil and watershed and recreational values. Thousands of acres which were denuded by fires in the early days are being reforested by tree planting financed by Federal funds.

The O & C area is divided into 12 relatively large sustained-yield units. Each is operated under a separate management plan, and an allowable cut has been set for it. The unit system insures that dependent communities are protected against the danger of timber depletion.

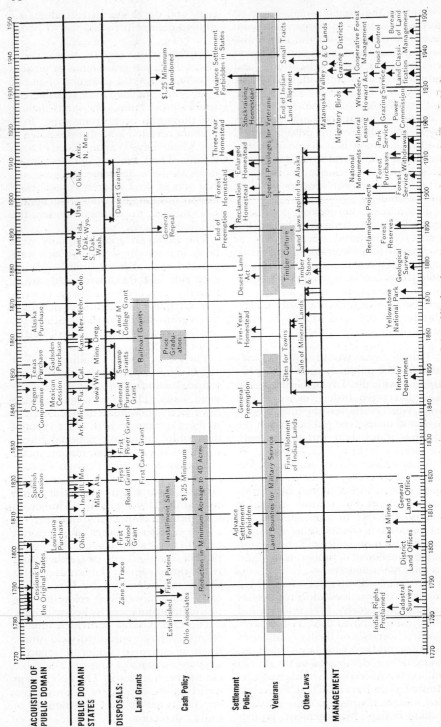

Highlights in the history of the public domain.

Timber access roads are being made at a cost of about 5 million dollars a year. They make it possible to market large volumes of timber that otherwise would be lost through mortality and decay. The road network has added greatly to the efficiency of the fire-control program.

The forestry practices have increased the timber harvest from the 500 million board-feet a year to the allowable annual cut of 660 million board-feet in 1958. The goal is an annual yield of 750 million board-feet.

Between 1938, when the O & C forest-management project began, and 1956, the total income produced was 102 million dollars—enough to reimburse the United States Treasury for all acquisition and management costs since 1916 and to yield a net return of almost 15 million dollars. Annual net returns to the Federal Treasury are nearly as much as the original cost of acquiring the property.

The complex ownership pattern of the intermingled public and private lands was recognized in the Taylor Grazing Act. The Congress realized that the remaining public-domain lands were not all in solid blocks but often consisted of a multiplicity of ownerships—Federal, State, corporate, and private. The act provided that Federal, State, and private lands might be exchanged to consolidate ownership so that management of public and private lands would be benefited.

A map of land status of any of the 11 Western States reveals the complicated ownership. The best land was reserved for Federal use or acquired by the public. National parks generally are solid units of Federal ownership. National forests were created mainly out of the public lands but nevertheless have substantial acreages of private, State, and appropriated public-domain lands within their boundaries.

Grants of land to the railroads and the States made the land pattern even more mixed up. The railroads, pushing westward after 1860 from the Missis-sippi and Missouri Rivers, generally were granted alternate sections of public land within 20 miles on each side of the right-of-way.

Most States, when they were admitted to the Union, were granted two sections of public land in each township for the support of schools. Utah, Arizona, and New Mexico were granted four sections of each township.

Land-exchange provisions of the Taylor Grazing Act and other exchange acts and the indemnity and lieu selection laws—laws that permit States to select unreserved public-domain land for the school sections and other grants of land they lost by reason of their inclusion in national forests and other Federal reservations—are used to improve the land tenure framework in national forests. The process of land adjustment, accumulation of management units, and land exchanges and transfers are continuing on the public domain. Though costly and time consuming, the process is necessary to make manageable units both for Federal lands and for lands occupied or used by private persons.

DISPOSAL AND SERVICE functions of the Bureau of Land Management are a continuing responsibility, although the management function is of emerging importance.

Classification is now a prerequisite to the transfer of the public domain to private persons, companies, corporations, and State and local governments as authorized by various land laws.

Before such disposals may be made under any law except the mining laws, the lands must first be classified as suitable for use under that particular law. This requirement is in section 7 of the Taylor Grazing Act. In writing this provision into law, the Congress, for the first time since the enactment of the preemption and settlement statutes, took affirmative action to prevent further unwise disposition of the remaining public domain.

Disposals of public lands are not made en masse, as was contemplated earlier in the public-land laws. Disposal activity now is a selective process. Lands that qualify under specific acts for disposal and are not needed for specific purposes by the United States or are not under management plans are subject to this process.

The disposal of minerals in the public lands is a primary and revenue-producing function of the Bureau of Land Management. Of the many mineral laws, the General Mining Law of 1872 and the Mineral Leasing Act of 1920 are the main ones. They are applicable to about 240 million acres of reserved and unreserved public lands, 60 million acres of private lands in which the United States owns the mineral title, and 58 million acres of lands to which the United States has acquired title. They apply also to more than 300 million acres in Alaska.

Oil, gas, coal, potash, phosphates, and certain other minerals are extracted from the public-domain lands under lease. The United States retains title to the land but disposes of the minerals.

Of more recent interest is the leasing and extraction of oil, gas, and sulfur in the outer Continental Shelf surrounding the United States. The outer Continental Shelf Land Act, enacted in 1953, recognized the sovereignty of the United States to certain submerged lands, seaward from historic boundaries of the maritime States of the United States. Tremendous resources of oil, gas, and sulfur are being prospected and developed through a system of leasing to private enterprise.

The Mining Law of 1872 provided for the disposal of the metalliferous and so-called hard-rock minerals. The unappropriated public-domain lands and most lands in national forests are subject to disposal under that law. To obtain title to the minerals, an individual, company, or corporation must first locate the minerals, identify such on the ground, and file a notice of location with the local county recorder. Certain annual assessment work is required by respective State laws. As long as the

individual has a valid location of minerals and is pursuing mining activities, he has a possessory right to the public-domain minerals. When he complies with the requirement of this law, he may apply for and obtain title to the land if he wants to.

BASIC LAND-TITLE RECORDS of all of the lands of the United States (not included in the Thirteen Original States and Texas) are maintained in the Bureau of Land Management. The records relate to the public-domain land still in Federal ownership and to all lands that were once public domain and have been disposed of by the United States. The records comprise more than 6 thousand volumes of cadastral survey field notes, 135 thousand plats of survey, 12 thousand volumes containing almost 7 million land patents, and 4 thousand tract books with more than 25 million notations affecting title or status of lands.

Recordkeeping is complicated because title to the surface estate or land itself is often separated from the mineral estate. The mineral estate may also be separated into those minerals occurring at and below the surface. Many land laws provided for disposal of public lands but reserved the mineral title to the United States. The public-land records reveal in whom vests the land and mineral title.

Thousands of individuals and Government workers consult the public-land records daily for title information.

The records originally were developed to provide for recording title of land as it passed out of Federal ownership. As the public-domain lands became more valuable, the Congress enacted laws that required reservations and management of resources by the United States. The change in emphasis has meant that the records must be modernized—a project that is designed to permit an almost immediate determination of the status of any federally owned tract or the minerals in it.

Land survey and identification is a necessary prerequisite to the use and disposal of public lands. The Bureau of Land Management is charged with the cadastral boundary surveys of the public-domain land, both reserved and unappropriated. The Congress, by the Ordinance of May 20, 1785, adopted the rectangular system of surveys. This system provided for the division of the public lands into townships 6 miles square. By running lines due north and south at 1-mile intervals and east and west at right angles, the townships are divided into 36 sections of 640 acres.

Cadastral surveys are, therefore, necessary to our total land-title system. Abstractors and title-insurance companies know that the land titles for lands outside of the Thirteen Original Colonies and Texas are derived from basic titles issued by the United States. These former public-domain lands now privately owned by individuals, companies, and corporations are described for the most part under the rectangular system. If one is to sell land, cut timber from it, or extract minerals, the land must be properly identified and described on maps and on the ground.

Although the rectangular system of surveys was initiated in 1785, there remains approximately 100 million acres in the United States and 362 million acres in Alaska yet to be surveyed.

ALASKA has by far the largest amount of public-domain land administered by the Bureau of Land Management.

Less than 1 percent of the Territory has passed into private hands. Some 95 million acres have been set aside for national parks, monuments, forest and wildlife refuges, oil and gas reserves, and other Federal reserves. Some 270 million acres are unreserved vacant public domain.

Alaska is developing rapidly, but its millions of acres of undeveloped land give it a frontier aspect. Disposal of the public domain in the Territory has been slow. Laws are available for the use and disposal of the lands, but the demand is not great. With increases in population, industrial activity, and improved agricultural technology, the

better lands in Alaska can be expected to reach a stage of development comparable to development in the States.

The Congress has recognized the recreational values of the public domain in Alaska by adopting legislation and appropriating funds to construct public campgrounds along the highways. Recreation has become a major industry in Alaska.

One of the more promising assets in the Territory are the 125 million acres of forests in the public domain. A 5-year forest survey begun in 1956 will provide a more precise inventory of the location, extent, volume, kind, and value of the timber resources of Alaska on the public domain.

Present estimates indicate that 40 million acres support commercial stands of timber, with a volume of 700 million cords. The principal timber species— white spruce, birch, cottonwood, and aspen—have desirable pulping characteristics. The remaining 85 million acres of forest land are classified as woodland. They are not considered commercial by present standards, but they have a high value for watershed protection, wildlife habitat, recreational use, and scenic purposes.

The volume of timber sales has been small—22.6 million board-feet in 1956—but the demand has been increasing. Timber and fuel wood on the public domain is locally important to settlers, miners, prospectors, trappers, and others who are entitled to its free use for their own needs.

The forestry program on the public domain in Alaska is in transition from one of custody to one of management. The primary job continues to be to protect the forest land and the 100 million acres of rangeland and tundra against fire.

Much of interior Alaska is dry. The precipitation range is 6 to 15 inches. Climatic conditions and highly flammable fuel types can mean dangerous and destructive fires. Immense distances, lack of roads and communication facilities, and difficult terrain complicate the problem of fire control.

The management of State lands.

The United States has title to about 408 million acres; the States own about one-fifth as much. The extent and history of these State-owned lands are discussed in this chapter, which tells how New York, Montana, and the Lake States acted to solve difficult, specific problems that arose from misuse of the land. It concludes with analyses of some proposals that have been made. By *Alvin T. M. Lee*, agricultural economist, State Experiment Stations Division, and *Hugh H. Wooten*, agricultural economist, Farm Economics Research Division.

THE STATES hold title to 80 million acres of land. More than 30 million acres of it are set apart for such purposes as wildlife preserves (4.9 million acres), parks (5.1 million acres), and forests and related uses (19.3 million acres). The remaining 50 million acres mainly are grazing lands held for income purposes, primarily for schools.

The public forest land—State, as well as Federal—is used mainly for timber production and watershed protection. Similarly, both State and Federal parks are for the same purpose—public recreation.

The great scenic parks can be considered as belonging to the entire Nation to enjoy, and the expense of maintaining them is shared by all, rather than by the States in which they are. Since most of the land in these national parks, especially in the Western States, was a part of the public domain, it was feasible for the Federal Government to have the acreage set aside for such special use. Many of the national forests likewise were started by the setting aside of existing public domain. Fish and wildlife lands owned by the Federal Government are used in the national interest, such as sanctuaries for migratory fowl. Individual States do not foster such sanctuaries because they could not easily work out uniform interstate regulations and programs for such purposes.

Water-storage areas for many of the great public reclamation, flood-control, navigation, and power projects are under the administration of the Federal Government because of the interests of several States in the available water, especially in streams flowing through several States. Military lands held strictly for national defense also are best held under Federal jurisdiction. Both Federal and State Governments have need for land for institutional and educational sites and other public facilities.

Remnants of the original public domain located primarily in the Western States are retained in Federal ownership. These 178 million acres are mostly grazing lands, which were withdrawn from homestead entry because of their low productivity.

About 46 million acres of the land in State ownership are used for grazing and other agricultural uses through lease to farmers and ranchers. Many of these 46 million acres of State lands and 178 million acres of federally owned lands are in the same general areas and are intermingled with 355 million acres of privately owned land.

Whether this public land should be all in Federal ownership, or all in State ownership, or transferred to private ownership has been the subject of much discussion. The many interests built up as a result of past policies preclude an easy and quick answer.

Why are 80 million acres still retained in State ownership when the great push of past land policy was to get land into private ownership? Is this land better suited to public ownership than to private ownership and is it better suited to State ownership than to Federal ownership?

An analysis of how the States acquired their large acreages and what their current policies and programs of land management are is the purpose of this chapter.

MORE THAN 50 PERCENT of all the State-owned land is in the 11 Western States. It is made up mainly of land remaining out of the Federal grants to the States for schools and public improvements.

Many of the Western States only recently have developed rational procedures for classifying land and getting it into the most suitable ownership and use. Land programs developed in these States therefore were developed after the States found themselves the owners of vast acreages. The Federal Government granted under various legislative acts 67,591,000 acres to these 11 Western States. The 47,298,532 acres in State ownership in these States in 1958 were nearly all part of the original grants.

California, Oregon, and Utah disposed of a major part of their grant lands, and Nevada disposed of all but a small fraction. The other seven Western States have retained most of the original acreage, having decided to administer it for income purposes. Some of the States still hold much of their original grants—no doubt because the terms of the enabling acts specified a minimum sales price so as to check reckless disposal.

The Great Plains States of North Dakota, South Dakota, Nebraska, Kansas, and Oklahoma received 20,-538,000 acres of Federal-grant land. Their State ownership in 1958 was 7,234,398 acres and consisted almost entirely of remaining Federal-grant land. Texas did not receive Federal-grant land, because it retained title to all public land when it entered the Union as a State. All of the Western States have relatively small acreages of public land in parks and wildlife reserves. Some of the acreage in these uses is land that the States purchased from private individuals.

Most of the State-owned land in the Western and Great Plains States is leased to ranchers for grazing. Some favorably situated tracts are leased to farmers for crop production. The types and period of leases vary by States. Much of the land is under oil and gas leases, and the States receive royalties on current production.

SPECIAL MENTION needs to be made of the Federal-grant lands given to the States as trust for the support of common schools, since they are such an important part of the total acreage in State ownership.

Nearly all of the remaining school lands are in the States west of the Mississippi River. A total of 77,523,000 acres was granted for this purpose to 29 States. Still in State ownership in 1954 were 42 million acres, not counting about 3 million acres of State school lands remaining in Texas and the school lands held by townships and counties in Mississippi, Louisiana, Texas, and a few other States.

Only eight States retained the major proportion of their common school-grant lands. Examples are Arizona, which has 8 million left out of a total of 8,093,000 acres; Montana, 4,280,000 out of 5,198,000 acres; and Wyoming, 3,091,000 of 3,470,000 acres. Other States retaining most of the school land included Washington, Idaho, Colorado, New Mexico, and South Dakota.

States that have retained about one-fourth to one-half of the original school lands include Utah, Nebraska, North Dakota, Oklahoma, and Minnesota. Utah has 2,500,000 of its original 5,844,000 acres. Minnesota has 1,017,-000 of its original 2,875,000 acres.

Kansas, Alabama, Illinois, Iowa, Michigan, and Ohio apparently disposed of all of their school-grant lands. Ten other States have only relatively small acreages remaining.

There may be various reasons why some States have retained large proportions of their grant land and others, often neighboring States, have disposed of nearly all of the land. Nevada has 8,571 acres remaining out of 2,062,000, but her neighbor, Arizona, has 8 million acres remaining of 8,093,000. Kansas disposed of the entire 2,908,000 acres, but Nebraska has retained 1,632,-000 acres out of 2,731,000. Whether it was better financially to sell the land and build up a trust fund or to manage the land for income depends on the sale price received for the land and whether full rental value has been and is currently being received for the land managed on a lease basis.

A report, "Public School Finance Program in the United States," Miscellaneous Publication 22, prepared in the Department of Health, Education, and Welfare, contains data on the school lands, school trust funds, and income received by the schools from these school lands and trust funds.

The estimated income from the school lands and endowment funds was 47,-117,000 dollars for the school year 1953–1954. This represented 0.6 percent of the total 7,712,738,000 dollars expended on common and secondary schools and 1.6 percent of the 2,938,-875,000 dollars of State aid.

The income from school land and the trust funds built up primarily from land sales and mineral leases represented a large proportion of the funds made available to schools in some States. In Nebraska the 2 million dollars of income represented 76.2 percent of the State aid and 34.8 percent of the total revenue for schools. New Mexico also relies heavily on this source of funds for operation of schools. The 7,972,000 dollars of income from school land and the school trust fund represented 23.7 percent of the total State aid and 19.2 percent of total school revenue in New Mexico.

This source of revenue is small in a few States, even though large acreages were granted for this purpose. Where most of the land was sold early in the history of the State, it is likely that sale prices were low. The sale and management of this type of land always is under pressure by special interests.

The management of the school land and trust funds represents a vast economic enterprise in the 16 Western States that received Federal-grant land. The combined value of the trust funds in 1954 was 435,262,000 dollars. Most of this is invested in United States and State bonds. Some is lent to school districts and municipalities. Some is in farm mortgages. A total of 32,818,000 dollars in annual interest and rental income was distributed to the schools in 1953–1954. Income to the Texas schools from its land and 228 million dollars of trust fund was 5,200,000 dollars in the 1953–1954 school year.

THE LAKE STATES also were granted millions of acres of public domain—Michigan 12 million acres, Wisconsin 10 million acres, and Minnesota 16 million acres—a total of more than 38 million acres. Among the more important grants were common schools, 4,879,000 acres; swampland, 13,747,-000 acres; specific internal improvements, 19,131,000 acres.

These States quickly disposed of the land in order to get settlers on the land and to get cash for public improvements. The southern part of the States was settled first. The forest was cut, and the land was cleared for agriculture. As the population grew, and land and timber became scarce, the wave of lumbering and settlement moved north into the pine forests. Only little of the grant lands remained in State ownership by 1920. Even much of the land submarginal for agriculture had been cleared for farming after the timber harvest.

The Lake States began to see much land moving back into State ownership in the 1920's. They suddenly became unwilling owners of millions of acres of cutover land and abandoned farms because the private owners could no longer make a living from the land and were letting it revert to the State or county through tax forfeiture.

The States since then have been building a positive program for continued public ownership of the land unsuited to agriculture. The land in State ownership in these States in 1950 was 4,403,000 acres in Michigan, 5,507,000 acres in Minnesota, and 531,199 acres in Wisconsin. As tax-delinquent land in Wisconsin reverts to the counties, the approximately 2 million acres of county-owned land should be added to make the figures comparable with those in Michigan and Minnesota.

The North Central States of Iowa, Illinois, Indiana, Ohio, and Missouri have relatively small acreages of State-owned land; the combined total is about 885,000 acres. These States received 28,512,000 acres of Federal-grant lands, of which 4,612,000 were trust lands for common schools. With the exception of Missouri, nearly all of this land in these States was suitable for agricultural development and was not hard to dispose of in the wave of westward expansion. Most of the land that these States now own was purchased for a variety of uses—forestry, parks, institutional sites, and wildlife reserves. There was need for land for these purposes. The land was not purchased for developing a public-land program. Missouri, however, does have a large area in the Ozarks not suited to agriculture, but the Federal Government rather than the State has developed a public program here.

Only two of the Southern States have sizable acreages in State ownership. South Carolina had 1,011,000 acres and Florida had 1,074,000 acres

in 1949. Florida since has had an active program of disposing of much of its holdings, which consisted principally of Federal-grant swamplands and other grant lands. The Florida acreage in 1954 was down to about 463 thousand acres. The South Carolina acreage is principally unclaimed swampland along the coast.

Five Southern States received considerable Federal grants of public domain—Arkansas 11,937,000 acres, Louisiana 11,432,000 acres, Mississippi 6,097,037 acres, Alabama 5,007,-000 acres, and Florida 24,206,305 acres. Nearly 1 million acres in each of these States were grants for common schools. Records show that these States had no other object than to dispose of their grant lands and to get it into private ownership and on the tax roll as quickly as possible. Only small acreages remain in public ownership. About 700,000 acres of the school lands in Mississippi are held by counties and townships.

Louisiana was the scene of large-scale lumbering in the early part of the century. It had a similar experience as the Lake States in that large areas of cutover land became tax delinquent in the 1920's and 1930's. By special law it had a lenient policy of permitting owners to redeem their land at low cost. This and the presence of oil throughout the area has made it attractive to own land regardless of the productivity of the surface rights, and the formerly tax-reverted land has been returned to private ownership.

Only two States in the East have extensive acreages in State ownership—3,100,000 acres in New York and 2,825,000 acres in Pennsylvania. Because of the early interests of the citizens in these two States to correct the thoughtless destruction of the forests and to protect the source of water supply, extensive State programs were developed. This accounts for the small acreage of Federal land in these States.

Pennsylvania for many years has had a positive program of developing its forest lands so as to manage the forests well and to protect watersheds. To keep families from getting stranded on land unsuited to agriculture has not been a major concern, although that has come about automatically on the land acquired by the State.

The development of the forestry program in Pennsylvania paralleled in scope and time the early program in New York State. The first public forestry work was the control and prevention of forest fires. Next came the purchase of land and the planting of trees. In both States the land acquisition program got under way before the turn of the century. Both States have similar policies in that the forest lands are used for multiple purposes—watershed protection, forestry, recreation, and wildlife.

The important types of programs in effect in the various States may be illustrated by a review of the development of the land programs in New York, Wisconsin, and Montana.

NEW YORK began early to develop a comprehensive program for the forest lands that seemed to be inadequately cared for under private ownership. The first settlers found a timber-covered State. Markets for timber were limited, and every person had an oversupply of wood. Many a settler had to burn up much good timber in order to get enough land for crops and pasture. Later, after extensive urban development, lumber markets opened up, and many settlers became lumbermen. By 1850 New York ranked first among the States in the production of lumber, much of which was exported. Extensive cuttings each year left larger and larger areas of unproductive cutover land subject to further ravages of fire. The heavy cutting of the virgin forest rapidly depleted the State's timber supply, and uncontrolled forest fires caused responsible citizens to seek public action. The water supply needed for the State's industries and the canals was being reduced because of the more rapid runoff after removal of the forests.

The first annual report of the Commissioner of State Parks of New York in 1874 stated that the land was abandoned for unpaid taxes as soon as lumbermen had cut the pine, spruce, and hemlock. It recommended that the wild lands then owned by the State be retained until the question of what to do about the forest reserves was decided. An act passed in 1883 prohibited further sale of State-held lands in certain counties in the Adirondack and Catskill regions. This withdrew from sale approximately 800 thousand acres, most of which had been sold by the State previously and had reverted for delinquent taxes.

A report of the Brooklyn Constitution Club in April 1885 had directed attention to the reduced flow of water in the Hudson River, the increasing frequency of forest fires, and the fact that forest fires destroyed excellent timber on mountain slopes where it was needed for watershed protection and where lumbermen had no intention of cutting.

A circular, No. 26, of the Federal Bureau of Forestry reported that more than 600 thousand acres of timberland were burned over in the spring of 1903. A total of 175 thousand dollars was spent in fighting these fires, which eventually rains put out. Timber and buildings worth an estimated 3.5 million dollars were destroyed.

Public agitation resulted in the adoption of the Forest Preserve Act in 1885. The act (with further restrictions prohibiting cutting on the forest preserve lands) was embodied in the State constitution in 1894. It is now section 1 of article XIV and contains the original wording in regard to the forest preserve: "The lands of this State, now owned or hereafter acquired, constituting the forest preserve as now fixed by law, shall be forever kept as wild forest lands. They shall not be leased, sold or exchanged, or be taken by any corporation, public or private, nor shall the timber thereon be sold, removed or destroyed. . . ."

The first act named the counties in

which the forest preserve was to be located. The boundary was drawn more precisely following the township lines in 1892 and is now referred to as the blue lines—the area within which the forest preserve is located. The Adirondack and Catskill Forest Preserve now embraces 2,468,000 acres.

The New York State Forest Preserve is a unique example of conservation in the United States. Because of the great concern for the protection of the Adirondack and Catskill watersheds and the extensive use of the area for recreation, the defenders of the forest preserve have been able to hold off the attack of those who would like to amend the constitution to permit commercial lumbering. The constitution is now interpreted to mean that no timber is to be cut. The only exception that has been permitted is the cutting of trees to permit the building of State highways and roads for the protection of the forest. Also permitted is the cutting of fallen timber that may be a fire hazard. Down and dead trees that are not a fire hazard cannot be cut. The preserve is a true wilderness.

The growing popularity of the Adirondack and Catskill Mountains for recreation may make this purpose as important as watershed protection. About 3 million acres, more than half of the land inside the park boundaries, are in private ownership. It is on the private land that increased commercial resort development will take place. The presence of State forest lands in a wilderness state no doubt enhances the recreational values of the private land.

The potential value of the timber in the forest preserve is demonstrated by the extent of salvage operations after the damage caused by a severe windstorm on November 25, 1950. Legislation enacted in January 1951 authorized the Conservation Department, until June 30, 1955, to remove the wind-damaged trees. Cleanup operations had been carried out on 115,178 acres by November 1954. The amount received for timber and pulpwood and for contracts to cut amounted to 1,146,-121 dollars. This was for the wind-damaged trees that might become a fire hazard if they were not removed.

Public action for better use of land in New York was first concerned with the mountain areas. They could not be developed for farming after timber harvest, and the wasteful method of lumbering endangered water supplies and navigation. Later it was observed that the longtime trend of land in farms was downward and that farming was being abandoned in other parts of the State. The area in farms was reduced by more than 2 million acres in 1880–1920, another 2.5 million by 1930, and still another 3 million acres by 1954.

A second program in New York was initiated in 1928–1929 to retire abandoned farmland to wildlife and commercial forest use. G. F. Warren and others in the New York State College of Agriculture in 1906 had begun studies which shed light on the problem of abandoned land in the State and served as a basis for this program.

The first study was a general agricultural survey of several townships in Tompkins County. The report of the survey, published in 1911, showed that the writers were thinking beyond the farm boundary. They noted that farmers were unaware of the value of their woodlots and that much of the land was better adapted to trees than to agricultural crops.

They wrote: "It would seem more reasonable if some plan could be devised that would exempt all forest land from taxation until the trees are cut. Such a law would unquestionably result in the planting of large areas of land to trees. . . . In many counties of New York there are farms that should never have been cleared. To reforest these lands is such a longtime investment that individuals hesitate to do it. If counties or cities should purchase and reforest some of these areas, it is probable that the next generation who are to pay the bonds that we are now voting for all kinds of purposes might have an easy means of raising the revenue."

The New York State College of Agriculture restudied selected areas in 1917 and again in 1927 to determine the rate of abandonment. A detailed study was made of Pharsalia Township in Chenango County in 1924.

L. M. Vaughan in 1926–1928 studied 15 abandonment areas, comprising 195,032 acres, in the State. He found 685 occupied farms and 764 vacant farms. About 25 percent of the occupied farms were not operated, and 40 percent of the cleared land was idle. Few men, except the operators of the farms, lived there, and there were no children on 47 percent of the farms. Most of the people were old. Crop yields and income were low. Many of the farms were sold and resold, and each successive occupant lost money, time, effort, and hope.

The conclusion was that because of the large acreage of abandoned farmland, the State was the only entity that could get the land reforested. Because natural reseeding was too slow, it was suggested that the State buy the land and replant it with adapted tree species—the job was too big for townships, counties, clubs, or individuals.

Concern for the people who were trying to farm the land was expressed: "The purchase of this land by a public agency would make it possible for the remaining residents to leave for sections of greater opportunity and would put an end to the exploitation of innocent persons which has been going on for the past century."

State aid to replace the lost tax base was suggested: "If a part of the land is removed from taxation and a corresponding reduction cannot be made in services, provision must be made to maintain the necessary local services without undue burden on the adjacent farmland."

Extensive studies were made of mortgage foreclosures, fire-insurance losses, school costs and attendance, and cost of roads. The losses and costs were greater as agricultural productivity dropped. A land classification system was developed as a guide for determining which land should be acquired by the State for reforestation.

There was much public discussion of the problem of abandoned land. To learn more about it, the legislature in 1928 set up a State Reforestation Commission and authorized it to investigate generally the subject of reforestation with particular attention to determining the location, value, and area of lands in the State unsuited to agriculture that might best be utilized for reforestation and to develop a plan for financing such a program.

The commission had the help of county supervisors, town assessors, Cornell University, and others, and decided that 1 million acres of idle or abandoned land in tracts of 500 acres or more would justify purchase and reforestation by the State.

The commission introduced a bill in the 1929 legislature, which was enacted into law and which is now section 3 of article XIV of the State constitution. The act authorized the Conservation Department to acquire for the State representative areas of not less than 500 acres of contiguous land to be devoted forever to growing and harvesting trees.

The aims were to retire permanently abandoned and idle farmlands from agriculture and to provide for a future supply of timber, public recreation, hunting, fishing, watershed protection, and scenic improvement. The department's policy was to acquire areas in which at least 50 percent of each 500-acre unit was cleared and suited for reforestation. The purpose was to prevent the acquisition of cutover forest land, which would be a mere land-buying program with little bearing on the agricultural problems.

This act did not apply to the areas already designated as the Adirondack and Catskill Forest Preserve. This new program was to be one of managing land for wildlife and commercial forests. The act authorized acquisition of about a million acres, but the annual appropriations were not forthcoming as scheduled because of the depression.

Up through 1949, 533,925 acres of submarginal farmlands in 363 areas in 34 counties had been acquired under this program at an average cost of 3.85 dollars an acre. At the end of 1956 this figure was 565,000 acres.

E. W. Littlefield, the director of lands and forests, reported in 1957 that an active program of land acquisition both for the forest preserve and State forests has been resumed, but progress may be slower because of high land prices. Legislation has been proposed to amend the State constitution to permit the sale of small, isolated tracts of 10 acres or less in size that are now outside the State forest preserve blue line. Proposals also exist for extending the forest preserve boundaries to include an area which would embrace 24 additional mountain peaks.

The State planning board in a summary report to the Governor in 1935 made a recommendation that remains State policy: "Careful surveys show that there is now a total of 5,800,000 acres of idle or submarginal farmland. . . . A large proportion of these submarginal lands, at least 4.5 million acres, should be gradually acquired by the State and used for timber production, for game and wildlife protection, for watershed protection and for public recreation. The State's present program for the purchase and reforestation of 1 million acres of submarginal farmland should be expanded so as eventually to include about 4.5 million acres."

There is yet a third forestry program in New York.

The State had much land in small tracts under 500 acres that were similar to the abandoned land that was purchased for reforestation. To get such tracts into a reforestation program, the Reforestation Commission sponsored a bill known as the county reforestation law, which became chapter 1947 of the laws of 1929. It was written into the State constitution in 1932 and is now section 3 of article XIV.

This article authorizes the board of supervisors in any county to acquire lands for reforestation and to establish and maintain forest plantations on lands already owned by the county. Counties may appropriate funds for reforestation projects and the State may contribute not to exceed 5 thousand dollars in any one year for any one county to defray a part of the expense of the work, provided the county appropriated and spent a similar sum on reforestation projects approved by the Conservation Department. Such land is exempt from State and county taxes but is subject to other land taxation on an assessment not to exceed the price paid for the land. Thirty-one counties were participating in this program and nearly 50 thousand acres were in county forests in 1954.

Tree planting has been a cornerstone of the New York State reforestation program. Open land has been planted almost immediately after purchase by the State. According to a report issued by the State Conservation Department in 1950, nearly 281 million trees had been planted on the submarginal farmlands acquired by the State. Between 1901 and 1949 the State planted an additional 85 million trees on the forest preserve and State institutional lands. The State furnished 337 million trees to individuals, municipalities, corporations, and semipublic organizations— a total of more than 703 million trees furnished by the State nurseries during 1901–1949—an average of more than 14 million trees a year.

New York State has had a three-pronged attack to carry out its forestry programs: First, getting land unsuited to agriculture out of circulation; second, planting trees at once so that it will return public revenue in the future and provide maximum watershed protection; and third, using the land for hunting, fishing, camping, and other types of recreation that do not interfere with the basic objective of timber production and watershed protection.

IN THE LAKE STATES, land programs developed later.

Michigan, Wisconsin, and Minnesota acted separately from 1928 to 1933 in developing land programs for handling the millions of acres of tax-reverted lands and in solving the concomitant problems of local government. The policies they developed were much alike because the problems they had to solve were the same. The State colleges of agriculture studied the problems and suggested programs for action.

One feature that did much to expedite the transfer of tax-delinquent land to the State was the shortening of the period between the beginning of delinquency and the sale and the subsequent redemption period.

The University of Wisconsin and the State Conservation Department published in 1949 a report by R. J. Penn and C. W. Loomer, who described the development of the land program in Marinette County. This county in northeastern Wisconsin typifies the timbered counties of the Lake States region and illustrates the problem and solution worked out in these States.

Marinette County was originally covered with white and Norway pine, hemlock and hardwoods on the highlands, and cedar, spruce, balsam, and tamarack on the lowlands. The lumber industry thrived from 1880 to 1910. Then the plow followed the ax. Many would-be farmers flocked to Marinette County after the First World War and were met by the many salesmen and speculators who had land to sell. The drop in agricultural and land prices in 1920 and 1921 soon dried up the stream of prospective buyers. The speculative owner ceased to pay taxes. Many settlers on the poorer lands could not meet mortgage payments. Discouraged, they moved away. Widespread abandonment of farms and tax delinquency became a major problem.

Wisconsin passed the forest crop law in 1927. It permitted private forest lands within a forest protection district to be taxed at 10 cents an acre annually and the timber at 10 percent of stumpage value, as a severance tax,

at the time of cutting. The State makes an annual payment to local taxing districts that matches the owner's annual tax of 10 cents an acre.

Marinette was one of the first Wisconsin counties to make wise use of the tax deed laws. The county took tax deeds to tax-delinquent land as soon as State law permitted. Thus the land was removed from the tax roll, and a realistic tax base was maintained for planning the county budget. Removing the land from the county tax roll also stopped State, town, and school levies, which formed a lien on the land prior to that of the county and had to be paid off before the county could get any return from the land.

The Marinette County Board on January 24, 1928, established a committee to work with local officials in developing an economic survey for the county to show trends in assessment, taxation, and resource development. The College of Agriculture assisted in the survey.

A committee of the State legislature also was studying these land-use problems which many other northern Wisconsin counties faced. As the result of a committee recommendation, counties were permitted to enter their lands under the forest crop law without annual tax payment of the 10 cents an acre. Another of its recommendations, enacted into law, was the annual payment by the State of 10 cents an acre for county forests to improve forests and to buy land to consolidate county holdings. Under this act severance taxes on county sales were increased to 50 percent.

Resolutions adopted in 1930 defined and named four forest areas in the county. Following the county committee's recommendation, the first step of the Marinette County Board was to establish county forest reserves and to enter forest land owned by the county under the Wisconsin forest crop law. The initial entry was 14,003 acres; by 1955 it was 227,853 acres.

The county committee early saw the need for consolidating the ownership of the county forests. To this end it made an ownership survey of its forest reserve areas and it purchased—with the county forest-aid funds from the State—scattered tracts of unoccupied wild land within these areas. By buying tracts from lumber companies that had no more interest in the land, the committee kept the land out of the hands of individuals who might have created problems of public service and fire hazards. Another blocking-in activity—the exchange of outlying tracts of county-owned, tax-reverted land for private tracts within the county forest boundaries—permitted lumber companies and some owners to consolidate their holdings. Others had opportunities to move out of the woods into communities with better public services.

The administration of tax-reverted lands is basic in the county land program. Marinette County, as did other northern Wisconsin counties, originally attempted to dispose of tax-delinquent land by sale to individuals at a flat rate of a dollar an acre.

A feature of a resolution the county board adopted in 1930 was a limit on the sale of county land. No land could be sold that was within county forest boundaries, was next to lakes, or had recreational advantages, unless the board authorized the sales. No isolated tracts could be sold if it meant future need for roads and schools. No tract was to be sold at less than the delinquent taxes.

A permanent committee of three members of the county board was created in 1933 and given authority to have general charge of all matters regarding sale of tax-delinquent land. It was instrumental in getting the county board to instruct the county treasurer to purchase all tax certificates at the county sales. The county thereby could take ownership to the land, perfect the title, and then retain it or dispose of it by trade, exchange, or sale in the best interests of the county.

In 1931–1948 the county sold 134,-025 acres of tax-delinquent land for 546,958 dollars—an indication that

considerable thought was given to deciding what tax-reverted land should be retained in county ownership and what should be returned to private ownership. It is possible that some of the land sold to private owners again reverted to the county through tax delinquency.

The development and execution of a sound, long-term program of administration of land resources required action of several kinds. More than land acquisition was needed to keep people from moving on land unsuited to agriculture. More was needed to keep settlers from remote areas, where costly public services would have to be provided for a few settlers who paid low taxes or none and could not make an adequate living.

The county board—with the guidance of George S. Wehrwein and W. A. Rowlands, of the University of Wisconsin, and C. B. Drewry, the county agent—instituted in 1933 an educational campaign to explain to the citizens the possibilities of guiding land occupancy under the Wisconsin Zoning Act of 1929. Nine months later the board adopted a zoning ordinance to be effective in the nine townships that favored the idea. More townships joined later.

The county board soon became aware of the need to move settlers out of remote areas so as to reduce the cause for high cost of government and to make effective the objectives of zoning. That was accomplished by direct purchase and by exchange of land. Sixteen isolated families on 1,120 acres were moved between 1936 and 1944.

This program was the forerunner of the larger isolated-settler purchase program in the Lake States, a program that could be useful only in counties that had effective zoning ordinances. Later 21 other families were bought out and helped to relocate elsewhere.

Marinette County is now benefiting financially from its forest holdings. At the suggestion of the county agent, the assistant county agent, and the district forester, the county board in 1941 de-

445509°—58——7

cided to try to sell aspen trees that were maturing and needed cutting. The sale in 1942 brought 2,640 dollars. Since that time, stumpage sales have been expanded to include several species for pulp and lumber. These sales have totaled 104,401 dollars since 1942.

The work of the Civilian Conservation Corps and the Works Progress Administration during the depression years of the 1930's did much to establish good forestry in Marinette and other forest counties. Several camps were established in the county, and forest-improvement work was carried out under the direction of the Wisconsin Conservation Department. The otherwise unemployed young men in the camps also built fire lanes, fire trails, and fire towers. They worked on stream and lake improvements and made surveys of forest types. They built a youth camp that can accommodate 175 persons. During the years 1933–1942 they planted 16 million trees in the county.

The Lake States now have well-established programs for conserving their timber resources and for getting maximum public benefits from large acreages of forest land. The programs embrace protection against fires; public purchase as a way of getting the abandoned cutover land back into productive status; the protection of public and private commercial forests against ill-planned settlement and use through rural zoning ordinances; special forest taxation laws to encourage private forestry; and the recognition of the value of recreational uses of forest land and lakes.

THE TYPE OF LAND owned by Montana, how the State came into possession of the land, and the programs for its use and management are similar to circumstances in most of the other Western States.

Montana received nearly 6 million acres of Federal-grant lands. Under the United States Enabling Act of February 22, 1889, the State received Sections 16 and 36 in every township, a total of 5,188,000 acres, for support of common schools.

Most of the State-owned land in Montana is school land scattered through the State in 640-acre tracts. The enabling act set the minimum selling price of grant lands at 10 dollars an acre. That was too much for grazing land, and the Congress later modified the act to make the minimum price 5 dollars an acre for all land classified as fit only for grazing. Apparently that also was high, because little of this land has been sold. Now the State board of land commissioners does not authorize the sale of any State land if the amount realized from such sale does not give a much better return when it is invested in bonds than the annual rental received.

A small number of acres is sold each year—for example, 25,069 acres in 1955 and 17,318 acres in 1956. The State retains mineral rights.

The enabling act provided that all money received from the sale of school-

STATE LANDS IN MONTANA	Original grants	Remaining June 30, 1956
Purpose of grant	(acres)	(acres)
Common schools	5,188,000	4,636,905
State University	46,720	41,420
Agricultural College (Morrill)	90,000	64,267
Agricultural College (Second)	50,000	18,230
School of Mines	100,000	60,308
State Normal College	100,000	66,403
School for Deaf and Blind	50,000	36,375
State Reform School	50,000	36,555
Other	186,226	125,162
Parks	1,439	1,439
Carey Act	92,280	92,280

trust land and timber and royalties from oil and minerals from these lands be invested in bonds of the United States, the State of Montana, counties, cities, and school districts within the State and that the interest earned be distributed annually to the schools. The same rules apply to each respective grant. The trust fund, exclusive of the value of the land, on June 30, 1956, was valued at 35,780,777 dollars, of which 30,661,177 dollars was credited to the common school fund.

The biennial report for June 30, 1956, said that 442,845 acres were under crop-share lease. The income from the State's share of the crops sold was 2,055,959 dollars. Land leased for grazing was 4,170,152 acres, which brought 434,399 dollars.

Montana in 1957 held title to 5,179,-344 acres of the grant lands received from the Federal Government. All State-owned land in 1949 amounted to 5,497,515 acres. Thus, the State had not purchased much land other than for parks, wildlife reserves, and miscellaneous uses. The program has been chiefly that of administering the scattered pieces of State-owned grazing, crop, and forest land and getting income from it.

A unique feature of the general land policy in Montana is the cooperative grazing associations, which were authorized under chapter 208 of the 1939 Session Laws.

This law was passed particularly for the localities in which operating ranch units were difficult to block out because of the patchwork pattern of small ownerships. The scattered tracts of State-owned lands, Federal lands, railroad lands, and various types of private lands mean that management of the State-owned lands without a cooperative grazing association would be only management for current income without consideration of long-term conservation needs. Controlled grazing to conserve range resources could be effected only with common management policies for all the ownership tracts within an area. The law enabled livestock operators to obtain control over the grazing land they use and thus has helped them stabilize their operations by controlling the intensity of grazing within the district. It helped put an end to uncontrolled free range and the overgrazing of the many absentee-owned tracts.

In 1949 there were 37 cooperative grazing associations, which cover 12,-381,786 acres—nearly 15 percent of the land area of the State. Most of the associations are in northeastern Montana. About 300 thousand acres of State-owned grazing land are within the boundaries of the grazing association districts, and their management contributes to the objectives of the grazing district program. Slightly more than 60 percent of the area within the districts is privately owned.

Establishment of the grazing districts makes it possible for the users of grazing land to control the intensity of grazing. It also provides a means by which the absentee owner, the State, the county, and the Federal Government may lease their lands at fair rates. Before the establishment of the districts, many of the scattered tracts of absentee owners were used under trespass as part of the free open range.

The Montana Grass Conservation Commission supervises the cooperative State grazing districts. The district officers have the power to buy, sell, and exchange land, allocate grazing rights, determine grazing fees, and to do a number of other things necessary to the successful operation of the district. The commission must approve plans for creating a district. The by-laws must be in accordance with the 1939 Grass Conservation Act.

A livestock operator within a district may obtain a grazing preference, whose size depends primarily on the amount of commensurate property he controls. Commensurate property is the privately owned or controlled land that furnishes feed for livestock in periods between grazing seasons. Commensurate property is called dependent commensurate property if it depends for its proper use on other land of which the rancher has had the use for a given number of years. People who own dependent commensurate property have first claim to preferences. If additional carrying capacity remains, the owners of commensurate property have next preference. Temporary permits may be issued from year to year to nonmembers and members if the carrying capacity exceeds the reasonable needs of commensurate property of member owners. Every livestock operator with cattle running at large must obtain a grazing permit.

One who lives within the district boundaries but does not use any land other than his own need not get a permit.

The members of the grazing districts have the choice of managing their range in large community pastures or blocking out the controlled land into units, which may be allotted individually. In the blocking out of contiguous tracts into an operating unit, an owner may in effect trade the use of his remote parcel of land for land that touches his main unit.

Taylor grazing districts (organized primarily in areas in which there is extensive Federal public domain) and soil conservation districts also exist in Montana. These district organizations have some of the same powers and objectives as the State grazing districts. The State grazing districts in Montana represent one form of State and local action to bring about better land use and greater economic stability to the community. Such a program allows maximum individual initiative and does not require that the State purchase the land in order to achieve social and economic objectives that are considered desirable.

NEARLY ALL OF THE STATES have some—not very much—land for demonstration forests, parks, institutional sites, and for fish and wildlife preserves. The large acreages of State-owned land, as we have said, are (in the West) primarily school lands granted to the States by the Federal Government; (in the Lake States) the cutover forest land forfeited for taxes; and (in New York and Pennsylvania) abandoned farm and cutover lands the States bought.

Public ownership of land—Federal, State, or local—usually is based on three objectives.

One is to own land for parks and wildlife reserves so that all citizens may enjoy their use.

Another objective is to acquire land to be used for some function of government—building sites, airports, capitol grounds, school grounds, and training bases, for example.

A third objective is to insure proper use of specific land resources so that they will remain productive for the benefit of the entire community. This objective involves large areas and is the one that is involved in all discussions of land and conservation policy.

Public purchase is a tool that may be used to shape desired land policy. Ownership in fee simple gives governing bodies and officials a right to determine management policies simply and efficiently without the tedious process of engineering consent but subject to mandate of the voting booth.

Much of the State-owned land in the Western States held in trust for common schools and other institutions is outside the scope of the objectives we listed. It is held presumably to earn income for designated institutions.

The use and management of most of the trust lands did not result from the adoption of basic land policies. State ownership of these lands appears to be a result of original plans gone awry. They were not sold because of various reasons. The minimum price set in the enabling acts often was too high. The few who hold leases at low rates want to maintain the status quo; and the dispersion of the trust lands often means that little public attention is brought to bear on the problem. The poorly conceived and managed programs for sale of public land in the past have made legislatures skeptical of any plans for selling public land. The loss of principal through bad investment of the trust funds possibly encourages the belief that land is the best investment, because the legislature can directly control its management.

Because forestry is a generations-long enterprise, some persons advocate State ownership of forest land. An individual may be forced to cut his trees prematurely because he needs money immediately, regardless of the greater returns he might get in time. Government, however, can wait.

Desired land policy can be brought about without public ownership if other necessary measures are taken within the framework of private ownership. These measures are principally special forest taxation, zoning, and arrangements for consolidating many small ownerships into economic units.

Purchase of land by the State (or Federal) Government to carry out certain objectives is resorted to sometimes because it is the easiest way. The same long-term objectives may be achieved if the members of a community look beyond a gain today and agree to restrictions for the good of the community and future generations.

Forest taxation usually is a modification or replacement of the property tax so that little or no taxes need be paid when a forest is growing into maturity and is not producing income to the owner.

A report, "Forest Tax Law Digest, 1956," published by the Forest Service, shows the status of forest taxation at the end of 1956. Twenty-nine States have forest tax laws.

Yield taxes are provided for in 15 States—12 optional and 3 mandatory. The yield tax exempts timber from payment of annual property taxes and imposes, instead, a tax when the timber is harvested. It is in the form of a gross income tax and must be paid by the landowner. The bare land usually is subject to annual property taxes.

Timber is exempt from property taxes in 11 States. The purpose is to encourage the reestablishing of forest growth in areas best adapted to forestry. There are no supplementary forest taxation acts in nine of these States. In 7 of the 11 States, the bare land is subject to the property tax. The land as well as the timber is exempt in three of them, and in one the assessment on the land is reduced to 20 percent. Idaho has a yield tax, which in effect recaptures at the time of harvest the exemptions that were made during the growing period. The other 10 States have no provision for recapturing at harvest the tax concessions.

Five States have a modified property tax, which fixes the assessment or tax rate at a given valuation or percentage.

Six States have severance taxes, which levy a small tax on the harvested timber products. Usually it is in addition to other taxes and is levied primarily to obtain special revenue to be used specifically to help forestry.

The millions of acres of cutover land that were forfeited for taxes probably would have remained in private ownership if the tax systems had been different. Property taxes, adapted to agricultural areas producing annual income, were extended to forested areas. Many owners who had cut-out-and-get-out ideas would not pay the relatively high taxes on land that would not produce income for another 30 to 40 years.

The yield tax appears to be the most satisfactory type of forest taxation as a means by which to raise taxes in a forest community, but it is only one of the tools to be used if good land use is to be fostered without outright public ownership of the land. It seldom has been used in the United States. It is mandatory in Louisiana, Mississippi, and New Hampshire. In the other States that have this tax, its use is optional on the part of the forest landowner, and only a small proportion of owners have elected to use it.

Zoning can do much to effect the development of desired land policy. It is not retroactive, however; it is a preventive tool, rather than a corrective one. It has met with favor in remote and sparsely settled areas, such as those in the northern parts of the Lake States. Its adoption to direct the use of private property in populous areas like New York and Pennsylvania is more difficult. Citizens do not like to have restrictions placed on the possible alternative uses of their property. If there are no sound alternative uses to the predominant use, restrictions are not objected to.

Other general classes of measures that can bring about desirable land use without public purchase are those that are developed to solve particular problems. An example is State grazing associations in Montana, which were developed to bring about improvement and security in the use of the many interspersed and small ownership tracts on the range. Declaration of certain roads as good-weather roads or seasonal roads would be a measure to prevent year-round occupancy in places where public services for permanent occupancy would cost too much. Some persons advocate such a plan for New York State. Land exchange has been used to consolidate ownership of State and Federal forests and also to remove isolated settlers from remote areas in public forests.

WHAT OF THE FUTURE? It is likely that measures other than public ownership will be strengthened and used more extensively to promote good forestry, conservation, and watershed protection. The extended period of high prices for forest products has made good forestry profitable. Wood-using industries have enlarged their private holdings, and more and more of them have adopted good forestry practices to insure continued yields.

The increased price of land has greatly slowed down programs of State acquisition of land for reforestation. It is likely that the Great Lakes States, Pennsylvania, and New York will strengthen their programs of management of State forests and that the chief acquisition activity will be to block in present publicly owned areas. In the other States, however, it is not likely that State ownership will be expanded much beyond present dimensions.

With good programs, managed in the public interest, and the necessity of long-term programs for forestry operation, it is not likely that the public will clamor for transferring the present State and Federal forests to private ownership. Michigan, Wisconsin, and Minnesota have yield-tax laws which encourage private forestry by relieving the owner of the burden of paying taxes on the value of the growing crop. New York and Pennsylvania, however, do not have laws for special forest taxation. The regular property tax, if strictly applied, is a hindrance to good forestry in private ownership. The Pennsylvania Legislature has enacted bills for special forest taxation, but the courts have declared the acts unconstitutional. Under such conditions, private ownership and operation of forest lands will be discouraged unless there are prospective subsurface values.

Acreages for parks, wildlife reserves, and other public purposes will increase as the population grows.

The future of the extensive acreages of scattered school-trust lands is more of a problem. It usually is a question not only of whether the land is best adapted to public or private ownership; it is first a problem of financial management, a determination as to what policy will bring the greatest and most sustaining income to the schools. A second consideration is whether the land will return more to the local community as well as the schools if it were transferred to private ownership and were added to the tax base of the community.

The kind of policy needed to promote conservation and wise use of land varies with the type of land resources in the various States and the patterns of government, tax structure, and customs built up over the years. The programs must be flexible so as to be adapted to the problems as they arise. State ownership of land is only one measure among the several needed for developing land programs.

Getting and using land in time of war.

The War and Navy Departments had the use of 52.7 million acres in 1945. The methods by which the land was acquired, the relocation of the people on it, the uses to which it was put, and its disposal when it was needed no longer were developed through discussion, legislation, and development of Government procedures. The experience has point for other programs and situations. By *Alvin T. M. Lee,* State Experiment Station Division, Agricultural Research Service.

SLIGHTLY MORE than 2.5 million acres of land were used by the War and Navy Departments of the Nation in 1940.

After the outbreak of the Second World War, the two Departments purchased about 6.75 million acres from private owners; leased more than 10 million acres from individuals, municipalities, and State governments; and had the use of slightly more than 33 million acres of public domain and other Federal land.

By the close of the war, these agencies had the use of 52,727,695 acres.

If all this land were in one piece, it would be larger than any one of 38 of our States. It would be about equal in size to Kansas or Utah and 1.5 million acres larger than Minnesota.

Many of the sites have been released from use by the armed services since the close of the war, but other sites have been acquired because of specific training needs and for the Atomic Energy Commission.

The total land used for military needs on June 30, 1955, was 23,462,430 acres. Senate Document 100 (the 84th Congress, second session) lists this total as follows: 7,057,305 acres for the Army, 10,231,901 acres for the Air Force, 4,170,067 acres for the Navy, and 2,003,157 acres for the Atomic Energy Commission. The size of these combined areas is equivalent to any one of the States of Indiana, Virginia, Kentucky, and Tennessee and larger than any one of 12 States.

Any one unit may be a few acres to several hundred thousand acres in size. Military camps and artillery ranges usually have 25 thousand to 100 thousand acres or more. Aerial training requires from 640 acres for ground bombing to many thousands of acres for more extensive training in flying and operating fighter planes and in air-to-air gunnery practice. Ordnance plants and storage areas usually comprise 5 thousand to 10 thousand acres to allow for a safety zone around the major installations. The space requirements for testing of missiles are so great that much of the testing is over vast expanses of water.

THE RURAL LANDS before they were acquired by the military may have had no use in agriculture, but some were highly productive.

Publicly owned land transferred or leased for temporary military purposes and land leased from individuals was primarily forest or grazing land before the war.

The land purchased from private owners had a wider range of uses and higher use capabilities. Of the land bought from private owners, about one-fourth was in cropland, one-third in pasture and range, and one-third in woodland and forest. (The rest had miscellaneous uses.) These were the major uses but not necessarily the best uses and the ones in which the land would yield the most satisfactory returns to the operator.

Ordnance plants have requirements as to site that nearly always place them on the best land in a community. They must be on land that can be excavated deeply and easily for heavy foundations. Deep soil has another advantage in that it will not carry explosive shocks so far as land with shallow, rocky soil. Adequate main-line railroad and highway transportation is necessary. Because much water is needed, the plants usually are near rivers. The large amount of hauling to be done demands that the land be reasonably level. The site must be in open country for safety yet close enough to population centers to insure an adequate labor supply. The cost of construction of buildings, highways, and railroad spurs can be held to a minimum only if sites with deep soil and level land are selected. Operating costs are cheaper on level land. Even in the best agricultural areas, such as Sangamon County in Illinois, the cost of the land was only about 2 percent of the total cost of the installation. This is a reason why construction authorities give relatively little consideration to agricultural productivity when deciding between alternative sites.

Ordnance depots, shell loading plants, and storage areas need not be near abundant water supplies, but otherwise they have the same requirements as to site as the ordnance plants.

Airfields are located on land as good as that for ordnance plants. Level land is needed for runways. Most of the site and the adjacent land must be open to avoid costly land clearing. Auxiliary and emergency landing fields usually require a level area of about 160 acres, used only for landing purposes. The main airbases are large, and some less level land may be used for barracks and grounds.

Camps built for prisoners and enemy aliens during the war contained a large proportion of cropland because it was intended that the occupants grow a part of their food.

Military camps and maneuver areas as a rule are located where there is a minimum of agricultural activity and thus on land not well adapted to crops. Exceptions include Camp Campbell in Kentucky and Tennessee, Camp Breckenridge in Kentucky, Camp Atterbury in Indiana, Fort Riley in Kansas, and Camp Adair in Oregon—in which 50 to 70 percent of the land had been used for crops. Nearly always are the camps placed in areas with two railroads. It is considered an advantage to locate a camp not far from sizable cities so that recreational facilities are adequate and varied enough for large numbers of men.

Bombing and artillery ranges and proving grounds usually are placed on the poorest land available. Of the 1,384,000 acres bought for this purpose from private owners, only 7 percent was used for crops before the war. These sites were mostly in the poorer grazing areas in the Western States and in extensive woodland areas in the Eastern States.

MORE THAN STATISTICS of acreages must be given, however. Human activities are involved when a public agency moves in to take over a large area of land and when it makes it available again for farming. Problems arise for the occupants and the communities.

The methods developed and problems encountered apply to all large scale Government acquisitions, use, and disposal of land. An account of them should give the reader a better understanding of how public agencies go about buying land and what the Government does to alleviate the problems caused by large-scale public-land acquisition for nonmilitary as well as military uses.

The acquisition of land for military sites and the other public purposes is different from the normal exchange of property in which a willing buyer negotiates with a willing seller.

When the property of all the owners in a community must be acquired, many will be unwilling sellers and will not want to move away. Moving means seeking new jobs, new friends, and new farms. Many will be too old to make the necessary occupational, emotional, and social adjustments easily. The acquisition of an entire community means the dismantling of churches, schools, and other facilities. The question always is, "Why does it have to be our community?"

It was estimated that the acquisitions of land by the War and Navy Departments during the war comprised about 100 thousand tracts of land that involved possibly 60 thousand families and 30 thousand farms.

Because of the inevitable resistance to being uprooted from one's home and community, ordinary purchase procedures would delay too long the Nation's wartime programs. Special powers therefore were granted whereby the agencies responsible for acquiring land for national defense could take over properties almost immediately and negotiate prices and other adjustments later.

PURCHASE OF REAL ESTATE for public use is first attempted through direct negotiation with the owner.

Two acts generally may be used to facilitate acquisition of property by the United States in the absence of voluntary sale by the owner: First, the General Condemnation Statute (25 Stat. 357, Aug. 1, 1888, 40 U. S. C. 257, 258); and, second, the Declaration of Taking Act (46 Stat. 1421, 1422, Feb. 26, 1931, 40 U. S. C., Sec. 258a–258e). Additional legislative authority was given in the War Powers Act (40 Stat. 241, July 2, 1917, 50 U. S. C. 171, as amended by 56 Stat. 177, Mar. 27, 1942, 50 U. S. C., Supp. V 632).

The General Condemnation Statute giving governmental agencies power to acquire property through condemnation provides a procedure by which title and possession may be taken by the Government but only after final judgment has been made by the court. This procedure often caused delay in beginning necessary construction and improvement.

The Declaration of Taking supplements the general condemnation procedure and is used concurrently with it. It provides that in condemnation proceedings title to land can be taken immediately by the filing of a declaration of taking and the deposit in court of the estimated amount of just compensation. The court may then pay the owners all or any part of the sum deposited in court upon receipt of application and satisfactory proof of title. As title passes immediately upon the filing of the declaration, it is possible for the Government to take possession at once and to carry on construction and improvement concurrently with acquisition activities.

The Second War Powers Act of March 27, 1942, provided: "The Secretary of War, the Secretary of the Navy, or any other officer, board, commission or governmental corporation authorized by the President may acquire by purchase, donation, or other means of transfer, or may cause proceedings to be instituted in any court having jurisdiction of such proceedings, to acquire by condemnation any real property, temporary use thereof, or other interest therein . . . ."

An important feature of the Second War Powers Act is that possession may be taken and the property may be occupied, used, and improved immediately upon or after filing of the condemnation petition. This is a special power conferred upon the acquiring agency to meet the contingencies of national emergency. Under this act, however, payment for the property cannot be made if there is disagreement on price or a flaw in the title until the cases are settled in court. Under it, the Government must pay an annual rate of 6 percent interest on the amount that is finally awarded to the person whose property was condemned.

The Declaration of Taking Act, in the absence of the War Powers Act providing for immediate possession, can be used for the same purpose. Title is acquired immediately, and the occupancy and use of the property can proceed forthwith. The court is given the power to fix the time within which and the terms upon which the parties in possession shall be required to surrender possession to the condemner. One of its chief points, through the immediate conveyance of title, is that a deposit can be made in the court of the estimated just compensation. Upon application of the parties in interest, the court may order that all or any of the money so deposited be paid to the condemnee as a partial or conditional settlement of the suit. This feature prevents hardship and saves the Government the costs of interest. Payment, under the declaration, is only to the account of just compensation to be awarded in the proceedings. The acceptance of payment therefore does not prejudice the case of either party. If such payment exceeds the final award, the Government can recover the overpayment. If payment is less than the final award, the Government makes an additional payment with interest.

The Navy Department conducted most of its wartime land acquisition under the General Condemnation Act and the Declaration of Taking Act. Thus immediate title was taken, and the final negotiations with the owners were carried out under the jurisdiction of the court.

The War Department used this blanket authority only when the land had to be used immediately. When it did so, the Department negotiated with the individual after filing the petition for condemnation and after the individual properties for which a price was agreed upon were withdrawn individually from the petition and the cases were settled out of court.

The several legislative acts authorizing acquisition of real estate apply with equal force to obtaining the use of the land through lease or easements and the extinguishing of mineral and other rights in the land.

PAYMENT FOR DISTURBANCE was discussed while the program of land acquisition was going forward, but no positive action was taken until the issue was brought to the courts in the General Motors case. In that instance, the War Department acquired a building that was under long-term lease to the General Motors Corp. The lease extended beyond the period for which the War Department expected to need the building. It was shown that the General Motors Corp. would be forced to undergo expenditures for moving equipment out, storing it elsewhere, and later moving it back again and incur damages in the process of moving. The Supreme Court ruled that General Motors was entitled to compensation for these costs.

This decision came late in the acquisition program, and most farm owners and tenants therefore did not benefit from it. The Farm Security Administration (which later became the Farmers Home Administration) helped low-income families who had to move by giving them grants up to 100 dollars toward moving expenses. That was of some help but was little compensation for the inconvenience and added expense experienced. Those who could not qualify as low-income families received no assistance.

ASSISTANCE AND DIRECTION in relocation was needed by many of the families who were bought out. Some were able to relocate without any help. Some wanted only information and financial assistance. The incapacitated needed help in the job of moving, besides information and financing. Since there was no compensation for disturbance, the displaced families suffered varying financial and physical hardships.

The county agricultural planning

committees or war boards, which were made up of county representatives of agricultural agencies and local farmers, worked in a coordinating capacity to help the displaced families. Their activities on relocation problems consisted essentially of surveying relocation needs; listing the available trucking, storage, rental, and related services; making lists of farms for sale; and maintaining an information office.

Government agencies and other organizations worked with the agricultural planning committees, but several also had programs that may have been carried out independently.

State agencies having programs of public assistance to the aged and to dependent children became involved in the relocation problem when their clients were in military purchase areas.

Philanthropic and semipublic relief agencies in some States came to the rescue of the incapacitated. In the Fort Knox area in Kentucky, for example, the American Red Cross stationed personnel at nearby villages so that families in dire circumstances could be interviewed and assistance could be given quickly and with the minimum of inconvenience. The Red Cross looked upon such a large-scale evacuation as a disaster, as disturbing as a flood.

Federal and State employment services helped those who wanted temporary employment to obtain priority for available jobs in the construction of camps or ordnance plants.

The relocation problems depended somewhat on the tenure status of the individual families. Farm owner-operators who had no debts could relocate with little difficulty, except for the inconvenience of waiting for payment and the need to make credit arrangements. Owner-operators of heavily encumbered property probably had little cash left after they paid their debts.

Tenants on the farms were compensated to the extent of their leasehold interests in the land, which as a rule included primarily their equities in the value of growing crops and seed-

bed preparation. The value of seedbed preparation was the cost of doing the job at prevailing rates in the community. The value of a growing crop was the estimated yield multiplied by the current price, minus the cost of bringing the crop to maturity and market. A tenant's share of such values as he had equity in depended on his contribution to the job or his share in the final crop.

The division of the proceeds was usually left to the decision of the tenant and the landlord. Each had a right to receive separate checks from the Government, but no payment was made until both had signed a release. If disagreement arose between landlord and tenant as to division of the proceeds for the item in which the tenant had an equity, the tenant frequently refused to sign a release. Then the property was filed under condemnation proceedings, and the determination of distribution of receipts was left in the hands of the court.

Tenants usually suffered more inconvenience and financial loss than owner-operators. Tenants often found themselves without farms because the normal season for leasing was past or because there were not enough farms for rent. Many who wanted to continue farming lost out on one crop year. This was a severe war-cost burden to a tenant and created a problem that found no satisfactory solution other than the part assumed by the Farm Security Administration.

The effort of the Farm Security Administration to develop a comprehensive program to help relocate displaced farmers through State defense relocation corporations warrants a special mention. For States in which there were at least 25 low-income farm families to be relocated on farms, regional FSA administrators had authority to establish corporations that would buy or lease lands and develop them for these people. They set up relocation corporations in 17 States and acquired 339,222 acres to be made available to displaced families.

One of the objectives of the relocation corporations was to hold to a minimum any secondary displacement, such as would occur if farm tenants elsewhere would be forced to move because the farms they were on were sold to families moving out of Government-purchase areas. The corporations tried to buy land that could be developed into additional farms. Much of it was under nonresident or corporate ownership. An example is a tract of 41,845 acres in Bates County, Mo., which was bought from the Scully Estate. It had 156 families on it. Plans called for subdividing the land into 382 family-sized farms, which would provide land for an additional 226 families.

Of the 339,222 acres purchased by the State relocation corporations, all but 4,745 acres were bought before July 1, 1942. This program was first started in Alabama, Georgia, and South Carolina.

Relocation activities through State defense relocation corporations were stopped by an opinion rendered by the Comptroller General of the United States on March 5, 1942. He held that these activities were not within the scope of appropriations made for the Farm Security Administration. The Appropriation Act of 1943 also directed FSA to stop direct loans for land purchased under the rehabilitation program except where directly specified under separate acts, such as the Bankhead-Jones Act and the Wheeler-Case Act.

MANY COMMUNITY PROBLEMS arose as the Government bought large tracts. Local governmental units, especially school and road districts, were dissolved or had to combine with others. Partially dismembered districts that were left that way had to reduce their services to the amount that could be supported by the reduced tax revenue that would come from the shrunken tax base. On the other hand, public services had to be expanded in areas where a great many workers moved in.

Some indirect benefits may have accrued from the increased payrolls, but they usually went to State and county governments and not to townships or school districts.

Only 37 counties in the United States had 10 percent or more of their area removed from the tax rolls because of these land-purchase programs. All of them suffered a noticeable loss in property-tax receipts. A far larger number, 745 counties, had less than 10 percent of their land area involved.

Smaller units, like townships and school districts, were affected more than counties. Up to January 1, 1945, 1,224 separate projects of 100 or more acres had been established by the War and Navy Departments; 172 of these involved 5 thousand acres or more. It is likely that the removal of 5 thousand acres from a local tax base would noticeably affect school and township finances.

Many local districts sought to obtain compensatory payments for loss of tax base on the grounds that it was unjust to place the burden of debt liquidation on the remaining properties. The War and Navy Departments had no authority to make such payments, however. The Departments could replace facilities by relocating roads, sidewalks, and powerlines if they were needed, but they had no authority to liquidate outstanding bonded indebtedness. Bonds are not encumbrances or liens on specific properties and accordingly must be retired by general taxation. As they are not liens, the vendors were under no obligation to pay them off, and the War and Navy Departments were not legally authorized to require their satisfaction. Any outstanding bonds had to be assumed by the portion of the taxing unit remaining.

Assessments levied against specific properties were a responsibility of the property owner, and had to be liquidated in the process of purchase by the Government. Current and all delinquent taxes had to be paid by the vendor before the Government bought.

Repeated attempts were made unsuccessfully to pass legislation during the war to permit the Federal Government to make payments in lieu of taxes to the taxing units in which it had purchased land for military purposes.

Closing of schools affected all of the families in the attendance district—those on farms not purchased as well as those within the purchase unit. Township and county roads near large training camps and ordnance plants usually had to be closed. The most necessary relocation of roads was financed by the Government.

Electric power and telephone lines on the land bought by the Government usually had to be relocated. Cemeteries that were in danger of damage by exploding shells or were in the way of construction were relocated at Government expense.

The influx of people to work at the Government plants and training areas created problems in housing and facilities. It was not easy to provide adequate living conditions for the thousands of construction workers who were to be in a community only a short time. Towns sometimes tried to give direction to the building boom by enacting zoning and health regulations.

Federal aid to local units of government was provided under the authority of the Lanham Act. Most of it went to cities and only a minor portion to the localities where large blocks of land had been removed from the tax roll.

Through June 30, 1946, the Federal Works Agency allotted 481,216,691 dollars for construction of public facilities and for public services because of the needs arising from new concentrations of population. Of the 359,605,457 dollars spent for public works, 8,275,474 went in the form of loans, 180,059,526 for Federal construction, and 171,270,457 as grants for non-Federal construction. Federal allotments for public services were mostly in the form of assistance in paying teachers, operating day nurseries, buying fire equipment, hiring additional policemen, and hiring persons for recreation centers.

Often the amount of aid exceeded the tax revenue that had been lost, but the communities could not have financed the needed facilities. It was a war need, and in most instances was temporary in nature.

Federal aid was in direct relation to the need for new schools, hospitals, and other types of public facilities occasioned by the influx of war workers. It had little relation to the loss of tax base. Pulaski County, where most of the land for Fort Leonard Wood was purchased, for example, received only 14,040 dollars for school operation, but the neighboring villages of Lebanon, Rolla, Waynesville, and Richland, which were within commuting distance of the fort, received more than 400 thousand dollars to enlarge and operate schools. The communities receiving such aid for the construction of schools, hospitals, water facilities, and sewage-disposal facilities possibly benefited after the war if the population remaining warranted the retention of these facilities. Many of the facilities were not needed after the military establishments were abandoned, however.

LEASING THE OPEN LAND in military sites to farmers when its only purpose was to form buffer strips for safety zones was looked upon as a possibility for increasing the production of food. Cropping such land helped control weeds and reduced maintenance costs.

A program for leasing military land for agricultural production, when it did not interfere with the primary purpose, got underway with the 1943 crop season and expanded to 377 thousand acres in 1944 and 1,145,993 acres in 1946, when the war was over. This was a new program, and it is still in operation. The Army in November 1956 had 992,894 acres and the Air Force had 674,313 acres outleased. Farmers who are known in the community operate within these sites under strict surveillance.

Leasing policies developed during the war have been continued in the outleasing of farmland. The principal provisions call for cash rental, revocation at will by the Secretary of Defense on 30 days' notice if needed, compensation to the lessee in the event of revocation, and the right of the commanding officer to enter the leased premises at any time.

The leasing program at each site is under the administration of the commanding officer. Suggested procedures that were developed by the regional and national staffs include consultation with county agents as to desirable crop rotations and soil management; subdivision of the tracts into units deemed most suitable for the locality; and the granting of first opportunity to lease the available tracts to their former owners.

Also, the acreage to be leased should be advertised wherever practicable. This may take the form of circulation of notices among former owners and others known to be interested and the posting of notices in public places. Negotiations may take place for the tracts to which no satisfactory sealed bids are received. The period of the lease may extend up to 5 years, and renewal may take place without advertising. Rental prices are substantially in accordance with the prevailing cash rental prices for comparable land in the locality.

Land that was formerly held under some type of Federal ownership usually is turned over to the former agency for developing an outleasing program. The agency reserves the right to take over use of the area whenever it may be necessary to do so. Supervision over use of the land, collection of rents, preparation of leases or permits, and similar matters are then the responsibility of the agency to which the Defense Department has given the job of land management.

THE DISPOSAL OF SURPLUS MILITARY LANDS was provided for under the Surplus Property Act of 1944. Under Surplus Property Board Regulation 1, issued April 2, 1945, the disposal of surplus agricultural and forest property was assigned to the Department of Agriculture; of grazing and mineral property, to the Department of the Interior; of housing property, to the National Housing Agency; and of other surplus nonindustrial real property, to the Federal Works Agency.

The Department of Agriculture in turn designated the Farm Credit Administration to handle its disposal job. In an amendment of Regulation 1, on February 23, 1947, the disposal of grazing and mineral property also was assigned to the Department.

In Regulation 16, November 16, 1945, a surplus airport disposal committee was established to function in an advisory capacity to the Surplus Property Administrator. This was necessary in order to conform to paragraph (c), section 13 of the Surplus Property Act, which required that surplus airport properties be disposed of in such a way as to promote the establishment of a nationwide system of public airports. Certain airports, particularly auxiliary airfields that were classified as not being suitable for continued use, could be assigned to the disposal agency having authority to dispose of such land. The Department of Agriculture has been authorized to dispose of several auxiliary airfields.

Section 12 of the Surplus Property Act provided for the transfer of surplus war property from one Government agency to another. Such transfers have priority over other disposals provided for in the act and must be at the fair value of the property as fixed by the disposal agency, unless transfer without reimbursement or transfer of funds is otherwise authorized by law.

Authority exists under section 12 for the transfer of forest land to the Forest Service, grazing land to the Department of the Interior, submarginal agricultural land to the Soil Conservation Service, and various other types of lands to other Federal agencies if they are best suited to public use.

A chief difficulty in making such transfer of the surplus land was that the law required that the requesting agency "pay" for land that the Federal Government had already paid for.

The transfer of surplus land to civilian agencies applies only to the land bought from private owners during the war. As a rule, land that was formerly in public ownership and was temporarily made available for military use automatically reverted to the former agency when it no longer was needed for military use. An exception existed for land on which substantial improvements had been made because of war use and which therefore was best suited to some other type of use.

Section 23 of the Surplus Property Act set forth the policies for the return of surplus real property to private ownership. It established priorities of the prospective buyers, policy on pricing, termination of priority privileges, and types of deeds that may be issued.

The order of priorities in the acquisition of surplus real estate and the type of real estate such priorities apply to under sections 12, 13, and 23 of the Act were worked out in Surplus Property Regulation 5. Government agencies, State and local governments, and nonprofit institutions may acquire any type of surplus real estate regardless of when the Government bought. Veterans have priority only to properties that are classified as agricultural, residential, or small business. Former owners have priority to repurchase any real estate except that classified as industrial. Tenants of former owners may purchase only properties classified as agricultural and bought by the Government after December 1, 1939. The right to purchase is extended by regulation for 10 days for public agencies and nonprofit institutions and 90 days to individuals after the date that notice of availability is published.

The priorities of Government agencies, State or local governments, and nonprofit institutions are continuing priorities in that they are not exhausted because of their effective exercise with respect to a given property. They may exercise their rights without any limitation as to number of projects or number of times.

Priority rights of the individual priority holders are more restricted. The rights of former owners and former tenants are limited to the specific projects in which their properties were located. Veterans and other persons intending to become owner-operators are not limited to specific projects in the selection of land. Their priority rights terminate when exercised once, however.

A former owner or his widow or children may exercise his priority rights. His priority relates to the property that is substantially the tract the Government acquired from him. If the tract is not available to him or is not wanted by him because it is no longer suitable for the purpose for which it was used when the Government acquired it, he may be offered a suitable substitute property in the same area. A former owner's rights, therefore, are limited to the project in which his former property is located.

Tenants of former owners may exercise their priority rights only with respect to substantially the same properties that they occupied at the time of acquisition. This right cannot be passed on to the widow or children. The right of a tenant cannot be exercised unless the former owner (or his widow or children if he dies) elect not to exercise their rights. Priority rights of tenants therefore are the most limiting of all priorities established by the act.

A veteran or the widow and children of a deceased serviceman could exercise his rights in the acquisition of only one property. Few choice tracts were available for these priority holders because a ranking priority holder seldom failed to exercise his rights on the productive properties. Veterans did not find many good properties in any one project, but they did have the advantage of making their selection from another project if suitable properties were not found in the first.

The management of tribal lands.

A staff assistant of the Technical Review Staff of the Secretary of the Interior here tells of a dark chapter in history—"the large-scale dispossession of the Indian occupants, who held or claimed large areas under nonintensive uses and under no right except that of aboriginal use"—and what has happened since to Indian lands, which now total 5? million acres despite many reductions. By *M. Wilfred Goding*

FEDERAL RESPONSIBILITY for the management of Indian lands is essentially that of a trustee.

Actual tenure of the Indian holdings is in a wide variety of forms, tribal and individual, which range from indeterminate use rights to fee simple.

The lands subject to trust that Indians use, control, or own total 53,376,-000 acres in the United States—39,-465,000 acres of tribal land, 13,328,000 acres of individual allotted land, and 583,000 acres of Government-owned land used in the administration of Indian affairs.

Nearly all these lands share two characteristics, which in one form or another have attached to Indian lands since early colonial days. They are protected against alienation and encumbrance. They are exempt from State and local taxation.

The Indian holdings nevertheless have been reduced continuously. Much of the reduction was inevitable, for at the beginning of white settlement in America some 800 thousand Indians held the whole continent by occupancy and use. The impact of succeeding tides of aggressive, land-hungry settlers, many of whom were beyond or without moral or other law, could result only in large-scale dispossession of the Indian occupants, who held or claimed large areas under nonintensive uses and under no right except that of aboriginal use.

Indian title, based on aboriginal occupancy, was officially recognized and protected by the Colonial Governments. England and Spain reserved to the Crown or the Colonies the sole right to negotiate with the Indians for the transfer of their lands.

The first colonists who showed concern for Indian rights and welfare apparently hoped to integrate the Indians into the colonial settlements Massachusetts Bay Colony as early a 1633 invited the Indians to the settlements to accept individual land allotments on condition that they "shall there live civily and orderly."

This policy was soon frustrated because the Indians lacked the colonists ideas about protecting property interests. They were not inclined to clea the land and follow the white settlers' agricultural pursuits. They were cheated in land transactions because land to them was not a commodity to be bought and sold for profit.

The Colonial Governments recognized the need to protect India property interests by prohibiting land purchases by individuals without the specific consent of the Governments.

This policy was followed when the United States, under the Confederation, issued a proclamation in 178 prohibiting all persons "from making settlements on lands inhabited or claimed by Indians without the limit or jurisdiction of any particular state

96

and from purchasing or receiving any gift or cession of such lands or claims without the express authority and direction of the United States in Congress assembled."

INDIAN LANDS have been at the focal point of the relationship of the United States with the Indian population from the beginning of the Government. Article 1, section 8, of the Constitution provides that Congress shall have the power "to regulate commerce with foreign nations, and among the several States, and with the Indian tribes." This constitutional provision recognized the Indian tribes as quasi-sovereign "domestic nations." In fact, the first treaty entered into by the United States, antedating the Constitution, was with the Delaware Indians in 1778.

The early attempts to bring the Indians into the landholding economy of the colonial frontier were followed by a policy of removing the Indian population from the frontier settlement areas: If the Indian could not be integrated, he was to be isolated.

The sharp trading of individuals and continuing efforts of many to separate the Indians from their lands caused resentment and bloody reprisals. The increasing movement of population to the west of the Appalachians resulted in intensified conflict, which the Government attempted to resolve by treating with the Indian tribes for relinquishment of their holdings and movement to western lands.

The policy of removing the Indians from the settlement areas east of the Mississippi reached a climax during the administration of President Jackson with the compulsory and tragic movement of the Cherokee Nation.

The forced movement of the Cherokee Nation from their traditional lands in the Southeast to the Indian Territory was probably the darkest page in the history of our Indian relations. The issues involved not only the Federal Government and the Indians. The State of Georgia initiated and pressed

the removal under the terms of the compact of 1802 with the Federal Government, whereby the area now forming Alabama and Mississippi was transferred to the United States in consideration, in part, for the purchase and extinction of Indian title to all land within the State of Georgia.

The Supreme Court decision in 1831 in the case of the Cherokee Nation v. Georgia left the Indians in a weak position for the protection of their traditional rights. It denied the jurisdiction of the Supreme Court on the technical grounds that the tribe was not a sovereign entity. This undermined the basic legal validity of all "treaties" with Indian tribes.

The next year, however, the Court ruled that the whole intercourse with the Indian tribes was vested in the United States and that the Cherokee Nation was a distinct community occupying a defined territory in which the laws of Georgia had no force. It was of this decision that President Jackson is reported as having remarked that, "John Marshall has made his decision, now let him enforce it." Jackson declined to enter the jurisdictional controversy and gave the Indians the choice of emigrating or complying with State law.

The Indian tribes by 1840 had surrendered nearly all of the territory east of the Mississippi, except a few reservations in Minnesota, Wisconsin, Michigan, North Carolina, and New York and the holdings of a few small groups, survivors of once powerful tribes, who maintained their ancient ways in scattered settlements throughout the Eastern States. The country west of the Mississippi, except for some settlements in Louisiana, Arkansas, and Missouri, was legally and actually Indian country at that time.

The years between 1851 and 1880, when new waves of settlers moved westward, mark the period of the fiercest armed conflict with the tribes that attempted to hold their own. Most of the Indian reservations were established then.

In general, the Indians were guaranteed permanent title to a reservation—land reserved for Indian use—in return for relinquishing to the United States large areas of land they claimed. Despite the extinguishment of Indian occupancy rights to vast areas, however, the settlers still coveted the undeveloped lands within the reserved areas. New treaties with Indian tribes diminished the area of such reservations for cash payments, annuities, or other considerations.

It has been estimated that by 1858 more than 581 million acres had been acquired by the United States in more than 400 treaties at a cost of less than 50 million dollars.

Negotiation of treaties with Indian tribes ceased in 1871.

THE POLICY of "individualizing" ownerships of Indian land was initiated with the General Allotment Act of 1887. Friends of the Indians believed that the only way the Indians could retain their land was for each family to be allotted a portion of the reservation area in severalty. These advocates believed that a share of individual land was all the Indian needed to become a successful independent farmer.

At the outset the act provided for the allotment of 160 acres to the head of each family. Lesser amounts were allotted to single persons and minor children, and issuance of patents in fee was to be withheld for 25 years. As the trust periods have run out, they have been periodically extended by special legislation. Reservation land not required to meet the allotments was to be purchased by the Government and opened to homestead settlement.

The Government, however, failed to provide the equipment and the vocational training necessary to make the Indians successful farmers. Many Indians were physically not able to undertake farming. Others did not know how or wish to learn to farm. Their lives, outlook, and inheritance were all against it; to try to force them into farming was to demand the impossible of many of them.

The allotment system eventually became a device for transferring Indian land to white settlers. Indians in 1887 owned about 138 million acres of land.

When the allotment system was brought to an end in 1934, their lands had shrunk to about 52 million acres. More than 59 million acres had been sold as "surplus" land. Nearly 23 million acres were sold by the original allottees. About 4 million acres were sold on behalf of the Indian heirs.

Of the lands remaining in Indian ownership, only 4 million acres were farming land, more than 45 million acres were classified as grazing lands, and the rest was timbered, swamp, or miscellaneous land types.

The distribution, as well as the value, of the remaining lands varied widely among the tribal groups. An example: 20 million acres, nearly half of the remaining grazing lands, were composed of the Navajo, Papago, and Pueblo Reservations in the Southwest. The allotting process applied to the best and most accessible farmlands. The result was that about 93 percent of the agricultural land and about 30 percent of the better grazing land went into individual allotments.

A serious byproduct of the allotting process was the scattering of holdings in uneconomic units, particularly in the Great Plains. This pattern of land tenure became more complicated when the original allottees died and the allotment descended in undivided interests to the heirs. Often it was possible only to sell the land, lease it, or not to use it at all.

Partly because of the complications as to heirs, leasing was first permitted by an act in 1892 in order to meet hardship situations. All restrictions on leasing were removed later. The Congress in 1902 authorized the sale of an ancestor's allotment by the heirs in an effort to solve the increasing complications of the land-tenure pattern.

Despite outright sale of much of these lands and many efforts later to consolidate and rationalize the pattern of landownership, the administration of the "heirship lands" remains a difficult aspect of Indian land management. It is estimated that more than 65 percent of all allotted lands remaining under Federal trust are now in heirship status.

THE COST of administration is burdensome, but no ready, fully acceptable solution has been found. Some persons advocate that a major financing program be established to buy such lands for tribal account, but no funds have been appropriated for this purpose in recent years. In some areas the tribal organizations have been using tribal funds to purchase the splitup allotment interests. Elsewhere corporate-type tribal-land enterprises have been established to take title to such lands by issuing shares in the enterprise in exchange for the individual holdings.

The Indian Reorganization Act of 1934 stopped all further allotments. It authorized land purchase and the restoration of ceded lands to the tribes and established a revolving loan fund to make possible more effective use of the land base. At the same time, sales of Indian lands were generally stopped, and a policy of retaining both tribal and allotted land for the use of Indians was emphasized. This shift in basic policy halted the long trend toward disposal of Indian lands. Indian holdings increased by nearly 4 million acres in the next several years. The new policy caused individual hardships, however, and, because exceptions were so limited, seriously curtailed the basic property rights of many competent Indian citizens. The policy was modified in 1948 to permit the competent Indian to retain or dispose of his property as he desired.

THE PROBLEMS of the Government as trustee for the landholdings of the Indians today arise from the complexities inherent in the nature of the lands involved, the diversity and multiplicity of the ownership interests, and the status of Indians as individuals and groups in the social and economic framework of the larger community.

It would be relatively simple if the responsibility could be discharged by the judicious determination of the competency of Indian individuals to manage their business affairs and thereby end the trust status. The Indian lands then would lose their special attributes. They could be alienated and would no longer be tax exempt. Understandably, some Indians are not inclined to press for a declaration that would result in the termination of such a privileged status.

The mixed-ownership pattern of lands on many reservations also presents problems of land-use management. An Indian owner of allotted land might have his personal interests advanced by an outright sale and termination of the trust, but it would be detrimental to the management and use of adjoining tribal lands.

The present sales policy is based on congressional statutory enactments that permit the sale of Indian lands. When an Indian makes an application under the applicable law for the sale of his trust or restricted land, the Bureau of Indian Affairs must comply with such a request if the facts indicate the action would be in the best interests of the Indian owner. The Government has no equitable right to deny arbitrarily such an application.

Before a sale is approved, an examination is made of the applicant's reasons for desiring a sale and his plans for using the money after he receives it. Indians in debt who cannot handle their affairs may be required to help prepare a budget before the sale of their land is approved to insure that the money from the sale will be used for their benefit.

The Bureau in 1955–1957 sold 927,-926 acres owned by individual Indians in response to written requests by the Indian owners; 292,488 acres were turned over to Indians who applied for fee patents and satisfied the Bureau of their competency to manage their affairs; and 122,414 acres of mixed tribal and individual Indian land have been taken by the Government for flood-control purposes with full compensation to the owners.

Even more difficult policy matters are entailed in the sale or liquidation of unallotted tribal lands. These are the lands held in common that can be sold only after specific authorization by the Congress.

The policy of restoring and increasing tribal holdings, which resulted from enactment of the Indian Reorganization Act of 1934, found much favor and acceptance. However, such a policy was contrary to the desire of the majority of some Indian groups to terminate the trusteeship of the Federal Government and to liquidate their holdings.

Not all Indian groups accepted the philosophy underlying that act. A number of tribes had long emphasized their desire to "terminate" the Federal trust relationship. Increasing land values have stimulated the desire of many tribal members to sell their holdings. The Congress, by concurrent resolution in 1953, enunciated a policy directed toward termination of Federal supervision as soon as possible.

That was followed by the enactment of several bills to terminate the Federal trust for a number of tribal groups, of which the Klamath Termination Act of 1954, relating to the Klamath Indians of southern Oregon, was typical. It provides that an appraisal be made of all tribal property and that each member of the tribe be given an opportunity to sever his tribal affiliation and withdraw his share of the tribal property or to remain and participate in a tribal management plan. As much of the tribal property as may be necessary to reimburse the withdrawing members will be sold. In any event, the Federal trust relationship was to cease at the end of 4 years. Because execution of this act has encountered unforeseen complexities and presented certain policy issues that have not been fully

resolved, the termination date was extended for 2 years by the Congress in 1957.

The high value of the Klamath Reservation timberlands is a strong inducement for many tribal members to sell their holdings. These lands, which have been managed as a unit under modern sustained-yield principles, are a major resource base for the economy of the area. Much concern is expressed that the partitioning and sale of the forest lands will result in destructive use. In order to avoid such a result, attention has been given to ways of proceeding under the act so as to assure continued conservation management. There is much support among residents of the area for acquisition of the lands by the Federal Government. This and other proposals were placed before the Congress.

ALONG WITH THE SALES of Indian land during the intervening years, there also have been acquisitions. More than 1 million acres were added in 1955–1957 to tribal holdings throughout the country as a result of congressional enactments and administrative acts by the Department of the Interior.

A total of 818,277 acres was restored to ownership of the Colville Tribe of Washington in 1956. The restored land was originally ceded to the Government by the tribe as "surplus" at the time the reservation was allotted. The tribe subsequently requested the restoration of the unallotted surplus. That was accomplished by legislation in 1956. The land is held in trust by the United States for the tribe on the same basis as other reservation lands.

The second largest addition to tribal holdings was the purchase by the Navajo Tribe of a ranch of 98 thousand acres in Arizona. The land is held by the tribe in fee simple title and is not in Federal trusteeship, but it represents a substantial increase in acreage available for use by the Navajos. The Pueblo of Zia added 41,216 acres, and the Pueblo of Jamez added 36,352 acres to their holdings. Both are in New Mexico.

Other acquisitions were for the Seminoles in Florida, the Yavapai Tribe of Arizona, the Kanosh Band in Utah, the Blackfeet and Flathead Indians in Montana, and the Shoshone and Arapahoes in Wyoming.

Purchases made by the Bureau in trust for individual Indians during the period account for nearly 20 thousand additional acres.

INDIAN LANDS held in trust by the Federal Government are administered for the use and benefit of the Indian owners in accordance with the policies followed by the Department of the Interior in managing the public lands under its jurisdiction. Accepted principles of conservation are the basis for specific treatment of forest lands, rangelands, irrigable lands, and general farmlands.

An increasing source of income to some Indians and tribes has been from mineral leasing. The total income from gas and oil on all reservations amounted to 41,007,075 dollars in 1956, and 2,881,532 dollars were received for other minerals.

The forest lands amount to an estimated 16 million acres. About 6 million acres are considered commercial forest land, more than half of which is in the Pacific Coast and northern Rocky Mountain States. About one-fourth is in the Southwest. Most of the rest is in the Lake States.

Most of the timber is sold as standing timber on the open market. Tribal sawmills operate on three reservations to utilize the annual harvest. The tribe is paid the fair market value of the stumpage used.

All phases of forest management and protection are supervised by employees of the Bureau of Indian Affairs. They designate the timber to be cut, measure the volume, collect payments, and distribute the receipts to the Indian owners. The Indian owners are encouraged to participate in the development of plans for managing the estate.

The consent of the owners is obtained before timber is sold. In 1956, 643,440,000 board-feet of timber were sold for 14,123,806 dollars.

Total administrative expenses for the fiscal year 1956 for Indian forestry operations amounted to 1,713,292 dollars, of which 505,246 dollars came from Indian tribal funds and 1,208,046 dollars from appropriated funds.

Rangelands amount to about 44 million acres, inclusive of forest lands grazed by livestock. They are managed so as to bring the maximum return to the Indian owners consistent with sustained production of forage. Indian owners are encouraged to use the range for grazing their own livestock. About 75 percent of the range is so used. General grazing regulations were adopted in 1931 to limit the grazing of each unit to the estimated capacity. Management methods have been improved steadily.

Cash receipts for the use of Indian rangelands in 1956 amounted to 2.8 million dollars. The value of grazing privileges on tribal lands and of the use of allotted land by the owners thereof was 3,475,000 dollars in 1956. Federal expenditures for range management amounted to 566 thousand dollars; and 600 thousand dollars were spent to develop watering places.

More than 2,170,000 acres of farmland and rangeland were covered by various conservation treatment works in 1956, and 11,069 farm and range conservation plans were completed during the year. The soil and moisture conservation budget for 1958 was 4,-638,000 dollars. About 80 percent of the conservation expenditures are borne by Indian landowners. The estimated return for the conservation investment is 21.56 dollars for every dollar of Federal conservation funds expended and 2.86 dollars for every dollar of such expenditure from all sources.

Irrigation works and facilities to increase the productivity of Indian lands were first undertaken by the Bureau of Indian Affairs 90 years ago on the Colorado River Reservation in Arizona. About 850 thousand acres, comprising 300 irrigation systems ranging from 100 acres to more than 120 thousand acres in 11 States, have been irrigated. About 190 thousand Indians live on these irrigated lands.

The construction or expansion of three major irrigation projects was under way or projected in 1958—the Colorado River Reservation in Arizona (65 thousand acres), the Navajo project in Colorado and New Mexico (113 thousand acres), and the Michaud unit of the Fort Hall project in Idaho (21 thousand acres).

Irrigation systems in use in 1958 provided about 3 acres per capita for Indians in the arid regions. Full development of all potentially irrigable Indian lands in the West would provide about 6.5 acres per capita. Under present law, construction charges assessed against Indian-owned lands within any Government irrigation project are deferred while the lands remain in Indian ownership.

The total annual cost of operating and maintaining the projects is approximately 3.8 million dollars, of which 800 thousand dollars is met by Federal appropriations. The rest comes from receipts from the water users and revenues from power. The part provided by the Federal Government is reimbursable in accordance with law and is provided to cover the share of costs for Indian landowners who cannot make such payments.

SOME PUBLICATIONS about Indian lands:

A Continent Lost—A Civilization Won: Indian Land Tenure in America, by Jay P. Kinney. The Johns Hopkins Press, Baltimore, 1937.

The Problem of Indian Administration (*Merriam Report*). Institute for Government Research. The Johns Hopkins Press, Baltimore, 1928.

Indian Land Cessions in the United States, by Charles C. Royce. The Government Printing Office, Washington, 1900.

Handbook of Federal Indian Law, by Felix S. Cohen, Office of the Solicitor, Department of the Interior.

Indian Affairs, Laws and Treaties. Five volumes. Compiled, annotated, and edited by Charles J. Kappler. The Government Printing Office, Washington, 1904–1941.

Indian Land and Its Care, by Edgar L. Wight, David P. Weston, and Clyde W. Hobbs, Bureau of Indian Affairs, Department of the Interior. The Haskell Press, Lawrence, Kansas, 1953.

Indian Land Tenure, Economic Status and Population Trends, Part X of the Supplementary Report of the Land Planning Committee to the National Resources Board. The Government Printing Office, Washington, 1935.

How we use our
private lands

—The land changes and the land
endures—Oranges do not grow in the North—Changes in the
Northern Dairy region—The use of land in the Corn Belt—Where
our cotton comes from—Changes in the land of cotton—The
general farming and tobacco region—Land and problems in the
wheat regions—Land-use problems in the Great Plains—The role
of land in western ranching

The land changes and the land endures.

Much of what is written in this chapter and this section is old stuff to some farmers, but others of us need to be told or reminded of the big, quick, new changes in farming, which have upset old patterns, opened possibilities, and given old words new meanings. By *Howard E. Conklin,* associate professor of agricultural economics, and *John W. Mellor,* associate professor of agricultural geography, Cornell University.

FARMERS TODAY do things with land undreamed of a few years ago.

They have new chemicals and machines to work with and plants and animals with new capabilities. They have developed new skills in planting, care, and harvesting.

They have accumulated much new knowledge about land—how it varies from place to place and how various areas of it perform when put to given uses in particular ways.

Farmers in the early days took the land as it came. They had to clear it where it was forested, but they had little basis beyond the type of the native vegetation for judging the way it would perform in agricultural use.

Accessibility probably was the characteristic of land to which they paid most attention. Differences in soil, climate, and topography, within local areas at least, were not highly critical under the low-pressure methods they used. A large share of their production was for home use. They had horses for power, so they could work odd-shaped fields on steep slopes.

The inherent fertility was important. Soils with a good natural supply of plant nutrients were more useful than low-fertility soils, no matter how deep, well drained, and level.

Farming today is a highly commercialized and highly specialized business. The entirely new set of input factors that farmers now have to work with has changed greatly the significance of many differences in land.

Many fields that could be worked with horses are ill suited to modern power units and large implements.

Soils that produce poor yields only because they lack fertility are not nearly so "poor" today as they were before science and the chemical industry developed suitable fertilizers.

Our progress in the manufacture of cement, structural steel, and large earthmovers, together with decisions to take a concerted action through Government programs, has brought water to millions of acres that formerly produced but a scattering of grass.

The introduction of crops like alfalfa has put a higher premium on well-drained, high-lime soils. Improvements in the genetic makeup of crop varieties have raised output ceilings on land best suited for growing them and so have left other land farther behind.

A more complete knowledge of the facts about the land differences and a deeper understanding of plant-land relationships have produced skills in the choice of crops, the timing of tillage and harvest operations, and the choice of fertilizers, rotations, and ways to control erosion that are fitted to individual farms and fields.

The joint efforts of farmers, scientists,

and industry in developing and adopting new technology have produced the outstanding progress that has been made in agriculture in this country.

Large numbers of workers have been released from farming to make cars, houses, washing machines, television sets, and the host of other things we want in addition to food and clothing.

American farmers have been able also to feed and clothe an increasing population from an acreage of agricultural land (farmland plus nonfarm grazing land) that has been slowly declining now for about 40 years.

Farmers, on a rather short notice, could further increase output from the land now in agriculture. It is a comforting thought, for, while surpluses may cause problems at times, our population is increasing, and there is no land beyond the frontier as there was a century ago.

Progress is good, but change brings problems. Some problems come from the upsetting of old patterns and relationships. Some exist only in the sense that change has opened up new possibilities, new horizons. Farmers face problems of both kinds today as they decide how to use their land.

THE CHANGES in farming have had diverse effects on the ability of various kinds of land to produce net income.

A farmer can turn out more today regardless of the land he is on, but some are not able to turn out enough more to maintain their position relative to farmers on other kinds of land. For some, too, the costs of increasing output are higher than for others. Farmers on land ideally suited to corn have been able to reap the full increases that hybrid corn makes potentially possible, but farmers on land where drought may limit yields have benefited less from the improved varieties.

Improved and less costly fertilizers have raised the income potential of farmers on sandy and gravelly soils that are level and in humid areas. Farmers on high-fertility, but poorly drained, steep, or otherwise handicapped land have seen their income possibilities decline as a consequence. Improved sprinkler irrigation equipment has brought advantages to farmers with water at hand, by comparison to their competitors less favorably located with respect to water supplies.

FARMING IS HIGHLY COMPETITIVE—so competitive, in fact, that farmers seldom think of their neighbors as competitors. The fact that so many farmers produce the same products and sell them individually in the same markets makes for—but masks—this competitive situation.

A farmer can pass ideas and tricks-of-the-trade to his neighbor or all his neighbors without the consequences a shoestore operator would suffer if he passed tricks-of-the-trade to the other shoestore operator in town. Yet it is to my disadvantage if the farmers of many communities can adopt an improvement that I cannot.

The competition in agriculture has brought gains or losses quickly to all competitors—gains to those whose resources have responded to the new inputs and losses to those whose resources have not responded.

Technological change in agriculture has made some kinds of land obsolete for farming. Some 8 million acres were in this classification in New York in 1958. It is land that once had a place in farming. Other land has responded so much more fully, however, to the new things that have come to farming that this land is now no longer needed. (Agricultural production in New York has increased by one-third, while 9 million acres have passed out of commercial production, 8 million becoming obsolete and 1 million going into urban and related uses.)

Changes in the competitive positions of farmers on various kinds of land that still have a place in farming have been less spectacular than farm abandonment, but just as real.

Land that can be farmed profitably at a higher level of output because of a new technique should in time sell for more money than land that has proved to be less responsive to this technique.

In that way, opportunities on various kinds of land, which still are adapted to farming, are supposed to be equalized—farmers will pay enough more for highly productive land to make their return per dollar invested no higher than the return they might have made on less productive but cheaper land.

This notion that all differences in land will be faithfully reflected in land prices has been assumed in economic theory for a long time.

People generally also cling to this idea. Their thinking often goes so far as to rule out the idea that land can really become obsolete for farming. Many seem to think that if farmers could learn the right way to handle "abandoned" land, they could prosper as well there as on any land. Enough instances, in which new techniques succeed in situations where all others have failed, occur to sustain this belief.

Actually, however, when you study the land market and the participants in it, you find little reason for expecting land prices to be a precise reflection of the income-producing power of farms.

There is no land market as such. It exists only as an artificial aggregation of many local transactions. Neither buyers nor sellers are fully acquainted with all the different kinds of land that produce the same product and that therefore are in competition with the land under consideration in a given transaction.

Farms vary widely and bear no grade stamp—like corn in a grain market or carcasses in a slaughterhouse. It is hard even to find out what the previous owner of a farm was able to make on it.

A farmer buying a farm is in much the same position a laborer would be in if he could get no more than a general idea of the wages paid by industries but had to make a deposit of 10 thousand to 50 thousand dollars to get a job—a deposit that might or might not be refunded when he quits the job. Under those conditions, many laborers would get stuck; for some of them, the jobs with a low deposit requirement would be the only alternative, regardless of the pay in other jobs. Most highly paid jobs would sell for more, but not for enough more, to equalize returns to laborers of equal ability on their time and invested capital.

Rapid technological change complicates the problem of deciding what a farm is worth. Many sandy farms were worth little 25 years ago. It was expensive or impossible to add fertility and water. Today it is less expensive.

The man who bought a sandy farm 25 years ago probably paid too much for it in proportion to the earning power it had then. But since then he may have made a lucky gain as a result of a technological change that caused others to suffer losses.

TECHNOLOGICAL CHANGE has come too fast and its consequences often have worked themselves out in ways that are too subtle for everybody to follow them closely. Statements like, "I can remember when . . ." and "this farm used to be the best in the county" indicate memories that are too long. The speaker may be living too much in the past. Yet one often hears such talk, and the thinking associated with it affects the prices of farms.

Because prices lag behind forces of change, which are continuous and rapid, a continuous discrepancy exists among farms on different kinds of land in the ratios of their prices to their producing power. This source of discrepancy is added to factors that would produce discrepancies in a static situation—a normal tendency to underestimate differences in producing power among farms and a land market that includes large numbers of people who can buy only relatively cheap farms. The result is an array of land prices that often are not related very closely to the incomes that will be won from the land during the next generation.

If we were to look further, we would

find that taxes also are not very closely adjusted even to current income possibilities in farming.

These discrepancies in land prices and taxes are among the major reasons why land is important to a farmer. The land a man farms will determine in a large measure the net income he can make, because it has an important effect on his receipts and expenses.

Although a farmer operates as efficiently and economically as he can, he cannot overcome completely the adverse effects of a poor buy in land. Not all poor buys can be avoided, of course, because no one can predict exactly the trend in technological change. Other technical innovations will come. Some will change the relative usefulness of different kinds of land.

Experience gives us some guide to the improvements we can expect in fertilizers, plants, and machinery. But the uncertainties in the types and degrees of change always will bring some unforeseen gains and losses to people who own land.

But changes in the competitive positions of farmers on various kinds of land are not the only consequences we see of the interaction between land and changing technology.

A farmer, to succeed, must choose his land wisely. He must also fit his farming to the land he picks. This, too, is becoming more important as time goes by. Annual expenses per acre now often approach or exceed one-half the purchase price of the land.

The task of tailoring the use to the land involves choices of the kinds of crops and livestock to be grown. It also involves choices of cultural practices; lime and fertilizer rates; the timing of planting, cultivation, and harvest; selection of insecticides and fungicides; rotations; and many more.

The farmer asks: What response can I get to more fertilizer for corn on my land? How will my land perform if planted to wheat? Would the east forty produce more corn if I plowed it in the fall? Would the back pasture produce enough more to pay for the cost of irrigation? Would the beans on that wet field respond enough to another dusting to make it worth while, or will their yield be limited more by wetness than by insects?

The answers a farmer gives to such questions determine how near he comes to reaching the income ceiling of his land. And the best answers change constantly as varieties, fertilizers, equipment, and other things change.

The problem of adjusting the kinds of land use can be separated from the problem of adjusting intensity, although both problems actually must be solved simultaneously to get a good answer for either. In other words: The question of whether to grow beans or corn on a field can be separated from the question of whether to use 200 or 400 pounds of fertilizer on the corn. But the relative profitability of corn and beans cannot be compared properly unless we know the net returns each will yield when grown in the most profitable manner.

The choice of the most profitable input levels and practices—the most profitable rates of seeding and fertilization, the most profitable amount and timing of seedbed preparation and cultivation, and the like—must be made for each of the important alternative crops according to the way the land responds. Then receipts and expenses at those levels can be estimated, net returns can be computed, and alternatives can be compared in these terms.

This process requires an intimate knowledge of land and its response to various treatments. The law of diminishing returns will come into play. Yields will increase rapidly in response to initial increases in most inputs, but responses to further additions begin to decline at some point.

The responses to the first increases (to additional fertilizer, say) and the point at which responses begin to decline differ, however, among different kinds of land. Costs of applying the fertilizer and other practices also may differ among different kinds of land— it costs more to plow steep land or to irrigate fields far from sources of water.

Each farmer could explore the response characteristics of his own land, but that would be costly and would take a long time. It is a job that can be done more efficiently by specialists who can study the combined experiences of many farmers, who can conduct controlled experiments on various kinds of land, and who can relate both experimental and farm experience to physical differences in land. With this background, the specialists can then prepare land classification maps on which they record their estimates of the response characteristics of all the various kinds of lands in large areas, such as counties and States. The maps are made available to farmers.

Work of this kind has been under way for many years. The classification of soils, one component of land, is farthest advanced. Classifications of topography, climate, and water supplies are moving ahead. Some efforts also are being made to classify land as a composite in terms of its overall response characteristics.

The problem of tailoring land use to the land reaches beyond the inputs that are used year by year.

It includes decisions with respect to what kinds and sizes of buildings should be constructed, what fences should be built and where, and what kinds of drainageways should be installed. Even the building of an adequate level of general fertility, the adjustment of soil acidity to a suitable point, the development of a favorable tilth in the soil, the layout of fields, and the installation of measures to control erosion are in part capital investments. These inputs have increased along with increases in the annual inputs we mentioned earlier. Yet many farms need heavy additional investments in these kinds of capital improvements.

Investments in capital improvements seldom increase the sale price of a farm enough to cover them, however, even when they would be a good investment for the farmer who continues to operate his unit for a number of years. (In most sections, buildings bought with the farm are less expensive than those built later, fertility bought in the land is less expensive than that bought in a bag, and so on.)

If the farmers of an area are stable and secure, they will make these investments and benefit by them. But if investment capital is scarce, tenure uncertain, or knowledge of the returns from various capital improvements deficient, a potentially productive area may become badly underdeveloped.

Many areas that appear to need more investment capital actually are areas that have been technologically displaced: The land cannot respond enough to pay for such investments. Classifications and descriptions of land need to be broad enough to include discussions of the responsiveness of the land to various kinds and amounts of capital improvements.

Actually, a large number of institutional arrangements modify what a farmer can and will want to do with his land. These include credit agencies, Government farm programs, property laws, and many other legal and organizational arrangements down to such things as the policies followed in the acquisition of highway rights-of-way.

Such elements also need to be tailored, if not to the land, at least to the farmers on the land. One form of tenure, of credit, even of property law, may work well in one place but not in another where the land is different.

Continued progress depends on maintaining a spirit of vigorous competition that will bring to able and energetic farmers rewards for ability and energy.

It depends also on maintaining a stimulating and helpful institutional climate within which farmers can make their daily decisions in ways that are consistent with the long-run goals of a progressive country.

It depends no less on a deepening of our understanding of the land resources with which farmers work.

Oranges do not grow in the North.

Everyone knows that cotton, tobacco, and vegetables are grown in certain places; that dairy farms may produce fluid milk or butter or cream; and that some land suitable for potatoes is used to grow soybeans. Why? Physical and economic forces give the answer and provide bases for outlining major type-of-farming regions, although modern technology has made agriculture more flexible. By *Ronald L. Mighell*, agricultural economist, Farm Economics Research Division.

LAND, as we have seen, no longer occupies the leading place among the resources used in farming in the United States. Its central place has diminished with the progressive advance of technology and the greater use of machines and other capital goods.

In today's farming systems, the annual value of the services of the capital goods used outweighs the value of the services of land by about 2 to 1.

Farmers no longer are close captives of their environment. They are able to control and direct natural forces in many ways. The picture of Man wrestling the raw forces of Nature with little more than his bare hands, as revealed in such works as Edwin Markham's Man with the Hoe, and Grant Wood's American Gothic, has been banished to the past. Present ways of using land in farming are as far removed from this former reality as today's mechanized ways of building highways are from yesterday's pick-and-shovel methods.

This means that farmland can be used for more different purposes than ever before. The properties inherent in the land are now less restrictive, and other resources determine oftener what the most economic use shall be. The characteristics of land nevertheless still set limits that influence the broad patterns of agriculture. The successful farmer is the one who learns how to cooperate with the natural and biological processes that are linked to land.

What determines how farmland shall be used in any area or region? Why are certain combinations of crops and livestock grown in one region, but not in another? Questions like these seek answers.

In general terms, two groups of forces—the physical and the economic—influence the use of farmland.

Physical factors are the ones that we think of in describing the land itself—climate, soil, topography, elevation, water supply, and the like. They are the properties that are naturally a part of the land. They were here before people occupied the land.

Economic factors have to do with man in his relation to the land—nearness to markets, communication facilities, public and private investments, patterns of ownership and management, and other institutional arrangements. The personal characteristics and skills of farm people in a region may be significant elements, too.

One group of institutional factors that is especially notable in international trade is referred to collectively as artificial barriers to trade. Many countries use tariffs, quotas, exchange restrictions, and other devices to "protect" themselves from the competition of others. Internal barriers to trade grow up even between sections and States in this country, sometimes in connection with such desirable objectives as efforts to promote public health and sanitation.

Economists began long ago to explain the different uses of land in terms of the principle of comparative advantage. This is a striking term. It means that which pays best.

Land used according to its comparative advantage is used to produce the commodity or combination of commodities that pays better than any other commodity or a combination of commodities under the given circumstances. This sounds reasonably simple, but the actual finding out of what pays best is often a complicated business. It cannot be discovered once and for all. Changing technology and changing conditions of demand and supply mean that comparative advantage is forever shifting.

Suppose we look at the physical differences in land. Some of them are so obvious that many observers have considered that they might explain completely the different uses of land. In this country, for example, oranges can be grown only in certain favored frost-free areas in California, Texas, Arizona, Louisiana, and Florida—not in Minnesota and Maine.

But even if there were no physical differences in land, there would be many different uses of land, because our wants and needs involve many different farm products.

LOCATION THEORY was first developed to explain how transportation costs determine the use of land. J. H. von Thünen, a German economist of the 19th century, was the first to analyze carefully this kind of location problem in a three-volume work, *The Isolated State*. He was fascinated, as many have been since, by the systematic spatial geometry that results if one makes a few bold, simplifying assumptions.

Von Thünen imagined an immense plain, in the center of which he placed his isolated city-state. In this self-contained economy, the natural conditions—the climate, soils, topography, and all the rest—were entirely uniform. Extension in space, or distance, was the only factor that made one place different from another.

He then worked out the pattern of a farm production that would arise about the city in terms of the concentric zones, which would minimize transportation costs. Bulky or perishable products, like fluid milk and fresh vegetables, would be produced in the inner zones nearest the city. More concentrated products—those with a high value per unit of weight—and the less perishable items would be produced farther out.

This kind of theory has been helpful in analyzing some of the aspects of the location of farm production. It explains, for example, why our butter, cream, and fluid-milk areas are located at varying distances from market.

Differences in the other physical characteristics of land, however, may have even more to do with the geographic distribution of farm production. Mainly because most of these other characteristics are distributed so irregularly, we have a seemingly haphazard production checkerboard.

Some areas have what is called an absolute advantage in production of certain commodities: Winter vegetables grow only in frost-free areas. Bananas grow only in certain tropical situations. Cotton grows only within a given temperature range. Tobacco grows only on certain soil types.

An absolute advantage is only an extreme form of comparative advantage, however. The usual situations are those in which any of a large number of products can be grown, but in which a few have relatively greater advantage. Frequently this is because the yields of the commodities grown are higher than yields in competing areas, but it may not be true: It may be only that the commodities are better in terms of value than competing products in the same area.

The principle of comparative advantage often is expressed like this:

"Each area tends to produce the products for which its ratio of advantage is greatest as compared with other areas or its ratio of disadvantage is least, up to the point where the land may be needed for some products less advantaged in the area in order to meet the demand for them at the prices that come to prevail."

This statement implies a supply-demand balance between areas. The role of demand in this process should be emphasized. An area may be capable of growing a fine crop of potatoes, for example, and yet in actual practice it will be used to grow only a fair crop of soybeans. The reason is that land capable of growing high yields of potatoes is relatively abundant in the United States and land capable of growing soybeans is not—relative to the country's need for each crop. Much land in the northern Corn Belt that would grow good potatoes therefore is planted to soybeans, which will bring greater returns. If our need for potatoes were to increase fourfold, with other needs remaining the same, some land would be withdrawn from soybeans and other crops and planted to potatoes.

AMERICAN FARMING is specialized more than farming in most countries, but this specialization does not usually express itself in single-product farming.

A combination of two or three products usually has a greater advantage in the use of land and other resources than any single product has. The seasonal nature of crop production and the uneven distribution of labor and machinery inputs open the way for special savings in dovetailing nonconflicting enterprises. Similar circumstances arise in livestock production. The interrelationships between feed crops and livestock often form the basis for profitable combinations in an operating farm unit.

Unique circumstances result in single-product specialization in a few highly specialized types of production. The growing of cranberries, for example, requires a heavy capital investment of a kind that is not suited to other lines of production. Citrus and many other fruits and nuts tend to be this way, too, for similar reasons. Some kinds of livestock production may be highly specialized. A notable example is the commercial production of broilers. Land is a relatively small item in broiler production, because standing room is about all that is needed.

Usually we take the family farm for granted as an integral part of farm production. Yet much farm production in the world takes place under other forms of business operation. Even in the United States, about 30 percent of all farm production occurs on large-scale farms with cash receipts of 25 thousand dollars or more. Many of them could hardly be classified as family farms.

Family farming has been defined in many ways. One definition is:

"A family farm or ranch is one which provides the main source of income for the farm family and on which the farm operator (owner or tenant) or members of his family make most of the managerial decisions, participate regularly in farmwork, and normally supply a substantial part of the labor needed to operate the farm."

This definition would include most family farm units except part-time, residential, and sharecropper units. About two-thirds of the farm production for sale comes from family farms.

The form of the farm operating unit may affect the choice of enterprises, the scale and efficiency of operation, and the comparative advantage of different farm commodities in an area. The status of the commercial broiler industry in 1958 is an example. Contracts between feed dealers or processors and farmer growers have so cushioned the risks and increased the efficiencies of operation that new specialized areas of broiler production have been built up rapidly.

Development of corresponding vertical integration in the production of fresh market eggs and in other kinds

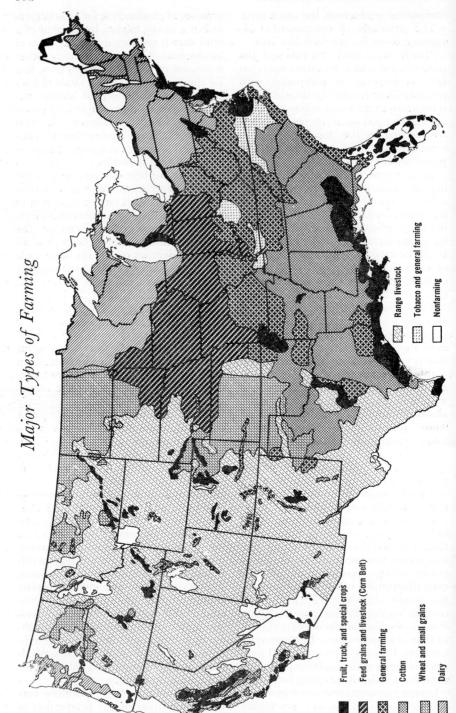

Major Types of Farming

Fruit, truck, and special crops

Feed grains and livestock (Corn Belt)

General farming

Cotton

Wheat and small grains

Dairy

Range livestock

Tobacco and general farming

Nonfarming

of farm commodities may have similar effects on the location of production and may change the comparative advantage of different areas. Bulk handling of milk and of feed grains and other farm supplies is a technological factor designed to reinforce other tendencies that may give differential advantages to some areas.

MAJOR TYPE-OF-FARMING REGIONS in the United States delineate some of the broad groupings of types of farming that characterize particular parts of the country. One should realize that these regions are only oversimplified and partial images of complex farming situations. Wide variations in type of farming occur in each region. Some of these variations have little in common with the type that appears to be most representative in a region.

The regions discussed in chapters that follow are the Northern Dairy region, the Corn Belt, the Cotton Belt, the wheat regions, the western grazing region, and the general farming region.

Of them, the Corn Belt is the most homogeneous in its agriculture, and Iowa is probably the most uniform part of the Corn Belt. Yet even in Iowa there are many contrasting types of farms. The Corn Belt probably contains within its elastic limits more highly productive land than any other area of equal size in the world.

The Northern Dairy region has rougher, less productive soils than the Corn Belt, but its cooler climate is better adapted to production of pasture and forage. That fact and the nearness of markets for fluid milk and other dairy products give it a comparative advantage in dairy production. A considerable amount of poultry and eggs is produced in the region, much of it on the specialized farms. Fruits and vegetables are grown in favorable locations.

The Cotton Belt has a long history, varied institutions, and a changing economy in which cotton has been migrating westward. In large part, the older eastern part of this belt has

445509°—58——9

shifted to other kinds of farming. Many significant changes are in progress there.

The wheat regions represent the result of a long evolution in application of modern technology to an ancient crop. Marginal costs of wheat production under full mechanization are so low as to challenge the traditional feed grains in many sections. Marked shifts in the use of land toward more permanent grass and livestock production are likely.

The western grazing region includes public and private land, much of which is suitable only for grazing beef cattle and sheep. Availability of water is frequently a limiting factor.

The general farming region includes a variety of general situations in addition to many small areas of specialized types of production like tobacco, peanuts, and fruits. Some of the general farming region lies between the two agricultural worlds of the Corn Belt and Cotton Belt.

Fruit, truck, and special-crop areas are shown on most generalized type-of-farming maps, but they are smaller areas of intensive specialization scattered so that they do not form a contiguous region. Areas along the Atlantic seaboard, on the shores of the Great Lakes, along the gulf coast, and in California offer special climatic and soil conditions that have comparative advantage for many fruits and vegetables. These areas formerly were too distant from markets, but the development of rapid transportation and refrigeration in transit has so reduced the cost and increased the feasibility of shipment as to give the more distant areas access to any of the largest markets.

The broad type-of-farming regions thus trace out the major effects of physical and economic forces. The distribution of physical resources is responsible for many of the boundaries indicated on the map—but command of modern technology and capital goods has given man control of the forces of Nature and has made agriculture more flexible.

Changes in the Northern Dairy region.

This summary of farming operations, history, and production in the city-dominated Northeast and Lake States concludes with the statement that recent trends are likely to continue indefinitely. The domestic market for farm products may expand, but the acreage of cropland and pasture may continue to decline. By *Herbert C. Fowler,* agricultural economist, Farm Economics Research Division.

DAIRYING is the main farm enterprise in the Northern Dairy region. More than half of the cleared farmland here is used to provide feed crops and pasture for dairy cattle. Farmers here receive more cash income from sales of dairy products than from the sales of all crops. They take in about twice as much money from sales of dairy products as from sales of meat animals. About three-fifths of the dairy farms in the United States are here.

Despite the relative importance of dairying, however, dairy products accounted for only 35 percent of total cash receipts from farm marketings in the region in 1956. Poultry and eggs accounted for 18 percent; meat animals, 16; feed crops, 6; truck crops, 5; other vegetable crops, 4; fruits and tree nuts, 3; oil crops, 3; food grains, 2; tobacco, 1; other crops, 6; and other livestock products, 1 percent.

In this discussion, we include in the Northern Dairy region all of the 11 Northeastern States, from the Canadian border to the Potomac River, and the three Lake States of Michigan, Wisconsin, and Minnesota.

A more precise delineation would include several additional counties in northeastern Illinois, northeastern Ohio, and northern Virginia. It would exclude several counties in southern Minnesota, which in reality are a part of the Corn Belt; several counties in western Minnesota, which are in the

Northern Plains (spring wheat) region; Aroostook County, in Maine, which is primarily a potato-growing area; and several other counties that for one reason or another are better adapted to the production of truck crops, fruit, tobacco, or poultry than to dairying.

The Bureau of the Census classified about half of the commercial farms in the Northern Dairy region as dairy farms in 1954. The proportion ranged from less than 30 percent in Delaware, Maryland, and New Jersey to more than 75 percent in Vermont and Wisconsin. Slightly more than a third of the commercial farms in Maine, Massachusetts, Michigan, and Minnesota were dairy farms. The proportion in the whole country was 16 percent.

Farms were classified as dairy farms if the dairy enterprise accounted for 50 percent or more of the total value of farm products sold. Sales of milk and other dairy products did not have to exceed 30 percent of the total if milk cows represented 50 percent or more of all cows and sales of dairy products, together with the sales of cattle and calves, amounted to 50 percent or more of all sales.

Dairy farms were the commonest type of farm in all States in the Northern Dairy region, except Delaware and New Jersey, where poultry farms were most numerous but where dairy farms led also in terms of land use.

Poultry farms ranked second to dairy

farms in southern New England, New York, and Pennsylvania on the basis of number of farms. Cash-grain farms were second in Michigan and Minnesota. Other field-crop farms were second in Maine and Maryland. Other livestock farms and general farms were relatively more important in the Lake States than in the Northeast, but they also were numerous in Pennsylvania.

The total value of milk and cream sold by all farmers in the Northern Dairy region amounts to nearly 2 billion dollars annually, or about half the national total. Census data indicate that dairy farms account for about 90 percent of the total. Sales of dairy products by operators of other types of farms are more important in Minnesota than elsewhere in the region.

More than 90 percent of the operators of dairy farms now sell whole milk rather than cream. The percentage was even higher in the Northern Dairy region and is increasing steadily. Minnesota ranked high in numbers of dairy farmers who sold cream (29 percent), but Iowa, a Corn Belt State, led in sales of farm-separated cream. Nearly 500 thousand American farmers sold cream in 1954, but only 10 percent sold enough to be considered dairy farmers. Farmers who sell cream frequently feed the skim milk to hogs and chickens. This practice increases the income from the nondairy enterprises.

THE TOTAL LAND AREA of the Northern Dairy region is about 235 million acres. A little more than a third is used for crops and pasture.

About half of the land is wooded, although much of the wooded area is better than some of the land that is farmed in other parts of the world. Some of it has been used for farming in the past and could be farmed again if we needed more farmland, but under present conditions it pays to raise more on fewer acres.

Although the population of the United States increased by about 27 percent from 1940 to 1956, the acreage of nonwooded farmland in the Northern Dairy region declined by more than 10 percent.

More land is used for dairying, however. The continued substitution of tractors for horses as the main source of farm power has made available for dairying and other uses a substantial acreage that provided feed for horses in 1940. Mechanization has made it more and more profitable to use some of the roughest cropland for permanent pasture and to farm the best land more intensively. These changes were encouraged by a quadrupling of farm wage rates, while the prices of tractors, gasoline, and fertilizer increased much less.

Dairy farming can compete with other types of farming in most of the Northern Dairy region for several reasons. Most of the farms are advantageously located with respect to city milk markets. Milk is highly perishable. In warm weather, it must be kept under refrigeration from milking time until it is consumed. Also, because milk is about 87 percent water, it is expensive to ship long distances. Most of the milk that is consumed in fluid form is produced within 200 miles of where it is consumed. The high cost of transporting fluid milk accounts largely for the fact that only 38 percent of the milk cows in the country are in the Northern Dairy region and that very little whole milk produced in the region is shipped as such far beyond its borders except on a temporary basis.

The region is too far north for crops that need a long growing season or that fail to do well in a cool climate. In years of early killing frosts, even corn does not mature in the northernmost parts of the region.

Although the climate is favorable for small grains like oats, barley, and wheat, the physical characteristics of much of the land are not favorable for them. Some of the fields are quite stony. Many are small because of the rough terrain. Large laborsaving machinery and equipment that can be used on most farms in the Corn Belt

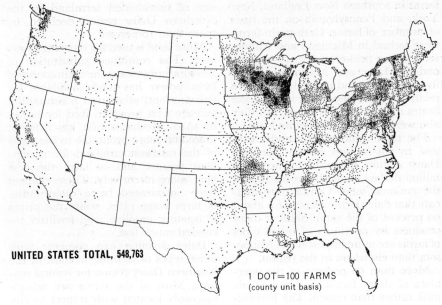

UNITED STATES TOTAL, 548,763

1 DOT=100 FARMS
(county unit basis)

Dairy farms in 1954.

and Great Plains therefore cannot be used advantageously on much of the land in the Northern Dairy region.

Dairy cattle can make good use of land that is difficult to plow. Some permanent pastures have never been plowed, and some fields from which hay is harvested each year have not been plowed in decades.

The Northern Dairy region has approximately 8 million dairy cows, of which about 6 million are on dairy farms. A dairy cow is one kept primarily for milk rather than for beef or veal. Calves on most dairy farms get less than 10 percent of the available milk supply.

Most of the dairy cows on commercial farms in the Northern Dairy region are in herds of 20 or more. About 10 percent in 1954 were in herds of fewer than 10 cows. About 27 percent were in herds of 30 or more.

Dairying in the Northeast differs from dairying in the Lake States in several respects. Although dairy farms in the Northeast accounted for about 55 percent of the total value of milk and cream sold by all dairy farmers in the entire Northern Dairy region in 1954, they accounted for only 48 percent of the total milk sold and 8 percent of the total cream sold.

Most of the milk that is produced in the Northeast is consumed as fluid milk or cream, whereas in the Lake States a much larger share is converted into evaporated milk, condensed milk, butter, and cheese.

The Northeast is a deficit area so far as manufactured dairy products are concerned, whereas the Lake States produce more manufactured dairy products than are consumed in the area. This accounts largely for the fact that the average price received by farmers for milk is about 1 dollar per 100 pounds higher in the Northeast than in the Lake States.

The average dairy farm in the Northeast is somewhat larger in total acres than the average dairy farm in the Lake States. The main difference is in acreage of woodland. They are about equal in terms of cropland.

Northeastern dairy farms are more specialized than those in the Lake States. Their operators raise fewer pigs, keep more cows, produce more milk, and buy more feed concentrates.

Most of the dairy farms in the Northern Dairy region are family operated. Fewer than 2 percent of the dairy farm operators in Wisconsin and fewer than 8 percent in New York spent as much as 2,500 dollars for hired labor in 1954.

THE TYPICAL family-operated dairy farm in the central Northeast (New York and Vermont) is a farm of approximately 200 acres. About 75 acres are harvested cropland. It has about 26 milk cows, 13 head of other cattle, about 90 chickens, and a pig or two for home use.

The total value of farm capital on such a farm in 1954–1956 was close to 28 thousand dollars, of which real estate accounted for 53 percent; machinery and equipment, 18 percent; livestock, 20 percent; and feed and supplies, 9 percent.

Some 4,400 hours of labor are used annually on farms of this size. An average of 16 percent of the labor is hired, but the percentage varies from farm to farm according to the availability of family labor. Farmers in this and other regions frequently exchange work with neighbors.

Hay and grass silage account for about two-thirds of the harvested cropland. Corn and small grains account for most of the rest.

Oats are the most important small-grain crop. Barley and wheat also are grown on some farms. Oats or another small-grain crop may be seeded as a companion crop for clover, alfalfa, or mixtures of grasses and legumes. The companion crop on many farms is cut green for hay or grass silage. Barley and wheat are harvested oftener for grain than for hay or silage on farms where they are grown.

Gross farm income on typical family-operated dairy farms in the central Northeast averaged 9,800 dollars annually in 1954–1956. Milk accounted for 84 percent of the total receipts; cattle and calves, 8 percent; and poultry and eggs, 7 percent. Produc-

tion expenses on these farms averaged about 5,750 dollars annually. Expenditures for purchased feed accounted for 35 percent of the total.

Machinery costs, including depreciation, repairs, and motor supplies, accounted for about 27 percent. Among the other items of expense, farm property taxes, depreciation charges on farm buildings and fences, and wages paid for hired labor were most important.

The average net farm income was about 4,050 dollars. This figure represents the return on the money invested in the farm business and the unpaid labor contributed by the farm operator and members of his family. It includes the value of products consumed by the farm family that were produced on the farm, the rental value of the dwelling, and the net cash income from farming, adjusted for inventory changes.

THE TYPICAL family-operated dairy farm in western Wisconsin from which milk is sold for processing is a farm of about 145 acres. It has about 65 acres of harvested cropland. It has 17 milk cows, 11 head of other cattle, and 110 chickens. An average of 3 litters of pigs are raised annually.

The total value of farm capital on such a farm in 1954–1956 was close to 22 thousand dollars, of which real estate accounted for 50 percent; machinery and equipment, 24 percent; livestock, 19 percent; and feed and supplies, 7 percent.

The labor used on such a farm averaged about 4 thousand hours a year in 1954–1956, of which about 12 percent was hired.

The chief crops on dairy farms in western Wisconsin are corn, oats (or other small grains), and hay, but corn and small grains are more important on dairy farms in this area than they are on dairy farms in the central Northeast. A larger percentage of the corn is harvested for grain in Wisconsin. Some of it is fed to hogs and to dairy cattle and chickens.

The acreage of hay (other than grain

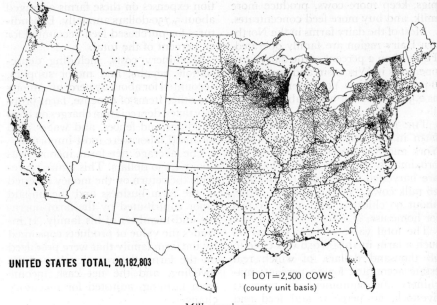

UNITED STATES TOTAL, 20,182,803

1 DOT=2,500 COWS
(county unit basis)

Milk cows in 1954.

hay) on western Wisconsin dairy farms is less than half the total acreage of cropland harvested. This compares with two-thirds of the acreage of cropland harvested on dairy farms in the Northeast. Because crop rotations are shorter on Wisconsin farms, the hay is of better quality and the average yield per acre is higher.

The average gross farm income on typical family-operated dairy farms was 6,450 dollars a year in 1954–1956. Milk accounted for 67 percent of total receipts; cattle and calves, 12 percent; hogs, 9 percent; and poultry and eggs, 9 percent. Farm production expenses averaged 3,850 dollars annually. Machinery cost, including depreciation, repairs, and motor supplies, accounted for 41 percent of the total. Expenditures for purchased feed constituted 19 percent of total production expenses, compared with 35 percent on dairy farms in the central Northeast.

Net farm incomes on typical family-operated dairy farms in western Wisconsin whose operators sell milk for processing averaged about 2,600 dollars a year. This is less than the comparable figure for typical family-operated dairy farms in the Northeast. It is also less than the average net farm income on similar dairy farms in Wisconsin that sell milk for fluid use.

Net returns from 1947 to 1956 were apparently about the same on dairy farms in the Lake States as on dairy farms in the Northeast, if farms of similar size and market outlets are compared.

Incomes on dairy farms in the two areas get out of line from time to time for several reasons—such as weather; the deviation in prices of milk in different markets from their normal relationships; and the changes in relative prices of milk, hogs, and feed grains, which tend to have different effects on incomes of dairymen in the two areas.

MOST DAIRYMEN in the Northern Dairy region own at least some of the land they use. About 92 percent of the dairy farms in New York State and about 83 percent of those in Wisconsin were operated by owners or part owners in 1950. Dairymen who own their farms can make use of their spare time by keeping up and improving their farm property.

The landlord and tenant of rented dairy farms in many instances are related. Often a son operates the farm as a renter until he inherits the property or until he can buy out the other heirs. More than half of the dairy farms that are operated by tenants in Wisconsin are rented on a livestock-share basis. The cash basis is somewhat commoner in New York.

Good dairy farms are seldom available for rent. The ordinary year-to-year rental agreement between owner and operator is usually not satisfactory to either party. The operator is not inclined under such an arrangement to invest in soil-building crops like alfalfa, and the productivity of the soil tends to decline.

Most dairymen in the Northern Dairy region own some farm real estate, but many have the use of additional land that they do not own. Research conducted by Richard G. Wheeler and Dr. John D. Black of Harvard University indicated that in 1945–1947 at least half of the commercial dairy farm operators in New England had arrangements for using land that was owned by others. Their studies showed that the proportion was as high as 80 percent in southern New England and 38 percent in northern Vermont.

Dairymen often obtain standing hay from their neighbors in this and other parts of the Northern Dairy region. They often pay little or nothing for it. The payment depends to a considerable extent on the quality of the hay and the amount of competition for it.

A dairy farmer occasionally rents pastureland from a neighbor. The rent paid for pastureland and whether or not the land is used at all frequently depend on the condition of the fences. Fences are not always kept up, especially when the owner keeps no livestock himself.

The opportunity that many dairymen have of cutting hay on nearby farms and estates and of renting additional pasture has helped to increase the output of milk on commercial dairy farms. It also has been one of the reasons for the relatively low yields of hay in areas like southern New England, where the number of dairy farms has declined rapidly. Yields of hay are usually higher on land dairymen own than on land from which they merely harvest the crop. One reason is that most of the land which dairymen use but do not own receives no manure, commercial fertilizer, or lime.

The average dairyman in the Northern Dairy region uses about 240 dollars' worth of commercial fertilizers and lime a year.

Purchased feeds also help to maintain soil fertility on many dairy farms—especially in the Northeast, where the average dairyman spends about 2 thousand dollars a year for concentrates. Other things being equal, farmers who buy substantial quantities of grain can keep more animals on a given acreage than those who depend largely on homegrown feeds. They therefore have more manure per acre.

THE USE OF LAND in the Northern Dairy region has changed a great deal over the years. In colonial days before much of the region was settled, production of farm products was almost entirely for home use. By 1840 a limited market for farm products was emerging in the industrial cities that were springing up along the larger rivers. Nearby farms were beginning to supply these growing markets with such products as meat, milk, butter, fruit, vegetables, hay, and firewood. More distant farms were able to supply some of the wool, hides, cheese, and small grains that were also in demand.

The development of inland waterways in the first half of the 19th century was a factor in the early growth of cities and the demand for farm products. Among the many canals that were built, the Erie, which connected the Great Lakes with the Hudson River, was undoubtedly the most important. Upon its completion in 1824, freight rates from Buffalo to New York City dropped from about 100 dollars a ton to less than 10 dollars.

Milwaukee, Wis., by 1862 had become the leading primary wheat market in the world, a distinction it held until 1873. Wisconsin farmers during this period received about 60 percent of their gross income from the sale of wheat and other crops and 10 percent from dairy products. Now they get 60 percent of their income from dairy products and 15 percent from crops. Wheat accounts for less than 1 percent of the total.

Dairy farms that sell fluid milk for consumption in large cities came into being in strictly rural areas when railroads were built. New York City received its first shipment of milk by rail in 1842 and its first shipment by refrigerator car in 1881. Much of the milk that was consumed in New York City before 1840 was produced within the city limits. Now practically none of the milk used in New York City is produced within a distance of 50 miles.

These developments in railroad transportation brought about drastic changes in the agriculture of the region. The number of sheep in New York State declined from more than 6 million head in 1845 to fewer than 2 million in 1900, while the number of dairy cows rose from less than 1 million to about 1.5 million. Feed grains replaced wheat on approximately 500 thousand acres, and the acreage of hay increased by about 50 percent. A substantial acreage was required to provide feed for horses in towns and cities as well as on farms.

Much farmland was abandoned after 1900 in the Northeast, but the acreage of land in farms continued to increase in the Lake States until about 1940. The decline in New York during the first half of the century amounted to nearly a third, while the increase in Wisconsin amounted to about a sixth. Numbers of dairy cows dropped by nearly 300 thousand in New York and increased by more than 1 million in Wisconsin.

Farm income, per farm, of dairy farms in the Central Northeastern States.

The development of motor transportation, the farm-to-market roads, and rural electrification improved considerably the competitive position of farms in outlying areas. More opportunities for nonfarm employment came to rural people, and part-time farming increased.

Mechanization gave further impetus to these developments. Many farms that had been large enough for several generations became too small to make efficient use of modern machinery and equipment. The mortality rate was especially high among hill farms and those with small fields and many stones. New York State lost a third of its farms and a quarter of its cropland from 1930 to 1954. Wisconsin, however, lost only 16 percent of its farms and none of its cropland.

The adjustments that farmers made to these latest advances in technology are reflected in the annual estimates of the Department of Agriculture relative to costs and returns by type of farm. From 1940 to 1956, for example, the average family-operated dairy farm in the Northeast increased by about 20 percent in total acres, 35 percent in number of cows milked, and 65 percent in total output of milk. The number of tractors per 100 farms increased from about 40 to about 160, while the number of horses per 100 farms dropped from about 270 to around 60. The constant-dollar value of all farm machinery and equipment per farm about doubled. Hours of labor used per farm declined by one-fifth, but hours of hired labor alone declined by two-thirds. The quantities of feed and fertilizer purchased per farm both increased by about 50 percent. The total value of farm assets per farm increased from about 10 thousand dollars to about 30 thousand dollars. Net farm income per farm increased from about 1,100 dollars to about 4,280 dollars. The purchasing power of net farm income increased by about 90 percent.

These changes reflect to some extent the decline in number of dairy farms. According to the census, there were 11 percent fewer dairy farms in New York State in 1954 than in 1950 but 7 percent more milk cows on dairy farms. A large part of the increase in average size of herd thus stems from the decrease in the number of farms.

Among the more important reasons for the decline in number of dairy farms is that some farm operators were able to find better paying employment elsewhere. Sometimes the initial cost of complying with new health regulations or of getting equipped to handle milk in bulk has been more than the farmer could afford or was willing to invest. And, as I pointed out earlier, many dairy farms in the Northeast are not well adapted to some of the labor-saving machines, like the field-forage harvester.

Farmers who have remained in business of producing milk have found it profitable to take over the share of the expanding market that the others relinquished. By so doing they have been able to spread their overhead costs over a larger volume of output and thereby increase their net returns.

This kind of adjustment also has occurred in the Lake States. The St. Lawrence Seaway project has provided some of the nonfarm employment opportunities that have enabled some dairy farmers to better themselves financially. In giving up farming, they helped to make it possible for the farmers who stayed in the dairy business to expand their output of milk without depressing the price unduly.

Many of the recent trends that have been observed in the Northern Dairy region are expected to continue for an indefinite period. It will take at least several years for the size of farms to catch up with modern technology.

Even though the domestic market for farm products is likely to expand, the acreage of cropland and open pasture will probably continue to decline in the Northern Dairy region. The extent of the decline will depend on many factors, including Government programs, how much cotton, wheat, and other farm products this country will be able to export, and the general level of business activity. In any event, however, the expected decline in acreage of farmland is likely to be more than offset by increases in crop yields in the country as a whole if not in the Northern Dairy region.

There may be times when trends in land use are temporarily reversed, however. Although the acreage of land in farms declined in New York State by about 27 percent from 1920 to 1954, it increased somewhat from 1930 to 1935 and again from 1940 to 1945.

In the more recent period it was the wartime demand for food that caused the increase. Milk production was subsidized, and many farmworkers were given draft deferments to bolster farm output. Large amounts of agricultural products were shipped abroad.

In the earlier period the great depression caused an increase in the acreage of farmland. Opportunities for off-farm employment were not sufficient to take care of the normal flow of workers from farming to industry. To make matters worse, some who had lost their jobs in industry were forced to rejoin the farm labor force until something better turned up. Some of these were already living on farms.

Eventually the country pulled out of the depression and the acreage of farmland in the Northern Dairy region resumed its downward trend along with the number of persons engaged in farming. And with a pickup in demand, earnings of farm operators improved substantially.

The use of land in the Corn Belt.

Here is grown about 40 percent of the world's corn. The future of this section will reflect the balance between demands for livestock products and the greater production that science is bringing. The march of technology, which has meant mounting investments in modern equipment and materials, may increase the Corn Belt's advantage in the production of corn and livestock. By *C. W. Crickman*, Northern Field Research Section, Farm Economics Research Division.

THE CORN BELT centers in the middle Mississippi River Valley. It is bounded on the east in Ohio by the foothills of the Appalachian Mountains and on the south by the rough topography along the Ohio River and the Ozark uplift in Illinois and Missouri. Its western and northern boundaries are established by the dry weather of the Great Plains and the short growing season and cool summer nights of the Lake States.

Land in the Corn Belt is generally level or gently rolling. The deep, warm, fertile soils are rich in organic matter and nitrogen. They are well adapted to the production of feed grains, soybeans, grasses, and legumes. Sufficient rainfall, well distributed throughout the growing season, hot days, and warm nights are also ideal for these crops.

To have level topography, fertile soil, generous rainfall, and favorable temperatures combined in so good a balance is rare. In fact, of the 100 million acres in the United States that soil technicians describe as excellent for grains, grasses, and legumes, about three-fourths are in the Corn Belt.

The Corn Belt is well named. The deep, black soils and the climate are nearly perfect for corn. The soils have the desirable characteristics of friability, aeration, water-holding capacity, and plentiful nitrogen.

The relatively flat topography permits an intensive corn-cropping program with modern laborsaving machinery. About three-fourths of the corn harvested for grain in the United States and about 40 percent of the world's output of corn are grown in the Corn Belt.

But the corn crop draws heavily on even the abundant fertility of the soil. It is particularly seasonal in its use of labor and equipment. To protect or replenish the structure and productivity of his soils and to spread the use of his labor and equipment, a Corn Belt farmer grows other crops with corn—chiefly oats, soybeans, wheat, and hay and pasture crops—in his cropping system. He seldom grows corn on more than half of his cropland. The oat crop is seeded in the spring before work on the corn crop begins and is cut in the summer when cultivation of corn is about over. Soybeans, the second most profitable crop in the area, are planted after corn and harvested earlier. Winter wheat is seeded in the fall when the harvest of other crops is mainly over.

Oats and wheat are the transitional crops in the rotation between corn or soybeans and the grass or legume soil-building crops that are essential to a program of soil maintenance and improvement. Oats and the forage crop are planted together. As the oat plant

122

is taller and matures more quickly than grasses and legumes, the oats can be harvested without much damage to the other crop. A primary function of the oats is to serve as a companion crop to the forage crop, shading out weeds and providing some protection from wind and sun while the young forage plants become established.

Thus the feed crops—corn, oats, and hay and pasture—and soybeans form the chief basis of the farming system in practically all parts of the region, not only in respect to the cropping program but also in selecting livestock enterprises to utilize the feed crops. The dominant crop, corn, which is primarily a meatmaking feed, is used chiefly for fattening hogs and beef cattle. About two-thirds of all the hogs and one-fourth of all the cattle and calves in the United States in 1954 were on farms in the Corn Belt.

Chickens are a minor enterprise, but farm flocks are kept on many of the farms. Between a fourth and a third of the poultry in the United States is in the Corn Belt. About half of the sheep and lambs "on feed" are fattened in the Corn Belt. Sheep are kept on a few farms.

The dominance of the corn crop and meat-animal production is more pronounced in the central part of the region. Even so, differences in topography and soils within the central section are chiefly responsible for three characteristic types of farming in the central part of the Corn Belt— cash corn, oats, and soybeans; hogs and cattle fattening; and hogs and cattle raising. Other types are dominant in the border areas.

Corn, oats, and soybeans are grown for sale on large farms in east-central Illinois and central Iowa. The level land has not been subject to serious damage from erosion even though it has been heavily cropped. Some farmers replenish nitrogen and organic matter in the soil by growing corn and an oats-clover combination in alternate years. In the fall the clover is plowed under as a green manure.

The cropping systems in the area generally produce a large supply of concentrated feeds, but not enough hay and pasture for a beef-cattle enterprise. Hog enterprises also are smaller than in other parts of the Corn Belt, because farmers believe they cannot afford to take the time from production of crops that would be needed to handle efficiently a larger hog enterprise.

Moreover, conditions that are favorable to a grain type of farming also are favorable to tenant operation of the land. Landlords usually prefer to receive a share of the crop as payment for use of the land. They also often prefer to seal for a Government loan or to sell their share for cash soon after harvest. Thus they frequently are not interested in providing buildings and fences; and, as their tenure is often uncertain, tenants cannot afford to put much money in the fences and equipment that are needed in livestock production. All these conditions are unfavorable to development of a livestock system of farming, even though the cropping system is built mainly around feed grains.

Cash-grain farms are the largest farms in the Corn Belt in both acres of land and total investment but the smallest in hours of labor used. The investment in 1954–1956 on a farm of 230 acres was 88,530 dollars. Crops were harvested from more than 80 percent of the land. The rotation of crops was usually corn, corn, oats, and soybeans, plus about 16 acres of hay. With this cropping system there is produced a large volume of concentrated feeds in proportion to forage from hay and pasture.

Hogs consequently are the most important livestock enterprise. The hog enterprise consists of about 35 hogs marketed annually. By feeding corn to hogs, farmers do a larger volume of business with only a limited addition to their investment in fixed resources. Thus hog feeding is a method of utilizing more fully the farm operator's labor and thereby increasing his annual income.

The cattle enterprise, as on about two-thirds of the cash-grain farms, is a combination of beef-cattle production and milk production. The herds are predominantly of the beef breeds. About half of the farmers who keep beef-breeding herds fatten a part or all of the cattle raised on the farm. The breeding herd of cows averages about seven head.

The net farm income on typical cash-grain farms from 1954 to 1956 averaged 8,220 dollars, which was somewhat higher than on hog-beef fattening farms. The relationship was reversed in 1947–1949, when prices for livestock were higher relative to prices for grain and soybeans.

HOGS AND BEEF CATTLE are the chief livestock enterprises on the areas of loessal—or windblown—soil, which border parts of the Missouri and Mississippi Rivers and usually are rolling.

A relatively high percentage of the land therefore can be used only for permanent pasture. The cropland is rich enough to produce good yields of corn, but it requires careful management—relatively large acreages of grasses and legumes to give protective cover and maintain organic matter—because of its slope and susceptibility to erosion. A common cropping system consists of two fields of corn, one field of oats, and one field of hay and rotation pasture.

The cropping systems include large proportions of corn to small grains and large proportions of high-quality hay to pasture. Both of these relationships are favorable to meat-producing livestock enterprises. Few farmers sell grain. In fact, in the most highly specialized livestock counties of the areas, some farmers regularly buy a considerable quantity of corn, notwithstanding the high production on their own farms.

Because hogs convert concentrated feeds efficiently into meat, they have first call on the corn grown. But even

with an optimum-sized hog enterprise, many farms in these areas have a surplus of corn. The abundant hay and pasture are utilized better when fed to cattle in conjunction with a concentrate ration. Beef cattle usually are selected in preference to dairy cattle, because fattening cattle use more grain in proportion to forage than do dairy cattle.

Fattening cattle on grain reaches its maximum development in the United States in feedlots on farms in these areas. Most of the feeder cattle are born on western ranges in the spring. Some of them are shipped to the Corn Belt in the fall as feeder calves weighing 350 to 450 pounds. Others are carried on the range over winter, are grazed the following summer, and move to Corn Belt feedlots as 600- to 700-pound yearlings. The heaviest movement of feeders usually is in October. The yearlings are fed to various weights and grades before they are sold for slaughter. Many are marketed in late spring and early summer. The largest volume usually comes in June. Calves, which fatten more slowly than yearlings, are marketed mainly in August and September. Thus the cattle-feeding operation has a production and investment period that may range from 3 to 12 months; 6 to 8 months is the commonest length of time.

Records from a sampling of farms indicate that about half of the farmers in these areas fatten cattle for market. About 10 percent of the cattle feeders fed lots of four carloads or more, and about 50 percent fed from one to three carloads. The rest fed less than a carload and confined their feeding operations largely to cattle of their own raising. Most farmers in the areas keep a small beef-cattle breeding herd. Those who do not fatten large lots of cattle concentrate more on breeding herds.

The typical hog-beef fattening farms may comprise 200 acres, of which 140 acres is harvested cropland. The investment was about 59,440 dollars in

1954–1956. About half of the cropland is used each year to produce corn. The other half is divided between oats and hay in a ratio of about 7 to 5.

The typical cattle enterprise consists of about two carloads of cattle fattened for market and a small breeding herd. The hog enterprise consists of about 150 hogs marketed annually, which requires farrowing about 30 litters of pigs. The ratio of spring to fall litters is about 2 to 1. The breeding herd of cows averages about six.

The net farm income on typical hog-beef fattening farms was about 6,720 dollars in 1954–1956.

Hogs and cattle predominate on the southern side of the Corn Belt—in southern Iowa, northeastern Missouri, and the adjacent counties in Illinois—where the land is rolling and there is more hay and pasture and a smaller supply of feed grains. More than a third of the land is in pasture. The smaller supply of feed grains is due to the scarcity of good cropland and the low yields on the land used for crops—conditions that favor a beef-cattle enterprise in which more emphasis is placed on grazing and less on fattening for market. The same conditions limit the production of hogs.

Typical farms in this area are about 220 acres. They had a total investment of 35,150 dollars in 1954–1956. The value of land and buildings here is about 100 dollars an acre. (It is more than 200 dollars an acre in the hog-beef fattening areas.) Less than half of the land is used for crops. The combination of crops is approximately a 3-year rotation of corn, oats and soybeans, and hay. The typical beef-cow herd includes 20 cows. The hog enterprise is about half as large as on typical hog-beef fattening farms. Net farm income in 1954–1956 was less than half as large as on the hog-beef fattening farms (3,040 dollars, compared with 6,720 dollars).

SEVERAL BORDER AREAS differ with respect to use of land and livestock enterprises.

Farms in the eastern part of the Corn Belt are smaller. The soils are lighter and better drained. Conditions favor production of soft winter wheat. Wheat is the dominant small grain in the crop rotation. Production of corn is no larger than is needed for the hog enterprise. Income from farming thus comes primarily from the sale of wheat and hogs.

On the northern side of the Corn Belt, in northeastern Iowa and northwestern Illinois, the glacial-drift soils are a much older formation than in either the Wisconsin drift or the loess soil areas in Iowa and Illinois. They are more leached and more acid and have lower inherent productivity than the soils of the newer formation.

A larger percentage of the farm usually is in hay and pasture than in other crops. The acreages of corn and oats are about the same. This use of the land results in a large amount of forage in proportion to concentrated feeds. Thus when farmers have set aside a supply of grain for hogs, the amount left bears a wide ratio to the supply of roughage and pasture.

Because the hog ration is mainly corn and production of oats is high in this area in relation to corn, the ratio of fattening grains to protein grains in the remaining supply of feed grains is favorable to dairying rather than to beef cattle. Also favoring dairying are the quality and carrying capacity of pastures. Pastures withstand the hot, dry period of late summer better in this area than in any other part of the region. Most of the milk is delivered to local creameries and condenseries.

The farming on the western side of the Corn Belt is a transition between corn and livestock feeding and wheat and range livestock. The acreage of wheat increases relative to both corn and oats. The low productivity of the hay and pastureland, chiefly because of low rainfall, means fewer cattle. The smaller production of corn means fewer hogs. More corn is sold from this part of the region than from the central livestock-feeding areas—partly because of the uncertainty of rainfall, which increases the variation in crop yields. To avoid the hazard of not enough feed in dry years, farmers tend to understock with livestock. Thus they have a livestock and cash-grain system of farming.

PRODUCTIVITY AND LAND VALUES in different parts of the Corn Belt are measured fairly well by the intensity of corn production because corn so largely dominates the systems of farming.

The intensity of corn production reflects the acre yield, proportion of cropland planted to corn, and the proportion of farmland that is used for crops. The relationship between corn production and land value therefore is closer in the central part of the Corn Belt than in the border areas, where corn has a less dominant position in the rotation.

Land values are highest in east-central Illinois in the central cash-crop area, where the average value of farmland in 1954 was 383 dollars an acre. Values ranged from 150 dollars to more than 300 dollars in the livestock-feeding areas. In areas where hay and pasture occupied more than half of the land, as in the hog-beef raising area in southern Iowa and northern Missouri, values generally ranged below 150 dollars an acre.

WE DIVIDED the Corn Belt into areas having different systems of farming chiefly on the basis of differences in topography and adaptability of the soil to crops. Wide differences in systems of farming on individual farms are due to those factors and others, such as size of farm, tenure, market outlets, control of capital or credit, and operators' preferences and skills. The variation in systems of farming is noticeable particularly in the border areas, where topography is rougher and several soil types are closely interspersed.

But farms also differ in the central Corn Belt as the quality of land, amount of capital available, and the level of management differ.

The need for grass and legume crops in the rotation is greater on low- to medium-quality land than on high-quality land. A limited amount of capital for operating expenses and annual capital investments restricts livestock production and favors a crop rotation that includes a large acreage of corn.

The level of management is reflected in the livestock system more than in the cropping system. Average managers tend to have a diversified livestock system that includes a dairy enterprise. Good managers tend to concentrate more on hogs and cattle fattening.

Superior management also increases efficiency of operation, which is reflected in net returns, particularly when the capital investment is adequate. The range in net return for well-organized, owner-operated, 240-acre Iowa farms at 1957 prices was from about 3,900 dollars with low- to medium-quality land, limited capital, and average level of management to about 17,800 dollars with high-quality land, adequate capital, and superior management.

FROM YEAR TO YEAR, the fixed resources—land, buildings, and to a considerable extent machinery—of each Corn Belt farm can be utilized in many ways. Land and climate give the Corn Belt an advantage over other areas in production of several crops and several classes of livestock. The alternatives are relatively close as far as returns are concerned.

Corn and soybeans are interchangeable in the crop rotation. The typical livestock enterprises—hogs, beef-cattle fattening, and poultry—can be instituted, expanded, contracted, or liquidated in a year or two. And the emphasis of many Corn Belt cow herds can be shifted from "kept for beef" to "kept for milk" at any time by feeding some of the calves and marketing the milk.

Thus the unspecialized character of the fixed resources and the relatively short period of production and investment for livestock give farmers in the

Corn Belt the ability to adjust readily and quickly to changing economic conditions. This is in contrast to the dairy regions, for example, where the specialized nature of capital and the absence of attractive alternatives make adjustment to change in demand slow and difficult.

A farmer in the Corn Belt may choose among his alternatives on the basis of his expectation of future prices. The usual price relationships give corn a profit advantage among Corn Belt crops, and most farmers plant as much corn as is consistent with their ideas of good use of soil and a balanced production.

In the fall when the size and condition of the corn crop can be estimated reasonably closely, the farmers make decisions about marketing the crop. These are foregone decisions for some farmers; they regularly plan to feed most of their corn to livestock, and their feeding programs vary little from year to year. But others adapt their corn-marketing plans to their expectations of future prices for corn, hogs, and cattle.

A farmer who expects the price of corn to be high compared with the price of livestock may curtail his livestock enterprises considerably and sell part or all of his corn. If he expects the prices of both corn and livestock to be relatively low, he may store his corn and take a price-support loan from the Government. But a farmer who expects the price of hogs to be high relative to the price of corn may decide to expand his production of hogs. He may expand his cattle-feeding program if he believes that prices of fat cattle will be high compared with the current prices for feeder cattle and corn.

The adaptability of agriculture in the Corn Belt is partly responsible for the phenomenon of the hog and cattle cycles. It also accounts for the relatively short duration of these cycles in production.

GREAT CHANGES have been made in farming in the Corn Belt. Energetic and resourceful operators have adopted new technology and improved production practices—hybrid seed corn, more fertilizer, and legumes and grass-legume mixtures in place of grasses on many acres of hay and pasture and soybeans, which were unknown to Corn Belt farmers not many years ago and now rank high in value per acre and acreage.

Formula feeds and associated additives are increasing the level of feed conversion by livestock. They also represent a transfer from the farm to industry of an important part of the work and the source of knowledge in the compounding and preparation of livestock rations. The benefits of scientific skill in formulation of rations thus become more widely available to livestock producers. Antibiotics were included in 1958 in about 90 percent of commercially mixed poultry starter, grower, and broiler feeds; about half of the poultry layer and breeder feeds; about three-fourths of pig and hog formula feeds; and about 5 percent of dairy and beef formula feeds. Antibiotics reduce death losses and increase output per unit of feed; adding them to creep-feeding rations for pigs may increase pig weights by 5 to 10 pounds at 8 weeks of age.

THE ADVANCE IN TECHNOLOGY has been accompanied by a mounting investment in modern machinery, equipment, and buildings, and by greater expenditures for fertilizers, feed, seed, and the many chemical and biological products used to promote the health and growth of plants and animals and to control the insects and diseases that attack them.

Records from annual samplings of 25 farms in Illinois during the past quarter century reveal that many changes have taken place.

The average size of farms increased 12 percent. The number of men employed (12-month basis) dropped 14 percent. The number of acres worked per man increased 32 percent. Total investment increased 65 percent per acre and 117 percent per man. Total cash receipts per farm increased 157 percent. Total cash expenses increased 202 percent.

The changes in the use of land included notable increases in acreage of hay, pasture and green manure crops, and soybeans, with corresponding decreases in wheat and barley. The proportion of the land in corn and oats remained about the same.

Crop yields per acre and livestock production per animal increased all along the line. The increase in crop production and livestock production per acre was 26 and 40 percent, respectively. The increase in total crop and livestock production per acre was 32 percent.

Output per man has been pushed up remarkably by farmers' investment in modern equipment and materials for putting advanced technology to work on their farms and by improvement in the managerial skill of farmers themselves. Total crop and livestock production per man increased 73 percent.

A similar story can be told for the whole Corn Belt. Any one of the changes alone may not provide an accurate measure of the change in efficiency of agriculture, but together they indicate the stupendous changes that progressive farmers are making in farming in the Corn Belt.

THE ADVANTAGE of the Corn Belt in the production of corn and livestock is likely to persist. The acreage of corn has declined since about 1925, but the reduction has been more than offset by increased acre yields.

The future should bring even higher yields that will lower the cost of producing a bushel. Mechanization, hybrid seed, fertilizer, and control of weeds, diseases, and insects will be important in boosting present yields.

New corn hybrids now in commercial production yield about 10 percent more an acre than those widely grown less than 10 years ago. Greatly superior agronomic characters of the new hy-brids reduce the costs of growing corn. Intensive research in progress shows promise of producing hybrids with greater resistance to corn borers and other pests and diseases. They will be important when diseases and insects strike.

New methods of production are gradually taking corn out of the soil-depleting category. It is likely that increased knowledge of soils and their management may permit continuous cropping of corn on the level, water-permeable soils in parts of the Corn Belt. So it is possible that the march of technology will increase—rather than reduce—the Corn Belt's advantage in the production of corn and livestock.

Livestock production has made significant gains in efficiency in the last two to three decades. Since 1935–1939, output per breeding unit has increased about a third. Forty percent more beef per cow and 20 percent more pork per sow is now being produced. Today's pig crop in the Corn Belt can be produced with about 15 percent fewer sows than in 1935–1939. These gains are primarily because animals have greater production capacity, more and better feeds are available, diseases and insect pests are better controlled, and management all along the line is improved. Master swine producers in Iowa saved three more pigs per sow in 1954 than the average farmer in Iowa did. This achievement is a still higher goal for further improvement through better management practices on farms.

Prospects in the Corn Belt during the next few decades depend on the balance between the expanding total demand of a growing population and the rise in per capita demand for meat and livestock products as against the increasing supply of corn and other feed grains that arises primarily from the advance in technology and the resulting boost in yields per acre. Present indications suggest that larger amounts of meat and other livestock products of high quality will be bought if they can be produced at prices that are attractive to consumers.

Where our cotton comes from.

This chapter, the first of two about the changing South, presents many details of the business of growing cotton—its importance in regional and national agriculture, the factors that determine where it is grown, yields, the growing use of machinery, acreages, the effect of Government programs, irrigation, and many more that determine how land is used. By *Max M. Tharp,* and *E. Lee Langsford,* Southern Field Research Section, Farm Economics Research Division.

MOST OF OUR COTTON is produced in the nine States of the Cotton Belt—the largest cotton-growing area in the world—and in New Mexico, Arizona, and California.

The nine States—Alabama, Arkansas, Georgia, Louisiana, Mississippi, Oklahoma, South Carolina, Tennessee, and Texas—accounted for 87 percent of the country's cotton acreage in 1954. Arizona, California, and New Mexico harvested 8 percent of the acreage. Most of the remaining 5 percent was in North Carolina, Missouri, and Florida.

Nearly half of all farmers in the Cotton Belt grew cotton, and a fourth of all land used for harvested crops was in cotton. Much of the cotton grown in the eastern part of the Cotton Belt is produced on small farms, but cotton farms in the Mississippi Delta, western Texas, and the three Western States usually are quite large. The acreage of cotton harvested in the three Western States averaged nearly 100 acres a farm in 1954. The average for the nine States in the Cotton Belt was 22 acres a farm.

Cotton, a subtropical plant, requires a long growing season and rather high temperatures. Climate largely determines where cotton is grown, but kind of land and economics also explain the location of cotton farms.

The northern boundary of the Cotton Belt follows closely the line of 200 frost-free days. The western boundary is limited to about the 20-inch rainfall line, except in places where irrigation supplements rainfall.

Production of cotton in areas that adjoin the Gulf of Mexico and the Atlantic Ocean is limited by the heavy rainfall during the fruiting and harvesting season, because it makes it harder to control insects, especially boll weevils. Dry weather at harvest means less damage to the open bolls.

Many different—but well-drained—soils produce good cotton. Poor drainage explains why cotton is not grown in some places in the Cotton Belt that would be suitable otherwise. Deep, level soils are best adapted to use of mechanical equipment. They are less apt to erode.

Cotton was harvested from about 17 million acres in 1955. In the major specialized cotton areas, 40 percent or more of the cropland used for harvested crops was in cotton.

The cotton crop is of even greater importance in terms of farm value, which averaged about 2.75 billion dollars a year in 1953–1955 for cotton lint and seed.

Great changes have occurred in the production of cotton. American farmers harvested about 42 million acres of cotton and produced about 14 million bales of lint in 1930. The harvested acreage had fallen to about 16 million acres by 1956, but production amounted to more than 13 million bales. Thus farmers in 1956 produced about as many bales of cotton as they did in 1930 with only 37 percent as many acres.

Yields of cotton increased about 87 percent in the 26 years from 1930 to 1957. The yield of lint cotton averaged about 192 pounds an acre in 1930–1934 and 359 pounds in 1952–1956.

Land selection, a shift in production among areas, the use of more and better fertilizer, improved methods of controlling insects and weeds, better varieties of seed, and irrigation are largely responsible for the increase.

The use of machinery in growing and harvesting cotton reduced the average number of hours of labor needed to produce a bale of cotton from about 260 in the 1930's to about 108 in 1955. About 541 thousand sharecroppers grew cotton lint in 1940—nearly twice the number in 1954. Not all of this reduction, however, was due to mechanization. The reduction in the acreage to comply with Government control programs also was a factor.

Lands on which machinery can be used have become more important since 1940. They have captured an ever-increasing share of the cotton production. Changes in price relationships between cotton and competing crops and livestock enterprises have also influenced shifts in cotton among areas. Production has moved westward into the semiarid areas of the Southwest, and a new "Cotton Belt" has emerged.

In the old Cotton Belt, east of the Mississippi River, cotton became the major crop because the area had an abundance of cheap labor to combine with the land to produce it. Because labor requirements for cotton growing were high, farms were small or cotton was grown by sharecroppers on small tracts as a part of plantation operations. During the 20 years to 1956,

however, farm wage rates rose about 300 percent. Thus, as laborsaving machines became available, it became economically feasible to substitute capital in the form of machines for labor on land suitable for mechanized farming. The areas best adapted to mechanization and the other improved techniques therefore have gained an advantage in production of cotton. In general, farms in the Southeastern areas are less well adapted to mechanization than the newer producing sections of the Southwest and West. Many farmers in the Southeast therefore could not grow cotton profitably— that is, their land could no longer profitably absorb the amounts of labor previously used to produce it. The result has been a relative increase in the importance of capital and a decrease in the significance of land as a factor in the production of cotton. Land values have not kept pace with those in other areas, and land has been shifted to crops using less labor and to pasture and trees.

Adjustments to the new technology of cotton production have varied greatly by areas. Reasons for these differences are partly explained by the characteristics of land and farms in the six major cotton areas.

ACREAGES OF COTTON GROWN and bales produced have changed since 1930. In the six areas—Eastern Coastal Plains, Piedmont, Mississippi Delta, Black Prairies of Texas, Texas High Plains, and the western irrigated area—they moved from east to west. These areas accounted for nearly 80 percent of our cotton production between 1950 and 1956.

The Eastern Coastal Plains in South Carolina, Georgia, and Florida accounted for about 10 percent of all cotton produced—somewhat less than in the 1930's. Soils there are light and often sandy. Some farmers specialize in cotton, but often peanuts and tobacco also are grown on a farm. Corn is the chief crop, on the basis of acreage harvested as a percentage of all cropland used for harvested crops. Corn usually is grown for feed. Yields are relatively low on most farms. Considerable mechanization has taken place in preharvest operations on cotton farms, but much hand labor is used in chopping and harvesting the crop. Vegetable crops that return a relatively high value per acre are grown in some parts. Pasture and forage crops are becoming more important as livestock enterprises are added to farming systems. The farms generally are small, and part-time farming has been increasing in places where nonfarm employment opportunities exist.

In the Piedmont area, which centers in South Carolina and Georgia and lies west of the Eastern Coastal Plains, farms are small, topography is broken, and much of the land is not suited to mechanized production. The proportion of the total acreage of cotton grown in this area remained fairly stable from 1930 to 1946, but it has declined sharply since 1946. Production has followed a similar trend. Piedmont farmers cultivated about 7 percent of the American cotton crop and produced about 9 percent of the lint in the 1930's. By the 1950's the acreage of cotton in this area was down to about 4 percent of the country's total. Production also averaged about 4 percent. Although many farmers in the area no longer produce cotton, the crop is ordinarily a major source of income for those that do. Most cotton farmers also grow corn, oats, wheat, and hay. Livestock farming and the acreage in improved pastures are rising.

The delta of Arkansas, Louisiana, Mississippi, and Missouri is a specialized cotton-producing area that is adapted to mechanization. The topography is level. The soils are deep and productive. Rainfall usually is adequate, but droughts may occur locally during critical growing periods, and many cotton farmers have turned to irrigation. Soybeans have become important. Corn, small grains, and pasture also account for a considerable acreage of cropland in many sections of the area. The acreage of cotton has increased relative to the national total since 1930. The acreage in cotton rose from an average of about 13 percent of the total acreage in the 1930's to nearly 17 percent in the 1950's. Production has remained at a high level. The delta accounts for more than 20 percent of the United States production in the 1950's.

The Black Prairie section of east-central Texas is a level and productive strip of black land. Farms averaged nearly 200 acres in 1955. Many had 500 acres or more. The area accounted for about 12 percent of the country's planted cotton acreage in the 1930's, but in the 1950's the acreage amounted to only 10 percent of the national total. Production was 5 percent of the total in the 1950's and 10 percent in the 1930's. Cotton farms predominate in most parts, but general farming is also significant. Yields of cotton are relatively low, but costs of production are also moderately low, and few alternative crops are so profitable.

About half of the cropland on the average cotton farm is customarily used for cotton. Corn, grain sorghum, and oats are important supplemental crops. The corn is harvested for grain. Large acreages produce pasture and hay crops. Beef cattle are the major grazing livestock, but there are many dairy farms, particularly in the sections near cities. Many farms here produce no cotton.

The Texas High Plains, a highly specialized cotton area, is in western Texas in a low-rainfall area. Acreage and production fluctuated widely between 1930 and 1956 on farms where cotton was grown without irrigation. In years when rainfall was adequate, the planted acreage increased and yields shot up. Much of the planted acreage was abandoned when droughts were severe. Farmers in the High Plains planted about 4 percent of the country's acreage of cotton in the 1930's and 8 percent in the 1950's. They produced about 3 and 7 percent, respectively, of the lint. The production of cotton under irrigation has increased rapidly in this area since 1946.

Irrigation has had a stabilizing effect on the acreage harvested. The acreage of cotton has increased, but since the Second World War the production has gone up even more—reflecting the shift to irrigation. The average number of bales produced in the High Plains, including both the dryland and irrigated cotton, was nearly three times as great from 1953 to 1955 as in a comparable period 10 years earlier.

Most of the farms are large, and one farmer may produce 100 bales each year. Most cotton farmers grow some grain sorghum, which is about the only adapted alternative crop and can be grown satisfactorily without irrigation in most years. Further expansion of irrigated cotton in the High Plains will be limited by availability of water and the price that farmers can afford to pay for it.

In the irrigated cotton areas of New Mexico, Arizona, and California, the acreages of cotton have increased rapidly, particularly since 1948. Many of the farms are large and highly specialized and mechanized. The topography is level, and the land is highly productive when it is irrigated. When a farm has rights to irrigation water, the value of the land is high. The acreages in cotton averaged less than 3 percent of the total for the country in the 1930's, but by the 1950's nearly 9 percent of the acreage was on irrigated farms. From an average of around 6 percent in the 1930's, farmers in the three States produced an average of about 20 percent of the country's total bales of lint in the 1950's.

GOVERNMENT CONTROL PROGRAMS have influenced the trends in the use of land and the production of cotton.

The Agricultural Adjustment Act of 1938 made certain provisions for setting cotton acreage allotments and marketing quotas. National allotments were broken down by States, counties, and farms. Individual allotments were based primarily on the past acreage history for the farm.

Farmers who harvested cotton from acreages in excess of their acreage allotments were not eligible to participate in the Government loan and price support program and were subject to a penalty on production from the excess acreage. Therefore few farmers planted any more than their allotted acreage, and many farmers in areas least adapted to cotton production planted considerably less than their allotment.

On the other hand, in sections best adapted to growing cotton, farmers planted as close as possible to their allotted acreage. This affected future allotments and therefore permitted minor shifts in cotton acreage between areas. One provision of the act specified that a farmer must have produced cotton at least one year in the previous three in order to receive a cotton acreage allotment. This provision influenced some farmers, who might otherwise have shifted to other crops, to plant cotton in order to maintain their base acreage for allotments.

Acreage allotments and marketing quotas were in effect for the cotton crops of 1938–1943, 1950, and 1954–1957. Allotments and quotas were suspended during the latter part of the war and the early postwar years. In the years when acreage allotments were not in effect, the acreage in cotton increased rapidly in the western irrigated areas, which had about 695 thousand acres in cotton in 1943 and produced about 6 percent of the lint. By 1953, the last year before acreage allotments were again imposed, however, these areas planted 2,586,000 acres of cotton and produced more than 21 percent of our crop.

The Acreage Reserve part of the Soil Bank Program, as operated in 1957, provided payments to farmers who reduced the acreage of certain crops below their allotted acreage. About 3 million acres of cotton were placed in the cotton acreage reserve program in 1957. This reduction of acreage did not affect future acreage allotments. Generally speaking, farmers with the least competitive advantage in cotton production participated in the Soil Bank Program.

The impact of other Government agricultural programs, such as the Agricultural Conservation Program, the Conservation Reserve Program of the Soil Bank, and other public efforts to conserve soil and water, have also influenced trends in the use of land. They have notably encouraged the shifts from cotton to pasture and livestock farming and to trees, particularly in the Southeast.

The drastic reduction in cotton acreage and shifts in land use have affected the farm population and labor force in the southeastern cotton areas. Farm population has declined as thousands of farm people have left cotton farms for jobs in the cities. Farms operated by nonwhite croppers decreased by 41 thousand, or 28 percent, from 1950 to 1954. The number of farms operated by white croppers dropped by 38 thousand, or 19 percent. The decline in sharecroppers continued as a result of the further drop in cotton acreage from 1955 to 1957.

Farm mortgage debt outstanding on farms in the Southeastern States more than doubled in the period 1950 to 1957. Land use in the older cotton areas is still in transition. Additional adjustments will be needed to stabilize the land use and agriculture of the areas most affected by the shift in cotton production to the West.

To INDICATE the relationship of land to other factors of production and to illustrate how cotton farms are organized, we give some details about three commercial cotton farms.

The average farm in the Southern Piedmont consisted of 177 acres, of which 58 acres were cropland. About 18 acres were in cotton. Corn and small grains were grown on about 32 acres of cropland. Hay was the only other crop.

Land and buildings, which were val-ued at about 13 thousand dollars, were the largest investment item. They constituted 85 percent of the total, or about 73 dollars an acre. Investment in machinery made up 11 percent of the total. Livestock accounted for the rest. This farm used work animals for part of the farmwork. The two dairy cows, the pigs raised, and the 50 chickens provided livestock products mainly for home use by the operator and his croppers. His four head of other cattle provided some cash income. A total of 4,280 hours of labor was used to produce cotton, other crops, and livestock. About 58 percent of the labor on the average farm represents work by the operator and his family. Of the rest of the hours of labor used, 31 percent was provided by sharecroppers and 11 percent by hired workers. Total gross income on the average Piedmont farm amounted to 4,500 dollars, about half of which was from the sale of cotton lint and cottonseed. Cotton grossed about 123 dollars an acre. Total expenses for the farm averaged 2,690 dollars.

Expenses for cropper and hired labor, machinery, and fertilizer were the major items of costs. After deducting total expenses from gross income, the farmer had left a net farm income of 1,814 dollars, or about 10 dollars an acre of farmland. This amount represented the return to him for his land, labor, management, and capital.

For the whole Piedmont, cotton farms vary in size and organization from the example we cited. A special study conducted on a sample of cotton farms in 1955 indicated that about 45 percent of the farms on which cotton was produced grew fewer than 10 acres in 1954. This group of small farms, however, accounted for only 14 percent of the cotton produced on all farms in the sample. Medium-sized farms, which more nearly approach the average (or illustrative) farm, made up 37 percent of all cotton farms and produced 32 percent of the cotton lint. Large farms that produced 30 acres or more of cotton in 1954 made

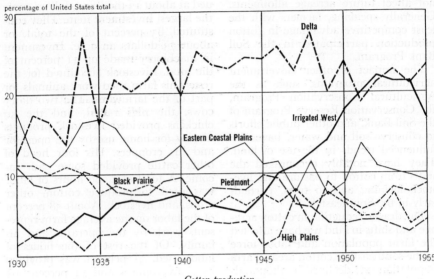

Cotton production.

up 18 percent of all farms in the sample and accounted for 54 percent of the production.

A SECOND EXAMPLE is a large cotton farm in the Delta area. It had 1 thousand acres, of which 613 acres were cropped. Cotton, the chief crop, was grown on 228 acres. A total of 175 acres was in soybeans. Undoubtedly more cotton would be grown on farms of this size in the Delta if acreage allotments permitted.

A total of 158,150 dollars was invested in the Delta farm—124,530 dollars, or 80 percent, for land and buildings, equivalent to 125 dollars an acre. Investment in machinery amounted to 17 percent of the total. Investment in livestock, mainly beef cattle, made up the remaining 6,710 dollars. A few work animals were kept for cropper use, but most of the cotton production was mechanized. Some cows were kept to supply milk for home use. The beef cattle and hogs provided supplementary cash income.

This Delta farm required an average of 32,510 hours of labor to produce the crops and care for the livestock during the year. Only 10 percent of it was performed by the operator and his family. Sharecroppers furnished 37 percent of the labor; hired workers furnished the rest.

Total gross farm income on the Delta farm averaged 62,500 dollars for the year. A total of 44,900 dollars, or 72 percent, of the income came from cotton. The gross returns from cotton averaged 197 dollars an acre for the crop. Other crops sold, mainly soybeans, contributed about 17 percent to the total gross income for the farm, and livestock sales made up the rest. Expenses for the year were 41,248 dollars. Hired and other labor, machinery costs, and expenditures for fertilizer, insecticides, and other crop costs were major items of expense. Net farm income to the operator for his management, labor, and capital averaged 21,270 dollars, or about 21 dollars an acre of farmland.

A study conducted in the Delta in 1955 showed that only 23 percent of the cotton farms (operating units) grew 100 or more acres of cotton in 1954. These farms were smaller than the farm used in the example, but they accounted for a high proportion of the cotton produced. About 44 percent of the farms were classed as of medium size, because they grew from 20 to 99 acres of cotton. The remaining 33 percent were small farms with fewer than 20 acres of cotton.

THE FARM selected as an illustration in the High Plains of Texas represents an average of irrigated cotton farms. It consisted of 314 acres. All the cotton was grown under irrigation. A total of 270 acres, or 86 percent of the farm, was cropland. Cotton was grown on 132 acres—half of the cropland and 42 percent of the farm acreage. The only other crop of importance was grain sorghum, which was grown on 134 acres. No workstock was kept.

The investment in land and buildings amounted to 73,130 dollars, or 233 dollars an acre, and constituted 84 percent of the total. The high acre value of this land results from its ability to absorb profitably large amounts of capital inputs, such as machinery and irrigation. As the farm was completely mechanized and had an irrigation system, the investment in machinery was substantial. It amounted to 12,970 dollars, or about 15 percent of the total investment.

Total labor used on the High Plains farm amounted to 8,290 hours a year—about twice as much as was used on the Piedmont farm to produce 58 acres of crops and about a fourth as much as was used on the Delta farm. The small amount of labor used per crop-acre reflects the high degree of mechanization attained on specialized cotton farms in the High Plains. Hired workers provided 71 percent of the labor. The operator and his family furnished the rest.

Gross farm income averaged 25,780 dollars from 1954 to 1956. A total of 20,500 dollars, or 80 percent of the gross income, was from cotton marketings. Grain sorghum, the other cash crop, accounted for most of the remaining 20 percent of gross farm income. Cotton grossed an average of 155 dollars an acre for each acre used to produce the crop. Total expenses on the farm amounted to 14,720 dollars, most of which was spent for irrigation, labor, and machinery. Net farm income amounted to an average of 11,060 dollars, or 35 dollars an acre of the farmland.

According to a survey conducted on a sample of representative cotton farms in the High Plains in 1955, no irrigated crops were produced on a third of the farms that year. Many of the farmers in the group that irrigated crops in 1955 did not have enough water and equipment to irrigate all their cotton. A fourth of the farms in the survey had fewer than 100 acres of cotton. Farms on which from 100 to 249 acres of cotton were grown made up 58 percent of the sample. Large farms with 250 acres or more of cotton constituted 19 percent of the farms in the sample.

Investments in land, not including buildings, account for half to nearly three-fourths of farmers' total capital investments in cotton areas. From 1946 to 1955, the value of all cottonland increased by an average of about 87 percent for the United States as a whole. Land values have risen most in such areas as the Texas High Plains and western cotton areas, where land responds well to irrigation and is adapted to mechanization. Land costs, including interest on money invested in land and real-estate taxes, constituted from 20 to 25 percent of the annual expenses required to produce our cotton crop in 1955.

If we look ahead, it seems certain that cotton production will continue to shift to areas in which land has a high potential for absorbing additional inputs.

In sections less favorable to the new cotton technology and mechanization, alternative farming enterprises will be substituted for cotton. Farms probably will continue to grow larger, and the number of farms will drop. Adjustments of this kind should bring about better overall land use; they should ultimately result in a more prosperous agriculture in the Cotton Belt.

Changes in the land of cotton.

The President of the United States in 1938 characterized the South as "the Nation's No. 1 economic problem." Evidence of the exciting progress since then is in a general conviction that the South is on the move; changes in the ownership and use of land; a decline in cotton acreage; a new emphasis on trees, grass, and grain; less erosion; more machines; improved farming practices; and a growing industry. By *G. H. Aull*, head, Department of Agricultural Economics and Rural Sociology, The Clemson Agricultural College, Clemson, S. C.

A NEW LANDSCAPE is shaping up in the part of the United States that extends south of Kentucky and Virginia and west to Arkansas and Louisiana and that once produced nearly all the cotton grown in this country.

Many persons call this the "Cotton South." Actually, however, there has never been a strictly "Cotton South," although it is true that cotton was the major source of cash revenue on most farms in the section. Much of the time, however, cash farm income was a minor part in total farm family living.

Cotton now has a less important place (particularly in the old cotton States). It may not be amiss therefore to point out that the maximum production of cotton in this country before 1860 had reached only about 4 million bales; even at the low yields then prevalent that would have required no more than 13.5 million acres, or less than one-fourth of the "improved land" then in farms in the South. Production dropped to fewer than 300 thousand bales in 1864, and not until 1870 did cotton production attain its former level. By that time the Bureau of the Census had begun to report acreages of the principal crops, and a total of 9 million acres was shown for "cotton harvested." The figure indicates that not more than 15 percent of the South's cropland was devoted to cotton in 1870. Ten years later this percentage had risen to 20, but even so about one-half of the Southern States that year reported more acres in corn than in cotton.

The largest acreage ever planted to cotton in the entire United States was a little more than 47 million acres in 1926. Even if all of this had been in the "Cotton South" and Oklahoma and Texas, it would have occupied less than a third of the region's improved land in farms and only one-sixth of its total farm acreage. (By contrast, a corn crop of 70 million acres is not unusual in the North Central States, where total cropland amounts to fewer than 200 million acres and total land in farms is fewer than 400 million acres.) In no Southern State has cotton ever occupied as much as a fourth of the land in farms. Even in its heyday, cotton provided the principal source of income on hardly more than one-half the farms in the South.

This is not to detract from the long-time, well-established economic importance of cotton farms in the South or the overall significance of the crop in the southern economy. It is simply to point out that from the beginning the designation "Cotton South" has been somewhat of a misnomer—especially when it was called "one crop Cotton South."

Many of the various types of livestock in the South were present in larger numbers before 1860 than since. For example, there were in the Southern States in 1860 approximately 3 million milk cows, 7 million other cattle, 5 million sheep, and 16 million swine. These numbers represented about one-fourth of the Nation's total of milk cows and sheep and nearly one-half of its other cattle and swine. The South in the intervening years has lost in livestock numbers relative to the Nation, and although a reverse trend has developed in recent years, the region has not since regained its former position in any major category of livestock.

A recognition of these facts may help one understand the emerging landscape, in which cotton is taking a less significant place (at least insofar as agriculture is concerned) and livestock is once again on the increase.

TO GET A CLEARER PICTURE of changes that are taking place, one needs to look at things as they were not 100 years ago but, say, in 1940, when more than one-half of all agricultural workers in the United States were "employed" on southern farms and were trying to make a living on one-third of the Nation's agricultural land, from which came only one-fourth the value of all farm products sold.

The average farmworker in the South then had access to fewer than 25 acres of cropland and 11 acres of pasture. Most of the cropland, moreover, was not very fertile and was highly eroded. The pasture was hardly more than an exercise lot for wornout milk cows.

In the Southern Economic Journal for April 1947, I wrote: "While the States in the western part of the United States have insisted on an average investment of approximately 12 thousand dollars as a prerequisite to the operation of a farm, we in the South have been content to do business with something less than one-third as much. On a per-worker basis, we have provided a farm job on a capital outlay of little more than 2,500 dollars. The average for the United States is approximately 5 thousand dollars, and industry asks at least 10 thousand dollars. . . . If the application of one 'dose' of manpower to each 2,500 dollars' worth of capital should result even in a gross return of 20 percent, the total available for distribution to both capital and labor (in southern agriculture) is only 5 hundred dollars, at least 1 hundred dollars of which must be classified as interest."

In the South in 1940 there were about 4.3 million farmworkers. To have provided each of them with an amount of capital proportionate to the capital of the average farmworker in the United States would have called for additional investments of something more than 10 billion dollars in agriculture in the South—an amount equal to that reported in 1940 and 50 percent more than the total of all the farm mortgage loans then outstanding in the United States. To put it another way: If the capital available in southern agriculture had been apportioned to its farmworkers at the same rate as to all the farmworkers in the United States, the total would have been exhausted by the time one-half of them had received their share and about 2 million of them would have been left without any capital whatsoever.

About 40 percent of the people in the South in 1940 were farmers, one-half of the farmers were tenants, and one-third of the tenants were sharecroppers. There was 1 tractor to each 11 farms and 1 truck to each 10. Only about 1 farm in 6 was receiving central-station electric service, and 1 in 8 had a telephone.

The time was ripe for change, and it was not long in coming. Spurred on by the upsurge of activity in the wake of the Second World War, the South has undergone an economic and social revolution. Viewing the landscape that has emerged since 1940, we get several definite impressions of what seems to be taking shape. They portend a brighter future for the region and its people.

THE FIRST of these impressions is so abstract as to defy measurement. It is found in the sometimes subconscious attitude of the rank-and-file southerner. It reveals itself in a contagious conviction that the South is once again on the move and that it has within itself the resources essential to its development. It spells an end to an attitude many held following the Reconstruction Era in the second half of the 19th century. Without this change in attitude, the other changes that are taking place might well be without substance and permanence.

Changes are evident in all areas of the economy and in the institutions, customs, and habits of the people, but the results are nowhere more apparent than in the ownership and use of land.

During the 15 years following 1940, for example, the total number of farms in the South declined nearly one-fourth, but the number operated by full and part owners increased more than 10 percent and the number operated by tenants decreased more than 50 percent. By contrast, the total number of farms in the United States during the same period declined 20 percent, the number of farm owners declined slightly, and the number of farm tenants dropped 50 percent. The percentage of tenancy meanwhile dropped from 48 to 29 in the South and from 38 to 24 in the country as a whole. In 1954, however, 45 percent of the Nation's farm owners and 59 percent of the Nation's farm tenants were in the South.

A picture of changes in the use of land is given in a special report based on the 1954 Census of Agriculture. For purposes of comparison, the report divides the South into four farm pro-

duction regions and comments on each:

"*Appalachian:* Land in farms has dropped from a high of 96 million acres in 1900 to 76 million acres in 1954. . . . Cropland harvested has fluctuated between a high of 25 million acres and a low of 19 million in 1954.

"*Southeastern States:* Land in farms reached a peak in 1950 largely because large grazing areas in Florida have been included as land in farms in recent years. Cropland harvested has declined by 8 million acres from a peak of 24 million acres in 1920.

"*Mississippi Delta:* The highest acreage of 51 million acres of land in farms was reported in 1950. . . . Cropland harvested has declined 2.5 million acres from the peak in 1940.

"*Southern Plains:* A fivefold increase in land in farms during the last 75 years characterizes this region. Pronounced fluctuations in the acreage of agricultural land are explained in part by difficulties in applying definitions of open woodland pasture in the areas of brush infestation in Texas. Cropland harvested has declined about 11 million acres from the peak of 46 million acres reached in 1930."

The rise in the number of ponds and reservoirs in the South has been spectacular. There were few farm ponds in 1945; in 1955 there were about 1 million—an average of two ponds for each five farms.

The outstanding change is the decline in cotton acreage—particularly in the Southeast. Between 1930 and 1954, the percentage of farmers growing cotton there dropped from about 60 to almost 30, and the cotton acreage harvested fell from about 16 million acres to 6 million. There was a further decline in harvested acres in 1957, when the figure for the Southeast was the lowest since about 1880. Yields increased to such an extent, however, that production has been maintained at a fairly constant level.

The number of commercial farms declined by 200 thousand, or 13 percent, between 1950 and 1954. The number of farms that had a total value of sales exceeding 25 thousand dollars increased 25 percent; the number of farms that had a value of sales of 10 thousand to 25 thousand dollars increased 12 percent; and the number of farms with sales of 5 thousand to 10 thousand dollars increased 14 percent. Commercial farms reporting sales under 1,200 dollars declined 25 percent from more than 1 million to fewer than 800 thousand.

The result was that the proportion of southern farms reporting sales of 5 thousand dollars or more increased from 1 in 10 to 1 in 8 and commercial farms with sales of less than 1,200 dollars dropped from 1 in 5 to 1 in 7. Even so, twice as many farmers in the United States as in the South had sales above 5 thousand dollars and only three-fourths as many reported sales under 1,200 dollars. Part-time and residential farms are relatively more numerous in the South, and a significantly higher proportion of southern farmers report nonfarm income exceeding the value of farm products sold—one-third in the South, compared to one-fourth in the rest of the country.

Farms are growing larger, but figures as to the number of acres in the average farm are misleading. In the South each sharecropper unit is enumerated in the census as a separate farm, although the cropper furnishes only his labor and all managerial decisions are the landlord's. A change from a sharecropper status to a wage status therefore considerably affects the statistical number and the average size of farms (also the percentage of tenancy) but has no material effect on the actual farm situation. There is the further difficulty of averaging the acreage in large commercial farms with the acreages in small, part-time and residential units. In South Carolina, for example, the average farm has changed little in size in a long time, but the large farms are getting larger and the small farms are getting smaller. This trend will likely continue.

THE SOUTH is fast becoming a land of trees and grass and grain. With only about a third of the Nation's total land area and less than one-third of its commercial forest land, the South accounts for more than one-half of the Nation's total net annual timber growth and only slightly less than one-half of the net annual timber cut of the country. For the first time in recent history, the annual growth of timber in the South exceeds the annual cut—and by a comfortable margin.

Much of the South's timberland is in farms. Timber and timber products (including naval stores) account for an increasingly larger proportion of farm income. More than half of all farm forest products sold in 1954 came from southern farms.

The South also leads in forest fire protection. Of 21 States reporting expenditures in excess of 500 thousand dollars for control of forest fires in 1956, 11 are Southern States. They provided nearly 40 percent of all State and local support for forest fire control in the entire country.

The figures on consumption of forest products in the South underscore the need for more attention to timber growth and forest fire protection. Nearly 100 pulp and paper mills in the South supply 40 percent of all paper sold in this country. Southern newsprint production in 1957 was at the rate of 500 thousand tons a year, and this is expected to increase threefold by 1975. The South produces more than half of the woodpulp manufactured in the United States.

The basis for this industry is the fast-growing southern pine.

THE SOUTH'S SHARE of the Nation's grassland also grows larger year by year. Opportunities for year-round grazing and emphasis on a "blanket of green" may cause this trend to continue. Cropland used only for pasture increased nearly 50 percent in the South in 1944–1954, but only 33 percent in the rest of the country. Other farm pasture increased nearly 10 percent here but lost ground elsewhere.

Acreage figures, however, do not tell the real story. Grass, a troublesome and costly enemy in cotton farming, is now encouraged, improved, and even fertilized to produce more milk, more pork, and more beef per acre and per man-hour of labor. One result is that for 10 years the number of farms depending primarily on dairy and other livestock has been increasing at the rate of about 2 thousand a year in the South but has been declining at the rate of 14 thousand a year in the rest of the country.

Along with more and better grasses, the South has made rapid strides in the protection of its soils against winter erosion through the use of cover crops. The acreage of such crops has increased fourfold since the Second World War. The economic implications of these changes are many and foretell the preservation of millions of additional acres against the ravages of winter and the conservation and enrichment of these acres for larger production of more commodities and at lower cost.

Some of these changes in land use are the natural result of a shift from mule to tractor power. Others are evidence of increased industrial employment opportunities, which have relieved much of the pressure of population on the land and have opened up new markets for a variety of farm products.

An overabundant supply of labor and also the absence of nonagricultural employment opportunities retarded the mechanization of agriculture over a large part of the South before the war. Since that time, no change in American agriculture has been more spectacular than the increase in the number of tractors and tractor-drawn equipment in the Southern States. Much of this was made possible by the withdrawal of large numbers of underemployed farm laborers into the military services and into nonfarm jobs.

The South as a whole in 1940 had only a quarter million farm tractors. Most of them were in Oklahoma and Texas. The number was 16 percent of the national total. It was only one-half the number reported in the Corn Belt, about the same as the number reported on the Great Plains, and only slightly more than reported in the three Lake States. By 1954, however, the number of tractors in the South had increased fivefold to 1,290,000—more than in the Corn Belt and more than in the Lake States and the Great Plains combined.

The widespread adoption of improved farming practices and the use of machines have greatly boosted yields per acre and per animal unit. Cotton yields which before 1935 were seldom as high as 200 pounds of lint an acre have not been below 200 pounds during any year since that time. The average was 300 pounds in 1946–1955, and more than 400 pounds an acre in 1956–1957.

No other section of the country has shown a more remarkable improvement in yields of small grain than the South in the same period.

On the basis of figures on gross farm production in the various parts of the United States and the number of farmworkers in each, the average production per worker in the South is only about two-thirds the average for the United States (including the South) and less than one-half the average for four of the six major sections outside the South.

These differences cannot be explained wholly on the basis of differences in the skills of individual workmen or in their use of particular items of equipment. They more likely spring from the fact that southern agriculture in the past has provided fewer productive hours of employment than has the agriculture in other regions.

Improvement in this regard has been constant, and the gap is rapidly becoming smaller. The problem is complicated by the fact that for every young man and woman needed to replace the adult members of southern farm families who die or retire, more than two farm boys and girls are available. Unless new nonfarm jobs can be made available to the sons and daughters of southern farmers at a rate at least equal to that for farm jobs, therefore, the resources on southern farms will continue to be divided among too many workers and the output per worker will continue lower than otherwise would be the case.

THE SOUTH is under strong compulsion to maintain and increase the gains it has made.

If nonagricultural employment in the region can be maintained at a high level, large numbers of southern-born farm boys and girls will not have to migrate to other areas (at great cost to themselves and their parents) nor be forced to stay in an agriculture that has too many underemployed persons. Southern industrialists have predicted the establishment of more than 3 thousand large industries in the region before 1965. About 300 of them will manufacture products not yet developed. Thousands of smaller plants and the trades and professions will need many workers. On the basis of the previous rate of change, it has been figured that there will be about 1.5 million fewer agricultural workers in the South by 1960 than in 1940—a drop of 75 thousand a year. An additional 1 million (50 thousand a year) meanwhile will have reached maturity on southern farms. They would not be enough, however, to provide the manpower for the new nonfarm jobs that may be available in the South by 1960. The number of employees in southern manufacturing plants increased by more than 1.5 million in the 15 years following 1939. At that rate, the number of industrial workers in southern establishments would reach nearly 6.5 million by 1969—3.3 million more than reported in 1954. Employment in southern manufacturing plants increased 20 percent between 1947 and 1954, payrolls increased 82 percent, and value added by manufacture increased 64 percent. The rate of gain in each instance was well above that for the area outside the South.

THE DEVELOPMENT of southern industry—preferably in rural areas—will undoubtedly leave the southern landscape with still fewer farms, but they will be better farms and will require more highly skilled operators. They will utilize still more machinery, produce an even larger volume of products, and require yet more supplies and services, but—being more productive and having larger market outlets—they will be in a better position to pay for them. Thus, while the products of southern agriculture flow in a larger stream from the hands of fewer but more advantaged workers, they will flow through the hands of more processors, refiners, and distributors into the hands of more consumers—all of whom will require the services of more people in the professions.

All of these things imply an increase in total employment in the South and a better distribution of labor and more income per worker.

That these changes are desirable and necessary is demonstrated in the production of cotton, in which the substitution of machine for handpicking on even one-half of the acreage normally planted would save approximately 100 million man-days of labor, the equivalent of 300 thousand men for a year or 5 times that number during the cotton-picking season.

Technological advances such as this and the current birth rate give the South a responsibility to find the equivalent of about 8 million new nonfarm jobs within the next 20 years. That is by no means an impossible task.

State and local governments in the South, ever alert to the need for balancing agriculture with industry, have been giving impetus to this change by modernizing their tax laws, improving their system of transportation, developing their facilities for export trade, and expanding their educational opportunities. In nearly every Southern State and in most of the counties there are development boards, which have a firm resolve to bring about further changes.

The general farming and tobacco region.

In this middle section of the country, which has many variations in land, methods, and utilization of labor, further industrial growth is needed to provide employment for farm people who are not now fully employed on farms. The same result could be obtained if some of them were to move to other sections, but then some market advantage to the region would be lost. By *W. Herbert Brown*, agricultural economist, Farm Economics Research Division.

THE GENERAL FARMING AND TOBACCO region is one of the most variable regions in the United States. Farms vary greatly in land use, size, degree of mechanization, and intensity of production.

This region centers around the middle Appalachian Mountains and the Ozark uplift of southern Illinois and Missouri. The southern boundary follows closely the line of 200 frost-free days. The northwestern boundary follows the foothills of the Appalachian Mountains, the northern edge of the rough topography along the Ohio River, and the Ozark uplift. On the northeast, the region extends to the milksheds of Baltimore, Washington, D. C., and Pittsburgh.

Land in the region is used for feed grains, tobacco, hay, pasture, lumber, and other forest products. A large proportion of the feed grains and roughage are fed within the region to beef cattle, dairy cows, and hogs.

The farms used to be less specialized than they are today. The continuing shift of grain production to the Corn Belt and regions farther west has led a few farmers to shift to production of fluid milk and others to shift to hogs and beef cattle. Significant numbers of fairly specialized types of commercial farms exist in most parts of the region. They include cash grain, dairy, poultry, livestock (other than dairy and poultry), and tobacco.

Dairying predominates in south-central Missouri. Tobacco farms predominate in central Kentucky, south-central Virginia, and central and eastern North Carolina. In other parts of the region, no single type of farming accounts for a majority of the commercial farms. General farms (those with no source of income accounting for more than 50 percent of gross sales) are important in most parts of the region, but they seldom account for a majority of the types of farms in a given area.

Most of the types of farming in this region also exist in adjoining regions. The Corn Belt is most like it in distribution of agricultural products sold. Both regions produce large quantities of feed grains, hogs, and beef cattle and some dairy products. The patterns of land use and the intensity of production vary greatly between the two regions.

Commercial farms in the general farming and tobacco region have about 30 percent of the farmland in cropland, 30 percent in pasture, and 40 percent in woodland. Commercial farms in the Corn Belt have about 70 percent of the land in cropland, 20 percent in pasture, and 10 percent in woodland. About 35 and 45 percent of the cropland, respectively, is used for corn in the general farming and tobacco region and the Corn Belt.

Commercial farmers in this region also use a smaller part of the cropland for oats and soybeans, but they use a higher proportion for hay than those in the Corn Belt. These commercial farms in the general farming and tobacco region in 1954 sold 30 dollars' worth of farm products per acre of land farmed, compared with 45 dollars per acre on Corn Belt farms. Topography is probably the chief factor in this difference in output per acre. Yields per acre are only slightly lower in this region than in the Corn Belt, but much of the farmland here is in less intensive uses, such as pasture and woodland.

Several factors contribute to the variety of the agriculture in this region. The soils vary from heavy clays to light, sandy soils, but corn, small grains, hay, and pasture grow well in most parts. Varieties suited to the local area have to be chosen, however. Alfalfa does well on well-drained, medium to heavy soils. Ladino, alsike, and red clover have a somewhat wider range in soil and moisture conditions. Lespedeza is well adapted to the lighter soils in the southern part. Temperature and rainfall make this region one of the best pasture regions in the country. The growing season is longer than in the dairy region, yet the summer temperatures are not too high for grass production as is the case farther south. In the southern part of the region, grazing is possible nearly the year round. Rainfall is reasonably well distributed through the year, but droughts in late summer often cut pasture production. Irish potatoes are grown on the light, sandy soils in a few areas, such as the Cumberland Plateau of Tennessee. Sweetpotatoes also are grown on the lighter soils in other locations, but neither Irish nor sweetpotatoes are major crops in the region.

Tobacco is raised in over half the region, but the production of specific types is highly localized.

Variety, soil, climate, cultural practices, and method of curing determine the type of tobacco produced in a given area. When the seed is taken from one area to another, the quality is changed. Expansion of the burley tobacco area in Kentucky and Tennessee during the 1920's was exceptional. Sometimes a physical feature forms a boundary between areas that produce different types of tobacco. In other instances, there is an overlapping between two areas in which two types of tobacco are grown. In only a few producing areas of the United States is more than one type of tobacco grown. Two such areas are the Miami district of Ohio and the Connecticut Valley.

Factors that determine quality and consumer preference determine the geography of tobacco production. Production has developed in areas to which buyers have gone to get the types of tobacco they need to meet demand of the consumers. Competition between areas is limited by the extent to which one type of tobacco can be substituted for another. The acreage of tobacco in a few counties in central Virginia that produce Virginia sun-cured, type 37, declined by 80 percent in 1920–1940 with the shift away from chewing tobacco and snuff. The acreage of cigar-binder tobacco in the Connecticut Valley declined by 60 percent in 1950–1957. Homogenized binders made from leaf scraps are replacing the leaf binders, and a shift in the location of production could occur if former users of leaf scrap tobacco buy leaf tobacco elsewhere to replace the scraps.

Price relationships generally have been such that any of these crops and associated livestock enterprises may be grown economically. Price relationships have changed from time to time, however, and have caused some shifting from one enterprise to another. Relatively high beef prices helped to stimulate the increase in beef cattle numbers in this region immediately following the Second World War. When several crops grow well in a region and the economic advantages of one over another are not large, local factors or personal preference determine the system of farming.

Topography often tips the balance in favor of one type of farming or another. Topography varies from generally level to very steep; rolling to hilly slopes predominate. Farms with relatively smoother topography are in the river valleys and a few other areas, like the central basin of Tennessee and the Bluegrass area of central Kentucky.

Farmers who have this kind of land have a wide choice in the type of farming followed. They may choose a cash-grain farm system and devote much of the land to row crops, grass, or corn.

There was a time when legumes were believed to be necessary in the cropping system, but it has been found that yields of corn can be maintained year after year on bottom land by using commercial fertilizer. Large supplies of nitrogen fertilizer at relatively low prices have stimulated this practice since the war.

When tracts of relatively smooth land are large enough to permit sizable fields, machinery can be used here just as well as in the Corn Belt and regions farther west. There is no reason why farmers on this kind of land cannot compete with farmers in the Corn Belt. Probably they will need to use more commercial fertilizer, but they have an advantage in producing for local markets in the area.

A commoner situation is the farm that has some level land but most of it is rolling or steep. The danger of erosion limits the extent of row crops. As there are no major cash markets for roughage in the region, the production of this land must be marketed through beef or dairy cattle. Farms with a combination of some bottom land and some upland frequently sell both grain and livestock or livestock products. The farmer needs more land to make a satisfactory income than the farmer whose land is all relatively level, because the upland must be used for less intensive crops. Farms with both bottom and steep land are scattered over much of the region, but they are common in areas adjacent to the areas of relatively level farmland and along the smaller rivers.

A farmer with moderately rolling or hilly land can farm much the same as a farmer with a combination of bottom and steep land, but the crop rotation will differ in that no land can be kept in row crops all the time, although row crops can be grown a small percentage of the time on the upland. Grain production on these farms supplies a high yield of concentrate feed. As the land becomes steeper, the farmer becomes more restricted as to practical alternative uses of the land.

Farms with a high proportion of hilly and steep land have shifted from corn and small grain to hay and pasture. Mechanization has given the farmer on the smooth land an advantage in grain production. Small fields and steep, irregular slopes are not well adapted to mechanization. Also, production of hay and pasture is better understood now than formerly.

The value of fertilizer and lime in roughage and pasture production has been known for a long time, but adoption of these practices has been slow. The Agricultural Conservation Program, the Soil Conservation Service program, and the unit test-demonstration farms of the Tennessee Valley Authority have stimulated the use of phosphate and lime on hay and pasture. The development of suitable harvesting machinery and the use of grass silage have made it easier to handle roughage. The large increase in farm wage rates relative to machinery since 1940 also has encouraged the shift from labor-intensive to labor-extensive systems of crop production. Beef cattle and sheep are well suited to farms with a high proportion of hilly and steep land and incomes may be relatively good if the farms are large enough.

Availability of markets also influences the type of farming in this region. The production of large quantities of roughage, the long grazing season, and the moderate quantities of feed grains produced make the region well suited to dairy production. The production of fluid milk, however, is limited by the markets available within the region. St. Louis is the only city in the region large enough to provide a market for large quantities of fluid milk. Some dairy production is scattered over most of the region to supply the needs of local markets. Bulk and perishability prevent shipment of fluid milk to larger cities to the north and east. Price relations before the war gave a decided advantage to production of fluid milk. The high cost of labor and high prices for beef and hogs have reduced this advantage, however. Some milk is produced for manufacturing purposes, but ordinarily there is greater advantage in other types of livestock farming. Beef, pork, and poultry products are needed for local markets. They could be shipped also to centers in the north and east.

The location of consuming centers influences the location of tobacco production very little. As tobacco is nonperishable and has a high value per pound, the small advantage gained by producing near consumer centers is offset by the demand for specific qualities of tobacco.

Size of farm also influences the type of farming followed. Small farms tend to have more intensive enterprises than larger farms on the same kind of land and location with respect to markets. Beef and sheep production usually give good returns per hour of labor spent, but a larger acreage of land is needed to utilize fully the time of the operator and his family and provide a good income to the farm family. Small dairy herds producing milk or cream for manufacturing often are better suited to small farms than sheep or beef cattle. The need for more intensive crops leads many operators of small farms to plant corn on steep slopes oftener than is consistent with good conservation. Tobacco fills an important place on small farms in areas where it is grown. It utilizes labor that could not be used

445509°—58——11

otherwise on these farms. Even so, many tobacco farms are too small to provide a good family income.

Small farms are especially numerous in the upland areas of Kentucky, Tennessee, Virginia, and West Virginia. Nearly half the commercial farms in this area in 1954 had fewer than 20 acres of harvested cropland. Three-fourths had less than 2,500 dollars of gross value of product; this means that the net farm income was probably less than 1,200 or 1,500 dollars. Improved practices, such as legumes, fertilizer, and lime, will add 200 to 400 dollars to the net farm income on farms in this size range, but the returns will still be low compared with industry and farms in many other areas.

Mechanization has been an important factor leading to larger farms. With the use of tractors, cornpickers, and combines, two-thirds of the labor used on corn and small grain can be eliminated. This means that the farm labor force can handle more crops, and farm operators are buying or renting more land to keep the farm labor force fully occupied. The average size of commercial farms increased from 3 to 10 percent in most parts of the region from 1949 to 1954.

Mechanization has been slower here than in the Corn Belt and regions farther west. At least a third of the farmers in the Appalachian Highland and the Cumberland Plateau use only horses for power. Small farms, rough topography, and lack of capital and suitable machines have retarded mechanization. Since 1940, however, several factors have encouraged mechanization: Higher farm incomes during and after the war helped to provide capital to purchase machinery; machines better suited to small fields have been developed; and farm wage rates went up to about 4 times the 1937 1941 level, while prices of farm machinery only doubled.

Farms that were large enough to need hired labor could be operated more economically with machinery than with hired labor at the higher wage rates. This means that industrial development pulled labor away from farms; mechanization—as is often said—did not force labor off farms. Other farms in the region, particularly the smaller ones, have always had a labor surplus or a labor force that was employed at a low rate of return.

Industry developed first along the Ohio River and in the larger cities that were readily accessible and had good water supplies. Industry since 1940 has spread to the smaller cities and has drawn labor from the hills around the cities. Improved transportation has made it possible for farm people to commute 30 or 40 miles a day to work in industry.

About 45 percent of the farms in the region in 1954 were part-time and residential farms. Farms once operated as full-time farms are now part-time farms. Many farms in the mountains, however, never were commercial farms in the sense that they produced much for sale.

A different situation exists in the coal mining areas of West Virginia and Kentucky. Employment in mining is declining, and other industries are not developing to take its place. These areas lack adequate transportation, and the main resources are labor and coal.

THE ROLE OF LAND in the agriculture of the general farming and tobacco region is exemplified by a typical livestock farm of 160 acres located in the Appalachian foothills of Ohio. Forty-four acres of the 160 acres in this farm are in cropland, 60 acres are in permanent pasture, and 56 acres are in woodland. The livestock consists of 12 beef cows, a brood sow, and 100 hens. Beef calves are kept over winter, fed out the next year, and sold as fat cattle.

The cropland part of the farm receives more attention than either the pasture or woodland. Corn and wheat are fertilized at about the recommended levels. The hay crop gets only lime. Corn yields 60 bushels an acre, wheat 20 bushels, and hay 2 tons. The yields of corn and wheat are about as high as yields in the Corn Belt. Permanent pasture, however, receives no treatment except clipping. Pasture production is low; it could be doubled by application of lime and phosphate. The woodland adds little to the cash income of the farm. The farm woodland once supplied fuel for farm use, but the importance of this function has declined with a shift toward coal and oil. Lumber for farm building is supplied by the farm woodlot.

The use of land accounts for only about 13 percent of the total inputs on this farm. Labor accounts for 30 percent. The rest goes for purchased items and the use of working capital. Labor has declined in relative importance in farm inputs, while purchased items and use of working capital have increased. The relative importance of land and buildings has not changed greatly.

The investment in land and buildings, machinery, and livestock amounts to about 21 thousand dollars—or 17,500 dollars per full-time worker on the farm. Sixty percent of the investment is in land and buildings, and the rest is divided equally between equipment and livestock. The investment in equipment per acre of cropland harvested is 97 dollars, compared with 40 dollars on cash-grain farms in east-central Illinois. The small acreage of harvested cropland accounts for the high investment in machinery and equipment per acre.

The gross farm income on a farm of this type and size is 4,900 dollars a year at 1950–1954 prices, or 3,060 dollars per 100 acres farmed. If interest is charged at 5 percent for the use of real estate and working capital, 1,420 dollars is left as a return to the operator and his family for their labor and management. Sixty-eight percent of the operators own all the land they farm, and 24 percent own a part of it. Therefore, very little of the income must be shared with landlords.

The net farm income on this typical farm can be improved by using some of the pastureland for crops and improving the remaining permanent pasture. A farm of this size, operated with modern machinery, however, is not large enough to permit the operator to utilize his time efficiently and to allow him to earn an income that will compete with off-farm employment. The maximum income on this farm at its present size could be obtained if it were operated as a part-time farm and the operator worked in industry. For this reason, some farm operators in the area have been adding to their farms, while others have started working off the farm.

THE ROLE OF LAND is somewhat different on commercial family-operated, tobacco-livestock farms in the Bluegrass area of Kentucky. Sixty percent of the gross farm income comes from tobacco, but tobacco occupies only 3 percent of all land in the farm and 14 percent of the cropland. Production of tobacco is becoming concentrated on an even smaller acreage of land.

The acreage of tobacco per farm dropped from 5.3 in 1937–1941 to 4.2 in 1954–1956. The yield per acre increased from 995 to 1,551 pounds during the same period, which was more than enough to offset the smaller acreage. Higher yielding strains of tobacco and more fertilizer per acre are largely responsible for the increase in yield. Although the production of tobacco is concentrated on a smaller acreage within the farm unit, the number of farms raising tobacco has not declined. This results partly from acreage allotments on tobacco. Acreage reductions have been somewhat greater in the major producing counties than in the outlying counties, where acreages per farm are smaller. The acreage per farm on farms with small allotments cannot legally be reduced below a specified minimum. Thus reductions must be larger on farms with larger acreages in order to bring down the total acreage.

Corn, small grain, and hay are grown mainly as feed for hogs, sheep, cattle, and workstock. Feed crops and livestock provide employment for labor and other resources when not used for production of tobacco.

The use of land accounts for 25 percent of the total inputs on the farm. The relative importance of land has not changed in the last 20 years. The proportion of total inputs, however, accounted for by labor declined from 53 percent in 1937–1941 to 42 percent in 1956. This decline in the relative importance of labor is less than on most crop and crop-livestock farms in the United States. Mechanization has been very slow on farms of this type. Only about 50 percent of the farms had tractors in 1956. Tobacco as it is now produced does not lend itself to mechanization. About 375 hours of man-labor are used per acre on tobacco.

Investment in machinery and equipment in 1954–1956 was 68 dollars an acre of cropland on tobacco-livestock farms, compared with 97 dollars an acre on livestock farms in southeastern Ohio and 40 dollars on cash-grain farms in east-central Illinois. The machinery inventory on tobacco-livestock farms is relatively low, but the investment per acre is moderately high because only 30 acres of cropland are harvested.

The investment in livestock, machinery and equipment, and land and buildings in 1954–1956 amounted to 22,630 dollars. Eighty-four percent of the investment was in land and buildings, 9 percent in machinery and equipment, and 7 percent in livestock.

Net farm income on a tobacco-livestock farm of 115 acres in 1954–1956 was 3,160 dollars a year. The return to the operator and family for labor and management was 2,340 dollars, or 82 cents an hour. Fifty-six percent of the farms are fully owned, and 17 percent are partly owned by the operator.

Tobacco farms in the Coastal Plain of North Carolina, where flue-cured tobacco is produced, differ significantly from those of the Bluegrass area of Kentucky. Type 12 tobacco is produced in the eastern part of the area, where the

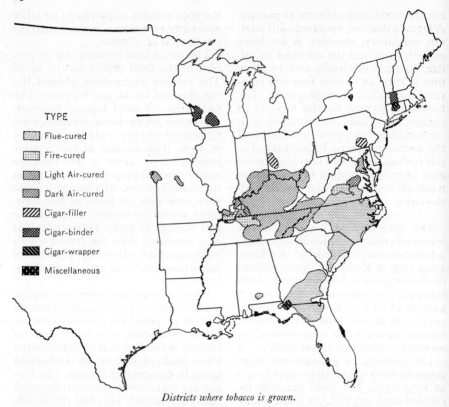

TYPE

- ▨ Flue-cured
- ▨ Fire-cured
- ▨ Light Air-cured
- ▨ Dark Air-cured
- ▨ Cigar-filler
- ▨ Cigar-binder
- ▨ Cigar-wrapper
- ▨ Miscellaneous

Districts where tobacco is grown.

soils are chiefly sandy loam. Type 11, a tobacco with heavier body and darker color, is produced in the western part of the area, where the soils are red clay loam or gray sandy loam. This area is located on the edge of the Cotton Belt, and cotton is often combined with tobacco in the farming system.

The average commercial family-operated tobacco-cotton farm in the area had 100 acres of total land farmed in 1954–1956. Crops were harvested from 40 acres. Tobacco occupied about 18 percent of the cropland acreage but accounted for 70 percent of the farm income. Cotton used 13 percent of the cropland and contributed 8 percent to the farm income. Corn and hay crops used a larger proportion of the land area, but these crops with the livestock enterprises add little to the gross farm income. Livestock are kept primarily for home use.

Even though the yield of corn has increased by 70 percent since 1940–1944, the average yield of 28 bushels an acre is low compared with yields in the Corn Belt. The yield of hay since 1940, has averaged about 1 ton an acre, compared with 1.5 to 2 tons in the Kentucky Bluegrass area and the Corn Belt. The soils, which are mainly sandy loam and sandy clay loam, are less well suited to hay and pasture grasses than the Kentucky soils. They are low in organic matter.

Much more labor is used on these farms than on the tobacco-livestock farms in central Kentucky or the livestock farms in southeastern Ohio. About 500 hours of labor are used in producing an acre of flue-cured tobacco, compared with 375 hours for burley tobacco. The acreage of tobacco on farms in the Coastal Plains is almost double the acreage in the Kentucky area. In addition, 120 hours per acre are used on cotton.

Mechanization has proceeded somewhat more rapidly than in the Kentucky area. Nearly 70 percent of the tobacco-cotton farms had tractors in 1956, compared with none in 1940. Investment in machinery amounted to about 65 dollars an acre in 1954–1956.

The total investment in land and buildings, livestock, and machinery and equipment amounts to 20,400 dollars, or 7 thousand dollars a worker. Land and buildings account for 84 percent of the investment; 13 percent is in machinery and equipment; and 3 percent is in livestock. Land was valued at 172 dollars an acre.

Because of the large amount of labor used on these farms and the higher expenditures for fertilizer, pesticides, and fuel for curing tobacco, land accounts for only about 14 percent of the inputs, compared with 25 percent on the tobacco-livestock farms in central Kentucky. Both land and labor have declined since 1940 relative to purchased goods and interest on working capital. The shift from wood to oil for fuel in curing tobacco reduced the amount of labor, but it also increased the amount of goods purchased.

Land supplies 14 percent of the total input on these farms and labor supplies 49 percent. The remaining 37 percent is from purchased goods and interest on capital.

Gross farm income is 40 percent higher than on the Kentucky tobacco-livestock farm, but net farm income is only slightly higher. The Coastal Plains farms have higher expenses for labor, fertilizer, pesticides, and fuel for curing tobacco.

The net farm income of an owner-operated tobacco-cotton farm was 3,315 dollars in 1954–1956. The operator and his family received 2,175 dollars, or 74 cents an hour, for labor and management after allowing for interest and investment. A tenant who rented on a crop-share basis received 1,735 dollars, after giving a third of the crop production as rent. Returns were 59 cents an hour, or about the same as the rates for hired labor during the same period. A cropper who rented on a 50–50 basis received about 53 cents an hour.

FUTURE DEVELOPMENTS in the general farming and tobacco region depend on demand for agricultural products, industrial development in the region, and new technology. The full impact of technological developments had not been felt in 1958. With continued industrialization in the more accessible parts of the region and at least moderately good demand for agricultural products, present trends may be expected to continue.

Farms will become larger as more machinery is purchased and more land is needed to utilize fully the farm labor force. As the smaller models of many machines can handle more work than is available on many farms in the region, more land is needed for their efficient use.

The trend toward grassland farming on the hilly and steep land very likely will continue as long as the demand for beef and dairy products continues to be good.

Adjustments in farm organization and practices could proceed faster if farmers had more capital. Frequently adjustments and new practices are very profitable, but farmers do not make the changes because they do not have the necessary capital. More favorable price-cost relationships would make these adjustments more profitable and also would provide additional capital. More credit of the type suited to small farms in a low-income area offers another opportunity to supply needed capital.

Further industrial growth is needed in the region to provide employment for farm people who are not now fully employed on farms. The same result could be obtained if some of these farm people were to move to other regions of the country, but some market advantage to the region would be lost.

Land and problems in the wheat regions.

Wheat can be grown in many sections of the United States. About one farmer in five and one crop acre in five grow wheat for sale and for other purposes. Many wheat producers are "suitcase farmers" and men with jobs in cities because wheat needs little attention between seeding and harvesting. The story of wheat, as told here, parallels the story—and the problems—of American agriculture. By *Warren R. Bailey,* Farm Economics Research Division.

ABOUT ONE CROP ACRE in five in the United States is devoted to the production of wheat, and about one farmer in five grows wheat as a commercial crop. For the crop harvested in 1956, about 60 million acres were seeded.

Wheat was a pioneer crop that accompanied land settlement as it progressed westward from the Atlantic seaboard. As each new area became a dependable source of wheat, older producing areas shifted some land to other crops, but some wheat was produced. It is still the most important crop in areas that were settled last, particularly in the Great Plains and the Pacific Northwest. In general, those are the drier areas of arable farming, and farmers there grow wheat not because the lands are especially well suited to wheat but because wheat produces more grain and more income than any other crop thus far known in these areas. Except in the Palouse in Washington, yields of wheat are lower in these areas than almost anywhere else east of the Mississippi River and north of the Ohio. The Palouse country, with its cool, rainy winters and its hot, dry summers, is well adapted to production of winter wheat.

In the Southern Plains, wheat makes good use of the moderate winters and the limited rainfall. In the Northern Plains, spring wheat makes use of the short summer growing season during which most of the precipitation falls.

Wheat was grown on about 6 million acres (which was 8 percent of the national acreage) in the Pacific Northwest in 1956; about 28 million acres (45 percent) in the central and southern Great Plains; 17 million acres (28 percent) in the Northern Plains; and about 9 million acres in the Corn Belt and Eastern States (14 percent).

The central and southern Great Plains had 36 percent of the national production that year; the northern Great Plains, 24 percent; the Corn Belt and Eastern States, 18 percent; the Pacific Northwest, 16 percent; and all other regions, 6 percent (on 5 percent of the acreage).

IN THE EASTERN WINTER WHEAT REGION, soft red varieties of wheat mostly are grown. Soft wheats are used mainly for pastry, cake, and biscuit flour, rather than for bread flour.

This area has ample rainfall and moderately cool winters, except in the north, where the ground usually is covered with snow during the coldest part. The wheatlands here tend to have the poorer soils, or at least those that are less well adapted to corn, soybeans, and oats. They include the Planosols of southern Illinois and Indiana, which are underlain by hardpan and hence

150

are poorly drained. They often remain wet until it is too late in the spring to prepare a seedbed and plant corn. The soils are usually better suited to seedbed preparation in the fall—hence the interest in fall-seeded wheat.

Also used for wheat are some of the shallower podzolic soils in Michigan, Ohio, Pennsylvania, and other States.

The deep, rich prairie soils of Iowa, southern Minnesota, northern Illinois, and northern Missouri are seldom used for wheat because wheat cannot compete there with corn and soybeans. The Podzols respond markedly to phosphatic fertilization, and yields of wheat generally are much higher now than they were 20 years ago before fertilization was commonly practiced.

Wheat is grown primarily as a cash crop. It is also used as a companion crop for grass seedings. It is seeded sometimes for late fall or early spring pasture. Some of our finest early lambs are produced on winter wheat pasture in the eastern winter wheat region.

THE HARD RED WINTER WHEAT REGION centers in Kansas, Nebraska, Oklahoma, and the Panhandle of Texas. It includes parts of some adjacent States.

Precipitation is 17 inches in eastern New Mexico and western Texas, 15 inches in eastern Colorado and Wyoming, and 30 or 35 inches in eastern Kansas and Oklahoma.

Much of the wheatland in the western parts is kept in clean-cultivated fallow every other year to permit soil moisture to be restored before the next wheat crop is seeded. Winters are moderately cold and generally dry.

All the important soils in the region are used for wheat. They include the Chernozems of north-central Kansas, the Red Chestnut soils of western Oklahoma, and the Brown soils of eastern Colorado, northeastern New Mexico, and the Texas Panhandle. The wheat is generally high in protein and is highly rated for breadmaking.

THE HARD RED SPRING WHEAT REGION

usually has winters too severe for winter wheat. The area includes North Dakota, South Dakota, northeastern and north-central Montana, and eastern Minnesota. The annual rainfall is about 15 inches in the west to about 25 inches along the eastern border.

Diseases (like scab and stem rust) and competition with corn, barley, and flax set the eastern limits of production. Wheat is alternated with summer fallow almost always in the drier, western part of the area.

Both the Chernozems and the Brown soils, which predominate in the region, are used for wheat. These lands have been farmed for 50 to 75 years, but only recently have they shown a response to fertilizer, notably phosphate.

Hard red spring wheat is noted for its high content of protein, which often brings it a premium in the market, and for its excellent breadmaking qualities. It is used extensively for blends that include weaker wheats.

Durum, a variety used chiefly for macaroni and similar edible pastes, is grown widely, particularly in North Dakota. The market for durum is much more limited than the market for bread-type wheats.

THE BIG BEND AND PALOUSE districts of Washington and adjoining parts of Idaho and Oregon constitute the chief wheat-growing region of the West.

The soil usually is covered with snow during the colder part of the winter. Annual precipitation is 12 to 20 inches. Fallowing the land every other year to restore soil moisture is commonly practiced wherever rainfall is less than 15 inches. Fallowing is done also to some extent in the Palouse area—not so much to conserve moisture as to help decompose the straw residue from the previous crop. Farmers use less fallow since they learned that decomposition can be speeded by nitrogen fertilization.

The principal soils used for wheat are the Chernozems (Palouse) and the Lithosols. The deep Palouse soils are of loessal origin. They are highly responsive to nitrogen fertilization. In Whitman County, Wash., an average of nearly 50 pounds an acre of nitrogen is applied, and the average yield is about 40 bushels.

Soft white winter wheat is the commonest type, although some spring wheat is seeded on fields that winterkill. Soft white wheats as a rule are not high in protein. They are used for pastry flour or as blends in bread flour.

FEW AREAS in the United States are wholly unsuited to growing of wheat.

Wheat is grown primarily as a cash-grain crop, but it often is grown for other purposes, particularly in the Eastern States. I mentioned its use as a companion crop and for late fall and early spring pasture. Wheat has found a place in some crop rotations in which a fall-seeded crop is desired because the land is more easily worked in fall than in spring.

Winter wheat is sometimes used in irrigated areas in the West in place of fallow to dry out the soil periodically. After the wheat is harvested, the land is fallow the rest of the summer.

The wide adaptability of wheat helps to explain why our capacity to produce wheat at times has exceeded market demand. This problem I discuss later.

LAND IS RELATIVELY more important in specialized wheat farming than in most other kinds of farming. It is easily the largest item of investment on wheat farms. Investment in land may be 3 to 10 times larger than the investment in equipment. A reasonably efficient wheat farm may represent an investment of 100 thousand dollars. It may have 15 thousand dollars in gross sales but may return the operator only 3 thousand dollars for his labor. Wheat farming, in fact, has become so efficient in the use of labor that it provides only part-year employment for most of the specialized wheat growers.

Wheat farming in the major wheat areas is an "extensive" type of farming—that is, relatively few inputs are added to the land. All the plowing, planting, and harvesting of an acre of wheat in the Great Plains, for example, can be done by only 2 hours of man labor and 1.5 hours of tractor time. In contrast, production of cotton may require as many as 100 hours of man labor and 10 to 15 hours of tractor work an acre. Once the wheat is seeded, particularly in the specialized producing areas, there is little more to be done until harvest. Wheat farmers sometimes spray to control weeds and insects, but ordinarily between seeding and harvest a man can do little to influence the outcome of the crop. He waits and takes what comes.

WHAT MANNER of men are they who produce wheat?

They are the conventional farmers who operate family-sized farms and may grow several other crops besides wheat—the Pennsylvania farmer, for example, who seeds wheat after the corn silage has been harvested.

The wheat producer is also the farmer in the Great Plains, where wheat is the dominant crop. He is the farmer who makes his home in Topeka but farms wheat in both eastern and western Kansas. He is the Texas farmer who may also grow wheat in Kansas and Nebraska. He is the rancher in Montana, Colorado, or New Mexico, who has a small acreage of level cropland in wheat. He is the farm machinery dealer, feed dealer, hardware merchant, banker, doctor, or lawyer who owns wheatland and rents it out or shares. He is the college student who, during summer vacation, harvests the current crop, reworks his fallow land, and seeds his next year's crop before going back to school in the fall. Wheat is the kind of farming that permits him to do this.

The wheat producer is any of these— or the man we usually think of as a farmer.

Because wheat growing does not take their full attention for the entire year, many wheat farmers have other part-time jobs or business interests—even in the Great Plains, where there is little urban industry. In fact, the incidence of nonfarm work is even greater in the Plains than in many other farming regions. The 1954 Census of Agriculture, for example, reported that one in three cash-grain (meaning wheat) farmers in eastern Colorado and western Kansas worked off their farms for wages, and about one in eight worked off the farm 100 days or more, or the equivalent of 20 workweeks.

The practice of combining other work with the farming is not unique among wheat farmers. Part-time farming is even commoner near large cities. I mention it because the combination might be least expected in the Great Plains. On the contrary, it is in character with the early settlement and the economic and cultural development of the Plains. When the Plains were first settled, the same people broke out the prairie sod and built homes, schools, churches, and stores. They now do the farming and at the same time operate the banks, the machinery repair shops, and the grain elevators. Many persons consider themselves farmers part of the year and during periods when crops are good. They depend on other sources of income at other times.

This intermingling of farm and non-farm interests partly explains why many wheat farmers no longer live on the farms they operate. For many decades after settlement, most farmers lived in the open country on farms they owned or rented. More recently, particularly since the Second World War, many have moved to town. In 1955, for example, about 30 percent of the cash-grain farmers in the 18 westernmost counties of Kansas lived off their farms. In Greeley, Hamilton, and Stanton Counties, the percentage was 40. Only a slightly lower percentage lived off their farms in the Colorado counties to the west and in the next tier of Kansas counties to the east.

Families of wheat farmers have found churches, schools, and other community services much more convenient since they moved to town. Nonfarm residence is prevalent in other specialized wheat-producing areas. This pattern of nonfarm residence may tend to coincide with the pattern of off-farm work.

Because wheat farmers can now live away from their farms, land has come to have a different aspect. Farming traditionally was a business and a way of life for the farm family; each member from the time he could walk had chores or a job to do and was a working partner in the business. But business and home are separated when the family lives in town. The farm becomes so many fields of wheat. The family's daily interests center in the town. Attitudes toward the land may change—not necessarily adversely.

Absentee operation spawned the term "suitcase farmer" for him who comes to the farm from his city home and "lives out of a suitcase" the few days he is seeding or harvesting.

Problems, including dust blowing, have been laid to the suitcase farmer.

Actually, however, it is often the hard-pressed, debt-harassed resident farmer who seeds when there is too little moisture. The suitcase farmer, who has greater choice of land, can select the more suitable lands.

Again, because wheat needs little attention between seeding and harvesting, the grower with the modern machinery can operate in widely separated locations. He can follow the seasons. Some individuals grow wheat in the Texas Panhandle and Nebraska, which are miles apart. The harvest begins in Texas and moves north as the summer progresses. Fall seeding dates vary widely, but generally they have a reverse pattern—they begin in the north and proceed south.

The ability to operate in different localities permits the farmer to work larger acreages with the same equipment, expand his scale of operations, and increase his efficiency with less equipment, overhead, and labor. Operating in separate localities also serves as a form of crop insurance against such hazards as drought and hail. The same storm is unlikely to hit both areas in the same season.

THE COMPARATIVE EASE with which young farmers can get started in farming is another characteristic of our main wheat-producing areas. Many start by using their fathers' machinery and renting land for a share of the crop. An industrious, dependable young man usually can rent the land he needs. He can soon acquire his own tractor and combine if things go well. Such golden prospects have attracted young farmers to the wheat sections and partly explain why the margin of cultivation has been pushed to poorer and still poorer lands. A young farmer eventually saves enough from his earnings for a downpayment on some land. As most wheat farmers do not attempt to own all the land they need to operate, he continues to rent additional land.

Part-ownership characterizes land tenure in the specialized wheat-producing areas. Part owners—not counting paid managers and institutions—comprise more than 40 percent of the operators. Part-owner farms are larger than full-owner and full-tenant farms and have more cattle and equipment.

Part owners include the operators whose managerial capacity exceeds their possession of investment funds and those who prefer to invest more of their own funds in operating capital rather than land.

Full owners oftener are smaller operators. They are older, and they work off the farm part of the time. Full tenants usually are the younger operators who are just getting started and who have not saved enough for a downpayment on a farm. In west-central Kansas, nearly half the tenant operators work off the farm for pay. One in six worked off the farms 100 days or more in 1954. Off-farm work was much less frequent among full owners and part owners. More of the part owners in north-central North Dakota worked off their farms than did full owners or tenants. More of the full owners in the Palouse area worked off their farms.

The usual rental in the specialized wheat areas is a share of the cash crops and a cash rate per acre on the forage crops and pasture. A typical share rent is one-third of the wheat, barley, grain sorghum, and similar grain crops. Cash rents for pasture and hay land vary widely.

Renting land is somewhat simpler, and fewer areas of conflict exist between landlord and tenant in the specialized wheat areas than in many other farm areas. That is because farming systems are simpler, production practices are more standardized, and management decisions are fewer. In a wheat-fallow area, there is no question as to the crop that will be grown. Once the crop is seeded, there are few further management decisions until harvesttime. At present, acreage restrictions on wheat have raised the question of which crops to grow on land removed from wheat production. Usually the alternative is limited to one or two crops.

HOMESTEADERS FIRST SETTLED the Great Plains in the 1870's and 1880's. Settlement continued until after the First World War.

Times and events had been exciting. Dodge City, in the Central Plains, was the railhead to which cattle from Texas and Oklahoma were driven for shipment to eastern markets. Large cattle companies from the South had moved into the central and northern parts of the Plains and were using the free public range. The Plains had been the scene of range "wars" between rival cattle outfits.

The homesteaders found lush native sod, which was relatively easy to plow. Wheat was one of their first crops. Homesteads were taken up in 160-acre tracts. Husband and wife could each file claim to a quarter section. Among the homesteaders were many who stayed only long enough to "prove up." Soon their land was available for rent or purchase by the real settlers. A farmer usually could acquire all the land he wanted or could operate.

The settlers had come from a more humid climate where 160 acres of crops was about all a man and his family could care for with the animal power and the crude tools he had. It was also enough to support the family.

They soon learned that the climate of the Plains was far different from what they were used to. The Plains country was drier. Rainfall was less dependable. Land in the western part of the Plains had to be left fallow every other year to store enough moisture to grow a crop. Twice as much land therefore was needed, but fewer tillage operations were required. In short, farmers found that they needed and could handle about three times as much land for an operating unit as was customary in the more humid Midwestern States.

Tractor power, self-propelled combines, and other large-scale machinery enlarged the acreage that one man could handle—about 300 acres on the eastern border of the Plains and 800 or 1,200 acres on the western edge, or even more for an especially good manager with adequate equipment.

Wheat has remained the main crop. The next alternative crop has been grain sorghum in the central and southern parts and barley and flax farther north. Most farmers have some cattle. Three in four cash-grain farmers have cattle, which graze land too stony or otherwise unsuited to cultivation. Small acreages of tame hay and other forage produce supplemental feed.

I MENTIONED that few areas in the United States are wholly unsuited to wheat production: The acreage capable of growing wheat exceeds the acreage needed for wheat. This fact in itself would present no problem. We also have more land than is needed for producing soybeans, corn, and cotton.

The problem arises because wheat growing is profitable throughout the country. In the specialized areas of the Plains and Pacific Northwest, wheat has an unchallenged claim on the land. The competitive position of wheat relative to other crops in the Eastern

States has been improved by new technology. Yields have increased from use of fertilizer, weed sprays, and improved varieties. The small combine-harvester has made the eastern wheat grower independent of the neighborhood's threshing rig. We consequently have excess capacity for wheat production.

This excess capacity is put to good use in times of national emergency. Wheat is a quick way to expand food supplies. It is easily transported to areas of need. At other times, however, a high production of wheat is a national problem.

To MEET this problem, we have legislation that limits the acreage in wheat and supports wheat prices at certain minimums. Other acts authorize the Government to subsidize exports of wheat and to pay farmers for not planting their allotted acreages of wheat. They are known as wheat programs. They have an impact on wheat farmers and on the way they use the land.

Without acreage allotments, the average wheat farmer in west-central Kansas would seed 320 acres and produce 4 thousand bushels of wheat. He seeded 240 acres and produced 2,600 bushels in 1955. With the acreage of wheat reduced, the farmers must find a profitable alternative use for the land taken out of wheat. The chief alternative in this section of Kansas is sorghum. Restrictions on wheat acreage encourage an increase in the size of farms.

Farmers in the specialized wheat-producing regions have been increasing the size of their farms for this and other reasons. But many farms are still too small for greatest efficiency. Farm enlargement comes slowly because it means fewer farms. Renting of land continues to be a facilitating factor.

Still another problem has arisen from the wartime and postwar expansion in wheat production. This expansion came not only within the major producing areas; it also extended into what are normally the drier parts of the western Great Plains. These areas were having unusually favorable weather at the time. Kiowa County, Colo., for example, had average yields of 19, 20, and 21 bushels per seeded acre in 1946, 1947, 1948, respectively; the longtime average yield is 6 bushels. These good crops came just when they were needed badly.

WE ARE FORTUNATE in having marginal lands with which to meet emergency needs for wheat, but those lands are not readily put back into a reserve status when the emergency has passed. They have acquired acreage allotments, the farmers have participated in wheat programs as have farmers on other lands, and the high yields and relatively good prices have become capitalized into land values.

Legislation in 1956—the Soil Bank—was designed to cope with this problem. Under the Conservation Reserve feature of this program, farmers have been paid to reseed cropland to permanent pasture.

The program provided that farmers sign contracts with the Government and agree not to crop the land for 5 years. For doing this, they receive five annual cash payments. In addition they agree to establish cover crops or pasture on the reserve land; they are reimbursed up to 80 percent of this cost, including their own labor. The payments were intended to be high enough to induce wide participation in the wheat-producing regions.

In the first year (1956–1957) of the program, 6.5 million acres were in the Conservation Reserve. About 2.7 million of these acres were in Texas, New Mexico, and Oklahoma; about 800 thousand acres in Colorado, Kansas, and Nebraska; and about 975 thousand acres in North Dakota, South Dakota, and Montana. Thus nearly three-fourths of the Conservation Reserve was in the Great Plains States. To the extent to which this program attains its objectives, the Western Plains will again return to grass and use for livestock.

The Conservation Reserve feature of the Soil Bank is not a new program, except in name. Payments to farmers for keeping land in conservation uses have been included in farm programs since the 1930's. But the 1956 act was the first that provided for long-term contracts—those extending beyond 1 year.

The purpose of the Acreage Reserve—another Soil Bank feature—is to reduce production of allotment crops and hence reduce Government-held surpluses. Under the Acreage Reserve, farmers sign 1-year contracts and agree to underplant their wheat or other allotments by a specified acreage. The payment per acre amounts to 1.20 dollars multiplied by the normal yield in bushels, in the case of wheat. Nearly 13 million acres of wheat allotment were signed up for the 1957 crop year.

Participation was highest in the southern and central sections of the Plains, where drought was extensive until the deadline date for signing up. Many wheat farmers participated no doubt because crop prospects were poor. Soil Bank payments seem less attractive when crop prospects are good. In the Plains, where crop prospects change widely from year to year, this can have a marked effect on participation. There has been too little time to assess the ultimate effects of the Soil Bank on the economy of the wheat regions.

FOR INFORMATION on how land is combined with other resources on farms in the Great Plains, we can turn to data assembled annually in the Cost and Returns series for family-operated commercial farms in the United States. This series is maintained by the Agricultural Research Service and is issued in the Agriculture Information Bulletin series of the Department of Agriculture.

THE AVERAGE COMMERCIAL wheat farm in west-central Kansas has about 715 acres of land. Of this, 525 acres are cropland and 190 acres are native

ORGANIZATION, INCOME, AND EXPENSES OF THE AVERAGE COMMERCIAL WHEAT FARMS, AVERAGES FOR 1954–1956

Item		West-central Kansas	North-central North Dakota	Washington-Idaho Palouse
Land in farm	acre	715	690	535
Total cropland	do	525	550	495
Wheat	do	220	165	170
Feed grains	do	70	120	85
Other crops	do	37	130	114
Fallow land	do	140	100	80
Other land	do	190	140	40
Livestock:				
All cattle	head	41	24	15
Cows milked	do	3	6	2
Pigs raised	do	3	12	13
Total labor used	hour	2,480	3,180	3,300
Operator and family	do	2,160	2,600	2,300
Hired	do	320	600	1,000
Value of:				
Land and buildings	dollar	59,000	26,000	125,000
Average per acre	do	83.10	37.68	233.64
Machinery	do	8,500	9,300	14,100
Livestock	do	3,500	2,650	1,700
Returns from farming:				
Total income	do	9,950	10,380	22,850
Income from—				
Wheat	do	6,230	3,950	13,280
Other crops	do	730	3,040	6,000
Livestock	do	2,730	2,020	1,565
Total expenses	do	4,820	5,320	9,550
Net farm income	do	5,130	5,060	13,300
Charge for capital	do	3,580	2,270	7,300
Net return to operator and family:				
Labor	do	1,550	2,790	6,000
Average per hour	do	0.71	1.07	2.61

pasture. About 220 acres of the crop-and are seeded to wheat. As about two-thirds of it is seeded on summer-fallowed land, the average farm has about 140 acres of cultivated summer fallow each year.

An average of about 40 acres, or one-sixth of the seeded wheat, fails to make a crop because of winterkilling, drought, or other hazard. If it rains after the wheat has failed, some of this abandoned wheatland is planted to grain sorghum the following spring. This possibility of planting a catch crop of sorghum on abandoned wheat-land is a unique characteristic of wheat-growing in the Southern Plains. It is the main reason why farmers seed wheat in the fall, despite poor soil-moisture conditions. They know that if the wheat fails, they have in sorghum another chance for income that year. Actually, the wheat that is "dusted in" in the fall, often makes a crop if rains come in time.

On the average, about 70 acres of grain sorghum and 40 acres of forage sorghum are planted each year. Forage sorghum provides the major source of winter forage for cattle. A few acres of oats or barley are seeded sometimes.

The average farm has about 40 head of cattle and no other livestock on a commercial scale. The number of cattle depends on the acreage of native grass that is used for summer pasture.

The average farm in this area represents an investment of more than 70

CHARACTERISTICS OF FARMS BY TENURE OF OPERATOR[1] IN THREE
WHEAT-PRODUCING AREAS IN 1954

West-Central Kansas	Full owner	Part owner	Full tenant	Cash-grain farms	Live-stock farms
All operators.................percent..	22	45	33	70	1?
Acreage per farm.................acre..	535	978	614	730	1,05?
Cattle per farm...............number..	37	64	35	38	9?
Farm operators—					
Who worked off the farm for pay....percent..	25	30	48	35	2?
Who worked off the farm 100 days or more.......................do....	11	7	16	12	?
North-Central North Dakota					
All operators.................percent..	35	43	22	69	?
Acreage per farm.................acre..	484	809	591	665	75?
Cattle per farm...............number..	22	34	23	21	6?
Farm operators—					
Who worked off the farm for pay...percent..	19	21	26	22	1?
Who worked off the farm 100 days or more.......................do....	6	4	6	6	?
Washington-Idaho Palouse					
All operators.................percent..	31	41	28	64	?
Acreage per farm.................acre..	460	2,203	1,170	1,494	4,16?
Cattle per farm...............number..	18	54	18	25	19?
Farm operators—					
Who worked off the farm for pay..percent..	37	22	30	27	3?
Who worked off the farm 100 days or more.......................do....	16	5	8	7	?

[1] Excluding paid managers, institutions, and other nonindividual operators.

thousand dollars. Nearly 60 thousand dollars is in land and buildings. About 8,500 dollars is in power and machinery. About 3,500 dollars is in livestock. Land and buildings thus represent more than four-fifths of the total farm investment. Only a part of the capital investment is provided by the farm operators themselves. According to the 1950 Census of Agriculture, the operators of cash-grain farms in west-central Kansas owned 37 percent and rented 63 percent of the land they farmed. Thus the average farmer owns about 34 thousand dollars of the total farm investment. His equity in most instances is considerably less.

Investment in land represents an important fixed expense. Suppose the farmer has a mortgage of 30 thousand dollars to be paid off in 20 years at 5-percent interest. If the mortgage is of the equal-payment type, the annual payment would be 2,407 dollars a year. A young farmer without financial reserves would find it hard to meet such a payment in a year of crop failure. A better arrangement for him would be a variable payment plan, in which the annual payment would reflect crop yields or gross farm income. Relatively few lenders offer this kind of loan.

About a third of the operators are full tenants. They have no investment in land or buildings, which are provided by a landlord. The usual rental is one-third of the crop and cash rent for pasture and forage crops. Tenants own only their machinery and livestock.

Nearly half the operators are part owners. As a rule they own slightly more than half the land they operate. Part-owner farms are larger than other farms; they average 978 acres, as compared with 535 acres for full owners and 614 acres for full tenants. Part owners probably own on the average about 55 thousand dollars of the estimated 95 thousand dollars of capital invested in their farm businesses. Full owners have about 57 thousand dollars invested in their businesses, and they own it all.

One should not infer, however, that ownership is the same as equity. Most farmers have less than full equity in the property they own. They are in debt for the rest.

The average wheat farmer in west-central Kansas had gross returns for 1954–1956 of 9,950 dollars and expenses of 4,820 dollars. Thus the net farm income was 5,130 dollars. This amount was available to cover earnings on investment and the labor and management of the operator and his family. If we subtract a charge for capital (figured at 5 percent) of 3,580 dollars, the remainder, which represented return to labor and management of the operator and family, was 1,550 dollars. This is equivalent to 71 cents an hour of labor input.

THE AVERAGE COMMERCIAL wheat farm in north-central North Dakota is nearly as large as the farms in western Kansas that I mentioned. Farms in North Dakota average about 690 acres. As in other parts of the Plains, their average size increased by nearly 200 acres since 1937–1941. Such a change has been consistent with the conversion from animal to tractor power and more and better equipment. Many farms are smaller than the average. Many are larger. For example, many farms contain 320, 480, or 640 acres, and some contain 800 and more acres.

These farms average 550 acres of cultivated land and 140 acres of native grass. About 165 acres of wheat, 120 acres of feed grains, and 130 acres of other crops are seeded each year. Both hard red spring wheat and durum are grown. A few farmers specialize in one kind or the other. The average yield of both kinds is about 13 bushels per seeded acre. These farms regularly have enough fallow land on which to seed about 50 percent of the wheat, although some fallow is used for other crops.

Flax was a favorite crop on new land in the Northern Plains during early settlement, when it was seeded directly on the freshly turned sod. Flax produced well because the new land was free from the diseases and weeds of the older areas. The land in time would become infested and unsuitable for flax. The acreage in flax and yields declined when all the virgin sod had been brought into cultivation. New disease-resistant varieties and selective herbicides have brought a revival of production of flax. Yields now average about 8 to 10 bushels, compared with 4 to 5 bushels in 1935. On the average, the farmers seed 60 to 70 acres each year.

Barley is the chief feed-grain alternative to wheat in the Northern Plains. It is somewhat better adapted than oats to the climate and soils. Some barley of malting quality is produced.

These farms average 24 head of cattle, of which six are milk cows. Many farmers depend on the sale of butterfat to cover current living expenses. They use the income from wheat and other crops to cover mortgage payments and general farm expenses. The number of cattle on a farm has increased from 16 to 24 since 1935.

THE VALUE OF LAND and buildings averaged 26 thousand dollars a farm, or 37.68 dollars an acre, in 1954–1956. The average value of machinery was 9,300 dollars and that of livestock 2,650 dollars. As farm operators own about 60 percent of the land they farm, their average investment in land is about 15 thousand dollars. Landlords have an average of about 10 thousand dollars invested per farm. The value of land and buildings on part-owner farms would average about

32 thousand dollars, as they are 30 percent larger than the average farm. The portion owned by the operator, about 54 percent, would average about 17,500 dollars.

A third of the farmers are full owners. Their farms average about 100 acres smaller than farms of tenants and more than 300 acres smaller than farms of part owners. About two farmers in five are part owners and one in five is a full tenant.

AVERAGE GROSS SALES of these farms in 1954–1956 amounted to 10,380 dollars, of which 3,950 dollars was from wheat. Other crops contributed about 3 thousand dollars to farm income. Livestock contributed about 2,000 dollars. Net farm income averaged 5,060 dollars per farm and returns to operator, and family labor averaged 2,790 dollars, or 1.07 dollars an hour.

These farms use about 2,600 hours of family labor and about 600 hours of hired labor annually. Farmers could step up their self-employment if they increased production of livestock, an adjustment that could be accomplished with present resources. The feed grains sold could be fed on the farm.

Wheat farms in north-central North Dakota have made substantial adjustments in scale of operation since 1935. They have important adjustments yet to make, however.

COMMERCIAL WHEAT FARMS in the Washington-Idaho Palouse are among the most efficient crop farms in the country. Farmers there are quick to use improved varieties of wheat. The use of fertilizer is widespread. The farms are well equipped and are organized on a scale to take advantage of this technology.

These farms average 535 acres. The average farm was 120 acres larger in 1958 than it was in 1938. The area under cultivation averaged 495 acres; 40 acres of other land were unsuitable for crops. These farms seed an average

of 170 acres of wheat, somewhat less than formerly because of acreage allotments. Without acreage restrictions, the farmers would grow about 250 acres of wheat.

The land diverted from wheat production is used for barley and dry peas, crops that are a regular part of the cropping system. Many farmers grow about 90 acres of peas and 70 acres of barley.

Because market prices of peas are rather sensitive to supply and demand, even a moderate increase in production has a softening effect on price. The acreage in peas therefore tends to be restricted.

Yields of barley are comparable to those of wheat. The cultural requirements are similar. The costs of production are nearly the same. Barley is inferior as a crop only because the market price for it is lower. Thus barley is a strong competitor for any acreage not in wheat.

THE CAPITAL VALUE of the average Palouse wheat farm amounts to 140 thousand dollars. Almost nine-tenths of that amount is represented by land and buildings. The value of machinery averages about 14 thousand dollars. The value of livestock averages 1,700 dollars. The operators own an average of about 40 percent—50 thousand dollars—of the land and buildings. The unencumbered equities of operators would be much less. The average landlord owns 75 thousand dollars of the farm capital.

Gross income in 1954–1956 averaged nearly 23,000 dollars per farm. Of this, 13,280 dollars was from sales of wheat, 6,000 dollars from other crops, and 1,565 dollars from livestock. Net farm income averaged about 13,300 dollars. After allowing a charge for capital, the return to operator and family labor averaged 6,000 dollars a farm, or 2.61 dollars an hour. Returns during this period were higher on the Palouse wheat farm than on wheat farms in north-central North Dakota and west-central Kansas.

Land-use problems in the Great Plains.

Further effort should be made in this high-risk area to retire certain low-grade cropland to grass, adapt agriculture to the variable climate, adjust production of wheat to market demand, apply recommended farming practices, adjust sizes of farms, conserve water, adapt crops, improve the range, and adjust institutions. By *John Muehlbeier,* agricultural economist, Farm Economics Research Division, and secretary, Great Plains Agricultural Council.

THE GREAT PLAINS, a vast region with its own characteristics and problems, is about 1,300 miles long and 200 to 700 miles wide. It extends from Canada nearly to Mexico. The Rocky Mountains form its western boundary. There is no clear demarcation for its eastern boundary, which is a transition zone through eastern North Dakota, South Dakota, Nebraska, and Kansas, through central Oklahoma, and into Texas. Parts of New Mexico, Colorado, Wyoming, and Montana are also in the Plains. A delineation of the Plains commonly used is the one shown in *The Future of the Great Plains* (Report of the Great Plains Committee, 1936).

Many of the land-use problems of the Great Plains arise from the nature of its climate. Rainfall is low and variable. The average rainfall in a wide zone running north and south is near the critical limits for the production of crops. In many years, crops are good, but years in which rainfall is below average follow, and crops fail. The more humid regions do not have this problem, or, if they do, it is in a lesser degree. Arid regions do not have it at all. C. W. Thornthwaite, in *The Great Plains*, attaches a great deal of significance to variation in precipitation in the transition area.

Extremes of temperature, periods of high temperature, a short growing season in the Northern Plains, and high wind velocities are serious hazards to crops. The wind increases evaporation of scarce water, intensifies drought, and causes erosion of soil.

The soils form a complex pattern. That further complicates the problem of adapting agriculture to the Plains. The soils differ in their capacity to absorb and hold water, resist erosion, and produce crops. They differ in the treatment they require and in the use that can be made of them in the production of crops.

Grasses are important in the Plains. The predominant species—buffalo, grama, and western wheatgrass—withstand or survive severe drought. Some of the taller grasses are present also, but they do not do so well in the dry years as the short grasses.

Compared to regions farther east, the Plains has relatively few trees, although many windbreaks and shelterbelts have been established. With proper care, they survive the rigors of the climate remarkably well.

The major types of agriculture in the region are livestock ranching, wheat farming, and a combination of grain and livestock production. The land area of the Plains totals about 363 million acres. About 331 million acres (91 percent) are in farms. Of the land in farms, 133 million acres (40 percent) are cropland, 195 million acres (60 percent) are pastured, and 11 million acres (4 percent) are woodland. Some cropland and woodland are also reported as pastured. About 7 million acres (2 percent of the land in farms) are irrigated. The Great Plains has fewer than 400 thousand farms and ranches. The average size is about 240 acres in some areas and more than 4 thousand acres in others. About two-fifths of them are cash-grain farms.

The population is sparse. About one-fourth of the inhabitants live on farms. Denver is the only large city, and it is on the western edge of the Plains. Distance is a major factor in the development of institutional arrangements that are adapted to Plains conditions.

The Great Plains contains about a fifth of the Nation's land and nearly a third of its cropland. It produces nearly two-thirds of its wheat and more than one-third of its cattle.

Farm income is highly variable. In a period of favorable weather, especially if it coincides with a period of high prices for farm products, income is high. Farm income drops sharply in dry years.

Many of the problems of the Plains may be traced back to the pattern of settlement, when the climatic limitations of the region were not given due consideration. The agriculture and institutions that settlers brought from more humid regions needed to be modified, and that has been a slow and painful process.

Progress has been made in adapting agriculture to the peculiar characteristics of the Plains. As evidence, one can list certain changes in size of farm and in land use, better farming, land treatment, development of water resources, improved varieties of crops and grasses, improvement of the range, better living conditions, more stable landownership, adjustment in institutional arrangements, supplemental off-farm employment, and the like.

A number of land-use problems require further attention, however.

Cropland with a very low average production that is cultivated at great risk or that deteriorates when farmed should be retired to grass. The average yield of wheat, for example, in some areas is less than 8 bushels per acre. Many years the crop is a total failure. Farmers are in economic distress in the dry years, and land deteriorates through wind erosion.

A detailed delineation of lands unsuited to continued cultivation is not available, but 15 million to 30 million acres may be in this category. But one has to be careful when he puts land in this category: Unless yields are extremely low, the land may produce more in wheat or in a drought-resistant feed crop than in grass. Risk and deterioration in the long run may be sufficient reason, however, to retire the land to grass, even though the return in the short run may favor wheat. Although some land may do well in wheat in favorable years, it is not practicable to shift it back and forth between wheat and grass because of the problem of establishing a stand of grass.

To locate the lands that should be retired to grass more precisely than has been done thus far will require further study of the occurrence and economic effects of drought, plus completion of soil surveys.

Various aids are available to help landowners and operators retire low-grade cropland. Among these are programs of research, extension, and technical aid to show how the job can be done and programs for cost sharing to ease the financial burden. For years, cost sharing for regrassing has been part of the Agricultural Conservation Program. A more recent addition is the Conservation Reserve of the Soil Bank. In the 2 years of its operation, nearly 3 million acres in the Southern Plains have been placed under long-term contract for regrassing. This is a significant shift in major land use in a short time. The drought undoubtedly was a motivating factor. Another new program that started in 1957 is the Great Plains Conservation Program (Public Law 1021). It also was designed to facilitate changes in land use through long-term contracts.

Still other steps could be taken to accelerate the retirement of low-grade cropland to grass. In the 1930's, several projects were established in the Plains in which submarginal land was purchased by the Federal Government, regrassed, developed, and then leased out under controlled grazing.

A study in 1957 by Loyd Glover, of the South Dakota Agricultural Experiment Station, showed that these projects were successful in bringing about necessary adjustments in land use, number of operators, and local institutions. To eliminate the need for long-term management by Government, it might be possible for it to buy land, correct the misuse, and resell the land with restrictions in the deed against cultivation. A step that could be taken to discourage misuse of land would be to give notice that the operators in certain areas would be denied the benefits of certain programs, including emergency programs, unless they followed recommended land-use practices.

There is reason to believe that at times some of the programs have contributed to expansion of wheat into areas not adapted to farming, or made it possible for production of crops to continue on land not suited to cultivation. This, of course, was not the intention of the programs, but it does mean that national programs must be studied continuously to assure that they will fit local conditions.

THE CONTROL OF WIND EROSION during severe drought is in the interest of landowners and the public alike in order to protect the land and keep blowing soil from damaging nearby farms and from endangering health. The Soil Conservation Service estimated that from 10 million acres to more than 15 million acres of land were damaged by wind each year during the blow season (November–May) in 1954–1955, 1955–1956, and 1956–1957; 1 million acres to nearly 5 million acres of crops were destroyed each year. In addition, from 10 million acres to more than 25 million acres were at times in condition to blow. Although the duststorms were more awesome in the 1930's than in the 1950's, the acreage damaged was about equal in the two periods.

At least two States, Kansas and Colorado, and possibly others, have granted county governments authority to control wind erosion when owners, after due notice, fail to do so. The costs of emergency tillage are assessed against the land. The mere fact that such authority exists is a stimulus to better care of the land. Another remedial measure available is a land-use regulation under authority of a soil conservation district. Such a regulation developed by local people, and voted on by them, could specify farming practices that may be required to prevent wind erosion.

ADJUSTMENT to market demand is difficult here. The Plains contains nearly three-fourths of the Nation's acreage of wheat and produces nearly two-thirds of the Nation's total supply. Furthermore, wheat is the principal crop in the Plains, and alternatives are limited primarily to grain sorghum in the Central and Southern Plains and barley and flax in the Northern Plains. With a supply of wheat that is large in relation to market demand, the region faces a difficult problem of adjustment.

We need studies of how the farm business can be adjusted to market demand, alternative cropping systems, and the effect of acreage-control and price-support programs on agriculture in the Plains.

While 100 million acres are suited to crop production, drought is always a threat. The farm business must be organized so it can survive the dry years and recover quickly when more favorable years return. Some of the effects of drought can be reduced by such measures as crop insurance and the use of recommended soil and water conservation practices. The saving in moisture is available for crops; better handling of the land reduces erosion.

WATER IS SCARCE in the Plains. In the drought of the 1950's in the Southern Plains, many communities were short of water for domestic purposes and for livestock. In many areas, farm operators who use underground water for irrigation have found their supplies sufficiently depleted so pumping has become more costly or impossible. In time, other areas will experience the same problem.

Opportunities exist for further development of water resources, but cost is an important factor, especially the cost of some of the larger irrigation projects. There is need for more comprehensive State water laws to protect investments in water development, particularly irrigation from ground water, and to direct new development in the public interest.

A LARGE ACREAGE of range is one of the resources of the Plains. In the Southern Plains, however, during the long drought of the 1950's much of the range deteriorated and is in need of rehabilitation. Some of it may need to be reseeded. Deferred grazing would facilitate recovery of the grasses. Cost sharing for deferred grazing is one of the practices authorized under the Agricultural Conservation Program.

Management of the range, including the proper rate of stocking, reseeding, water development and water spreading, brush eradication, and production of adequate supplemental feed, require the constant attention of the ranch operator. This determines the condition of the range and, in large measure, how well the rancher fares in the drier years. Research can help with all these problems, including determination of the lowest cost alternatives.

RESERVES should play an important part in the management of the farm business in an area such as the Plains, where good years may be followed by crop failure. These reserves can take various forms, such as water supplies, feed, soil moisture, equity in land, machinery and livestock, crop insurance, liquid assets, and the like. In planning reserves, however, their cost needs to be taken into account. There is a limit, for example, to the amount that may be profitable for a rancher to invest in feed for protection against a prolonged drought, not knowing when the drought may strike. Certain reserves involve carrying and opportunity costs. In localities where drought may run 5 years or longer, very large reserves would be necessary to carry the livestock enterprise without drastic reductions.

MANY UNECONOMIC UNITS disappeared as the number of farms in the Plains dropped from more than 500 thousand in 1940 to fewer than 400 thousand in 1955, but quite a number remain, especially in some of the transition areas. For a fourth of the farms in the Plains, the annual value of products sold is in excess of 10 thousand dollars; for half the farms, the annual value is from 2,500 dollars up to 10 thousand dollars; and for the remaining fourth, the annual value of products sold is less than 2,500 dollars. Although many of the smaller farms are occupied by older or less active people who do not want larger farms, many are run by young families, who are eager and able to operate larger units and need credit and other help.

Some credit from the Farmers Home Administration, the Farm Credit Administration, banks, and other private institutions is available. Constant attention needs to be focused, however, on the particular needs of families in the lower income group. Furthermore, the loans must be adapted to conditions in the Plains. Care needs to be exercised to assure that credit is not used to perpetuate uneconomic farms nor improper land use.

GRASSHOPPER NUMBERS in the Plains frequently build up until serious infestations exist, especially during periods of long drought. Crops and grasses in large areas are sometimes eaten into the ground. Fields thus laid bare are subject to wind erosion. Some species of grasshoppers migrate and become a threat to the neighboring areas. This makes control of grasshoppers a matter of interest to the public as well as to the individual farmers whose crops they are destroying.

In 1957, after a long drought, nearly 24 million acres of land were seriously infested by the grasshoppers. Control measures were required on 12 to 15 million acres in order to protect crops and grass.

A large-scale program, under the supervision of the Agricultural Research Service, is available for control of grasshoppers on rangeland. One-third of the cost is paid by the Federal Government. Cropland is excluded from the grasshopper-control program.

A grasshopper-control program in the Plains needs to be based on accurate forecasts of infestations. It should be flexible so it can be put into operation quickly in areas in which an outbreak threatens; in drought disaster areas in which infestations become serious, it should include both cropland and range.

WEATHER-AGRICULTURE RELATIONSHIPS are important in a region in which climate is a limiting factor. Areas that differ with respect to the occurrence of drought need to be delineated. That is, each area thus delineated should be relatively uniform within its own boundary, in frequency, duration, and intensity of drought. This involves research on the weather patterns of the region.

Equally essential is the completion of the soil survey work, which would make it possible to delineate areas that are relatively uniform with respect to climate and soils. From work of this kind, the people of the Plains would acquire a better understanding of the farming hazards or risks in each area, and the differences between areas. It could become an important guide to agricultural programs.

The Soil Conservation Service accelerated its soil survey and land-classification work in 1955 and gave priority to the part of the Plains that is most in need of land-use adjustment. This land classification indicates the physical conservation needs of the land.

Land can be classified in various ways, depending on the purpose to be served. Additional classifications that take into account physical and economic factors need to be developed. They would be useful for taxation purposes, as aids in credit programs, and for other purposes.

CROP FAILURES are common in the Plains because plants are unable to survive such natural hazards as severe drought and extreme temperature. From 10 to 20 percent of the cropland is often abandoned. In parts of the Plains, abandonment sometimes has reached 50 percent. Progress has been made in improving crops and cropping systems. This has reduced the risks of farming, but much remains to be done. Further research on the mechanism of plant growth is essential to progress in the adaptation of plants, cropping systems, and cultural practices to Plains conditions. The result would be more stability in production of crops and less economic distress in the dry years.

About two-thirds of the precipitation in the Plains is lost by evaporation alone. Reducing this loss by 25 percent in a 20-inch rainfall zone would result in a saving of moisture equivalent to 3 inches of rainfall. This could be the difference between a crop and a crop failure.

There is need for more study of the underlying processes involved in the loss of water by evaporation from the soil and to methods of control.

Attention needs to be given to the intake of water into the soil, to the moisture retention characteristics of soils, and to the use of soil moisture by plants.

New field practices are needed for more efficient use of precipitation.

If a major breakthrough could be achieved through basic research on this problem, great benefits would accrue to the agriculture of the Plains.

DROUGHTS of disaster proportions will continue to strike. Despite everything individuals can do to protect themselves, disaster relief programs will be needed at times to alleviate distress. Programs need to be developed that can be put into operation quickly and are suited to local conditions.

The Plains has relatively few industries. The region depends largely on agriculture. The industries it has, however, add to stability and aid in the adjustment of population. As additional industrial plants are located in the Plains, still greater stability will be provided. The industrial development should be encouraged.

In a region of variable income, sparse population, and great distances, such as the Plains, new institutional arrangements need to be developed so that the people will have the same essential services as those in the more densely populated regions. Progress is being made in this direction. A few communities have planned health services and facilities that are adapted to the Plains. Adjustments are being worked out in local school facilities. To provide higher education without duplication of facilities in each State, agreements have been worked out whereby one State will pay another for the students it sends. Adjustments of this kind need to be accelerated.

One of the innovations in the region is the Great Plains Agricultural Council. Its purpose is to analyze the problems of the region, develop possible solutions, promote the adaptation of research, extension, and action programs to conditions in the Plains, and foster cooperation on an attack on the problems of the Plains. The Council, which is an advisory body, provides for an exchange of ideas. It was formed in the early 1930's as various agricultural leaders felt a need to work together on common problems. It has continued to function since on the adaptation of the agriculture to Plains conditions. Local committees of farm people and representatives of various agencies in many counties function in the same way. The extension of this activity to more counties would greatly facilitate the adjustment of agriculture.

The Great Plains Agricultural Council carries out much of its work through the use of committees. These are: Controlled climate-plant growth laboratory committee (to outline need for regional laboratory and outline areas of work in which research would be conducted); forestry committee (to facilitate tree growing in the Plains); information committee (to publicize the work of the Council); health committee (to facilitate the adaptation of health services and facilities to the conditions peculiar to the Plains); insect control committee (to facilitate adjustment of insect control programs to the needs of the Plains); irrigation committee (to outline research needed on problems of irrigation farming and irrigation development); Plains research committee (to activate regional research projects on problems of the Plains); program implementation committee (to foster program planning at the local level); range management and livestock production committee (to outline research needed in this field); soil moisture research laboratory committee (to outline need for regional laboratory and outline areas of work in which research would be conducted); and tenure, credit and land values (to outline research needed and to facilitate research in these and related fields). A number of these committees have functioned for many years.

Individual landowners and farm operators must take the initiative in solving the land-use problems of the Plains, but various programs of research, education, technical aid, and cost sharing can show the way and reduce the financial burden. Some directional measures may also be necessary. Progress has been made. The effect of the recent drought would have been even more severe than it was if this had not been the case. We expect further progress.

The role of land in western ranching.

Land is the main resource in livestock ranching in the West. The forage it provides can be converted into economic uses only by grazing animals. The rancher must care for his animals so they can do the most economical job of harvesting. He must care for his land so that it will support the highest number of animals consistent with efficiency and conservation. By *M. L. Upchurch, head, Western Field Research Section, Farm Economics Research Division.*

LAND IS RELATIVELY more significant in ranching than in any other major type of farming. The very words "livestock ranching" bring to mind the expanses of prairie, desert, and mountain range that we link with grazing.

More than half of all land in the United States is used for grazing. Some of it is in farm pastures, but most of the acreage is in the rangelands of the West. Much more than half of the total investment on most livestock ranches is in land.

The western livestock region covers roughly the western half of the United States. About three-fourths of all land in this region is used for grazing. The rest is in cropland, mountains, and forests that are not grazed, military and other reserved areas, and urban and industrial areas. The soils and climates, of which there are many different ones in this region, determine the amount and kind of forage and the season of grazing use.

The land used for grazing generally is unfit for any other agricultural use. The soil may be too poor or rocky for cultivation. The climate may be too dry and the summers too short for crops. Some areas may be too remote from market to make crop production profitable.

Therefore ranchers have little choice but to continue livestock grazing, regardless of the price levels for their product, the costs of operation, or the productivity of the land itself.

Most of the western rangeland will continue to be used for grazing, despite competition from other livestock-producing regions, price levels, and the other hazards of ranching.

To be sure, any one rancher may go broke and quit the business, but the rangeland itself will continue to be used for grazing, if it is used at all. Grazing is the residual economic use.

Even though most rangeland cannot be used successfully for other types of agriculture, surprisingly little land in the West is so poor that it cannot be used for grazing. There are a few nearly barren areas, like the salt flats in Utah and parts of the desert in southern California, western Arizona, and southern Nevada. A few areas of the rockier, more barren mountains, and some of the densely forested areas of northwestern California and western Oregon and Washington have no grazing.

No one knows for certain just how scant vegetation has to be to preclude some kind of grazing use. Some of the near-desert land may be grazed only in years when rainfall is favorable, or it may be grazed for only a few weeks following rains. Other dry areas may be grazed only by sheep in winter, when snow provides enough water for them. Still other areas may be grazed briefly in spring or summer when water and vegetative conditions are favorable.

A rule of thumb is that land that will not support at least five or six animal units on a section of land for the grazing season probably cannot be used economically for grazing. On the other hand, the better rangelands of the West will not provide feed for more than about 60 animal units a section during the grazing season. The more productive land usually has soils and rainfall suitable for crops. Among the few exceptions are some of the higher mountain meadows that can be stocked properly at heavier rates, although the growing season is too short for crops.

In general, however, an acre of rangeland has a relatively low productivity. Many acres are needed for a reasonably efficient ranch. Even a small, family-operated ranch may have 12 thousand acres. This simple fact gives ranching and the management of rangeland its unique character.

A RANCHING ECONOMY supports a sparse population. Distance becomes an important factor in the social and economic organization of ranching communities. The usual community services of schools, churches, and libraries do not exist or are costly.

The relatively low productivity and the relatively large acreage in an operating unit make it difficult for the rancher to have close control over rangeland.

Rangeland is seldom used only for grazing range livestock. Western range areas, particularly those in the national forests, are primary sources of water. They are the vital watersheds. They are habitats for game. Many areas are important for recreation. Forestry and grazing often are companion uses.

These multiple uses of rangeland make many different persons interested in the management of a range area: The rancher, whose livestock graze it; the hunter, because deer and elk may use the area; the irrigation farmer, the industrialist, and the urban householder, because range areas are the source of water; the State, because it controls the game and the appropriations of water; the vacationer, because he camps and fishes there; the lumberman, because the area may supply logs or other forest products.

Each tries to influence the management so as to further his particular interest. The extent to which each is successful depends on the ownership of the land and on other institutions through which management decisions are made and exercised.

A little more than half of the land used for pasture and grazing in the western range area—355 million acres —is in private ownership. Public land comprises 286 million acres, and 42 million acres are Indian land.

Indian land is not public land. It is held in special trust. Indian ranchers use most of it, either in common with other ranchers or in individual allotments. Non-Indian ranchers lease some of it for grazing.

PUBLIC LAND is used by ranchers either under lease or permit, as prescribed by law and the rules of the administering agencies. State-owned land is leased for grazing. Most leases are like those that might be made between individuals. The leases in some States provide for renewals on expiration. They are also transferable, so that a leasehold has many of the attributes of ownership in fee simple.

Federal land, most of which is administered by the Forest Service of the Department of Agriculture or the Bureau of Land Management of the Department of the Interior, is allotted to ranchers under a system of permits. Permits are given to eligible ranchers under the rules prescribed by each.

Ranchers use private land alone or private land in combination with various forms of public land. The rancher's ability to control such land in achieving his own interests is limited by the large acreages he must police and manage and by the control he has over the land he uses through ownership, lease, or permit.

Private ownership in fee simple normally gives the owner a high degree of control. A rancher who operates large acreages, however, may be unable to exercise precise control in a real physical sense. In areas where big game abounds—as an example—the rancher may not be able to prevent grazing by the animals. He may not be able to exclude hunters or others from access to the land. Sometimes this lack of precise control may affect greatly the product he reaps from the land.

His control over the public land he uses is subject also to the limitations imposed by the permit from the administrative agency. The reality of multiple uses then makes itself felt. Grazing on a public range allotment may be conditioned by one or more additional uses at the same time. The allotment may be open to hunters or fishermen during the grazing season, or the grazing season may be cut short to make way for a hunting season.

A further unique characteristic of the use and management of rangeland, as compared with cropland, lies in the fact that the rancher's harvesting machines are the animals themselves. Management of livestock under range conditions is somewhat more complex than operation of a mowing machine or a combine harvester. The grazing animals may not harvest the range forage uniformly, in the proper amounts, or at the proper stage of growth to get maximum production from the land.

The science of range management has lagged behind technological developments elsewhere in agriculture. The State agricultural experiment stations, the Department of Agriculture, and other research agencies only recently have devoted very much attention to the use of rangeland. Now the young science of range management is making rapid strides.

Ranchers also have intensified their efforts toward better management of grazing land. More and more of them are "farming" their ranges by controlling undesirable plants, seeding desirable ones, using fertilizer, and following other practices in order to achieve more efficient production.

Good management of rangeland no longer is a matter merely of turning grazing animals loose to seek what forage Nature may provide. Good management requires close watch on the part of the rancher over the livestock, the way they graze, the use made of different range plants, the condition and development of the plants, and many other facets of rangeland use. It may require control of noxious vegetation, seeding of usable plants, and the development of water and fences.

Besides the basic problems of low productivity and lack of full control, the rancher is faced also with relatively high risk and uncertainty in his use of land. The great variation in productivity of rangeland from year to year requires flexibility in number of animals and seasons of grazing and causes a variable output. The rancher at times may not be able to graze his land at all, or he might have to dispose of his livestock or obtain feed from other sources. Either may be costly.

I have said that many different range conditions exist in different parts of the West. Range conditions actually may differ from ranch to ranch or even within the same ranch. Certain broad areas or types of rangeland nevertheless can be defined.

The Northern Great Plains mostly is rolling or flat. Medium and short grasses are the dominant vegetation. Many sheep graze here, but this country usually is better suited to cattle. Generally 7 to 10 months of grazing are provided. Native hay or alfalfa and other forages from cropland are the main winter feeds.

The Southern Great Plains is mostly shortgrass country. Mixtures of semidesert species and winter and early spring-growing annuals and shrubs exist. Yearlong grazing is common. Supplemental feeding of crop feeds and cottonseed cake or pellets may be

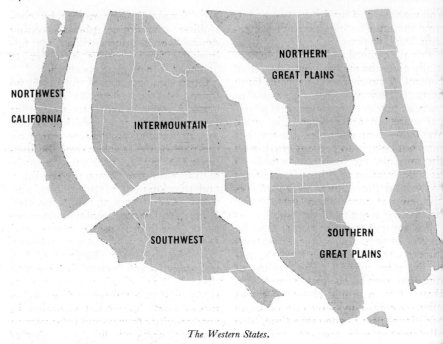

The Western States.

practiced during short periods in winter and occasionally at other seasons when drought limits range feeds.

The intermountain region has many range types. The lower country supports a complex of desert and semi-desert grasses and shrubs, which are used mainly as winter or spring and fall grazing. Higher elevations slope into the pinyon-juniper, oak brush, and timber types. Much of the rangeland is used seasonally. Livestock often must be moved long distances among spring, summer, fall, and winter ranges. A higher proportion of the rangeland in this area is in Federal ownership than in other major range areas.

The southwestern range region has desert-shrub types at lower elevations, grama grasslands in southeastern Arizona and southwestern New Mexico, and a wide mixture of feed types in the pinyon-juniper and forested zones. The desert lands are used rather precariously by sheep and cattle. Speculative inshipments of livestock for grazing are common when seasons are favorable. Cattle ranching is usually on the grama grasslands, where grazing is yearlong, or nearly so. Cottonseed cake or other feeds may be needed during the winter. These cattle ranches are rather productive and stable. Only occasionally are they plagued by severe and prolonged droughts. Lands of higher elevation are used mainly as summer range for cattle and sheep that are wintered in the irrigated valleys or on range at lower elevations.

The California range region is unique in that the main range feed is annual grasses and legumes that grow in winter and early spring. The winter rains and dry summers provide abundant feed in late winter and spring but very poor feed in summer and fall. Ranches therefore have developed a system based on inshipments of stocker cattle in the fall for grazing until the spring, when they are marketed. Another common practice is to graze cows on the range during winter and spring and move them to irrigated pastures and croplands in the Central Valley in summer and fall.

Most of the land in the northwestern range region once was forested. Range livestock grazing there is largely on cutover land or on the small areas of natural grasslands.

I HAVE DESCRIBED the range regions in broad terms. Climate mainly determines the characteristics of rangeland and largely dictates how the land can be used best. Therein lies one of the rancher's major problems as he tries to carry on a profitable business within the natural environment.

Livestock must have feed at all seasons and more at some seasons than others. Yet range forage plants do not grow in all seasons. The task of balancing feed supplies with feed requirements season by season and year by year always is a primary problem. The rancher's success in meeting this problem largely determines his success in the business.

Ranchers who needed winter feeds have acquired cropland or some other means of producing at least part of the winter feed they need. Ranchers in seasonal range areas strive to acquire a balance in their spring, summer, fall, and winter range or other supplies of winter feed.

Each rancher in each region and in each locality must solve the problem of seasonal feed balance in his own way. The efforts and the results have far-reaching effects on the profitability of ranching and on the value placed on certain types of rangeland in a locality. For example, the rancher who is short on spring range can afford to pay high prices for that type of land. Thus he may use his other land and resources more efficiently.

The rancher also faces the problem of feed supplies from year to year. What can he do when drought reduces his feed supply? He may overuse his range for short periods and even sacrifice some weight on his animals, but he soon finds himself in a grave situation if feed is not forthcoming.

He may sell some or all of his cattle to bring his feed requirements in line with his supply. But cattle forced onto the market by drought often are not in shape to sell for a good price. Often they compete with many other cattle in the same condition.

He may buy feed to carry him through until his ranges are again productive. The many ranchers who use this solution get help from the Department of Agriculture, the railroad companies, and the States in various ways. Widespread drought is a drain on feed supplies, and purchase of feed to maintain range herds is often costly, even with the outside aids.

He may try to provide his own reserves of feed and carry them over from good years to meet drought or other hazards. But can—or should—the rancher afford to maintain an inventory of feed large enough to meet the prolonged and unpredictable drought? The long droughts of the 1930's in much of the range country and of later years in the Southwest would have exhausted the feed reserves any prudent rancher might have tried to provide.

Also: Can the rancher who might be able to carry over reserves of feed afford to feed it to his own stock? Feed is in high demand during droughts. A rancher who has feed might be able to sell it for more than it would be worth to him as feed for his own stock. The question must be answered in terms of each situation when it arises.

THE PLACE OF LAND in ranching can be described by presenting a few situations of different types.

A ranch differs from a farm in that a major part of the income is from livestock and a chief source of feed is range forage. Many farms specialize in livestock but depend mainly on crop feeds and cropland pasture.

The size, organization, and operation of individual ranches depend on several factors: The type, topography, and location of the different tracts of land available; ownership and management limitations prescribed by the ownership; the kinds and relative amounts of feeds produced on the rangeland and on cropland on the ranch or in the locality; the abilities and preferences of the rancher; and the amount, costs, and skills of the available labor.

Some ranches do best as a cow-calf business. Others are best as steer ranches. Still others are most profitable as sheep ranches.

I cite a steer ranch in Montana as an example. It has about 6,400 acres of upland prairie land that makes excellent summer range. About 4,400 additional acres of rough land, much of it with southern slopes, is suitable for winter and early spring grazing. Used for native hay are 260 acres of meadowland. The supply of irrigation water is somewhat limited in late summer, so yields of hay are not high.

The grazing land is made up of private and public lands intermingled. The rancher owns about two-thirds of the acreage. The rest is public land, which he uses under permit from the Bureau of Land Management. The hayland and ranch headquarters land is privately owned.

Because of the supply of winter feed and the topography of the spring range, this ranch is not adapted to cow-calf operations. Each fall, by the first of November, the rancher customarily has bought about 350 head of long-yearling steers. He puts them on the winter range and feeds them hay as necessary. Considerable feeding usually is required in January and February. The cattle are kept on the range nearest the headquarters during these months to make feeding easier.

The steers are moved to summer range about the middle of May. This area is adequately cross-fenced and watered to permit the stock to use the range feed efficiently with a minimum of movement. The primary aim is to put as much weight as possible on the animals. They are moved gradually and slowly from pasture to pasture and end the grazing season on especially good range just before they are shipped in late September.

This ranch is well adapted to steers. Young animals can be bought in the fall when normally the price is at a seasonal low. Winter range and supplies of hay are adequate to rough the animals through until spring except during an occasional severe winter when some feed must be bought. The spring and summer range is of a type that puts rapid and solid gains on the animals. Normally this ranch produces about 115 thousand pounds live weight of beef a year, the difference between the weight of the animals bought and the weight of the animals sold. The ranch operates with little hired labor.

This kind of operation is subject to considerable risk from falling prices. The investment in livestock is high and is in the nature of a cash expense each year. A drop of a couple of cents in the cattle market from one fall to the next could easily wipe out the entire profit for the year. The rancher usually buys and sells on the same market, however. Losses sustained one year may be more than regained in another.

The land, including buildings and improvements, represents an investment of 134 thousand dollars, although probably it would cost considerably more if bought today. Machinery and equipment, feed and supplies, and livestock represent a total investment of about 8 thousand dollars. Steers purchased each fall cost perhaps 35 thousand dollars, but this amount is considered an expense rather than an investment.

Land and the forage it produces is the dominant factor on this ranch. The steers are merely a means for harvesting and selling the grass. The haying operations and other aspects of ranch activity are ways to facilitate the harvest of range feed by the steers themselves.

A COW-CALF RANCH in the Southwest is another example. It normally carries about 150 animal units of cattle. About 100 are cows. The rest are replacement heifers, bulls, and a few calves and steers carried over. It covers 7,200 acres, only 810 acres of which are owned. From the State the rancher leases 2,050 acres, which have been leased in connection with this ranch for many years. The rest is Federal land and is used under yearlong permit from the Bureau of Land Management.

This ranch is in a truly yearlong grazing area. The main source of feed at all seasons is from the range itself. Cottonseed cake or pellets are fed during periods of drought or occasional winter storms. The range feed is usually most limited in spring, before summer rains bring on the current year's growth of weeds and grasses.

Calf crops are not very high, partly because of the low level of nutrition during the spring, which should be the most active breeding period, and partly because of the rough topography and brush, which make it difficult to get all cows served in season.

One might think that with a low calf crop, the rancher could do better by growing out older animals rather than depending on sales of calves as a major source of income. With the type of forage on this ranch, however, it is almost impossible to get satisfactory gains in weight and finish on older animals. Even though the ranch is not highly productive as a cow-calf unit, it is relatively more profitable when used in this way than in any other.

All of the grazing land on the ranch can be used at any season, although not all the land is grazed all the time. Lack of stock water at times on parts of the ranch precludes much use even when forage is available. No doubt more adequate water development and fencing would permit this rancher to manage his range more effectively.

About 30 acres, mainly in alfalfa, at the ranch headquarters are irrigated. More land could be farmed if water for irrigation were available. Only enough irrigation water is available for horse feed and for a little hay for the "hospital bunch." Purchased high-protein concentrates are depended on for the main supplemental feed.

Calves, cull and dry cows, and surplus bulls normally are marketed in early fall. Replacement heifers and some of the late smaller calves and perhaps a few yearling steers are over-wintered if the supply of range feed is fairly good. A few cows or calves may be marketed at any time, depending on their age and condition, the supply of range feed, and the prices and prospects of the market.

Drought and shortage of range feed are the rancher's greatest hazards. The years 1953 to 1956 were particularly difficult in the area. All animals except the herd of cows and the current year's calf crop were sold in the summer of 1953. All calves were sold early in the fall, and the cow herd was culled closely. New bulls were bought in the spring of 1954, but supplies of feed continued to be short, and further culling was done throughout the year. Loans were obtained in the winter of 1954–1955, and grain feed was purchased under emergency programs. With the continuing drought, further sales of stock were made and additional emergency supplies of feed were purchased.

When rains and the spring grass failed to come in 1956, the remaining cattle were sold. Every means available to the rancher to keep the ranch a going concern had been exhausted. Drought had wiped out many years of work to build a good cow herd and a good range-management program. With the return of rains, he must rebuild his herd and rejuvenate the range, possibly by incurring heavy indebtedness. Both are slow and costly undertakings.

ANOTHER EXAMPLE, that of a sheep ranch in the Northwest, presents a different type of land use and operation. The rancher owns about 2 thousand acres of mountain foothill rangeland suitable for spring and fall range. This land is used with about 21 thousand acres of similar Federal land under permit from the Bureau of Land Management as a spring and fall range.

Summer range is obtained on a national forest. The summer range allotment covers an area approximately 3 by 6 miles in extent, but with only about 8,700 acres open and usable for grazing. All land in the summer allotment is Federal, except about 60 acres in scattered mining claims.

Winter feed is obtained from irrigated land in the Snake River Valley. The rancher owns 142 acres of irrigated farmland, but rents additional hayland or buys hay at other farms. The purchased hay usually is bought "in the sheep"—that is, sheep are moved to the farm where hay is grown and are fed there.

This ranch operates about 3,500 ewes of a Rambouillet crossbreed and uses mutton-type bucks of several breeds. Lambs are dropped in February while the sheep are still on the winter hayfields. This is earlier lambing than is common among most range sheep operations. It is made possible by feeding the ewes hay in winter and by providing lambing sheds or tents as protection from storms in late winter.

The ewes and their lambs are formed into three bands early in March and moved to spring range about 60 miles distant from the winter quarters. Sheep once were trailed long distances between seasonal ranges. Now movements are made by motortrucks on most ranches.

The sheep graze on the spring range until the middle of June. They start at the lower elevations and gradually work up until they reach higher foothill parts of the range at the end of the season. Shearing is done on the spring range in permanent shearing sheds and corrals.

Sheep are moved by truck to the mountain summer allotment the middle of June, about 40 miles. Both spring and early summer feed is excellent. Under these conditions, the ewes give maximum milk and lambs grow rapidly. Most of the lambs are ready for market by mid-July. Lambs ready for sale are shipped at that time. Ewes without lambs are then formed into a

single band for the rest of the summer.

Ewes still with their lambs are put in another band and are herded on the choice feed to get maximum growth on the lambs. The remaining lambs usually are shipped between mid-August and the first of September.

Ewes are then brought to farm stubblefields and irrigated pastures for the breeding season. Breeding in this way shortens the breeding season and requires fewer bucks than breeding on the range. After the breeding season, at least part of the ewes may be returned to the spring range for 2 to 3 months of fall grazing.

The rancher owns about one-tenth of his spring-fall range. The rest is Federal land under Bureau of Land Management administration.

He owns none of his summer range, except for a few acres originally alienated as mining claims, on which he has constructed the pens and loading chutes needed to handle the sheep. The summer range is administered by the Forest Service.

The rancher owns an irrigated farm of 142 acres of cropland that produces about half of his winter feed needs. He buys hay and feeds on other farms in the community.

This type of ranching operation requires a high order of managerial ability. Close coordination between sheep numbers and the method and time of movement of the sheep, on the one hand, and the management plans of the Forest Service, the Bureau of Land Management, the private landlord, and the rancher, on the other, is essential for successful operations.

THE THREE RANCHES in the illustrations are typical of a type of ranching in each of the areas, but they are not average. The average ranch is somewhat smaller than those I described. Many ranches are too small to provide satisfactory incomes to the ranch families, except under abnormally favorable price conditions and are too small to provide full employment to the rancher and his family.

Some financial aspects
of land use—Distribution of income from farmland—
How do you put a value on land?—Appraisal of farm real estate—
The market for farm real estate—The mechanics of land transfer—Borrowing money to purchase land—Insurance against losses on farms—How taxes affect the land and farmers—Getting started in farming is hard

Distribution of income from farmland.

The questions are simple: What is land worth? What is income from farmland? Who gets it? What does the land earn? On the answers depend changes in the use of the land, prices paid for land, the amount of land farmers use, the net amount that land can earn in any one use, and so on. The answers are based on no simple calculations. Taxes and public programs are among the factors that affect income from land. By *Virgil L. Hurlburt*, agricultural economist, Northern Field Research Section, Farm Economics Research Division.

WE USUALLY DEFINE income from farmland as the payment received for the use of the land. Our general meaning is clear, but we encounter difficulties when we try to make actual calculations, separate the income from land and the income from other resources, and distinguish between what land income is and who gets it.

We have to think in terms of the earnings of land as one of the factors in production—there must be some type of allocation of total farm returns among the many resources used in farming.

We have to think also in terms of the payment received as a reward for use of land—to set what land actually contributes to production apart from what land as a factor gets as a reward.

Land in the long run should receive as a reward for its use a payment that is exactly equal to its actual contribution to production. In the short run, there are many variables, differences in calculation procedures, and overlooked costs, so that the two are seldom the same.

Many diverse forces can affect the amount and the distribution of income from land. The more obvious are prices of farm products, costs, and relations between prices received and prices paid.

Anything that can affect the farm economy also affects the income from the land—all the influences of location with respect to markets for the services that land provides, the advantages of quality, and the kinds and amounts of other resources used with land.

A farm operator has a given set of resources—land, buildings, machinery, livestock, operating capital. Whether these resources are owned, hired, or rented need not confuse the issue; the pertinent point is that these different resources are combined in production.

For a given period, such as a year, the operator has fixed amounts of land, buildings, machinery, and the like. He adds to them some variable inputs of labor and capital (within the limits of his available operating capital) and produces a gross value of product or a gross return.

Let us assume that his records of costs and returns are realistic and complete. Total returns exceed total costs. What part of the total return is made up of earnings from land?

This question can be answered accurately if the operator knows from experience his additional costs and additional returns over a range of output. It can be answered reasonably if he knows that the return on the last unit of each type of variable input is above its cost. But this detail of information is not usually available. Often data on costs and returns are not complete.

Nonetheless, many operators know from experience which of their practices pay. They know also that each input contributes to gross product and therefore should share in the total return. They may or may not know that for their purpose in allocating returns the earning rate within the farm is more realistic as a basis for determining factor earnings than is some opportunity-earning rate outside the farm.

The average rate of return in the farm business—the total annual returns divided by the total annual costs—may be the most realistic and reasonable procedure for allocating returns to the different resources. By this calculation, income from land is the annual land cost times the rate of earning in the farm business.

The major differences of opinion concerning the calculation of land income generally center on the question of how to distribute total receipts in a business. How do land earnings differ from the reward attributed to land for the contribution it makes in production? Opinions vary among owners, tenants, lenders, and technicians.

THE CONSEQUENCES of results from using one method of estimating land income compared with another are many. Overestimation or underestimation of the income causes changes in use of land and of other resources. People own, control, and use land because of its capacity to produce income and to provide nonmonetary services. Their estimates of relations between land costs and returns, compared with those between costs of and returns from other resources, determine how much land they use and how they use it in combination with other resources. Estimates of income-producing capacity affect the prices paid for land. The price paid in turn affects the net amount that land can earn in any one use. Comparisons among uses determine whether land is used for agri-

culture, residence, industry, transportation, or recreation.

Within a farm business, an overestimate of land income prompts the individual to buy or rent more land, when his money could earn greater returns if used for fertilizer, weed spray, livestock, or drainage. Likewise, overestimation or underestimation influences the decisions made by nonfarmers as to investments in farm real estate.

WHO GETS THE INCOME from farmland? Here we must note the difference between land income and the claims or demands on income by individuals, families, or business organizations.

An operator uses farm income for both business and family purposes. Taxes and mortgages have first claim on income. From this viewpoint it is unimportant whether it is the land, the labor, or the fertilizer that earns the income in the farm firm.

But neither the legal claims nor the demands for family living determine the earnings of the factors. These claims determine the use of income. From the viewpoint of use of income, returns above costs may be used in any way that the claimants decide. There is no effect on resource use and production, except as investment requirements in the firm and personal desires for use of money compete for the funds available.

Who receives income from land in the individual firm and in the United States as a whole? The question differs from questions that deal with allocation of returns to factors of production. The issues become these: Who owns the factors? What is the effect of the distribution of ownership of factors on the distribution of incomes among people? What are the effects of claims, custom, and change on the distribution? Do landowners receive the income that land earns in the production process?

The answers vary by type of case. An owner-operator receives the income his land earns. What he does with it is another question. He may be heavily in debt, delinquent in taxes, and unable to meet his obligations. His creditors may exert their claims and collect from him. If the debt claims are not met, title to the land may change, and the new owner receives the income. These complexities should not be allowed to confuse the issue of who receives the income from land in an owner-operated farm. Income from land automatically accrues to the owner. The amount that he attributes to land depends on his assumptions or estimates as to income for his labor, management, buildings, machinery, and other inputs.

Farms rented for cash raise the question of whether the rental payment is the same as the land earnings. This depends on the method used in calculating land earnings. If both land and buildings are involved, part of the payment is for the use of buildings. Usually no distinction is made in practice; the two are combined into one lump sum. The owner makes the division between the two as sources of income.

Usually there is a lag between change in farm income and change in cash rent. Cash rents change slowly. The difference between cash rent as a customary payment and land earnings may be one of the reasons why relatively few farms are rented for cash.

The same types of questions apply to the farm that is rented on shares, but the adjustment to changes in prices of products and to rising or falling farm income is faster than in the case of cash rent. Whether the landowner receives the full amount that land earns is a matter of definition and calculation; it depends on the details of the individual leasing arrangement.

Annual payment for use of land is a share of products for about 70 percent of the land operated by tenants in the United States. How much of the share of product is defined as land income in the individual case or for a State or region depends on the assumptions made concerning income from other resources. Part of the rental payment is an income from buildings, seed, fertilizer, lime, or other inputs furnished.

The evidence we have suggests that under share leases only a small fraction of landowners receive as payment for use of their land the exact amount that land contributes to earnings on the farm in which it is used.

Rental arrangements are surprisingly similar over wide areas. Shares of crops, such as the 50–50 share on corn, are standardized from farm to farm. These general terms cannot be presumed to fit all rented farms equally well. The fault rests in the terms of leases—not in leasing as a form of land tenure. A workable agreement can be made to distribute income to owners of the resources on the same basis that each resource contributes to the earnings in the firm.

MANY OF THE DIFFICULTIES in estimating income from farmland result from the failure to distinguish between what land earns as a factor of production and the annual cost of obtaining the use of land. The two are related. One affects the other.

Customary practices in conducting farm businesses further confuse (rather than help clarify) the situation. The difficulty arises because some of the resources used are bought in regular markets and are paid at the regular market prices.

An example: Fertilizer is bought and used at a specific price per ton. Labor is hired at a given rate per month or per year. Both have their own market prices. Both are subtracted from gross farm returns. This procedure is proper and correct, in terms of the claim they have on income in the farm business. Neither labor nor fertilizer shares in the profit or loss of the firm. But rewarding such inputs at cost does not solve the problem of distributing returns above cost or suggest the answer to the question of how to allocate profits or losses.

From the viewpoint of earnings, the measurement problem is to determine the income-earning power of each input. This is necessary so the operator can plan the farm business. From the viewpoint of rewards, the question is: Who gets the income that the input earns? Who gets the reward cannot be used to determine the income earning of the input.

Profit or loss accrues to the farm operator—the one who makes the decisions and takes the risks in the farm business.

To DETERMINE HOW TO distribute profits in the farm business you have to establish a profit-and-loss account: Determine the amount that each factor contributes to gross income. Reward at cost all factors that are bought and used at their specific market prices—fertilizer, lime, hired labor, tractor fuel, spray materials, and so on. Designate as profit (or loss) any excess (or deficit) between factor earnings and factor costs. Treat this as profit, rather than as reward for the use of any one factor.

The importance of a profit-and-loss account in the farm business rests on its effect on decisions about how resources are to be combined to bring the greatest net returns.

If an earning is calculated for each factor, no one factor is arbitrarily rewarded with the profits (or loss) from others. This is particularly important for land, which is the largest single input in most farm businesses. Profits from other factors are often allocated to land and thereby in practice are designated as land income. This tends to overestimate the economic importance of land and causes competitive bidding beyond the price warranted by the actual earnings of land.

We need to know more about the actual earnings of all inputs, including land. We need to separate earnings from rewards at the farm level and at the area and national levels.

TAXES are among the other factors that affect income from land.

Many conflicting opinions exist about the effect of taxes and who pays them. Property taxes are levied on real estate and are a first claim on earnings as well as a legal claim on title. Specific assessments are made on land. Does the land actually pay the tax? The answer is not so simple as it would appear to be.

Property taxes are an overhead cost to the farm business. Although assessed to land and collected from the owner of land, the tax can be paid only from income of the business as a whole or from other income of the landowner. Until land is combined with other resources, it has no income. This works out the same whether the farm is owner operated or tenant operated. The landowner is responsible for payment of the tax.

The usual procedure in both owner- and tenant-operated farms is to calculate a gross return to land. Land taxes then are deducted as a cost. The balance is supposed to represent the owner's return on his investment in land. But does it?

I CONTEND that property taxes are a separate and distinct type of cost. People do not invest money in taxes as a production cost in the same sense that they invest in land, machinery, seed, and fertilizer. The landowner cannot arbitrarily pay more taxes to increase gross returns or pay less taxes to lower costs. Any cost-accounting procedure that handles property taxes purely and simply as a land cost therefore gives an erroneous picture of the actual net earnings of land.

A more realistic way to determine the earnings of each factor is to subtract property taxes from gross farm income and then allocate the balance to the different factors. Here again, the distinction is between what land actually contributes to production and what the land—the owner—receives as a payment.

If property taxes were charged as an overhead cost to the farm business rather than as a land cost, the calculated earnings of land would be somewhat higher. The difference between land income calculated by charging taxes as an overhead cost of the business versus charging them as a land cost would be less than the present land tax per acre. Land would still bear a large share of the tax cost, because land is a large proportion of total inputs in the farm business.

Property taxes are one of the items of cost that affect choice of farms by buyers. Differences in rates between tax districts influence decisions of buyers. Tax structure is thus imbedded in the structure of land prices. And land prices as a cost are one of the determinants of land returns.

The actual effects of property taxes on the use of land and on income as a whole are probably less important than are their reputed effects.

Changes in taxes, particularly increases in taxes, apparently receive more attention than do changes in other phases of the agricultural economy. This is in keeping with tradition and custom. Taxes are usually "too high." Part of the outlook on taxes no doubt results from the fact that the direct benefits of expenditures of tax funds for schools, roads, and police protection are less obvious to individuals than are personal expenditures for automobiles, beefsteak, and television.

The capital gains tax undoubtedly influences the prices that investors are willing to pay and what is done with land. Potential buyers are aware of the difference between the tax rate on capital gains and that on annual income.

We have no data to prove that the prices of land and the income from land reflect the actions of those who take advantage of the provisions of the laws. Knowledge of these provisions is present as an inducement to action, however. Expenditures for land improvements are an allowable deduction for income-tax purposes. Only a part of the increase in value is taxed when a property is sold. The thinking investor has an income incentive to bid up the price of land and to make capital improvements beyond their current income-earning effects in the farm business.

MANY PUBLIC PROGRAMS affect the amount and the distribution of income from farmland.

Some of the programs are so much an accepted part of the continuing process of social change that we may not question or notice their indirect effects. The change in the use of land from agricultural to residential is an example. Tax funds are used to provide the public facilities needed and wanted by people who move outside the city limits. The existence of the facilities is in itself an encouragement for more people to move to the country. The whole movement causes a rise in the market price of land and necessitates increased property taxes.

Increased costs lower the net income of land used for farming. A drop in income encourages the transfer of land to nonagricultural use. It is estimated that land in urban areas increased by about 395 thousand acres a year between 1945 and 1954. It no longer produces farm income. The trend will continue, but it will have little effect on total income from farmland because the areas involved are only small fractions of land used for agricultural purposes. But the small areas involved do not deny the need to plan carefully each area of urban development to increase the advantages and reduce the costs of change.

Public programs have long affected the ownership of land. Sales at nominal prices, preemption, acreage limits in homesteads, and other phases of the public land acts gave many people claims to income from the land. The history of American development would have been quite different if the land policy had been patterned after the Crown grants in the Colonies.

Another program is the Farm Credit Administration, whose history is a chronology of change in agricultural finance. What might interest rates on mortgages have been otherwise? How many more farms would have been foreclosed had it not been for the refinancing program of the early 1930's? The amount and the distribution of income from land today are not what they would be without the 25 years of price-support programs. Market prices of many products have been above support levels at times and below support levels at other times. Farm incomes have been favorable and depressed. Whether support levels were too high or too low, effective or ineffective, and necessary or unnecessary are debated issues. There is little doubt, however, that the existence of the programs has removed some of the uncertainty as to the income from farmland.

PROMISES OF SUPPORT at designated percentages of parity have acted as floor prices for producers of basic crops. Reduction of uncertainty, through the existence of floors, has been an incentive to production. The belief that farm income will not be allowed to continue its downward trend has been reflected in the farmland market. Prices of farmland continued to advance in 1955 and 1956. Evidently the prospects for land income are still sufficient to warrant investment in land by farmers and others.

Land performs a strategic function in distributing the benefits from price-support programs. Compliance, a prerequisite to benefits, is established on the basis of acreage allotments per farm. One must own or control land to receive price support. Inasmuch as the benefit is tied to land, the program creates the incentive for at least part of the benefits to be capitalized into land values.

Any restrictions on production also strengthen the interest of farm operators in obtaining more land. A larger acreage means a larger allotment. Machinery, equipment, labor, and available operating capital can be used to capacity on the larger acreage. Each producer who is interested in buying land to add to his operating unit has at least one important question to answer: Does the income I can attribute to land warrant the price I must pay to get it?

ONLY GENERAL STATEMENTS can be made about trends in income from farmland. The only regularly published estimates are the estimates of net rent paid. Conclusions about income for any one year or a period of years must be based largely on assumption as to relations between several variables. One must also keep in mind the distinction between what landowners receive as a gross return from several factors. The difference is that between land earnings and rewards.

Because gross farm income includes returns to many other factors, changes in farm income do not reflect adequately the changes in land income.

Calculations of income from land as the contribution of land to the earnings in agriculture in any one year are complicated by what happens to livestock prices. A rapid rise (or fall) in the price of beef has a tremendous effect on farmers' realized gross income and on net income. The index of prices received by farmers for meat animals changed from 361 in 1948, to 409 in 1951, and to 296 in 1953. How much of the difference in farm income that resulted from a drop of 20 dollars in the price of beef within a period of a year should be reflected in the income from land?

The same type of question applies to other livestock, whether on the range in Montana, the feedlot in Iowa, or the dairy farm in Wisconsin.

The practical answer is to separate crop and livestock enterprises for cost accounting and income calculation purposes. A farm that produces any type of livestock is essentially two businesses organized vertically. Crop products are inputs in the livestock side of the combined businesses. Land income logically must be calculated in terms of the value of the crops produced and sold to the livestock enterprise. Whether the livestock enterprise makes a profit or a loss is another, though related, question. Crop and livestock enterprises are tied together in one operating firm. Failure on the livestock side spells failure for the business as a whole—possibly foreclosure or bankruptcy. Relations between crop and livestock production within farms are part of the explanation of why trends in returns from livestock also affect land values.

Data on farm income and costs are not detailed enough to permit a reliable estimate of land earnings as a part of farm income. Crop and livestock enterprises cannot be separated accurately, as there is no feasible way to separate the costs in the aggregate data for States and areas. This can be done for one farm if cost-returns data are complete. Even then some charge to (and income from) land must be included in the livestock enterprise. Land makes a contribution beyond the value of the crops produced, in the form of feedlots and the like.

Income from land is sometimes estimated by applying the current rate of interest on farm mortgages to current land values. The value of land only (excluding buildings) was estimated at about 85 billion dollars as of March 1, 1957. If an interest rate of 5 percent is allowed, the annual return to land would have been about 4,250 million dollars, or 12 percent of realized gross farm income in 1956.

The estimate of 4,250 million dollars, made by applying the mortgage interest rate to the market value of farmland, is a fairly realistic estimate of the annual cost of using farmland. It is an inaccurate, oversimplified, and even erroneous estimate of land earnings. It is in error because: The interest rate is a cost indicator and because (if all other costs are handled in the same way) there is no explanation of what happens to the excess or deficit between total costs and total returns in the individual farm firm or for the State or Nation.

Net rent to landlords is also used as an estimate of return to farmland. It is probably a better estimate than is interest on land value, but it only partly indicates the contribution of land to value of production. Net rents of landlords are calculated by subtracting selected expenses of landlords from their gross rents. This assumes that landlord expenditures for operation and maintenance earn only their costs in the firms. Any excess above cost is thereby arbitrarily allocated to land.

THE ACREAGE used for agricultural production has remained fairly stable for many years. The quality and value of land has increased since 1940, however. But even greater increases took place in the other resources used. That means that for the Nation and for the average commercial farm, land is now a relatively smaller part of total inputs than it was in the past. Mechanization and other forms of technology have increased capital requirements per farm, and therefore income from land should be a smaller part of farm income than it was in 1940 or 1945.

The value of land in 1910 was 69 percent of the value of the physical assets of farming; in 1956, it was 60 percent. The changes in physical assets do not include the changes in operating costs, such as extra fertilizer.

The total value of real estate tripled between 1910 and 1955, whereas current operating expenses increased about sixfold. Thus the trend in income from farmland is downward relative to farm income and total national income.

WHAT ABOUT THE FUTURE? Most of the answers will be given by individuals who make decisions for their own actions. There is little prospect that public programs will be developed to control prices of farmland or to regulate the distribution of income from it. Requirements in administrative detail alone practically preclude direct control programs—but many public actions will have influence in the future. Among them are highway construction, price support for farm products, and taxes.

What can the individual—you—do? He can think and act more in terms of what land actually contributes to the value of production and less in terms of what the owner receives as a reward.

How do you put a value on land?

Loans, taxes, rentals, and sales of farmland and even efficiency of production often depend on the changing, indefinite thing we call "value." Here an agricultural economist explores the bases of values—expected income, amenity factors, prices, the land market, past sales, improvements, and mineral rights. Knowledge of them is highly important to many persons who every year must put a value on a piece of land. By *William H. Scofield*, Farm Economics Research Division.

THE VALUE placed on farmland and buildings for sale, tax, or credit purposes has a dollars-and-cents meaning to every landowner. For the half-million persons involved in market transfers each year, fixing that value may be the most important business decision they have ever made. The size of one's tax bill depends in part on the valuation the assessor makes.

New mortgage loans totaling more than 2 billion dollars and secured by farm real estate are made annually. A fifth of this amount comprises the insurance premiums and reserves invested by life-insurance companies. What happens to the market value of farmland therefore can be of concern to every holder of life insurance.

How would you go about evaluating land and how, indeed, would you define land?

Land in a strict economic sense is a natural resource that consists only of the soil and the topographic, climatic, and location features associated with it.

Yet varying amounts of capital and labor are incorporated with practically all land used for agricultural production. Land therefore seldom is valued apart from the structures, man-made fertility, and other improvements that have been made on it.

Furthermore, land is multipurpose. It can contribute to the production of many products and yield intangible services and satisfactions. Its value cannot be separated from its use or from the capital and labor that must be combined with it to make it productive.

So we are concerned with the valuation of a bundle of productive resources that together constitute farm real estate. I use the terms "land," "farmland," and "rural property" interchangeably in this chapter to mean farm property as it is bought, sold, and valued in the market.

THE WORDS "value" and "price" have many meanings.

Value is the intrinsic worth of any good or service for satisfying human wants.

Price is simply a measurement of value in terms of money.

A price is established whenever one sells farm real estate. The value of a particular farm or of all farms in the country can be estimated on the basis of the price at which a relatively few properties have been transferred or in terms of the income that is expected to be received in the future.

Records of farm sales in Brown County, Kans., for example, show that 41 properties were sold at an average price of 129 dollars an acre in 1953. The total value of all farms in Kansas was estimated at 4,150 million dollars that year, or an average value of 83.56 dollars an acre. All farm real estate in the United States was estimated to have a market value of about 116 billion dollars on March 1, 1958.

Because price is the chief economic regulator in our economy, the prices established for farmland determine how much land will be combined with other productive factors in a particular farm business and in agriculture as a whole.

Market forces seek constantly to find the correct proportions of the various productive factors to be combined so that each will yield the same return. If land is high and labor is cheap relative to land, more labor is applied to a given tract of land.

If machinery is cheap relative to labor, additional machinery will be used to the point at which the return from the additional machinery will just cover its cost.

Because farmland (with buildings) represents about three-fourths of all physical assets used in agriculture, the valuation placed on land relative to other productive factors affects the efficiency with which food and fiber is produced.

If land is overvalued, the individual farm operator may so deplete his capital by the purchase of a farm that he has too little money left to buy the necessary machinery and livestock and to meet current operating expenses.

If land is undervalued, it may encourage wasteful use or an extensive level of cultivation.

ANTICIPATED FUTURE INCOME from farmland provides the primary basis of value.

Income may derive from the sale of farm products.

Income may also derive from such intangible services and personal satisfactions as view, historical association, community advantages, location with respect to persons and places, and the sense of security achieved from ownership of land. Such amenity values vary considerably among different groups, individuals, areas, and times. They may add to or subtract from productive value. Because a farm is both a business and a home, amenity values usually raise market values somewhat above those that would be justified by productive value alone.

Only two things are needed to arrive at the productive value of farm real estate. If an annual net income of 10 dollars an acre is expected from farmland and the acceptable rate of return is 5 percent, the capitalized value of the land is 200 dollars.

The valuation process for land is no different from that for stocks or other resources from which income is derived. The difficulties arise in separating the net income from farmland from the income obtained from the other resources used in farm production.

Rents paid for the use of land provide one measure of the income derived from it. If rents are paid in cash, net rents can be used as a measure of land income to be capitalized. Nearly three-fourths of all land is rented for a share of the crops or for a share of crops and livestock, however. In order to use this form of rental income, future yields, as well as future prices, must be estimated.

Estimation of future prices of farm products is a difficult problem in valuation because it requires also some estimate of general economic trends. Because one cannot predict these trends with certainty, the level of values established at any particular time is based on the collective judgments of both sellers and buyers as to the most probable prices that will prevail for farm products in the future.

Past prices are an imperfect guide, but one relies heavily on them in the valuation process. More errors in valuation have been made with respect to price expectations than with respect to quantities of farm products to be realized or the rate to be used in capitalization.

Some experts maintain that these problems of estimating future prices and net income from land make the capitalization method of valuation unworkable in practice. The method sometimes produces results that are inconsistent with market or sales values. In areas where farmland seldom is rented, it is difficult to determine net land income on the basis of rents. Then one relies more on sales prices as a measure of value. I discuss this basis for valuation later.

The idea that "normal" values of farmland could be determined received much attention in the 1930's.

Credit agencies particularly sought such a standard to guide their mortgage policies. By limiting mortgage loans to a fraction of such values, they hoped to insure the safety of their funds and to minimize the necessity of foreclosure.

Certain assumptions with respect to prices of farm products and costs of goods and services used in farm production were necessary to establish normal values. Average prices received for farm products in an earlier period when prices and costs were assumed to be in balance usually were taken. Because the parity concept relied heavily upon the period 1910–1914 as representing normal conditions for agriculture, the calculation of normal values for farmland were also tied to that period. Levels of values that would prevail with other assumed levels of commodity prices and costs also were derived, based on the relationships in that period.

As prices of farm products and farm income moved progressively upward after 1940, the normal values for farmland which were based on the 1910–1914 or 1935–1939 relationships became more and more unrealistic. Lenders were slow at first to adjust upward the basis for normal values. They believed that previous price relationships would return when the war was over. When postwar price adjustments did not occur, further modifications in the concept of normal values became necessary. Less attention is given today to the idea that long-range predictions as to future levels of land values can be made with any certainty.

The concept of normal values rested on the expectation that the economy would be static. Advancing farm technology and the growth characteristics evident in our general economy since the end of the Second World War represent important new factors that were not recognized in the original concept. Nor was adequate recognition given to the form and duration of the Government programs for agriculture that have evolved. Modifications in these programs that are likely to occur in the future also should be taken into account.

THE VALUATION OF FARMLAND takes place in a market that is unique.

We often speak of the land market as though it were similar to those that exist for farm products, but actually it has few of the usual characteristics of a market. The term "market" implies a known number of trading centers where prices are established and goods or services are exchanged.

If a marketing system is to perform well its basic functions of establishing prices and distributing goods and services, it should have several characteristics. A free flow of information among suppliers and prospective buyers is essential. All parties should know the quantities available and the quantities needed at any particular time. The goods or services to be exchanged should be sufficiently mobile so that surpluses and deficits in various parts of the country can be corrected. The commodities should be identifiable by grade or quality so that sellers and buyers can arrive at a price with full knowledge as to what they are pricing.

The market for farmland has few or none of these characteristics. Prices are usually established between seller and buyer without making others aware that a farm or tract is for sale. Prospective buyers often restrict themselves to a small geographic area. They seek only a particular tract that best suits their needs and disregard all others. A prospective buyer in New York or Chicago faces an impossible task if he tries to learn of all the farms that may be for sale in Iowa at any particular time. At best, he can select one from perhaps a dozen that he is able to inspect and appraise. Usually, also, the seller brings his property to the attention of only a few potential buyers. Real-estate brokers and national listing services seek to correct for this limited geographic scope of the land market by multiple listing services, catalogs, and personal contacts with other brokers. Only a small fraction of all farms are sold through such channels, however.

Public auction provides more nearly the ideal of a broad market that permits competitive bidding. Property to be sold at auction usually is advertised throughout a county, and the maximum number of prospective buyers have a chance to bid. Only about 10 percent of farm sales are made at auction, however.

The almost complete lack of any grade or quality standards for farmland is a serious limitation to a more efficient market: A carload of No. 2 winter wheat is priced and ownership is transferred, and neither buyer nor seller sees the wheat.

The west half of the southwest quarter of section 12, township 9, range 1 east of the 6th principal meridian is a specific parcel of land, but its legal description reveals nothing as to its value. It could be a swamp, a sand dune, or a field that can grow 100 bushels of corn to the acre. Actually, it is a tract of 80 acres in Seward County, Nebr. It sold for 10,300 dollars in the fall of 1956. Only a personal inspection and detailed appraisal could determine whether that was a reasonable market value.

Despite these obvious limitations of the land market, the forces of supply and demand operate to establish a level of prices in much the same way as they do for other goods and services. In effect, hundreds and possibly thousands of small local markets exist in which sellers and buyers make valuation judgments daily.

A level of values becomes established in each community. This level reflects people's judgments as to productive and amenity values. Factors like weather and crop conditions, trends in prices of farm products, and general economic and political developments are appraised constantly to learn their possible effects on future returns from farmland.

Value judgments concerning land are slower to change than those for most other productive factors. This stems basically from the fact that land yields a flow of income over an extended period, and a change in income for a year or two is not too important unless people expect it to continue. Higher farm earnings for a single year (or even for several years) are largely discounted unless it seems certain that they will continue for a considerable period. Even then, the full increase (or decrease) is seldom reflected in land values.

The amount and rate of response in an area depends on how fast individual farmers can adjust their production to take advantage of favorable prices for certain commodities and the relative importance of the land and nonland inputs in the production process. Thus changes in the prices of crops usually have a more direct and immediate effect on the price of land than do changes in the prices of livestock or livestock products.

SELLERS AND BUYERS use past sales in their communities as a guide in setting their asking and offering prices. This method of valuation has several limitations. Because no two farms or parcels of land are identical, considerable judgment is needed to adjust for the differences that exist between the properties used as a standard and the particular property for which a value is desired. More important, the acceptance of recent prices as a standard assumes that they are a true indication of value.

A study of the circumstances of each sale often reveals that personal factors have modified the price that would have been indicated by the earning capacity of the property. Particularly is that true of the amenity values—. the intangible ones that vary among individuals. One person may want a property because it is near other land he owns or is close to relatives. Another person may attach more value to a property because it reminds him of southern Minnesota or is near a good school or is in a community that he considers desirable.

Some types of amenity values—highways, schools, nearness to towns—become well established and can be measured by observing past sales. Other types stem largely from the personal preferences of the individuals who buy and sell. They cannot be measured in the aggregate.

Although average sales prices in a community or county provide a general guide to the value of specific properties, they must be used with caution. The inherent physical characteristics of farmland vary so widely, even in small areas, that both sales prices and productive values show a wide range.

A sample of 2,249 sales in the western Corn Belt in 1955–1956, for example, showed an average price of 162 dollars an acre. Even if we disregard the highest and lowest 10 percent of the sales, a price range of from 60 dollars to 345 dollars an acre remains. Although the range is normally less for smaller areas, some knowledge of the proportion of all sales prices that were made near the average is desirable if one is to use the sales price comparison method.

IMPROVEMENTS TO FARMLAND present a special problem of valuation. Such improvements as buildings and fences are easily identified and can be valued separately. Others, such as tile drains and past management practices, are so much a part of the land that separate valuation is seldom possible, except as they may be reflected in crop yields.

A common procedure for valuing buildings and other structures for which replacement costs are obtainable is to determine the cost of rebuilding them and then to adjust it for depreciation and obsolescence. It is hard to determine the expected life of various types of buildings and to make proper allowance for functional obsolescence.

New methods of handling and storing hay and forage crops and more efficient housing for livestock have reduced greatly the economic value of many farm buildings that were put up a generation ago.

Many farmhouses that were designed to accommodate a much larger labor force than is now used on farms also have suffered from obsolescence, even though they remain structurally sound.

The economic or productive value of farm buildings often is appreciably less than would be obtained by the cost-less-depreciation method. But because buildings seldom are sold separately from the land, their market value can be only approximated by observing the difference in sales prices of comparable farmland with and without buildings. On this basis for valuation, all farm buildings were estimated to have a market value of 24.6 billion dollars on March 1, 1957. This amount was about 22.5 percent of the value of farm real estate and the lowest proportion since annual estimates were started in 1940.

This downward trend in the value of farm buildings relative to bare land followed the rapid increase in size of farms, which has created a surplus of farm buildings in some areas. The economic value of buildings on farms that are combined with others is sharply reduced, even though on a cost-less-depreciation basis they have the same value as before. In some areas, notably the western Corn Belt and the Great Plains, sales prices of farmland without buildings are often nearly as high as those for farms with buildings.

The same distinction between the cost of replacement and economic value that exists for farm buildings also applies to other capital improvements that have been made. Once such investments are made, they cannot be recovered without sale of the entire property. The basis of value tends to be the additional income that can be realized from them, but it is difficult to separate such income from the income obtained from other factors.

Some investments, like land clearing, drainage, and irrigation, often add more than their cost to the sale price of a farm. Others are often of value only to a particular owner, and their cost can be recovered only partially in the market.

SUBSURFACE RIGHTS have become an important new factor in the valuation of farmland in some parts of the country.

Increasing demands for oil and gas have extended explorations into areas that previously were believed to have little promise. Present and prospective owners consequently have become more conscious of the three-dimensional legal nature of land.

Ownership of land in fee simple extends below the surface and indefinitely upward; the separation of title into the subsurface, surface, and air right portions is permitted. For all practical purposes, airspace in the open country has ceased to be recognized as privately owned because control of aviation has been assumed by the Federal Government. In approaches to airfields and in downtown business areas, air rights often are valuable property rights.

Rights to minerals that may exist below the surface can be conveyed by mineral deed in much the same way as other interests in real estate. Although mineral rights usually refer to oil and gas, they also include lignite, salt, coal, taconite, metallic ores, and many other substances. A mineral deed may specify only certain minerals, or it may convey ownership of these minerals for a specific term of years. A seller of farmland, by specific wording in the land deed, may retain all, part, or none of the mineral rights. The fraction of the mineral rights that "go with the land" is important in influencing sales prices in some areas.

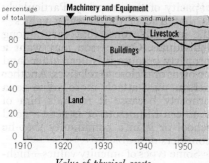

Value of physical assets.

A study in three counties in Oklahoma showed that sales prices of land with all mineral rights were 10.25 dollars to 32.10 dollars an acre higher than similar land that was sold with none of the mineral rights. In Smith County, Tex., in the heart of the eastern Texas oilfield, land sold with all mineral rights intact brought an average price of 45 dollars an acre in 1945, but land with all rights reserved sold for 17 dollars an acre.

Owners of mineral rights may receive an income from the rights in several ways. The commonest, in terms of acreage, is through the granting of oil and gas leases to oil companies that wish to explore and develop such resources. Such leases are written usually for 5 or 10 years; they specify an annual rate of payment per mineral acre. A mineral acre is the number of surface acres times the fractional part of the mineral rights owned by a particular lessor. When competition among companies is strong, a bonus may be paid when the lease is signed initially. The oil company retains its rights to develop and explore a particular tract as long as it makes the annual lease payment, within the initial term of the lease.

Owners of mineral rights are estimated to receive at least 500 million dollars annually from lease payments. Rates of 50 cents or 1 dollar per mineral acre are common in localities where prospects for production are moderately good, but can range much higher in or near proved areas.

If oil or gas is found in commercial quantities, royalty payments are made to landowners and other holders of the oil and gas rights in producing acreages. The customary royalty is one-eighth of the oil and gas produced and marketed from the tract.

Although income per acre from royalties is much larger than that from leases, it is concentrated among fewer recipients. In the 13-State area extending from Montana and North Dakota southward to New Mexico, Texas, Louisiana, and Mississippi, royalties paid by oil companies have ranged from 562 million dollars to 751 million dollars annually since 1948. In this area, income from lease bonuses and annual rental payments have totaled about 275 million dollars annually since 1950.

Coal, lignite, lead, and many other minerals also are often mined on a royalty basis. If coal is close enough to the surface to permit strip mining, full title to both the surface and the coal vein is usually acquired by the coal company, as stripping operations largely destroy the surface for farming purposes. The land may still have value for forestry or recreation after the stripping operations have ceased.

Royalty rights may be valued and transferred separately from mineral rights by a royalty deed. This conveys a specified share of the owner's royalty if and when oil or gas is produced. A landowner whose title includes mineral rights may sell the land and part of the mineral rights but retain part or all of the royalty right. The owner of royalty rights has no control over the granting of leases and does not share in the lease payments. The only income that can be derived from royalty rights consequently is the income realized when oil or gas is actually produced.

Because the occurrence, amount, and quality of mineral resources cannot be determined without extensive exploration, followed by drilling operations, the valuation of the various kinds of interests in minerals is highly speculative. Further, even when mineral resources have been located, they are subject to depletion and exhaustion and the total income to be derived from them cannot be known in advance. Even so, the amount of mineral rights that go with the land is often a point of bargaining when farmland is sold.

Value per acre of farm real estate.

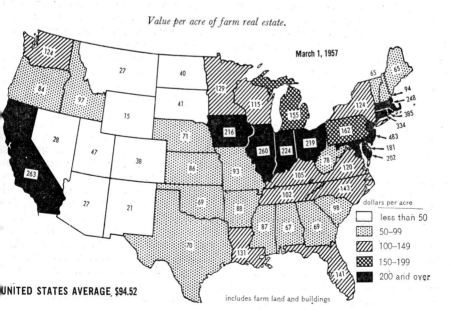

UNITED STATES AVERAGE, $94.52

includes farm land and buildings

Appraisal of farm real estate.

The previous chapter stressed the theory of land value and difficulties in fixing values. This one has a more practical approach to methods of estimating farm productivity and value as a basis for farm loans, tax assessments, farm ratings in Government programs, land classification, and the purchase, sale, and condemnation of farms. The major techniques involved in two of many methods of appraisal, which may be varied with the purpose, are cited. By *William G. Murray*, Department of Agricultural Economics and Rural Sociology, Iowa State College, and *Joseph Ackerman*, managing director, Farm Foundation.

A FARM can be appraised in many ways, but the more important methods can all be reduced to two—comparisons of income and sale value.

A physical inventory is the first step in both. It gives a detailed picture of the farm to be appraised.

To clarify the procedure, we list each of the inventory items covered in an actual appraisal. Individual appraisals vary in the emphasis they place on the different items. For example, a description of fruit trees and irrigation works may be required in an orchard area, but not in a Corn Belt farming area.

Legal description is the first step in a systematic appraisal. This identification should be established beyond any doubt by the use of maps and the exact wording of the legal description.

County plat books or similar local maps provide quick reference guides for locating the farm to be appraised with regard to towns, roads, schools, and other local features. The plat book generally shows farm boundaries and the name of the owner at the time the plat map was prepared. If the farm boundaries are not clear—as in instances where fractional tracts or irregular boundaries occur—you can get accurate information from the county office where the official county plats are kept.

Each tract of land has its own legal description, which distinguishes it from all other land. It is the legal description that appears on the deed of transfer. Since this subject is discussed in a later chapter (page 206), we mention here only the special concern of the appraiser.

The two major systems in the United States are metes and bounds on the one hand, and rectangular survey on the other. The appraiser's task in both instances is to make sure that the legal description fits the boundaries of the farm exactly.

A good practice to follow in reading rectangular survey descriptions is to work backward, starting at the end and taking individually each unit separated by the word "and."

Here, for example, is a legal description: *NE¼ NE¼ NE¼ of Section 10 and NW¼ and N½ SW¼ of Section 11 in Township 83 North, Range 24 West of the 5th Principal Meridian.*

It would be handled as follows: The location of township and range and sections would be noted first. In Section 11 the SW¼ would be located and the north one-half of this unit would be outlined as part of the farm. Then the NW¼ of Section 11 would be outlined, and so on. The total acreage of this farm should be 250 acres, more or less.

As a test of your ability in this respect, you may want to check this acreage for yourself and at the same time draw the boundaries of the farm.

An appraisal map is a common part of a detailed appraisal. The preparation of this map, which one sketches in roughly as he makes a systematic trip over the entire farm, calls for a ready knowledge of the soils of the area. The objective is to provide a picture of the soils on the farm so that someone who has not seen the farm can visualize it.

The appraisal map should show the area of different soils which vary in their producing ability. For example, if roughly 35 acres are sandy, droughty soil, they should be shown; if 80 acres are highly productive silt loam soil, the areas where this soil occurs should be mapped.

Abbreviations or legends are used commonly in detailed appraisal maps to indicate the name of the soil, its surface soil depth, and the percentage of slope.

Drainage, permanent pasture, orchards, timber, farmstead, and other features of the landscape are included on the appraisal map. In fact, any important physical factor that affects the value of the farm should be noted on the map in order to make the inventory complete and authoritative.

Aerial maps save time in preparing appraisal maps. An aerial map in appropriate scale, usually available at the local ASC office, can be traced to get the major outline of the appraisal map. The details can then be filled in as one systematically walks over and inspects the farm.

A soil auger or spade should be used on this trip to test the depth of the surface soil and the quality of the subsoil. Depth, the third dimension of the land, is frequently overlooked, but it is often the most important factor in determining the productivity and value of a farm.

Estimating soil productivity is the next step. The appraisal map can be used to estimate the number of acres of different kinds of soil. Then the yielding ability of these different soils can be estimated for the major crops grown on that soil. If we are appraising rangeland, the carrying capacity of different types of range can be estimated.

This estimation of productivity is a difficult step, but it is essential because differences in productive capacity provide the main basis for determining the final appraisal values. Information as to yield by counties and for different types of soil is becoming more readily available. Soil survey publications of the Department of Agriculture and the State agricultural experiment stations are invaluable.

The appraiser must be able to recognize differences in productive characteristics. In the cotton territory, he has to be able to identify high, medium, and low cotton-producing land; in the Corn Belt, high, medium, and low corn-producing land; and in range areas, high, medium, and low carrying-capacity range. The use of bench-mark yields for certain soils and constant observation and comparisons with reported yields help one to acquire this ability.

CROPPING SYSTEM AND MANAGEMENT can be estimated with the information available on soil productivity. For general farming areas, this step calls for an average rotation with estimated crop yields. Estimates in range areas would be made on total carrying capacity of the ranch. The likely production would be estimated on an annual basis in areas that produce fruit and vegetables.

A danger in this procedure is failure to make proper allowance for management and the use of fertilizer. A poor soil may produce well in the hands of a top operator who uses ample fertilizer. An excellent soil may produce low yields in the hands of an inept

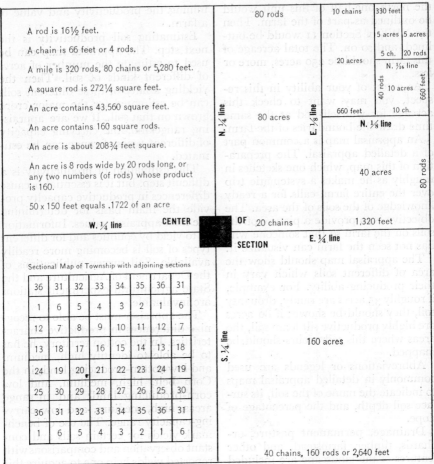

A rod is 16½ feet.

A chain is 66 feet or 4 rods.

A mile is 320 rods, 80 chains or 5,280 feet.

A square rod is 272¼ square feet.

An acre contains 43,560 square feet.

An acre contains 160 square rods.

An acre is about 208¾ feet square.

An acre is 8 rods wide by 20 rods long, or any two numbers (of rods) whose product is 160.

50 x 150 feet equals .1722 of an acre

Sectional Map of Township with adjoining sections

36	31	32	33	34	35	36	31
1	6	5	4	3	2	1	6
12	7	8	9	10	11	12	7
13	18	17	16	15	14	13	18
24	19	20	21	22	23	24	19
25	30	29	28	27	26	25	30
36	31	32	33	34	35	36	31
1	6	5	4	3	2	1	6

A section of land—640 acres.

manager who uses poor seed and no fertilizer and does a poor job of seedbed preparation, cultivation, and harvesting. An appraiser should see the inherent qualities of the land independent of management.

BUILDINGS, including both the dwelling and all other farm buildings and improvements attached to the land, have to be inventoried in a detailed appraisal. We include only buildings attached to the land with a foundation or other means that make them part of the farm real estate.

At this stage we are interested only in the physical aspect of the buildings—not their dollar value. We are concerned with measurements and a description of their condition, capacity, adaptabiliy, and arrangement.

Just as we inventoried the soil to determine what it could produce, so also we want to estimate what the buildings will contribute. We want to know, for example, how much grain storage is available on a grain-producing farm and the condition of the storage facilities. In this inventory, buildings should be studied from the standpoint of their usefulness. What is the present and likely utility of an old horsebarn?

Classification of the farm or of the land by itself completes the physical inventory. In this step we assign to the farm or land a class number or letter that conveys to the reader the kind of a producing unit it is. All of the various physical aspects are summed up in one number or letter in this classifying process. For example, if we have 5 classes, A through E, and the farm we appraise is assigned the letter "B," this denotes a definite quality of physical assets, which will be described in a legend or scale accompanying the classification rating.

The classification process is explained in the chapter on page 362.

THE INCOME METHOD can be used for valuation after the physical production estimates for a farm or tract of land have been made. The process of arriving at an income value involves three important steps or techniques. These are estimating gross income, estimating expenses, and capitalizing net income to obtain what is called income value.

Gross income can be estimated under a landlord-tenant situation or under owner operation. Income is estimated by both methods in some appraisals. In localities where renting is not common, the owner-operation method is usually preferred.

The landlord-share method is desirable in places where renting is common.

The landlord-share method has the advantage, other things being equal, because fewer expense items need to be estimated. It also provides a preliminary basis for land valuation, because the rent represents the annual value of the land—that is, the value for the use of the farm for a year. This rental value for a year is a gross figure, from which estimated landlord expenses have to be deducted to arrive at the annual net income value.

Income items that should be considered in a farm appraisal are shown in appraisals of the Federal Land Bank and the Farmers Home Administration.

445509°—58——14

The Federal Land Bank appraisal gives estimates for both owner operation and landlord-tenant arrangements.

The Farmers Home Administration appraisal contains a detailed estimate of owner-operator income because the loan based on one of these FHA appraisals may represent a large percentage of the farm value and accordingly must be tied closely to the specific income potentialities of the applicant for the loan.

Selection of prices received for farm products is an important and difficult step in the income estimating procedure. The choice of price levels—whether it be 20-cent, 25-cent, or 30-cent cotton, or corn at 1, 1.25, or 1.50 dollars a bushel, for example—sets the general level for income, expenses, and land values. The major requirement in the selection is a clear recognition of what is being done—namely, making an estimate of what is likely to be the price level in the years ahead, with declining emphasis on the years progressively farther in the future.

Some appraisers and appraisal agencies prefer to use an average of some recent period as their estimate of the future, say the past 10, 15, or 20 years. This procedure, applied mechanically, sometimes produces strange results. More common is the selection of price estimates which, although roughly in line with recent price levels, are the best judgment of the appraiser or appraisal agency regarding what is likely to occur in the next few years. The prices used in the Federal Land Bank and Farmers Home Administration appraisals can be noted as an example of this type of estimate.

The American Society of Farm Managers and Rural Appraisers in cooperation with the Doane Agricultural Service since 1950 has issued a series of standard prices which they recommend for use in estimates of income. These standard prices are selected by a committee of appraisers and agricultural economists after reviewing all available information. The committee, for example, set a corn price of 88 cents a bushel in 1950, 1.04 dollars in 1051, 1.10 dollars in 1952, and 1.15 dollars in 1956. A similar committee in Canada recommends grain prices for use in farm appraisals in Canada.

The estimated prices, once they have been selected, can be applied easily to the expected physical production to obtain the total estimated gross income. This gross income includes all livestock sales as well as crop sales in owner operation.

Expenses are troublesome because they usually are more numerous and their total is higher than would appear at first glance. The first expense item is the total property tax on land and buildings. The actual taxes paid can be obtained directly from courthouse records. A better estimate of future taxes can be made by examining the records for a number of years to determine the trend.

Information should be obtained on school building projects and other plans that may have an important bearing on future property tax levies. Special levies, such as those for drainage ditches, also should be checked at the courthouse or wherever the tax or drainage district records are kept.

Improvements, repairs, maintenance, and depreciation are the next major items of expense. Here the inexperienced appraiser may be lost, because the cost of keeping up and replacing buildings, fences, water systems, tile drains, and other improvements can amount to a sizable figure.

Observation and familiarity with actual expenditures for insurance, building repairs, and the like are helpful in making reliable estimates. Farm management records, which may be available at the State agricultural experiment stations, usually indicate actual amounts spent for repairs and replacements. Figures like these provide good benchmarks for the appraiser.

Other expenses include seed, fertilizer, and such miscellaneous items as management expense on rented farms. Many other important farm operating expenses have to be estimated on owner-operated farms. They include costs of machinery, fuel and oil, feed, livestock, veterinary help, and the like. The appraisal of the Farmers Home Administration is especially helpful in showing the list of expenses of the owner-operator.

When the expenses are all added and the resulting total is subtracted from the gross income, we have the estimated annual net land income of the farm. This net income can be considered as a total for the farm, or the total can be divided by the number of acres to obtain an estimated annual net income per acre—a figure that commonly is used when farms are quoted as worth so many dollars an acre.

Capitalization of the net income is the next step we follow when we want a capitalized value. Not all appraisers or appraisal agencies take this step. Some agencies, like the Federal land banks and the Farmers Home Administration, use estimated annual net income as a check on their appraisal of land value but do not capitalize this net income into value.

The capitalization process is a division of the income estimate by an interest or capitalization rate estimate to obtain a capitalized value. It is indicated by the formula $V=a/r$. If our estimated annual income is 7.50 dollars an acre and our estimated interest or capitalization rate is 5 percent, the resulting value is 150 dollars an acre. An alternative, such as the farm mortgage interest rate or one slightly higher (to reflect the additional risk in the whole farm value), often is used in selecting a capitalization rate.

Another way to explain the capitalization rate is to state the situation in reverse. If farms are currently selling for 150 dollars an acre and the prevailing annual net income per acre is 7.50 dollars, the rate of return is 5 percent.

One of the dangers connected with capitalization, emphasized by critics of the process, is the ease with which estimates in the income, expense, or capitalization rate can be changed slightly to obtain the desired capital value. By reducing expenses 50 cents an acre, the value in the foregoing example can be increased 10 dollars an acre or to a total of 160 dollars an acre. If the capitalization rate is raised to 6 percent in the same example, the resulting capitalized value is reduced by 25 dollars, and the total is lowered to 125 dollars. Those who use the capitalization process have to be consistent in their estimates in order to avoid these pitfalls.

Nonincome or intangible features exist on most farms. It is hard to place a value on them because we cannot measure physically the influence of location, highways, schools, churches, distance to town, and similar factors.

Even more difficult to determine are the intangible influences of attractiveness of farm home. Valuation of these features has to be conducted almost entirely by comparisons of sale values.

COMPARISONS OF SALE VALUE are basically a method of appraisal in which farms sold recently are analyzed and compared with the farm that is being appraised.

A scale of sale values for farms of different quality is established in the appraiser's mind, and when the quality of the farm in question has been measured, its appropriate sale value is evident from the sale-value scale.

An example: If an average farm in a given community is selling for 200 dollars an acre and if the farm being appraised is considered (after a physical appraisal inspection) to be slightly lower than the average for the community, its appraisal value will be fixed at slightly below the average, or at, say, 190 dollars an acre.

The appraiser's chief problem in using the sales-comparison approach is to obtain reliable sales information. A growing body of useful data is being accumulated in that field. First, on a State and national scale are the index figures issued by the Department of Agriculture for three different dates each year—March 1, July 1, and November 1—in the publication, Current Developments in the Real Estate Market.

A more detailed explanation of these figures is given in the chapter on land valuation, which precedes this one.

The second source of estimates of value is the Bureau of the Census, which issues figures for all States and counties every 10 years and at 5-year intervals in between. The latest was in November 1954. These census-value figures are especially helpful in establishing benchmarks. For example, the county values can be traced from census to census and can be compared with the overall State or national trend. In one State, for example, counties in one area had the same census values in 1950 that they had in 1910, while in another area of the State, where drainage and other improvements had been made, the census values in 1950 were almost three times the 1910 values.

Additional information is available in some States from the State agricultural experiment stations. In Iowa and Minnesota, for example, annual averages are obtained from surveys by real-estate brokers for different parts of the State and for different qualities of land.

Actual sales prices of farms are collected and analyzed in some States, notably Kansas and Nebraska, in connection with assessment-sale ratio studies. In these studies, as with all surveys of actual sales, care should be taken to determine how closely the sales represent an average of the farms in the county. In some instances, the number of poor farms sold is proportionately higher than for better farms in the area. The reverse situation may hold in other instances.

The appraiser's duty is first to collect and analyze the available sales data. With them he can formulate an accurate estimate of sale value for different qualities of land in a given area. In the appraisal of an individual farm he will be able to use nearby actual sales as basic evidence in establishing his estimated sale price of the farm.

A comparison of sale value and appraisal estimates of income value provides evidence on the nonincome or intangible features of a farm. Before making the comparison, the sale values must be adjusted to put them on the same level with the estimates of prices of farm products, or the product-price estimates must be brought in line with the sale values. When these adjustments have been made, the excess of sale value over income value equals the value of the nonincome features. The appraiser can divide this amount and attribute what he thinks is appropriate to such factors as location, attractiveness of buildings, and the like.

BUILDINGS AND LAND we have treated thus far as a unit in the appraisal. This is the proper approach in the main because the farm is usually sold as a unit. But some appraisals, especially tax assessments, call for separate appraisal of land and buildings.

When buildings are valued separately, the cost of replacement less depreciation is usually the method followed to set the top limit on value, with special attention to economic obsolescence or lack of usefulness.

Many farm buildings, such as horsebarns, no longer have much value because of changes in farm production methods. Some buildings, especially grain storage bins and certain livestock buildings, have a definite earning value, and this value shows up in the sale value estimates of the farm. The same is true of dwellings.

An important check of separate land and building values is a comparison of their combined total with the estimated value of the farm as a whole as determined by a sale value and net income appraisal. An appraiser frequently will find that the total of his separate figures for buildings and land amounts to more than his appraisal for the farm as a whole.

THE TYPE OR PURPOSE of appraisal largely determines the specific form of the appraisal report. The main types are loan, purchase and sale, tax assessment, and condemnation.

Loan appraisals include a great deal of income information, especially on detailed physical inventories of the soil and crop producing features of the land. The purpose of the appraisal is to provide a reliable index of how much income the farm can produce over the period of the loan. This information enables the loan agency to determine the expected yearly income, which in turn indicates the owner's ability to pay interest and the appropriate size of the loan. Because loans are made for long periods, the emphasis in the appraisal is on long-run estimates of probable net returns, with special notations on such hazards as erosion.

Purchase-and-sale appraisals should include most of the income detail of the loan appraisal, but the main emphasis is on the current sale-price situation. Nonincome features usually receive much more attention than in a loan appraisal. Any special aspects of the surrounding land-value market, such as demand by neighboring farmers for unimproved land to add to their farms, are important. Sometimes it may pay the seller to dispose of his farm in three or four units to competing nearby farm owners rather than to sell his farm as a single unit.

An appraisal for a buyer may involve a special survey of alternative farm purchases in several communities. The appraiser may need to compare the land market in these different communities as well as the quality of the individual farms available to give the buyer an indication of the relative advantages of buying farms in the different communities.

Tax assessments are a special type of mass appraisal in which the major objective is uniformity between individual tracts. The chief problem is not to establish the exact sale price but to place each landownership unit in its proper value relationship to every other unit in the tax district. If one land tract is worth twice as much as a second land tract, the tax assessment of the first should be twice that of the second. The resulting tax levies in this situation will then be equitable. Too often the tendency has been for assessors to conform too closely to the average—the low-value properties are overassessed and the high-value properties are underassessed.

Condemnation appraisals require strict adherence to legal procedure and correctness because they may become the center of a court battle. The major objective is a value that compensates the owner for the property being taken. In ruling on this difficult term, "compensation," the courts have usually agreed that it means the fair market price—that is, a price that enables the owner to obtain an equivalent place.

If a farm is condemned for an airstrip or highway, the compensation value will be what it would cost the owner to buy an equivalent farm. When only a part of a farm is taken, the compensation should include damages that represent the difference between the value of the present farm and its value after the portion is taken. These damages should include the loss

the owner might incur in having his farm reduced in size below that which is the most profitable to operate.

Another problem in condemnation cases is changing price levels for real estate. If the owner whose farm is taken does not immediately purchase another farm, he may find his compensation inadequate to buy an equivalent farm if the price level of farms should rise. The courts cannot help in such situations because the value fixed for compensation is the fair market value at the time of the taking.

The appraiser in preparing any appraisal report, whether it be for a loan, purchase, sale, or condemnation, will want to examine his report carefully; make certain the legal description is accurate; verify soil, crop yield, and production figures, income items, expenses, and sale value information; and check income against sale value.

If the appraisal report is in order in every detail, the appraiser should insert the date of inspecting the farm and certify to the correctness of the information he has included in the appraisal by affixing his signature.

Changes in dollar value of farmland.

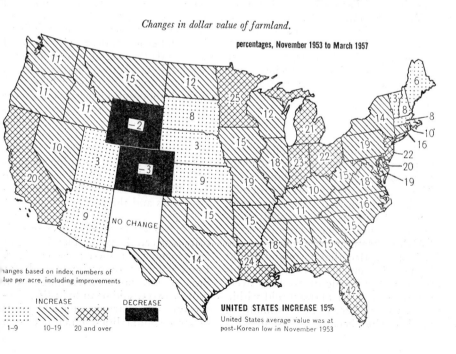

percentages, November 1953 to March 1957

Changes based on index numbers of value per acre, including improvements

INCREASE
1–9   10–19   20 and over
DECREASE

UNITED STATES INCREASE 15%
United States average value was at post-Korean low in November 1953

The market for farm real estate.

The price of land usually reflects net farm income—but not always. Net farm income had declined 25 percent by the end of 1955 from a peak in 1951, but land values were up 4 percent. The reasons for these and other changes, which have a bearing on farm welfare, credit policies, and public programs, are cited in this survey, which has great meaning for people who want to buy land. That, it seems, includes nearly everybody. By *Paul L. Holm* and *William H. Scofield,* agricultural economists, Farm Economics Research Division.

CHANGES IN THE MARKET VALUE and rate of transfer of farm real estate, which represents three-fourths of all physical assets in agriculture, are a barometer of the economic position of agriculture.

They have broad, significant implications with respect to farm welfare, attainment of farm ownership, credit policies, and Government programs.

Data pertaining to changes in value per acre, volume of farm sales, extent and method of financing farm purchases, and related aspects are of value to lending agencies, tax officials, other Government agencies, and persons concerned with the purchase, sale, or the financing of farm real estate.

We review trends in market values of farm real estate since 1940 and the various economic forces that have been responsible for them. We use the terms "farm real estate," "farmland," and "land" interchangeably to include land, buildings, and such other fixed improvements as are normally conveyed as a unit when a farm is sold.

Value means market value, or the estimated price that farmland would bring if it were offered for sale. This value may differ slightly from the average sales price for all land sold within a county or State. We use estimates of market values because no system exists for reporting the actual sales prices of all farms sold.

The Department of Agriculture maintains observation posts throughout the country to obtain reports as to what is happening in the farm real-estate market. The system was started in 1912. Farmer-reporters provide estimates on many agricultural subjects. One of the items asks them for their estimates of the market value of farmland and the number of farms sold in their localities. A special group of dealers in farm real estate and others familiar with the farm real-estate market was added in 1926.

These unpaid observers include more than 20 thousand farmers, who report three times a year, and about 10 thousand special real-estate reporters, who are reached by mail twice a year. Data from both sources are summarized, and reports for general distribution are published three times a year. They provide a continuing picture of changes in market values and the reasons for them.

A CLOSE RELATIONSHIP exists historically between the price of land and net farm income, but there are exceptions. Land values seldom rise so high (or drop so low) as farm earnings for a year or two would seem to justify. Factors other than farm income and prices of farm commodities sometimes have become important in the land market.

The general trend in prices of farmland in 1940–1953 agreed closely with changes in farm income and commodity prices. Generally rising prices of farm products during and just after the Second World War meant higher returns from farming; they, in turn, supported higher prices for land.

Buyers of farm real estate and lending agencies displayed considerable caution during the early war years. Land values rose slowly at first because of uncertainty as to how long the high levels of farm income would continue and the recollection of the serious consequences that followed the collapse in the land market after the First World War.

Most of this caution later seemed without basis. A postwar depression did not occur. International tensions and foreign-aid programs brought about a rising general price level. Farm income continued to increase and to exert an upward pressure on farm real-estate values. Land values rose 98 percent from 1942 to 1948. The level of values at the end of 1948 was more than twice as high as in 1940 and about the same as the peak in 1920 after the First World War.

The first decline in 10 years occurred in 1949. It reflected the drop in prices of farm commodities and general economic activity, which started late in 1948 and continued through 1949. The outbreak of hostilities in Korea in July 1950 introduced several strong inflationary factors in the economy, and the downturn in land values was checked. Land values increased by 26 percent in the 2 years that followed. They reached a then-record high by mid-1952 that was 33 percent above the 1947–1949 average.

The downturn of the prices of farm commodities that began in the second half of 1951 halted the upward trend in land values. Values turned downward later and continued so until early 1954. Then an unusual development occurred. Land values turned upward, even though farm income continued to go down. Net farm income had declined 25 percent by the end of 1955 from the alltime high in 1951, but land values were 4 percent above their mid-1952 peak. Although farm income rose by 4 percent in 1956, land values increased by 7 percent. Thus in early 1957 land values were 15 percent above the 1953 low, despite the decline in farm income. This is the longest period in 40 years of record in which land values have moved counter to farm income.

Regional changes in farm income and land values have been similar to those at the national level, although the rates of change have varied.

Two characteristics should be noted, however. First, farm income has remained considerably below the high level of 1951 in all regions but one. Second, land values have increased in all regions since 1954. In the west-north-central region, farm income in 1953 equaled the 1951 level, but it has since been below that level.

VALUES OF FARMLAND in most States followed the national pattern during the war and postwar years until 1948–1949. Substantial declines in 1949–1950 were recorded in all except North Carolina, Mississippi, Minnesota, Iowa, Illinois, Missouri, South Dakota, Idaho, Arizona, and Utah.

Values advanced in all States after 1950, and by mid-1952 or early 1953 new high levels were set in all States except Iowa, Missouri, South Dakota, and Nebraska. Only Iowa, South Dakota, and Nebraska reported values on March 1, 1957, that were below the peak in 1920.

More variation is evident in the movement of average values in the States since the post-Korean peak in 1952. Trends in 31 States were similar to the national movement—that is, values declined through 1953 and then started an upward climb that has continued. The increase in most States ranged between 10 and 20 percent.

Values of farmland did not decline in 1953 in 11 States; they continued the upward trend that started in 1950. All except Michigan were Atlantic or Gulf Coast States. The increases since 1950 ranged from 21 percent in Rhode Island to 99 percent in Florida. Increases in seven of the States amounted to more than 50 percent.

Land values in a third group of States declined after 1952. Five of the six States in this group were in the West. They experienced serious drought during most of the 1952–1957 period. The decline was sharpest, 10 percent, in Colorado. The smallest drop, 1 percent, was in Utah.

Values of farm real estate were at, or equal to, the highest levels of record in 38 States in early 1957. Seven of the remaining 10 States were in the western half of the country; the other three were in the eastern half. Values increased in 1956 in all States except those in the drought area of the West. Declines of 2 and 3 percent were reported in Nebraska, Wyoming, Colorado, and New Mexico. Increases of 6 to 9 percent were typical in the eastern half. Florida led with a gain of 17 percent. These changes brought the United States index of average value per acre to a record high level of 147 percent of the 1947–1949 average.

The estimated market value of farmland in the United States was a record high level of 109.5 billion dollars, or 94.52 dollars an acre of land in farms on March 1, 1957.

Average values per acre were highest in several Northeastern States, where large cities add potential site value to much of the farmland, and in the central Corn Belt and California. Values averaged lowest in the Mountain States because of extensive areas of arid grazing and nonirrigated cropland. Irrigated land in these States is valued as high as comparable land in the Corn Belt.

Farm buildings accounted for 22.5 percent of the value of farm real estate, or 24.6 billion dollars, on March 1, 1957. This represents a national average of a little more than 5 thousand dollars per farm. The Northeastern States continued to show the highest value of buildings per farm and also the highest proportion of the value of farm real estate represented by buildings. In most of these States, and in Michigan and Wisconsin, buildings represented 50 percent or more of the value of farm real estate. Buildings accounted for about a fourth of the total value in the Southeast, but in the western half they seldom exceeded 15 percent of the total value.

THE COMBINED EFFECT of factors other than prices of farm products has been strong enough since 1954 to continue to push values for farmland upward, even though farm income and prices for farm products were lower. Most of the explanation for this unusual trend lies in the nonfarm sector of the economy and in the advancing technology.

The high level of business activity, a slowly rising general price level, and increasing needs for space for a growing population have helped to sustain the demand for farmland. Efficient use of many of the new technological developments requires larger operating units. Because many thousands of commercial farms are still too small for efficient use of available labor and machinery, farmers have continued to bid actively for the limited acreage of land that is for sale. The factors that contribute to strong demand also tend to reduce the acreage of land offered for sale in many areas.

DEMAND AMONG FARMERS has been sustained partly by the desire of present operators to enlarge their farms. Many thousands of farmers who wanted to realize the full benefits of farm mechanization and other advances in agriculture felt the need for more land. Reduced prices for farm products after 1951 were not accompanied by reductions in the cost of the things farmers buy. This squeeze between costs and prices received encouraged a faster adoption of improved fertilizer and seed, more efficient feeds, better breeding practices, and more efficient management without increasing the acreage. But many farmers found that they needed more land to use efficiently the labor and equipment they had. Some machines are profitable only if the initial cost and annual depreciation can be distributed over a large total output.

The cutback in crop acreage as a result of the national acreage-allotment and price-support program also gave farmers an incentive to acquire additional land with allotments—particularly in sections that depend largely on a single crop, such as wheat or cotton, and have few alternative crops. In such situations, unit costs often can be reduced by enlarging the operating unit to obtain a larger acreage allotment; the cost of machinery per unit of farm output of machines can be held down and labor can be kept profitably employed.

Both the farm-purchase and farm-rental market provide an opportunity each year for a limited number of farmers to make adjustments of this kind in the size of their farms. Census data show, for example, that although the total number of farms declined by 11 percent between 1950 and 1954, the number of owners who rented additional land increased by 5 percent and the average size of their farms increased by 6 percent. The average size of farms operated by full owners increased by 7 percent.

The farm-enlargement process has continued since 1954. It has proceeded most rapidly in the wheat areas, where purchases for farm enlargement made up nearly three-fifths of all purchases in 12 months that ended March 1956. Such purchases nationally represented a third of the total, an increase of 14 percent since 1954. A steady increase has occurred since 1950, when only 22 percent of all farms and tracts purchased were to be added to other farms.

Much of the land added to other farms was operated as single farms before sale. Nearly half of the tracts added to other farms in 1956 were of this type.

In the western Corn Belt, the number of single farms that became part of another farm increased by nearly 50 percent in the 1954–1956 period. The increase was nearly 40 percent in the wheat areas. Nationally, a slow but steady decline in the proportion of all sales that were single farms before they were sold has also been evident.

Many farmers decided to leave farming during this period partly because they could not acquire additional land. Favorable alternative employment opportunities because of the dispersal of industry and the continuing high level of nonfarm employment helped to make the move easier. By far the largest proportion of these farmers left without financial loss from the sale of their farms. With prices of farm real estate at, or near, record high levels and demand from neighboring farmers strong, usually they were able to recover more than their equities and satisfy credit obligations.

NONFARMER DEMAND for farmland was strong during and immediately after the war, when the high returns from land made it a good investment. Farmland was considered to be a good hedge against inflation and a safe investment for the savings that had accumulated during the war, when consumer goods were scarce. Other investments may yield higher returns, but many persons view farmland as a safe and desirable long-term investment.

The prospect of a growing population and a fixed supply of land is believed to assure a slow but steady increase in the price of farmland.

Apart from such considerations, many people prefer farmland because it is a tangible investment that the owner can see and manage. Some attach a prestige value to ownership of land. Farmland provides a retreat in case of emergency or economic adversity. Plans for eventual retirement on a farm also enter into the decisions of many people to buy farmland. Retirement-income plans that many workers now have permit more persons to carry out such retirement-living plans without depending on the income of the farms they may buy.

About a million acres are taken by residential and industrial uses, highways, and other nonfarm uses yearly. A somewhat larger area is withdrawn from the farm real-estate market and held for such future uses. The price of much of it is based on the expectation that it may be suitable for nonfarm uses in the future. In such a market situation, location with respect to population centers, existing or anticipated highways, and industrial plants becomes a major determinant of market prices. Prices of farmland in such areas have become increasingly insensitive to changes in farm income, and asking prices for many farms are often higher than can be supported by prospective farm income.

Unlike the back-to-the-land movement of the 1930's, which had its origins in unemployment and insecurity, much of the recent interest of city people in land grows out of the general growth of population and the dispersal of industry. The movement can be observed in the ribbon development along highways and in the widening suburban fringe. High levels of income and employment have made the move possible. Better highways and the availability on the farm of the comforts of living previously found only in the city have helped accelerate the trend.

Many of the smaller farms that would not be economical units are attractive to prospective purchasers who have nonfarm jobs and who do not expect farms to pay for themselves. They often attach values to the intangible factors of location, condition of dwelling, and other attributes that have little bearing on agricultural productivity. Thus they establish a higher level of market prices than would prevail otherwise. This type of demand has helped to sustain or raise market prices of many that could not be operated profitably as full-time farms.

Many of the factors that contribute to a strong demand for farmland also limit its supply. Present owners see advantages to continued ownership of land that are similar to those prospective buyers see. Nearly half of all farmland sold is bought by farmers. Consequently, when conditions make ownership of farmland attractive for farming purposes, it is as attractive to present owners as to prospective buyers.

A frequent observation in many farm communities has been that "land is in strong hands." Owners generally have not been under strong financial pressure to sell because mortgage debt has been low in most instances, and supplemental income from nonfarm sources has been available. Favorable returns from farming during and just after the war left most farmers in a generally sound financial position—a situation that further restricted the supply of land on the market.

A record high proportion of landowners are farm operators who have substantial investments in machinery, equipment, and livestock. They have been reluctant to liquidate their large investments in order to realize a profit from the sale of land alone. It would mean changing to new occupations.

Many nonfarmers who hold land primarily for its annual return apparently still consider farmland a satisfactory investment, even when returns have declined. This desire of investors to retain ownership of land apparently stems from three main considerations.

First is the tendency to value farmland in terms of original cost, which in most instances would be less than the current value. When this is done, the annual rate of return, on the original cost, would be higher than if current market value was used.

Second, tax savings from ownership of farmland can accrue to individuals with certain levels of income from nonfarm sources. Any possible tax saving could be considered as part of the return to farmland, thus making it more attractive than farm income alone might indicate.

The third consideration arises from the nature of the landlord's costs under prevailing share-renting arrangements. His costs typically include taxes on real estate, repairs and maintenance of buildings, and a share of certain crop expenses, like those for seed and fertilizer. As landlords do not share in many of the cost items that are paid by farm operators, the cost-price squeeze has been less severe on nonoperating landowners.

Records for a sample of farms operated under crop-share leases in northern Illinois, as published in Illinois Farm Economics for January 1956, showed that in 1952–1954 the tenant's expenses amounted to 75 percent of cash income. The landlord's expenses took only 35 percent of gross rental income. A 5-percent increase in the cash expenses paid by each party consequently (with no change in income) would reduce the tenant's net income by 15 percent and the landlord's income by only 3 percent.

The increasing amount of capital-gains tax payable if land is sold has come to have increased importance as a deterrent to sales. Unless owners had an adjusted cost basis substantially above original cost, the tax would cut heavily into the proceeds from a sale, particularly on land bought during the early 1940's. Such taxes normally are not assessed if a farm is passed on in the family by inheritance. The current market value of the property at the time of transfer becomes the new cost basis, and the question of capital gains can be postponed to some future date. It can be delayed indefinitely by the inheritance process.

The voluntary transfers of farms accounted for three-fifths to three-fourths of all transfers in 1940–1956. They occurred at the highest rate in history in 1945, when the title to 310 thousand farms changed hands by voluntary sale. A steady decline followed until 1953, when the number was only 139 thousand. A slight increase occurred later, although the rate in the 12 months that ended in early 1957 was below that for any of the years in 1941–1953.

Distress transfers—foreclosures, assignments to avoid foreclosure, bankruptcies, and related defaults—declined from 16 percent of all transfers in 1940 to fewer than 1 percent in 1947. They later increased to about 5 percent of the total.

THE FREQUENCY of distress transfers is a barometer of economic conditions in agriculture. A severe economic stress means greater numbers of distress transfers. The largest number—nearly 223 thousand farms—occurred in 1932. The number declined from 1940 through 1947, when an alltime low of only one farm in each thousand farms in the Nation was sold because of financial pressure. A gradual increase followed, but during 1956 the rate was still lower than at any time before 1944. In 1956, 9 thousand farm sales were estimated to have occurred because of financial difficulties.

Sales caused by delinquent taxes have followed much the same pattern as distress transfers, although they account for a smaller share of the total—fewer than one farm in a thousand since 1945.

The remaining types of transfers—inheritances and gifts, administrators' and executors' sales, and other miscellaneous or unclassified transfers—occurred at a nearly constant rate, ranging from 12 to 16 farms in 1 thousand farms since 1940.

FARMERS ARE THE LARGEST class of buyers of farm real estate. They account for about 70 percent of all purchases.

A shift in the composition of the farmer-buyer group is apparent, however. Owner-operators have increased in numbers, and tenant-buyers have declined. Forty-six percent of the farmer-buyers in 1940 and 58 percent in 1956 already owned land. Tenants declined from 49 to 35 percent of the total in this period. Some of the decline in purchases by tenants is due to the decline in the total number of tenant farmers since 1940.

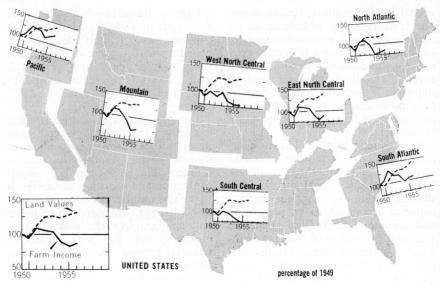

Income of farm operators and farm real-estate values.

The proportion of all farms bought by nonfarmers changed little in 1940–1957. They have amounted to one-fourth to one-third of the total.

Fewer than 50 percent of all sellers in 1940 and nearly 70 percent in 1946 were farmers. Minor fluctuations around this level continued through 1956, when farmers made up 69 percent of all sellers.

Nonfarmer sellers have declined in importance. This group sold 44 percent of the farms in 1940. In 1956 they accounted for only 14 percent of all sales. The decline was due largely to a decline in sales by lending agencies. Such institutions, particularly insurance companies, in the early 1940's had a large inventory of farms that they had acquired by foreclosure in the previous decade. Although these properties had been largely sold by 1944, a few have continued to sell each year since. Sales by lending agencies in 1956 amounted to less than 1 percent of all sales.

The sale of farms to settle estates is estimated to account for about 15 percent of all sales each year. Sales of this kind in some areas represent a significant part of the total supply of land on the market.

The decision to buy a farm usually involves the problem of obtaining suitable financing. The amount and terms of the credit available consequently are an important aspect of the farm real-estate market.

Farm-mortgage credit has generally been available during and since the war years. Credit agencies tended to revise lending policies in line with higher level of land values during the 1940's. Competition among lenders helped to maintain favorable interest rates and to assure an abundant supply of farm-mortgage credit.

The proportion of all farm purchases that were financed with some form of credit has trended almost steadily upward since estimates were started in 1944. The proportion rose from 42 percent of all purchases in 1944 to more than two-thirds of the total in the year that ended March 1, 1956. Active farmer-buyers have used credit more frequently than nonfarmers. Those who were formerly tenants have used credit more frequently than those who already owned land.

The amount of money borrowed in relation to the purchase price declined steadily from 1941 to 1951, but it increased later. It amounted to 61 percent of the purchase price in 1955. Dollar debt per acre has increased more than 3 times since 1940. The average size of all new mortgages has increased by about the same amount.

Part of the increase in the size of debt in relation to the purchase price of farmland is due to the relatively high frequency of purchase to enlarge farms. In these situations, a prospective buyer can utilize his existing farm as security for the land to be added. Thus the amount of cash required as a downpayment often is less than it might be otherwise. In addition, the use of purchase contracts, which usually require 30 percent or less of the purchase price as a downpayment, has increased in recent years.

With two in three farm purchases financed with borrowed funds, sources of credit have become more and more important in facilitating farm transfers. Nationally, sellers (primarily individuals) provided all of the credit required to finance 37 percent of the credit-financed sales in 12 months to March 1, 1956. The proportion ranged from less than 30 percent in the Corn Belt, the Northeast, and the cotton areas, to more than half of all credit sales in the Mountain and Pacific Coast States.

The high occurrence of seller financing can be explained partly by the increased use of purchase contracts, which provide the seller with a tax advantage under certain circumstances. In some areas, however, it may indicate the reluctance of conventional lenders to make farm-mortgage loans in amounts sufficient to meet the needs of potential buyers with limited cash for downpayments.

A seller who is under pressure to make a sale or who is personally acquainted with the buyer and considers him a good risk often is willing to accept a lower downpayment than other lenders. In other instances, sellers may prefer sizable mortgages or contracts to full payment. They may not be familiar with other investments and may consider the farms previously owned to be the best security for their funds.

About the same proportion of farm purchasers were financed by commercial banks as by insurance companies (19 and 18 percent, respectively), but the two classes of lenders operate in different areas. Local banks financed nearly half of the credit purchasers in the Northeast. The general farming area in the east-central section and the tobacco area also showed a relatively high frequency of financing by banks. Banks financed less than 10 percent of all farm purchases in most farming areas west of the Mississippi River.

Insurance companies have been most active in the farm-mortgage field in sections where average loans are large and risk is low. The Corn Belt, the winter wheat area, and the western cotton area had the highest proportion of farm purchases that were financed by insurance companies.

Federal land banks financed a tenth of all farm purchasers. These banks in 1955 made about 18 percent of the total number of all farm-mortgage loans, many of which were used to refinance existing mortgages or other indebtedness, rather than to buy farms.

MANY OF THE FORCES that have been present in the farm real-estate market since 1940 existed in 1958. They may continue to affect the market for land and consequently the general economic position of agriculture.

The strong demand for land to enlarge existing farms is likely to continue. The expanded highway program and further dispersal of industry seems likely to create additional areas in which location value, rather than productive value, will assume new importance in the land market. Land for living space could well become of even greater importance as a price-making factor in the future as the population continues to grow.

The mechanics of land transfer.

Anyone who buys, sells, or bequeaths land gets involved in many technical points, which may seem needless to one who is unaware of all the problems. This chapter gives a wealth of practical information about selecting a farm, negotiating for it, drawing up contracts, arranging to buy it, getting a mortgage or credit, paying for it, and providing for it. By *Charles L. Stewart,* Department of Agricultural Economics, University of Illinois, and *Stanley W. Voelker,* Department of Agricultural Economics, North Dakota State College.

YOU HAVE A GREAT DEAL at stake when you buy a farm. It may be the biggest investment you will ever make. The land must provide a home and a means of livelihood for you and your family.

You must know in advance that you can get title to the land you select and be certain that you will not be dispossessed because of some irregularity in the transfer or flaw in the title.

Exacting legal rules must be adhered to when dealing with real property in order to attain this certainty of expectation. You may have the impression that property law is burdened with needless technicalities, but you will abandon that idea if you consider all the problems that are involved.

First of all, you should do a great deal of thinking and planning before you buy a farm. It also is important that you consult an attorney before you enter any agreement concerning the purchase of land.

You should inspect some of the farms you know are for sale. You can tap the wealth of information that is available in your county courthouse concerning land in the county.

The county recorder will explain the techniques of land identification. You probably know that a common designation, such as the "Sellers farm," usu-

ally is not the legal description of a farm. A legal description is based on a survey of the land. Different types of survey are used in various parts of the country.

The Thirteen Original Colonies followed the metes and bounds method: The surveyor began at some point in the boundary of the tract to be described and then recited the courses and distances from point to point around the tract. Boundary disputes were common because the monuments used often were stumps, rocks, or other items that lacked permanency.

This system is still used to describe irregularly shaped tracts, but more permanent monuments than stones and stumps are used.

An example of an old metes and bounds description might be: "Begin at the middle of a large, white pine stump standing in the west side line of Simon Vender Cook's land and on the south side of the main road that leads to the new city, and there is also a fence that stands a little to the west of Simon Vender Cook's barn, which said fence if it were to run cross the said field southerly, would run to the middle of said stump; and running thence north 2 degrees east 19 chains and 50 links to a small white oak

206

tree"—and so on, until one gets to the point of beginning.

The Federal Government recognized the weakness of this system and on April 26, 1785, adopted the rectangular survey. It applies to 29 States and Alaska. It does not apply to the original Colonial States, the other New England and Atlantic Coast States (except Florida), and West Virginia, Kentucky, Tennessee, and Texas.

Under this system a north-south line, called a meridian, and a baseline running east and west were established through the area to be surveyed. The surveyors started at the intersection of the meridian and baseline and divided the area into squares 24 miles on each side. These areas were further subdivided into squares, called townships, 6 miles on each side. The townships in the row next to and parallel to the baseline were designated as township 1, north or south, and the other rows parallel with the baseline were numbered accordingly (township 2 north or south, and so on). The rows formed by the squares parallel to the meridian were numbered in a similar fashion and designated east or west but were called ranges rather than townships. Later each township was divided into 36 squares. Each is a mile on each side and contains "as nearly as may be" 640 acres. Because the north-south lines of the survey merge at the North Pole, the north side of a township is about 50 feet shorter than the south side. Every fifth row of townships is measured the full 6 miles for each township.

The deficiencies that result from this are placed in the north and west rows of sections of a township. These fractional sections occur in sections 1 through 6 on the north side and sections 6, 7, 18, 19, 30, and 31 on the west. Sections are further subdivided into tracts of 40 acres, or what is known as a quarter-quarter section.

A typical description using this system might be: "The southeast quarter of the southeast quarter of section 9 township 3 north, range 2 west of the Xth principal meridian in Blank County."

Some tracts have been subdivided into blocks and lots. This is accomplished by making a survey of the tract and drawing a plat. The plat is then certified by the surveyor and is signed by the owners.

After you have acquired a working knowledge of the records, you will do well to spend some time going over them in order to get the correct legal descriptions of the farms you are interested in, a list of the mortgages or other encumbrances on the land, and the approximate purchase price paid by the present owner.

You can get the valuations placed on the properties through the recorded considerations for transfer, the revenue stamps, the mortgages accepted by financial institutions with known maximum loan limits, and the county assessment rolls for general property tax levies. (The Internal Revenue Code provides that revenue stamps in the amount of 55 cents per 500 dollars of consideration shall be attached to instruments transferring land. This does not apply to encumbrances remaining at the time of sale or to any instrument given to secure a debt.)

You should also get a list of the prices recently paid for other land in the vicinity and the amount of property taxes levied annually against each farm and the amount of delinquent taxes, if any. You can get this information in the offices of the county treasurer and county clerk or auditor.

You also should check to see whether any special districts have been organized in the area for purposes of drainage, flood control, water conservation, and irrigation and, if so, the amount of special assessments levied by such districts against the land.

When you have this information, you are ready to inspect the farms you have in mind in order to get an idea as to what a reasonable value might be. You talk with each owner.

You decide that the Adolph Sellers' farm suits your needs. You feel that

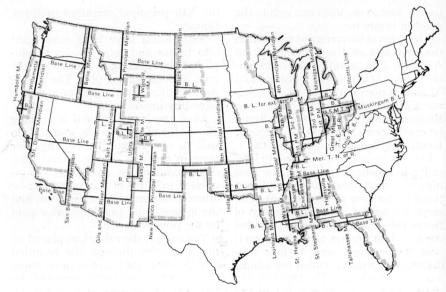

Location of the several prime meridians and their base lines.

Mr. Sellers will accept the price you are willing to pay—60 thousand dollars.

You are not sure how to make the offer. To clear up this point, you visit your attorney. People sometimes do not seek legal advice until after the offer has been made and accepted; they may feel this is not an important phase of the transfer. Failure to obtain competent legal advice at this stage, however, can lead to many pitfalls, because a binding contract results once the offer (in writing) is accepted. The offer basically is nothing more than a promise, which in this instance would be conditional upon a return promise being given to sell. The statute of frauds requires that a promise to transfer or to buy an interest in land must be in writing and signed by the person to be charged.

You and the attorney, after discussing matters, decide that the following details are to be included in the offer to purchase:

1. The legal description of the real estate to be covered by the offer.

2. A list of items, such as movable hog houses, water systems, and hay in the barn, that are to be included in the sale. Some items known as fixtures are difficult to describe as either real or personal property and often lead to litigation. The best approach is to itemize them in the offer.

3. Mr. Sellers must provide a warranty deed to the premises as opposed to a quitclaim deed.

4. The full names of the parties, which are designated "buyer" and "seller."

5. Whether the property is to be taken subject to an existing mortgage.

6. The date on which possession is to be given, such as March 1 of the next year.

7. Mr. Sellers is to pay the real-estate taxes until the date that possession is given. The buyer is to pay for unexpired insurance on buildings after date of possession.

8. The purchase price shall be 60 thousand dollars, 20 thousand dollars to be paid in cash on March 1 and the balance to be paid on July 1.

9. This offer is conditional on the buyer's securing a 20-year mortgage at 4 percent (or other specified rate).

10. This offer must be accepted by August 1 of the current year.

11. Within a reasonable time after acceptance of this offer, the seller is to furnish an up-to-date abstract of title showing a "marketable" title.

It may be necessary to include other items in the offer under certain conditions. Getting points such as these clearly understood is not to be taken lightly. You should ask your lawyer to explain any details you do not know.

Perhaps you are wondering why the offer, as we outlined it, specifies that the seller is to deliver a warranty deed rather than a quitclaim deed.

In a warranty deed, the grantor (that is, the seller) promises that he has good title in fee simple, that the real estate is free of encumbrances, and that the buyer will not be disturbed in his possession because of any legal claims existing in the seller's chain of title. The effect of these promises is to give the buyer a claim for money damages against the seller in case the seller's title later proves to be defective.

A quitclaim deed does not contain these promises. As its name suggests, the grantor merely transfers whatever interest he might have in the premises, without any implication that he has a good, marketable title. If the grantor really does have good title, a quitclaim deed will convey title just as effectively as a warranty deed. Usually, however, quitclaims are used only for releasing minor realty interests for the purpose of clearing title or for consolidating the interests of two or more coowners into one ownership.

After your lawyer puts the offer in full detail into written form, it is given to Mr. Sellers. If the terms are agreeable to him, he accepts in the manner requested. Usually in this type of transaction, a space is provided on the offer where the owner may express acceptance by signing. You must be sure to get the signatures of both Adolph Sellers and his wife, Jane Sellers. Otherwise the wife may be able to retain certain rights in the land, commonly called widow rights or dower rights. A husband may have similar rights. The only safe solution is to get

445509°—58——15

Township 3 North, Range 2 West of the Principal Meridian

Dividing an area into townships.

Section 9. Township 3 North, Range 2 West of the Principal Meridian

Sections 1 through 6 on the north side and 7, 18, 19, 30, and 31 on the west side are fractional sections.

A township divided into sections.

signatures of both husband and wife.

The initial contract we have just discussed is commonly referred to as an offer and acceptance contract, a binder contract, or an earnest money contract. If all the conditions are met, title to the farm eventually will pass to you.

One of the conditions in the binder contract is that Mr. Sellers must provide a "marketable title," which is

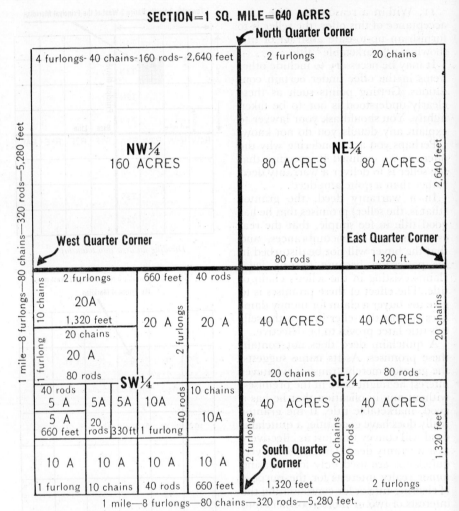

Section of land showing acreage and distances.

defined by the courts as one that an ordinary, reasonably prudent buyer of real estate, acting on competent legal advice, will accept.

You will have to look to your attorney for advice on this matter. The lawyer will examine the title history, with the help of an abstract provided by Mr. Sellers, and will prepare a summary of his findings, called an opinion on title. An abstract is a condensed history of the recorded transactions that deal with or affect a speci-

fied piece of real estate. It is prepared by an abstractor, who is a specialist in this field and who keeps elaborate records for this purpose.

If any defects exist in the title, it will be necessary for Adolph Sellers to remedy them. Some defects may be simple to correct. Others may require judicial action. Still others may be impossible to remedy. In any event, this is an important step in providing protection for yourself.

Another method of checking and

protecting real-estate titles is by title insurance. Under this system, you would contract with an insurance company to insure the title of the land you are buying. Before entering into the contract, the insurance company will check the real-estate records. If the records show that the title is in order, it will issue a policy of insurance.

If a tract index is maintained at the county courthouse, the attorney may check the records himself and write an opinion for you on the basis of this. This is essentially the same as the first method we discussed, except that the attorney does not have the benefit of abstractor service before writing the opinion.

Some States have used the Torrens system of registration of title to land. By a judicial proceeding, title to the land is registered in the name of the owner. The owner is given a duplicate of this certificate of registration. Before he can sell the land he must turn in this duplicate and a new certificate will be issued to the buyer. For various reasons, this system has not been widely used in the United States.

Let us assume that the title opinion prepared by your attorney revealed no defects in Sellers' title to the land or that there were only minor defects, which Sellers was able to have corrected without much delay or cost. In either event, Sellers was able to deliver a "marketable title" under the terms of the purchase agreement.

You recall that this purchase contract was conditional upon your obtaining a 20-year mortgage loan of 40 thousand dollars at 4 percent interest. As it turned out, arrangements for such a loan were made with the local agent of a lending corporation. The loan was to be paid off in 40 semiannual installments of 1 thousand dollars each on April 1 and October 1 of each year, beginning with October 1 of a specified year, plus interest on the unpaid balance at the rate of 4 percent per annum. Before the company had agreed to make the loan, its appraiser had appraised the Sellers farm to determine its security value, and the company's legal department had examined and approved the abstract of title.

Closing the sale involves several steps: Preparation of the deed of conveyance from Sellers to you; preparation of the note and mortgage from you to the lending corporation; signing and acknowledging the various instruments; payment of the amount due Sellers under the terms of the purchase agreement; and delivery of the various instruments to the proper parties. Your attorney can be helpful in each step.

In order to effect the various steps in the closing procedure as expeditiously as possible, your attorney may suggest that you, Mr. Sellers, and your wives meet at his office. The agent of the lending corporation might also be present.

The warranty deed from Sellers to you will probably be on a standard printed form. In order to fill in the blanks on this form properly, your attorney must know a number of things, the first of which is the name of the seller (termed the "grantor" or "party of the first part" in the deed form) exactly as it appears on the deed by which the seller has acquired title. He also must know whether the seller was married and, if so, his wife's given name and initial. In this case, the grantor blank will be filled in with "Adolph G. Sellers and Jane M. Sellers, husband and wife, of Smithfield Corners, parties of the first part."

The second thing your attorney must know is the exact name of the buyer (termed the "grantee" or "party of the second part" in the deed form) and whether title is to be taken as sole owner, as joint tenants, or as tenants in common.

If you and your wife take title as tenants in common, each of you will have an undivided interest in the land, which share can be transferred by deed or will to someone else independently of the other owner; if one of you should die, the deceased's interest will pass to his or her heirs.

On the other hand, if you take title

as joint tenants, the survivor will acquire full title upon the death of the other, and the heirs of the deceased will not have inherited any interests in the property. Under the laws of most States, either one of you could destroy the joint tenancy by transferring his or her interest to someone else, in which case the joint tenancy automatically would become a tenancy in common.

The type of title is important, not only because of its effect on the future conveyance and inheritance of the property, but also because of differences in the amount of State and Federal inheritance taxes to be paid if one of you should die. We give a more detailed discussion of the important subject of inheritance in the final section of this chapter. Let us assume that you and your wife decide joint tenancy is more advantageous than tenancy in common or sole ownership. Your attorney will fill in the second group of blanks with "Robert C. Byers and Edith M. Byers, his wife, of Smithfield Corners, as joint tenants with right of survivorship, and not as tenants in common, parties of the second part."

A third thing the attorney has to know is the full price of the land in order to determine the amount of revenue stamps to be placed on the deed. The exact purchase price generally is not stated in the deed. Instead, a phrase such as "One dollar and other valuable consideration" is used. Statutes in one or two States, however, require that the exact purchase price be shown in the deed. Failure to place the proper amount of revenue stamps on a deed does not affect its validity, but it does render the buyer and seller liable to a fine.

The seller customarily pays for the revenue stamps.

Your attorney will also need the correct description of the land. He can get this from a previous deed listed in the abstract, but he will probably check it to be sure it is accurate. The attorney also must know whether Mr. Sellers is reserving any right in himself, such as a right-of-way or a portion of the min-

eral rights, and whether there are to be any exceptions to the general warranty of the seller that "property is free and clear of all encumbrances," such as unpaid special assessments of an irrigation or drainage district or an unpaid mortgage to be assumed by you, the buyer.

MORTGAGES usually are prepared on standard printed forms. You may be surprised to learn that the wording of the mortgage instrument reads as if you were actually transferring title to the farm to the mortgagee (that is, the lender).

As a matter of fact, a mortgage instrument is similar to a warranty deed, with two important exceptions. A mortgage contains a defeasance clause, under which the mortgage deed becomes void and ineffective upon fulfillment of the conditions set forth in the instrument, which in most cases would be the repayment of the note. A mortgage conveys only legal title, with equitable title (that is, the right of possession and use) remaining with the mortgagor.

Trust deeds are commonly used for the same purposes as mortgages, especially in cases where two or more lenders join in making the loan. Under a trust deed, the borrower transfers legal title to a third person, called the trustee, to be held in trust for the benefit of the lender, whereas a mortgage transfers legal title directly to the lender. The legal effect and foreclosure procedure for the two types of instruments are similar, and we here make no distinction between the two.

Your attorney will have Mr. and Mrs. Sellers sign the warranty deed to you and your wife before a notary public, after cautioning them to use their first names and middle initials, exactly as they appeared in the first paragraph of the deed. You recall he insisted that both Mr. and Mrs. Sellers sign the original purchase agreement with you. This was to obligate both of them to sign the warranty deed when the time came. He would have insisted that both Mr. and Mrs. Sellers sign this deed, even though only one of them was the title owner of record, in order to extinguish any dower, curtesy, and homestead rights, which might interfere with your future occupancy and use of the farm.

Dower right is the interest a woman acquires in the property of her husband. Curtesy right is the interest a man acquires in his wife's property. Dower and curtesy rights are not recognized in about half of the States. The statutory provisions governing dower and curtesy rights vary greatly from State to State, but generally the rights amount to a life estate in a portion of the property owned by the other spouse. With few exceptions, neither dower right nor curtesy right is destroyed by the will left by the landowning spouse. If both husband and wife sign the deed, however, the nonowning spouse is deemed to have waived her dower right or his curtesy right, as the case may be.

Most State legislatures have adopted homestead exemption statutes to protect part of the value of the family home from claims of creditors. The statutory limitations on the amount of land which may be claimed as a homestead vary widely among the States. The limitations are expressed in terms of value, such as 1 thousand or 5 thousand dollars, or in terms of area, such as the dwelling and up to 160 acres. In many States, in addition to being an exemption from debt, the homestead right is also a special kind of estate in land, which continues in the surviving spouse after the death of the landowning spouse. In some of the States, the survivor's interest amounts to a life estate in the homestead; in a few others, it is a title in fee simple. Homestead rights are in addition to any dower or curtesy rights.

Since you and your wife will acquire the Sellers farm as joint tenants, both will have to sign the promissory note and mortgage deed to the lending corporation. Even if the farm were deeded to you as sole owner, the corporation probably would insist that your wife also sign the mortgage as a waiver of her dower and homestead rights.

THE NEXT STEP is to pay for the farm. There is more to this step than just your handing over a check for 60 thousand dollars. Your attorney will prepare a closing statement, or final accounting of all financial matters concerning the sale, based on various stipulations in the purchase agreement between you and Adolph Sellers.

This contract provided that the real-estate taxes and the premiums on the fire and windstorm insurance on the building were to be prorated between buyer and seller as of March 1. Let us assume that Mr. Sellers has not paid the current year's real-estate taxes, amounting to 421.56 dollars. Inasmuch as these taxes are obligations against the land, you will have to pay them eventually, but the proration stipulation in the purchase agreement gives you a claim against Mr. Sellers amounting to two-twelfths of the amount of the taxes, or 70.26 dollars. On the other hand, if Mr. Sellers paid the taxes before the closing date, you would owe him ten-twelfths of the amount of the taxes, or 351.30 dollars, in addition to the purchase price of the farm.

Let us also assume that 16 months before the March 1 closing date, Mr. Sellers had taken out a 3-year fire and windstorm insurance policy to protect the buildings, the premium of which had amounted to 414 dollars. This policy, which still has 20 months to run, could be put in your name by getting the consent of the casualty-insurance company. Under the terms of the proration stipulation in the purchase agreement, you will have to pay 230 dollars for the unexpired value of the policy, 20/36ths of 414 dollars.

The representative of the lending corporation that is financing your farm purchase will give you a cashier's check for 40 thousand dollars, which you must endorse to Adolph Sellers. In addition, you will give Mr. Sellers your personal check for 19,659.74 dollars. The lawyer will give the mortgage and promissory note for 40 thousand dollars to the lending corporation's representative. He will also take the warranty deed to the county recorder's office to be recorded, with instructions that the deed be sent to you after it has been recorded.

Since it is customary for the land seller to pay for the internal revenue stamps, which must be placed on a deed before recording, Mr. Sellers will give the attorney a check for 66 dollars to cover this item.

You must pay your lawyer his fees for professional services (examining the abstract, drawing the deed, preparing the closing statement, and so forth) and the recording fees, which he will have to pay when he presents the deed for recording.

Although the closing procedure we have described is typical, it should be remembered that the steps vary somewhat from one land transfer to another. For example, if there is no prepaid insurance on the buildings, obviously there would be no proration of insurance premiums. In some cases there is no provision for real-estate taxes. This is frequently the case if the closing takes place near the end of the tax year (in which case, the seller might have paid all the taxes) or near the beginning of the tax year (in which case the buyer might pay all of the taxes).

Most of the variations in the closing procedure stem from differences in arrangements for financing the transfers. For example, if you had enough cash on hand to pay the entire purchase price of this farm, the closing procedure would consist mainly of delivery of the warranty deed from Sellers to you and payment of the purchase price to Sellers, either with or without proration of prepaid insurance premiums and real-estate taxes.

If there is an unredeemed mortgage outstanding against the farm that is being transferred, the closing procedure includes two additional steps—

payment of the amount of principal and interest due the mortgagee (that is, the mortgage holder), who in turn executes an instrument (known as a satisfaction of mortgage or release) as evidence that the debt has been discharged and that the mortgage has become void and ineffective. This satisfaction is signed, acknowledged, and recorded in much the same manner as a deed, and it appears on all subsequent abstracts of title.

But what would be the situation if you have enough cash to buy out Sellers' equity—that is, the difference between the sale price of the farm and the unpaid balance of the mortgage—but not enough to pay off the mortgage?

One way to handle this would be for you to assume the mortgage. In this case, the deed from Sellers to you includes a special clause describing the mortgage (usually by giving the book and page number of the recording), which you and your wife expressly assume and agree to pay. The closing procedure consists mainly of delivery of this special warranty deed to you; proration of insurance premiums and real-estate taxes; and payment to Sellers of the amount of his equity.

Although you and your wife in this example obligate yourselves to pay off the mortgage, Mr. Sellers should recognize that he still may be held liable for the debt if you fail to pay it. He contracted with the mortgagee to repay the debt when he put the mortgage on the farm in the first place, and nothing he and you agree to do can relieve him of this obligation. The assumption of the mortgage by you actually means that there are now two promises to pay the mortgage. In case of default, the mortgagee can proceed against either of you or both you and Sellers, or he can proceed against the land by instituting a foreclosure action. Of course, the mortgagee can release Mr. Sellers from his promise to pay, but that is a different matter.

There is another item of interest regarding assumed mortgages. It would have been desirable, although not legally necessary, for the assumption clause in the deed to have shown the unpaid balance of the mortgage that you assumed. The reason for this is that internal revenue stamps are not required for that part of the sale price represented by the assumed mortgage.

In this example, if the sale price had been 60 thousand dollars and the unpaid balance of the mortgage had been 20,500 dollars, stamps would have been required for only 39,500 dollars of the purchase price, or 43.45 dollars' worth of stamps, instead of 66 dollars' worth.

IT IS A COMMON practice in various parts of the country for sellers of land to supply credit to the buyers. Transfers financed by sellers are of two general types: Deed to the buyer, with the seller taking back a mortgage to secure payment of the debt; and sale under installment purchase contract, with legal title remaining with the seller until all or a specified portion of the purchase price has been paid. In some localities, an installment-purchase contract is known as a contract for deed, a bond for title, or a land contract. Some installment contracts provide that when a certain proportion of the sales price has been paid, such as two-thirds or three-fourths, the seller will give the buyer a deed to the land and take back a mortgage to secure payment of the remaining portion of the sales price.

Under the deed-and-mortgage type of seller financing, the closing procedure would be similar to our first illustration, in which a mortgage company lent you 40 thousand dollars to finance the purchase, except, of course, that you would draw a mortgage deed and promissory note in favor of Mr. Sellers.

If you had purchased the farm under an installment-purchase contract, however, the closing procedure would have been considerably different. The main step would have been the preparation of the lengthy and detailed installment contract to replace the original purchase agreement between Mr. Sellers and you. The essential features of the new contract would have been: The names of the buyer and seller and their wives; a description of property being sold; the total sales price; the amount of the downpayment; a schedule of the due dates and amounts of each installment payment; the interest rate on deferred payments; the seller's pledge to deliver a warranty deed to the buyer upon the latter's fulfilling his part of the contract; the buyer's promise to keep the buildings insured in favor of the seller; and the promise of the buyer to pay the real-estate taxes and any special assessments for drainage or irrigation when due, to maintain soil fertility, to refrain from committing waste, and to keep the fences and buildings in good repair.

Installment contracts must be signed by both the seller and buyer. If either is married, the spouse should sign also. In most States, these contracts can be recorded, especially if the signatures have been acknowledged before notaries public, but some buyers do not record their contracts—a poor business practice, because recording is a protection to the buyer.

In some installment sales, the warranty deed is not drawn and signed by the seller until the buyer has made his final payment. The more common practice, especially if the contract is to run for more than a year or two, is to draw the deed at the same time the installment contract is signed. This deed is signed by the seller and his wife before a notary and is delivered to a disinterested third party, known as an escrow agent, who holds the deed in trust for the buyer. When the buyer has completed his part of the contract, the escrow agent delivers the deed to the buyer, who then records it. An individual can act as escrow agent, but the recommended practice is to have a legal firm or financial institution perform this function. One convenient arrangement for both buyer and seller is to name the seller's bank as the escrow agent. The bank is given both the deed and a copy of the installment contract. The buyer makes his payments to the bank, which inserts the date of receipt and the amount of each payment on the contract and credits the seller's checking or savings account with the proceeds.

There are many different ways of setting up the repayment schedule in installment contracts. The payment dates may be annual, semiannual, quarterly, or monthly. Some contracts provide for relatively small payments during the early years and larger payments toward the end of the contract period. Other contracts provide for equal periodic payments on principal, which means that the interest payments become smaller and smaller as the debt is retired. Other contracts establish amortization schedules in which all periodic payments of principal plus interest are equal. Still other contracts provide for variable payments based on the amount of crop production and agricultural prices each year.

You note that installment sales and deed-and-mortgage sales are for the same purpose—namely, to provide a mechanism by which the seller can provide land credit to the buyer. What, then, is the difference between the two methods of seller financing?

If the buyer is able to make all payments as they fall due, there may be little practical difference between the methods. Under either one, the buyer gets possession of the farm at time of closing, his equity in the property increases as he makes his periodic payments, generally he can transfer his equity to someone else during the period of indebtedness, and eventually he gets title to the property free and clear of all encumbrances.

Legally, however, there is a big difference between the two methods—the rights and remedies of the buyer and seller under one method are determined according to the law of mortgages; under the other they are determined by the law of contracts.

The legal differences between the two methods are brought into focus whenever the buyer defaults—that is, fails to make a payment within a short time after it is due. The law of mortgages varies considerably from State to State, but in all of them the defaulting debtor is given a right of redemption, which can be extinguished only by foreclosure sale at which the interests of both the mortgagor and the mortgagee are sold at public auction to the highest bidder. The proceeds of sale are applied to the foreclosure costs and amounts due the mortgage holder for interest and principal. Anything left over after these payments goes to the debtor. If the debtor can raise the money, he can remove the default at any time during the foreclosure procedure and the period of redemption. Because of delays, time requirements for foreclosure procedures, and the redemption period, 2 years or more may elapse between time of initial default and date when the debtor's redemption rights are finally extinguished.

There is even greater diversity among the States in the rights and remedies of buyer and seller in the case of defaulted land contracts. In some States, the seller can terminate a defaulted contract upon short notice and retain all payments previously made by the buyer as liquidated damages. Legislatures of some States have attempted to mitigate the harshness of abrupt termination by requiring the seller to give 30 days' written notice before canceling the contract or by establishing a redemption period between default and cancellation, the length of which depends upon the proportion of sales price already paid. In several States, the most important remedy of the seller is a judicial action for strict foreclosure of the contract, the courts being empowered to grant a short redemption period before the seller can regain the property. In all States, however, the mortgage method of financing gives the buyer more protection in case he defaults than does the contract for deed method, in that he has more time within which to remove the default and he has a chance to recover part of his investment.

Now LET US JUMP ahead 25 years. You have reared three children. One son, Richard, is farming in partnership with you. Mary and Henry are married and live in town.

If you should die intestate—without leaving a valid will—and your wife and three children survive, what would happen to the farm? The answer to this question depends on how you and your wife held the land and on the State statutes governing descent.

There are three possibilities.

First, if the land title was in joint tenancy, your wife will have rights of survivorship. This means that she will take title to the entire farm. A minimum of judicial proceedings will be required if this is the case. (Georgia appears to be the only State in which joint tenancies have been converted into tenancies in common. Survivorship, which is the most important characteristic of a joint tenancy, is permitted in some States only where expressly provided for by the creating instrument. An attempt to convey a joint tenancy to a husband and wife in other States will create a tenancy by the entireties, which also has the characteristic of survivorship.)

Second, if you and your wife held the land as tenants in common, each of you had an undivided interest in the farm, but neither of you has any right of survivorship. She therefore will retain her own one-half interest after your death, but your interest will pass by the law of inheritance. Your widow, under law in a number of States, would acquire one-third interest in your one-half interest, and the remaining two-thirds interest of your half would be divided equally among the three children. In many States, your widow may, as an alternative, claim dower interest in the real estate owned by you at the time of death. (At common law, the dower interest was a life estate in one-third of all land to which her husband had held title during the marriage.)

Third, if the title was in your name as sole owner, the entire farm would descend according to State laws of descent and distribution. According to Illinois statutes, for example, your widow would take a one-third interest in the farm, and the remaining two-thirds would be divided among the three children. Depending upon State laws of descent, your widow may take a dower interest if she chooses.

IF YOU AND YOUR WIFE prepare a mutual will, devising the farm to your son Richard, the following results would be possible:

First, if the land was held under joint tenancy, your widow would acquire your interest on your death under her right of survivorship. Richard would acquire complete title upon the death of both you and your wife.

Second, if the title was held in tenancy in common, your widow would retain her one-half interest after your death and Richard or his heirs would take the remaining one-half interest. Upon your wife's death, Richard or his heirs would acquire her interest, thus giving him (or them) title.

Third, if the title was held by you as sole owner, the entire interest would pass to Richard or his heirs on your death. In some States, this would be subject to statutory provisions whereby your widow could (if she chooses) claim a life estate in part of the land under her dower or homestead rights or a fee interest under a statutory right.

Another method of transferring the farm to Richard might be by escrow deed. Under this system, Richard would contract to purchase the farm, and the deed to the property, signed by you and your wife, would be deposited with a third person to be delivered to Richard on compliance with the conditions of payment. This approach prevents the title to the farm from becoming involved in probate proceedings after you and your wife die.

Thus you can wisely plan for three phases: Original acquisition of the farm, retention of the land, and disposition of the property.

Borrowing money to purchase land.

No simple set of rules will insure the successful use of land credit. An ideal financing arrangement for a farmer who buys a given farm at a given time may not apply to his neighbor. The best way to finance the purchase of a farm depends on the financial condition of the buyer, the date of purchase, the sale price, the size and type of farm, and source of credit, among other things. By *James A. Munger*, agricultural economist, Farm Economics Research Division.

TWO-THIRDS OF THE PEOPLE who bought farms in 1956 had to borrow money to do so. For the satisfaction of ownership and the hope of more income, security, and comfort for themselves and their families, they were willing to assume debt obligations and risk the possible loss of earnings, life savings, and home.

Not only were they concerned individually: The problem of credit financing of farm ownership has social, economic, and political significance, which has made farmers and farm lenders conscious of the responsibilities that accompany the use of credit for buying farms.

To evaluate the role of credit in financing landownership, one needs to review the basic need for land credit and trace the historical development of our land-credit system.

The traditional manner of transferring land from one generation to another has created a continuing need for credit to finance ownership of land. When a farmer of one generation retires or dies, his farm is taken up by someone of a younger generation. That would present no problem if the title to the farm were transferred in its entirety to someone who would be willing and able to operate the farm. Often, however, that is not the case.

It is customary in our society for the children of a farm owner to inherit equal shares of the farm. The children who do not remain to operate the farm usually like to have their shares in cash, a practice that creates the problem of financing the shares that are withdrawn from farming. Moreover, as many children of farmers live in cities, the money invested in farms not only leaves the farm in each generation, it may leave the agricultural areas.

The transfer of land through inheritance or sale has led to a heavy and constant demand for money to be used to buy farms. The amount of capital that must be refinanced each generation depends largely on the price of land.

The total value of all farm real estate was nearly 110 billion dollars in 1957. Most of it must be refinanced within the next 30 or 40 years, assuming constant prices for land. Much of it will be savings that the buyers have accumulated. The rest must be borrowed.

CREDIT FOR FINANCING landownership in the United States dates from colonial days, when farming operations were financed often with the aid of credit secured by land. The purchase and sale of land in the more settled areas was carried on much the same as it is today. Land was cheap, but no organized land-credit market

218

existed and there was a serious shortage of credit.

The Federal Government became directly involved in the problems of land credit after the Revolution.

In order to speed up the sales of public land to raise revenue and promote development of the West, the Congress enacted legislation that permitted the Government to accept a small downpayment at the time of sale and collect the rest later.

But the Government had difficulty in collecting the full purchase price, low though it was. Many settlers did not have enough income to pay for the land and had no other way of obtaining funds. This situation led to the repeal of the credit provisions in 1820.

Public land was sold on a strictly cash basis after 1820, and at reduced prices. The Government thus sought to stimulate purchase without extending credit. The need for land credit was further reduced by the passage of the Homestead Act in 1862, under which public land in the West was given under certain conditions to frontier settlers.

Disposal of public land during the 1800's promoted landownership in the West with only a minimum use of credit, but the need for borrowed funds was increasing rapidly in the more settled areas, particularly in the East. Good farmland was scarce in many communities, and competition among buyers led to higher land prices.

Most of the more productive free land was gone by 1900. Then a sharp rise in farm income at the time of the First World War brought a boom, which reached a peak in 1920. The average value of farm real estate increased from 20 dollars an acre in 1900 to 69 dollars in 1920.

Banks, life-insurance companies, individuals, and miscellaneous lenders increased their volume of farm-mortgage loans outstanding from 3,208 million dollars on January 1, 1910 (the first year for which farm-mortgage debt estimates by type of lender are available), to 8,449 million dollars in 1920. Many prospective farm buyers nevertheless were unable to obtain credit.

As land prices continued to rise, farmers who could not borrow funds became critical of the credit system—the lack of credit, terms of loans, interest rates, and commissions. And with reason: Real-estate loans commonly were made for terms of 5 years or less; interest rates were 8 to 10 percent; commission charges were high.

The high prices of land and a shortage of adequate credit in some areas contributed to a rise in farm tenancy, because after 1900 many tenant farmers found it harder to buy land without credit.

The Federal Government took direct action. The Congress in July 1916 passed the Federal Loan Act, which created the Federal land banks and the joint stock land banks.

The 12 Federal land banks were organized on a cooperative basis. Their loans were made through local cooperative associations.

The joint stock land banks were semiprivate institutions. Their loans were made through local farm-mortgage representatives.

Both systems were given Federal assistance and supervision. Both were designed to obtain funds from the large investment markets and to lend the funds to farmers in all parts of the country on long terms and at low rates of interest.

The Federal land-bank system with its local cooperative National Farm Loan Associations of borrowers is similar in many respects to farm credit institutions in Denmark and Sweden. In Denmark "credit associations," which are cooperative associations of borrowers, issue bonds and lend the money raised on first mortgages on farm real estate. In Sweden cooperative "rural mortgage associations" of borrowers obtain funds for first-mortgage loans from the Royal Mortgage Bank of Sweden, which in turn obtains funds by issuing debentures on the security of the mortgages. The term of loan in Denmark may be as much as 60 years.

Land prices fell sharply in the early 1920's following a decline in prices of farm commodities. Many farmers could not repay mortgages contracted during the land boom. A wave of farm-mortgage foreclosures and bankruptcies swept over distressed sections. Foreclosures increased from 4 per 1,000 farms in 1920 to 18 per 1,000 farms in 1926. Liquidation of mortgages through foreclosure and increasing caution on the part of both farmers and lenders caused farm real-estate debt to fall after 1923. Debt held by individuals and banks decreased more rapidly than total debt as many of these lenders liquidated their investments in farm mortgages.

The decline in debt held by individuals and banks during the 1920's was partly offset by the increased loan activity of life-insurance companies, Federal land banks, and joint stock land banks. These lenders refinanced many farm mortgages on a long-term basis, but the number of farm foreclosures remained high during the entire decade.

The general economic depression of the 1930's and a severe and prolonged drought in the Great Plains caused a crisis in the farm-mortgage market. Farm owners who were already burdened with heavy debt loads faced economic ruin. The average value of farm real estate fell from 49 dollars an acre in 1930 to 30 dollars in 1933. Many owners found themselves with a mortgage debt higher than the total value of their real estate. Deterioration in the national financial structure, which caused lenders to be short of funds, made the situation worse.

The tide of foreclosures rose to 39 per 1,000 farms in 1932. Farm real-estate debt declined steadily as mortgages were canceled through foreclosure. Many banks and insurance companies stopped making new loans.

The Government then reorganized and enlarged the system of public and semipublic farm-credit agencies.

The first step was the establishment of the Farm Credit Administration in March 1933. It brought together into one administrative unit almost all federally sponsored farm-credit agencies existing at the time. The Federal system of land banks is an important unit within the Farm Credit Administration.

The Emergency Farm Mortgage Act of May 1933 liquidated the joint stock land banks and created land bank commissioner loans. These loans were direct Government loans made by the Land Bank Commissioner in Washington, D. C. Commissioner loans were designed to help distressed farmers refinance their mortgage debts. The authority to make commissioner loans expired in 1947.

The Farm Credit Administration is now an independent Federal organization, which supervises a broad system of public and cooperative farm-credit agencies. It coordinates the activities of the many credit units that make farm loans, but the Farm Credit Administration itself does not make loans.

The Farmers Home Administration (which is a part of the Department of Agriculture) also provides long-term credit to agriculture. It was called the Resettlement Administration when it was established in 1935. It became the Farm Security Administration in 1937, and its present name was adopted in 1946. An important function is its program of loans to tenant farmers for farm purchase. That program was established under the Bankhead-Jones Farm Tenant Act of 1937.

With the aid of two distinct credit systems to promote farm ownership, the Federal Government attempted to bolster the sagging farm-mortgage market of the 1930's. Millions of dollars in farm mortgages held by private lenders were refinanced by Federal land bank and land bank commissioner loans in an attempt to stem the tide of foreclosures.

Foreclosures gradually declined after 1932 to a rate of 10 per 1,000 farms in 1940. Despite improvements in the farm-mortgage system, many of the farmers who bought high-priced land in the 1920's were tenants in 1940.

Experience gained during the depression in the 1930's led to a revision of long-term lending practices. Policies initiated by Federal credit agencies were adopted by private lenders. Terms were extended to 20, 30, or even 40 years at low rates of interest. Repayment provisions provided for small annual or semiannual payments over the length of the loan instead of one lump-sum payment.

Farm real-estate debt amounted to about 6 billion dollars at the beginning of the Second World War. Farm income improved substantially during the war years, but land values remained relatively low. Farmers were able to pay off their long-term debts, so that in 1946 the total farm-mortgage debt was 4.8 billion dollars, the lowest point since the high of 10.8 billion dollars in 1923.

Farm income and land prices went up rapidly in the postwar years. The average value of farm real estate increased from 53 dollars an acre in 1946 to 95 dollars in 1957.

Purchasers of land are again faced with the problem of finding adequate credit. The farm-mortgage credit system, however, is now well organized and more able to supply sufficient credit than in 1935.

Life-insurance companies and commercial banks became active in the farm-mortgage field after a temporary withdrawal during the 1930's. Total farm real-estate debt stood at 9,908 million dollars on January 1, 1957. Individuals, the most important type of lenders, held 3,153 million dollars in loans. Life-insurance companies were second with 2,477 million dollars. Federal land banks held 1,722 million dollars; banks held 1,386 million dollars. Miscellaneous lenders accounted for 880 million dollars, and the Farmers Home Administration had 290 million dollars in loans outstanding. Private lenders accounted for 7,896 million dollars, or 80 percent of the total debt;

public or semipublic agencies held 2,012 million dollars, or 20 percent of the debt.

The establishment of a well-organized land-credit system is a comparatively recent development in American agriculture. Advances of the past 50 years exceed those of the preceding three centuries. The problems of obtaining credit with which to finance farm ownership are not entirely solved, however. The trend toward increased commercialization in farming is likely to create an even greater demand for long-term real-estate credit.

THE CORRECT USE OF CREDIT is just as important as its availability in financing farm ownership. Many farm buyers have had little trouble in borrowing money but have had difficulty in paying it back. It boots little to buy a farm one year and lose it a few years later.

The buyer's financial condition is of prime importance in determining how a farm should be financed. His financial condition includes his estimated future income and savings as well as his income and savings at the purchase date.

A buyer usually can reduce the risks of borrowing by making a substantial downpayment. The size of the downpayment needed to protect his investment varies with changes in both the prices of farm commodities and in the value of land. When land prices are low, a relatively small downpayment will establish an adequate equity. This equity will increase as the price of land rises, and both the borrower and lender will have greater protection. When land prices are high, a large downpayment is needed to protect the buyer from losing his entire equity if land values decline.

Another way to reduce risks is to keep a reserve of funds in addition to the downpayment. A farmer who uses all his funds to make a downpayment may be in bad shape in a year of low income. He would be better off if he made a smaller downpayment and kept back enough funds to carry him through a lean period.

Lenders base the size of their loans largely on the value of the security offered. Most farm buyers have difficulty in borrowing more than 50 to 60 percent of the purchase price. Many lending agencies also place increasing emphasis on the borrower's ability to repay. His financial condition thus is a chief factor in determining not only the use but also the availability of credit.

The sale price of a farm is related closely to the date of purchase and the size and type of farm.

Most farm operators have no trouble in deciding on the type of farm they want to buy. The decision usually depends on the interest and experience of the buyer. The best type of farm for any buyer obviously is the type that satisfies his needs.

The size of farm to buy requires more thought. A farm should be large enough to provide an adequate living for the owner and his family and the money needed to pay off the mortgage debt. It is usually a mistake for a farmer to buy a farm that does not meet these qualifications, unless he can rent adjoining land or has an outside source of income. The national trend toward larger, more commercialized farms points up the weak competitive position of small farms.

Deciding on the correct time to buy a farm and the price to pay usually means much time and thought on the part of the prospective buyer.

In general, the price of land reflects the attitudes of buyers and sellers. In periods of high farm income, people become optimistic, and the price of land goes up. When farm income goes down, people become pessimistic, and the price of land drops.

The ideal situation is to buy when prices are low. Land that costs 200 dollars an acre this year may be expensive when compared with a price of 180 dollars last year, but it may be cheap in relation to next year's price of 220 dollars. The main difficulty lies in determining whether current prices are high or low in relation to future prices.

A prospective buyer can usually make a reasonable offer for a farm if he takes advantage of all available sources of information. An examination of all farms for sale in the community will give a buyer some idea of current land prices. This is especially important if he does not live in the community. A study of deed records, which usually are kept in county courthouses and are open to the public, also may help.

The economic measure of the value of a farm is its ability to produce income. Productivity can be determined only by careful inspection of the physical characteristics of the land. Offering to buy land on the basis of what one sees from the road is risky.

One method of estimating the exact price to offer is to compute the net rent that the farm will bring and compare it with other investments. For example, if a farm will bring 5 dollars a year net rent an acre and the rate of return on other investments is 5 percent, the farm would be worth 100 dollars an acre. One gets this figure by dividing the interest rate of other investments into the net rent of the farm (5 dollars divided by 5 percent equals 100 dollars).

The basic price of 100 dollars can then be adjusted up or down according to the buyer's judgment. An unusually fine home may prompt the purchaser to pay slightly more for the farm. The absence of good schools may cause him to offer less. The final purchase price, however, should not be out of line with the long-run, income-producing capacity of the farm. A borrower must remember that his ability to repay his debts depends largely on future income from the farm.

Choosing a lender is the prospective farm owner's next task.

The best advice is to shop around for the best deal. Farmers seldom buy a tractor without first comparing several makes and models, but often they accept the first loan offered. This practice can cost the borrower a great deal of money, and it may even result in the loss of his farm.

A buyer must be familiar with the various types of loans, repayment provisions, and interest rates in order to choose a suitable lender.

THE MOST COMMON TYPE OF LOAN for the purchase of land is the real-estate mortgage loan. The buyer receives money with which to purchase a farm, and the lender receives a claim against the real estate to secure the payment of the loan when it is due.

A deed of trust is sometimes used for the same purpose as a mortgage. The title to the real estate passes to a third party, or trustee, who can sell the property if the loan is not paid.

Sales contracts, although not loans in the usual sense, provide a means of buying land with a relatively small downpayment. The lender keeps the title to the land until the buyer pays the total price or gets a mortgage for the unpaid balance.

Mortgages, deeds of trust, and sales contracts are designed to reduce the risks of lenders. These credit instruments are necessary not only to protect lenders but to attract large sums of money to the land-credit system. Farm buyers would have a hard time finding a loan if they could not offer some form of security.

The size of the downpayment is usually much smaller for land sold under sales contracts. Lenders who have acquired land through foreclosure often are willing to sell the land under contract for a small downpayment or sometimes with no downpayment. On the other hand, loans secured by mortgages usually do not exceed 50 or 60 percent of the sales price. The choice of credit instruments often depends on the buyer's financial condition at the time of purchase.

The size of loan and repayment provisions on long-term loans should be geared to the borrower's expected income situation. This principle has been overlooked too often. Both the lender and borrower have been unduly optimistic, especially during periods of high farm income.

Several methods of payment are commonly used in farm-mortgage loans. Each borrower has to decide which method best meets his needs.

THE STRAIGHT-END LOAN calls for payment of annual interest charges during the life of the loan (usually 5 years or less). The principal is due in a lump sum when the loan matures. This was a common method of payment during the 1920's and earlier, but its use has declined.

Most borrowers who use the straight-end loan intend to renew or refinance the loan when it becomes due. This might be a satisfactory arrangement if the borrower could renew the loan whenever necessary. Farmers generally are unable to predict their future. A buyer who uses this method becomes dependent on the willingness and ability of the lender to renew. The method involves relatively high risks for the owner.

Some purchasers can use the straight-end method to good advantage. For instance, a farmer who wishes to sell his farm and buy other land may take out a short-term loan that can be paid in full when his first farm is sold.

A PARTIAL-PAYMENT LOAN, a form of end-payment loan, has an added provision for small annual payments on the principal along with the usual interest payments. The term of this loan generally is longer than that of the straight-end loan. It ranges up to 10 or 15 years.

This method of payment is somewhat less risky than the lump-sum plan. A typical loan of 10 thousand dollars for 10 years may call for annual principal payments of 200 dollars. Thus the owner would gain equity of 2 thousand dollars in the farm during the life of the loan if the price of land remained constant. But the borrower would still have to arrange to refinance the remaining debt of 8 thousand dollars.

AMORTIZATION LOANS were first used widely by the Federal land banks. The usual amortization loan calls for annual or semiannual payments of interest and principal, which are arranged to pay the debt completely within the life of the loan.

The amortized loan has become increasingly popular with both lenders and borrowers. It encourages the farmer eventually to own his farm free of debt while providing maximum protection for the lender by reducing his investment each year. These loans are commonly made for 20 to 30 years. A few range up to 40 years.

Two amortization plans are in common use by lending institutions. The standard plan calls for equal payments each year during the life of the loan. The proportion of each payment that represents interest is high at first, but it grows smaller with each succeeding payment. This is because the balance outstanding on which interest must be paid is reduced with each payment. As the interest payment decreases, the amount paid on the principal increases because all the payments are the same.

The Springfield plan calls for equal payments on the principal but for declining interest payments. The borrower pays a fixed amount each year on the debt, but interest payments decline as the balance outstanding grows less. This plan is the same as a partial-payment loan, except that the payments continue until the entire debt is paid.

The net effect of the standard and the Springfield plan is the same. Both plans call for full payment of principal and interest during the term of the loan. The initial principal payments are higher under the Springfield plan. Thus the Springfield plan would provide more protection if the price of land should decline. Some borrowers prefer the Springfield plan because the decreasing annual payments give them a feeling of progress in paying the loans.

Variable or flexible payment loans are a relatively new development. In some parts of the country, such as the Great Plains, crop yields and farm income may vary widely from year to year. Farmers in those sections are unable to meet their loan payments in some years. They have more than enough income in other years to pay their annual installments. Variable payment loans are designed primarily for high-risk areas.

The variable or flexible payment loan is just what the name implies. Payments vary each year depending on prices, yields, or incomes of borrowers. Mortgage contracts based on income or yields generally have been more satisfactory than those based on prices. High prices are of little benefit to a farmer who has had a crop failure.

OPTIONAL PAYMENTS give borrowers an opportunity to pay any part or all of the loan before the mortgage comes due. This is a great advantage to the farm buyer, as he can make substantial payments during good years and thus reduce the possibility of losing the farm during a period of low income. Optional payments also permit the borrower to save money by refinancing the loan when the interest rates decline.

Lenders often specify the times at which optional payments are to be made. This prevents the lender from losing money if the loan is paid too soon. A loan of 2 thousand dollars at 5 percent interest will return 100 dollars to the lender in the first year. If the expenses of making the loan amount to 125 dollars, the lender may specify that optional payments cannot be made until 2 or 3 years have elapsed since the loan was made.

Reserve payments also serve to reduce the risks of borrowing. This feature, which was promoted by the Federal land banks, allows the borrower to make advance payments, which are held in reserve. Reserve payments earn interest; they can be used to meet annual payments in poor years.

INTEREST RATES are of direct concern to both lenders and borrowers. Attempts by borrowers to get lower rates and resistance to these attempts by lenders have led to much controversy and legislation.

The cost of borrowing money is determined largely by economic factors. Lenders do not lend their money unless they receive compensation from the borrower for its use. The amount of compensation (or the interest rate) demanded by lenders depends on the supply of money, risk of loss, cost of making loans, length of loan, type of security, size of loan, and State and Federal laws that pertain to loans.

The upper limit on rates is set by State laws. The Federal Government has also influenced rates by sponsoring credit agencies specifically designed to establish low interest rates throughout the country.

Interest rates on farm real-estate loans vary significantly from one region to another. The average interest rate in the West in 1910 was above 7 percent; it was 5.5 percent in the Northeast. The spread between regions gradually decreased, mainly because of the impact of relatively uniform interest rates charged by the Federal land banks.

Interest rates are highest in the Western and Southern States. This fact generally can be explained by the size of loans, amount of risk, and availability of credit in those States. The cost of making a loan of 10 thousand dollars is not much greater than that of making a loan of 1 thousand dollars. The lender usually charges a higher rate of interest on the smaller loan in order to get the same return. The Southern States particularly have a large proportion of small loans.

Interest rates usually are higher in high-risk areas. Some lenders will not make loans there, and others demand higher rates as a protection against loss.

Farmers in Western States are far removed from the important investment centers of the East; that explains in part the higher rates in the West.

COMMISSION CHARGES must be paid on some loans in addition to interest payments. The borrower usually pays

these charges when the loan is negotiated; they help to pay the cost of making the loan.

Commissions are either a flat fee for each loan, a fixed percentage of the amount loaned, or a combination of both a fee and a percentage. For example, the commission on a loan of 10 thousand dollars may be 200 dollars in the form of a flat fee. It would be the same regardless of the size of the loan. The lender may prefer a 2-percent commission charge instead of a flat fee. This charge would amount to 200 dollars on a loan of 10 thousand dollars. Or the lender may combine a fee of 100 dollars with a 1-percent commission. The total charges are the same for all methods in this example. In actual practice, a large borrower usually would have less expense with a flat fee, while a percentage commission would be cheaper for a small borrower.

FARM MORTGAGE LENDERS are commonly divided into six major groups: Federal land banks, Farmers Home Administration, life-insurance companies, banks, individuals, and miscellaneous lenders.

The Federal land-bank system is a cooperative credit organization composed of the Land Bank Service of the Farm Credit Administration in Washington, D. C.; 12 Federal land banks, each of which serves a farm-credit district consisting of one or more States; and more than 1 thousand national farm-loan associations in all parts of the United States and Puerto Rico.

The land banks and associations were established by the Federal Farm Loan Act of 1916. The banks were originally capitalized almost entirely by the Federal Government, but public capital was replaced with funds from the local associations so that the system became entirely farmer owned in 1947.

The land-bank system is under the general supervision of the Farm Credit Administration, which is responsible for coordinating the activities of the banks and associations and for administering the laws governing them.

The land banks and their local associations are organized much the same as any cooperative. A farmer-borrower becomes a member of a national farm-loan association by purchasing stock amounting to at least 5 percent of the loan. The associations in turn own the stock of the land bank, and the users of the land-bank system are also the owners.

Federal land-bank loans are secured by real-estate mortgages. The banks borrow additional funds for lending purposes by using the mortgages as security. The chief source of funds of the land banks is the sale of farm-loan bonds to commercial banks, private corporations, and individuals.

The land banks also handled land bank commissioner loans from 1933 through July 1, 1947. These loans were made from Federal funds provided by the Federal Farm Mortgage Corporation; they were usually higher risk loans than land-bank loans. All outstanding land bank commissioner loans were sold to the land banks on June 30, 1955.

The land banks have lent more than 6 billion dollars to farmers since they first began to operate in 1917. They negotiated an additional 1 billion dollars in loans for the Federal Farm Mortgage Corporation. More than a million farmers have received long-term real-estate loans through the land-bank system.

Only farmers who own or buy land can get a land-bank loan. All loans must be secured by a first mortgage on real estate. They cannot exceed 65 percent of the normal long-run value of the property. Terms of these loans are 5 to 40 years; 30 to 35 years the most common term. Each land-bank loan must be on an amortization plan, and the borrower usually is permitted to repay the loan at any time without penalty.

Interest rates on land-bank loans are low. The law specifies a maximum rate of 6 percent, and rates actually charged have ranged from 4 to 6 percent, except for a temporarily reduced rate of 3.5 percent, which was in effect from July 11, 1933, to July 1, 1944. Year-to-year changes in rates on new loans are usually caused by changes in the price of the money that the land banks must borrow for their lending operations. A rate of 6 percent was charged by three land banks in November 1957. The other nine banks charged 5.5 percent.

Federal land-bank loans outstanding on July 1, 1957, amounted to 1,847 million dollars. The average size of land-bank loans made during the last half of 1956 was 8,940 dollars.

THE FARMERS HOME ADMINISTRATION offers a supervised credit service to farmers who cannot borrow from other sources the funds they need.

To be eligible, a borrower must be unable to obtain sufficient credit elsewhere at the rates and terms prevailing in the community. He must also have had farm experience, and he must be a citizen of the United States. Loans are made for the purchase of family-type farms only. The loan cannot exceed the average value of all family-type farms in the county.

A qualified farm buyer can borrow up to 100 percent of the fair and reasonable value of the farm. Loans are made for terms of up to 40 years. The farming operations of the borrower are supervised to the extent necessary to insure efficient and successful farming practices. A borrower must refinance his loan through a private or cooperative lender whenever he is able to do so.

All loans are made through county offices, which are in the county seat. Applications from veterans with farming experience receive special consideration.

Interest rates on direct farm-ownership loans of the Farmers Home Administration are lower than those of any other major lender. Rates have ranged from 3 percent in the 1930's and 1940's to 4.5 percent in 1957.

Funds loaned by the Farmers Home Administration are appropriated directly by the Congress. The funds available in any one year are some-times exhausted before the needs of all qualified borrowers are met.

A unique feature of the farm-owner-ship program is the provision that per-mits loans up to 100 percent of the purchase price of the farm. This fea-ture enabled many tenant farmers, particularly those in the South, to buy a farm with no downpayment.

The Farmers Home Administration also insures farm-mortgage loans made by private lenders. Borrowers must meet about the same requirements for insured loans as for direct loans. The chief difference is that insured loans are limited to 90 percent of the bor-rower's investment. The borrower must be able to make a downpayment of at least 10 percent, plus a mortgage insurance charge of 1 percent.

A prospective farm buyer should not overlook the possibility of obtaining a loan from the Farmers Home Ad-ministration if he cannot get adequate credit from other sources. Farm-own-ership loans are amortized, and bor-rowers are permitted and encouraged to make prepayments.

The total amount of loans from the Farmers Home Administration is small in comparison with loans of other lenders. Direct farm-ownership loans amounted to 305 million dollars on July 1, 1957. The average loan made in 1956 amounted to 12,310 dollars.

LIFE-INSURANCE COMPANIES hold more farm-mortgage loans than any other institutional lender. They began to make loans secured by farm mortgages in 1850 or so, and since then have been an important source of credit.

Insurance companies were the larg-est institutional holder of farm mort-gages from 1910 until 1933. During the depression of the 1930's, the com-panies curtailed their lending activi-ties. Many companies acquired a large number of farms through foreclosure. They were not anxious to invest more funds during a period of low farm in-come and declining land prices. Life-insurance companies began to expand

their loans shortly before the Second World War. They again led other in-stitutional lenders by the end of 1947. They held about 2,465 million dollars in mortgage loans on January 1, 1957.

Insurance companies commonly in-vest some of their reserves in real-estate mortgages. The companies hold these reserve funds to pay policyhold-ers or their beneficiaries. When they invest the funds, the companies try to obtain the highest rates of return con-sistent with a high degree of safety. They are not obligated to make loans to farmers, and they may make more or fewer new farm loans at any time.

The companies tend to concentrate their loans in the low-risk agricultural areas and to make rather large loans in order to service a large volume of loans at low cost. Insurance companies are most active in the Corn Belt and adjoining States. The average size of loans they made in the second half of 1956 was more than 16 thousand dol-lars. Loans of all other lenders aver-aged 6,800 dollars.

The home offices of many large life-insurance companies are rather far re-moved from agricultural areas, and ordinarily their loans are made through branch offices, local agents, or banks.

Life-insurance companies offer amor-tized loans for terms up to 40 years. Repayment plans often are patterned on the borrower's special needs.

Their interest rates usually are high-er than those of the Federal land banks and the Farmers Home Administra-tion, but they generally are lower than rates of banks and individual lenders. Rates on loans made by major com-panies in the first part of 1957 were 5 to 6 percent.

Insurance companies are forbidden by law in most States to make loans in excess of two-thirds of the appraised value of the farm. Farms usually are appraised on the basis of normal values, but companies' policies differ.

BANKS have long been important in financing farm ownership. A farmer who needs credit is likely to seek a loan from his local bank before he tries any other source. Banks were one of the few sources of credit for farmers during the 1700's and early 1800's.

The volume of real-estate loans of banks more than doubled between 1915 and 1922. This rapid expansion in loans, which was followed by an agricultural depression in the next two decades, caused serious trouble for rural banks. Many banks were unable to collect their loans and were forced into bankruptcy. Bank loans shrank steadily during the depression. After the Second World War, however, banks began to increase their volume of loans. On January 1, 1957, they held farm-mortgage loans amounting to 1,386 million dollars.

Banks lend the money their patrons deposit with them. Those funds are not well suited to making long-term loans. Demand deposits may be withdrawn from the bank at any time, and time deposits can be withdrawn on short notice.

Banks tend to concentrate on short-term loans to farmers for production and living expenses and the purchase of livestock and machinery. This leaves less money for them to lend for farm real-estate loans.

Some banks make long-term amortized loans, but most bank real-estate loans are lump-sum or partial-payment loans made for 5 to 10 years. Banks often are willing to renew these loans when they become due, particularly if part of the loan has been repaid during the original term.

A bank loan usually is not suitable for a farmer who borrows most of the purchase price of his farm. Such an owner has little hope of repaying the loan within 5 or 10 years, and he must face the problem of refinancing his debt every few years. He probably would be better off with a long-term amortized loan. But owners who need to borrow only a small proportion of the value of their farms may find it more convenient to take out a small bank loan that can be paid in full within a few years.

Interest rates charged by banks tend to be higher and less competitive than those of other lenders, although this situation has changed gradually in some States in which public credit agencies are most active. Most banks in 1957 charged about 6 percent interest on mortgage loans.

Banks also act as loan agents for life-insurance companies and individuals. A banker may arrange for a loan to be made by another lender, or he may make the loan himself and later sell it to an individual or credit institution. Banks thus stimulate the flow of mortgage credit from lender to borrower.

INDIVIDUALS are the chief single group of farm-mortgage lenders. We know less about them than about any other major group of lenders because they, unlike institutional lenders, are not required by law to prepare and publish records of their activities.

Individuals who hold farm-mortgage loans fall into three general categories. One group is made up of former owners who have accepted a mortgage as partial payment at the time they sold their farms. Others make loans to help a relative or friend buy a farm, or they may take a mortgage when they transfer the farm to their heirs. A third group comprises individuals who like to invest savings in farm mortgages.

Individuals held more than 50 percent of the total farm-mortgage debt until the depression that followed the First World War. High losses caused many individuals to liquidate their investments in farm mortgages, and by 1940 the Federal land banks were the largest lender in the field. Individuals regained first place after the depression. They accounted for about 32 percent of all mortgage loans in 1957.

The average term of loans made by individuals is generally shorter than that of loans made by most institutional lenders, and average interest rates are relatively high. Rates fluctuate greatly among lenders. Rates on loans between members of the same family are usually low, while those on loans made to persons outside the family may be high.

Short-term loans from individuals are not a very satisfactory means of financing farm ownership. Individuals do not have the large financial resources institutional lenders have. The seller of a farm is sometimes a good source of credit. He knows what the farm will produce and can judge how much the buyer will be able to pay each year. A former owner often is willing to accept a mortgage or sales contract, particularly if he considers the farm a good investment.

MISCELLANEOUS LENDERS are mostly mortgage-loan companies, merchants, and dealers. They held about 9 percent of all farm-mortgage debt on January 1, 1956.

Mortgage-loan companies are located in many rural communities. They make loans with their own funds or act as agents for other lenders. Some of their mortgages are sold to life-insurance companies.

Merchants and dealers make loans mostly for the purchase of machinery or supplies and take a real-estate mortgage as additional security.

Miscellaneous lenders have no loan policies in common. A farm buyer who uses this source of credit should make sure that interest rates, terms, and repayment provisions are in line with loans available from other lenders.

CONTINUING PROBLEMS of land mortgage credit should be recognized by both lenders and borrowers.

Uncertainties caused by fluctuations in farm prices and incomes continue to be the chief problem in financing the ownership of land. Lenders and borrowers have often overestimated their ability to solve this problem. The high incidence of farm foreclosures in the 1920's and 1930's was primarily the result of failure to anticipate the declines in land values and farm incomes that occurred after the debts were contracted.

The causes of uncertainties as to price and income are often beyond the control of individual farmers and the lenders, but the adverse effects of these uncertainties on a long-term debt obligation can be reduced if changes are anticipated and provided for in the mortgage contract.

Both lenders and borrowers should recognize that fluctuations in farm prices and incomes will affect the borrower's ability to make payments on his mortgage. A borrower can reduce future risk by making a substantial downpayment and by keeping additional funds in reserve.

Borrowers who are permitted to anticipate future payments in good years are less likely to become delinquent in years of low incomes. Risks also are reduced when the mortgage contract provides for payments that vary with crop yields or income. Mortgages with variable-payment provisions are not yet common, but a usual practice of institutional lenders is to defer principal payments—and sometimes interest payments—when a borrower has a poor year.

Much of my discussion has been about the problems involved in borrowing money to buy land. Borrowing involves problems, and sometimes farmers get the idea that they should avoid debt, or if debt cannot be avoided it should be repaid as soon as possible. Often neither idea is true.

A farmer by borrowing money may be able to buy a farm that is better than any he could rent and will give him a better income. Every borrower should try to have an adequate reserve for his future mortgage payments. But after that, he may be better off not to reduce his mortgage ahead of schedule. It may be better for him to improve his farm instead and add to his livestock and machinery. Money wisely spent in this way should add to his future income and may make him more secure than if it were used for debt reduction. A farm may be mortgage-free and yet be too small or too poorly equipped or have too few livestock to insure a secure living.

Insurance against losses on farms.

Insurance does not prevent loss. It spreads the losses of a few among many. By paying a small, definite amount annually, a person gets assurance that his burden of possible losses may be distributed over a period of years. Insurance can help stabilize farm income by assuring that even in the event of a disaster a farmer will have some cash to meet his obligations. By *Ralph R. Botts* and *Robert C. Otte,* agricultural economists, Farm Economics Research Division.

ALL INSURANCE companies try to follow certain common principles.

They must establish premium rates for each class and degree of risk. Enough risks must be carried to give a reasonably stable experience. The company must be safeguarded against adverse selection and too great a concentration of risks.

Premiums must equal or exceed losses within relatively short periods of time. Aggregate losses must not vary too greatly from year to year, or impractically large reserves will be required. Losses must occur by chance, for otherwise there would be no basis for averaging.

We discuss here only the forms of insurance that cover loss of farm property (including buildings and their contents) and farm products, before and after harvest and while still on the farm. Other forms of insurance may be important, however, to farmers and others—automobile, life, health and sickness, employer's liability, workman's compensation, old age and survivorship (social security), and other forms of property, personal, and liability insurance.

FIRE AND WINDSTORM insurance is needed by farmers more than by any other group.

Farm buildings seldom are of fire-

proof construction. Firefighting facilities often are far away, and a fire may bring total loss.

Farm buildings also are more apt to be damaged or demolished by wind than other buildings because of their construction and the higher, unobstructed wind velocities to which they are subjected.

Loss of the farm buildings means loss of a place to live for the farm family and impairment of its means of livelihood.

Both stock and mutual insurance companies offer fire and lightning and windstorm insurance on farm buildings and personal property, such as machinery and household equipment.

Mutual companies include the farm mutuals, which have at least one-half of their insurance on farm property, and the general-writing mutuals.

Within a given State, the stock and general-writing mutual companies ordinarily use the same rate manuals covering farm property. The mutuals, however, usually declare dividends (about 20 percent) when policies are renewed.

The stock and general-writing mutual companies offer term policies and 1-year policies. The premium for a 3-year policy is 2.7 times the annual premium; for a 5-year policy, it is 4.4 times the annual premium. An example: If the premium for an annual policy is 10 dollars, a 3-year policy would cost 27 dollars and a 5-year policy would cost 44 dollars. For a general-writing mutual company that has a 20-percent dividend rate, the renewal premium at the end of 3 years would be 21.60 dollars, instead of 27 dollars; for a 5-year policy, the renewal premium would be 35.20 dollars, instead of 44.

Rates of the stock and the general-writing mutuals vary according to loss probabilities associated with a number of factors. The use (dwelling or barn), wall construction, roof flammability, and location and the presence or absence of lightning rods, a central heating plant, and sometimes fire extinguishers all affect rates. Another factor is the availability of fire-department services—whether the fire department is within a specified distance from the farm, there is telephone service, and at least 3 thousand gallons of water are available for the use of a fire truck.

Farm mutual companies other than the crop-hail mutuals may be classified as specialized fire (and lightning) companies, which do not cover the windstorm peril; the fire-wind mutuals, which cover wind and hail damage to property other than growing crops, in addition to fire and lightning; and the specialized wind mutuals, which usually cover only wind and hail damage (to property other than growing crops).

Most of the fire-wind mutual companies also cover property damage from such minor perils as vehicles, explosion, riot, smoke, falling aircraft, and, less often, overturn of machinery. A few may cover theft of machinery or livestock, or both, and loss of livestock on highways. Some of the specialized fire and specialized wind mutuals cover these additional perils.

Hereafter, we shall call the specialized fire and the fire-wind companies farm fire mutuals, because both types of companies write fire (and lightning) insurance and have at least half of it on farm property.

Many of the farm fire mutuals were organized as assessment cooperatives in the 1870's and 1880's. They operated in limited areas and made assessments after losses were incurred. They insured mainly against damage to buildings by fire and lightning. There was little uniformity in the wording of policies. Livestock was the chief source of power on farms, and there was little investment in or insurance on equipment. Because values were low, the amounts of insurance provided were low.

Significant changes have occurred, particularly as to volume of insurance carried, services performed, and financial soundness of the farm fire mutuals. There are fewer companies, but they have increased greatly their volume of business. The proportion of companies carrying at least 10 million dollars of insurance trebled between 1936 and 1954. The increase came partly from the acceptance of nonfarm risks and partly from the rise in value of farm property, including machinery.

Other changes include the coverage of additional perils, including windstorm, a greater accumulation of safety funds or reserves, and wider adoption of the practices of collecting advance assessments and using standardized policies.

The 1,743 farm fire mutuals on December 31, 1954, had 28.8 billion dollars of fire (and lightning) insurance in force, of which about 85 percent was on farm property. That was about 5.5 times the volume of fire insurance carried by these companies 40 years earlier. About 11.4 billion dollars of the 28.8 billion dollars of insurance also applied to the windstorm peril. In addition, 64 specialized windstorm mutuals carried another 7.7 billion dollars of windstorm insurance, making a total of 19.1 billion dollars of such insurance in force at the end of 1954.

The Corn Belt and Lake States have a greater concentration of farm mutuals than any other region. Seventy-one percent of the farm fire mutuals were located there. They carried about 64 percent of the total farm mutual fire insurance in force at the end of 1954. Moreover, 83 percent of the specialized windstorm mutuals, which carried 96 percent of the insurance on the books of such companies, also were in this region.

About one in three farm fire mutuals were covering the windstorm peril in one form or another in 1954. Only one in five did so in 1946.

As more farm fire mutuals make windstorm insurance available to members, more and more specialized windstorm mutuals add fire and related perils to their coverages. Eventually there may be only one type of farm mutual—the wind-writing fire mutual. The inclusion of both perils and others in one policy should result in some savings in overall operating expenses.

Many farm mutuals include in their policies a provision for the payment of up to 10 percent of the amount of insurance on household goods and personal property if they are damaged or destroyed when off the policyholder's premises. For example, with 2 thousand dollars of insurance on personal property, a policyholder may claim up to 200 dollars for clothing damaged by fire while it is in storage or at a dry-cleaning establishment or laundry in a nearby town.

About two-thirds of the farm companies, including specialized windstorm and fire mutuals, use 5-year policies. These companies usually make assessment levies annually, however, to pay losses and operating expenses and to build up safety funds.

About three-fourths of the fire mutuals and three-fifths of the specialized wind mutuals charge flat rates that are applicable to all classes of farm property. They do not classify rates according to fire-loss or wind-loss probabilities. These rates vary widely, even as State averages, but they tend to be lowest in the Great Plains, Lake, and Corn Belt States and highest in the Northeastern, Appalachian, Delta, and Southeastern States. In Minnesota, for example, they averaged 15.5 cents per 100 dollars in 1954, compared with 75.1 cents in South Carolina.

One reason for these low loss and assessment rates of the farm fire mutuals is their practice of inspecting properties before acceptance for insurance. About nine in ten follow this practice. About two-thirds of them also inspect properties both upon acceptance and when policies are renewed. Only about one in ten companies also inspect properties during policy terms.

Most farm mutuals now have safety funds or reserves and about seven in ten use reinsurance. Reinsurance is a transfer of part of the ultimate liability for loss from one company to another. It enables a company to insure high-valued farm properties more adequately and also to iron out the year-to-year fluctuations in the cost of insurance to members.

In all forms of property insurance, the company may pay the claim at either the actual value of the property or the amount necessary to repair or replace it, taking depreciation into account. Any payment, however, is limited to the amount stated in the policy. Partial losses thus are payable in full unless a deductible amount applies.

Most losses from windstorms are small. For example, old roofs or barn doors that already need repairs may be damaged. Some companies therefore include in their policies deductible clauses, under which the amount specified is deducted from all windstorm claims. This may also be offered on an optional basis along with a full-coverage policy. Under a 50-dollar-deductible clause, for example, that amount would be deducted from a claim of 75 dollars, and the insurance would pay only 25 dollars. Nothing would be payable on a claim of 50 dollars or less.

Deductible clauses mean lower premiums. A farmer who keeps his buildings in good shape is likely to favor this kind of insurance, as it does not require him to help pay the maintenance claims of his neighbors. A major loss, which would hurt him most would still be covered almost in full.

If a farmer has obtained a loan from the Commodity Credit Corporation on farm-stored grain, he is not responsible for the loss of such grain if there has been no negligence on his part. The Commodity Credit Corporation will assume any loss of sealed grain from causes such as fire or windstorm but not losses from insect infestation, vermin, or rodents. If insurance covered such grain and there were a loss, probably the farmer could not collect from his insurance company. He would have suffered no financial loss. As far as he is concerned, the provision in the loan agreement serves as a substitute for insurance on sealed grain.

ALL-RISK FEDERAL CROP insurance was available on one or more crops in 818 counties in 1957. More than 330 thousand producers were insured. Wheat, cotton, flax, corn, tobacco, soybeans, barley, oats, dry edible beans, peaches, and citrus fruit, sometimes were insured under separate contracts. Many different kinds of crops also were covered in some places under multiple-crop insurance. In all, 23 different crops were insured in one or more counties in 1957.

This insurance covers the unavoidable natural causes of loss, including drought, flood, hail, wind, frost, winterkill, lightning, fire, excessive rain, snow, hurricane, tornado, wild animals, insects, and plant diseases and such other unavoidable causes as may be determined by the Federal Crop Insurance Corporation, which makes the insurance available. Drought has been the commonest cause of losses.

This coverage is essentially a guarantee. (Citrus fruit is an exception.) The insurance cannot exceed area-average costs of production, which are often considered to be 60 percent of the county or area-average, long-term yield. The coverage is progressive. It builds up by stages as the crop ma-

tures—somewhat in line with the increase in investment as additional production costs are incurred. The maximum coverage applies to a crop that is harvested.

The grower is indemnified for the difference between his coverage and the bushels (or other units) he produces. Any deficit in production is valued at a predetermined price per unit. If there is a loss of quality, the actual production is valued at a lower price while the coverage is valued at the predetermined price. This program insures yield and quality but not price and income.

Under multiple-crop insurance, the coverage in yield units for each crop is converted to dollars by using the designated price. These dollar coverages are then combined. The production of each crop later is converted to dollars in the same way. The difference between the combined coverage and the combined valuation is the amount of the indemnity.

Combining several crops under one coverage reduces risks. Each crop is subject in part to different risks, and good production of one often offsets poor production of another. The farmer receives a premium reduction for this diversification of risk.

Under another plan, several crops may be covered under one contract, with the option that losses are still settled separately on each crop. Rate discounts for diversification do not apply as under the other plan.

Under Federal crop insurance, all farmers in a given area, which may be as large as a county, have the same coverage and pay the same premium rate. Coverages and rates are on file in the county offices. Insurance must be obtained before specified closing dates. A policy is continuous, but failure to pay premiums before a specified date automatically terminates the contract. Premiums do not include the expense of operating the program; that is borne by the Federal Government.

A farmer cannot buy Federal crop insurance to cover certain fields, as he can in the case of crop-hail insurance. He must insure all he has in the county or none. Settlements by fields result in the payment of some losses that would be avoided on an overall basis, and the latter more nearly measures the loss to the farmer. High production on one field may offset low production on another. This balancing of high against low production is more likely to occur with large acreages and widely separated tracts than with smaller acreages and contiguous tracts.

Federal crop insurance is essentially an all-risk yield guarantee, but this is not quite true of citrus (not tree) insurance. Citrus contracts cover the principal hazards of freeze and windstorm, and one minor hazard, hail. The policy is a multiple-peril, not an all-risk, contract. Moreover, losses are settled on a percentage of damage, rather than a deficit-yield, basis.

Peach (not tree) insurance was offered experimentally in 1957 in one county. Growers can elect coverage at 100, 150, or 200 dollars an acre. A normal yield per acre is established for each insured orchard. When production drops below the coverage in bushels (dollar coverage divided by fixed price per bushel), the grower moves into the loss category. But he bears the first 40 percentage points of the percentage of damage. A deductible clause of this kind holds down losses and premium costs.

As an example of the peach insurance, suppose a normal yield of 400 bushels were established for a particular orchard. If the farmer elects 200 dollars of coverage, his effective guarantee is only 60 percent of that figure, or 120 dollars an acre—because of the deductible feature. The 200-dollar coverage divided by the 400 bushels of normal yield provides a fixed price (50 cents), at which any production is valued. If only 100 bushels are produced, they are valued at 50 dollars (or 50 cents a bushel), and the indemnity is 70 dollars (120 dollars minus 50 dollars).

For all crops except tobacco, Federal crop insurance terminates when the crop leaves the field. Tobacco losses cannot be determined until the insured tobacco has been weighed and sold at the auction market and the average market price has been determined. The insurance therefore also covers tobacco while it is in the curing barn.

MULTIPLE-PERIL CROP insurance was offered for the first time in 1956 in seven States by about 60 stock insurance companies.

A few companies attempted to write all-risk crop insurance many years ago, but the projects were not successful. The contracts were written against loss of income from the crop by any cause, and price declines were more important causes of loss than crop failures. The insurance of price would be desirable if it were feasible, but prices are determined largely by human actions and are not predictable.

Factors that affect production are largely physical and can be predicted in some measure. Also, because price declines in a given year affect most producers, the spreading of risks becomes almost impossible.

The 1956 multiple-peril crop insurance program got started late, and fewer than 100 policies were sold. These policies covered the perils of drought, plant disease, insect infestation, freezing, windstorm, flood, excessive moisture, excessive heat, and some minor hazards. The insurance was available on corn and soybeans in specified counties in Illinois, Indiana, Iowa, Minnesota, and Nebraska and on tobacco in Kentucky and Tennessee.

The insurance was offered as a supplement to crop-hail insurance. A normal yield was established for each insurable crop for each area. A farmer could get crop-hail insurance for half that figure, valued at a fixed price per bushel. In an 80-bushel area, for example, a farmer could get crop-hail insurance on corn for up to 100 dollars an acre (or 40 bushels times 2.50 dollars a bushel).

In most areas, 30 percent of the hail insurance was applicable as crop insurance (30 dollars, for example). If, because of the occurrence of a named peril, only 30 bushels were produced, they were valued at 75 cents each, or 22.50 dollars, and the indemnity amounted to 7.50 dollars an acre (or 30 dollars minus 22.50). Stated in another way, the guarantee under crop insurance was equivalent to placing a valuation of 30 percent of the fixed price on each bushel of deficit yield below half of normal for the area.

CROP-HAIL insurance is used by more and more farmers as protection against financial loss because of hail damage to growing crops. Much of the increase in this insurance has been on corn and soybeans in the Midwest and on tobacco and cotton in the Southeast.

About 55 mutual and 85 stock companies offer crop-hail insurance. It is also available in three States (North Dakota, Colorado, and Montana) from State hail departments.

From 42 to 93 percent of the premiums paid by farmers were returned to them as indemnities in 1950–1956. Losses were particularly high in 1956.

Claims are based on the percentage of damage as determined by inspection. A farmer having 1 thousand dollars of insurance and 40-percent damage is paid 400 dollars. He can obtain lower rates by taking out a deductible policy. In this example, under a 10-percent deductible clause, the farmer would receive only 300 dollars, but his premium would be lower.

The policy shows the total amount of hail insurance on a crop and also a per-acre figure. The farmer may claim a loss on any part of the insured acreage. Buying insurance late in the season does not reduce the premium, because the probability of loss increases as harvesttime approaches.

The insurance may be taken on a general or a deductible policy.

General policies usually contain minimum-loss clauses under which no loss of less than a specified percentage is payable. Losses that equal or exceed this minimum amount are payable in full. Under a 5-percent minimum-loss clause, for example, nothing would be payable on hail damage of 4 percent or less; but if the loss amounted to 5 percent or more, that percentage of the insurance on the damaged acres would be payable. This eliminates small claims, for which settlement costs are high in proportion to the indemnities paid.

Deductible policies are particularly well adapted to areas in which hail risk and premiums are high. The deductible may be as low as 10 percent or as high as 25 percent.

Farmers tend to take hail insurance when their crop prospects are good. Before taking it, the farmer should consider the alternative protection provided by different policies in relation to needs and costs. Suppose a crop starts off well and gives promise of bringing in 2 thousand dollars. Suppose, further, that the premium rate under a general hail insurance policy is 10 percent (or 200 dollars). The farmer may decide to carry part of the risk himself and spend only 120 dollars for insurance. This would buy 1,200 dollars on a general policy, or enough to carry 60 percent of the value. The same premium (120 dollars) might buy a 10-percent deductible policy for 1,500 dollars or a 25-percent deductible policy for 2 thousand dollars.

If a loss of less than 50 percent occurs, the largest indemnity would be paid under the general policy. The 10-percent deductible policy provides the greater protection against losses between 50 and 70 percent. The 25-percent deductible policy is most valuable for protection against losses of more than 70 percent.

Deductible crop-hail insurance can be used in combination with all-risk crop insurance. The latter covers loss from any cause (including hail) but is limited to area-average costs of production. There would thus be some duplication with a general crop-hail policy, which covers cost of production as well as possible net income.

Less duplication occurs when crop prospects are good than when they are poor, and the amount of duplication may be reduced by using a deductible clause on the crop-hail policy.

Standing grain and soybeans are insured against fire (and lightning) loss by some stock and mutual companies, particularly in the Northwest. Insured fields must be specifically described. Companies in some States make the insurance available as a supplement to crop-hail insurance. The fire insurance applies to all fields covered by crop-hail insurance. The two coverages expire at the same time.

LIVESTOCK insurance against death from fire (and lightning), windstorm, and related perils may be obtained from most stock and mutual insurance companies. Lightning is the commonest cause of loss.

A farmer may obtain a different amount of insurance on each specifically described (usually high-valued) animal; or he may insure all animals of a kind, as personal property, for a blanket amount. In the latter case, a specified maximum amount of insurance usually applies to any one animal.

Many companies, including more than a third of the farm companies, also use a pro rata clause in settling livestock losses that occur in connection with blanket or herd coverage. The amount of insurance on the herd or class of animals is prorated over the number of head owned at the time of loss. With such a clause in effect, the company is liable for the least of three amounts with respect to an animal: The prorated amount, the specified maximum, or the actual value of the animal.

All-risk mortality insurance on livestock, covering accidents and disease, as well as other perils, is uncommon, although it was widely available in the 1920's. One large company now writes all-risk livestock insurance on horses and cattle only—not range cattle. All insured animals must be kept under daily supervision and care. Indemnification is made only upon the death of the animal. Other companies offer all-risk insurance on show animals, breeding stock, and racehorses. A few make it available on the livestock of 4–H Club members and Future Farmers of America or as coverage on animals while in transit.

A comparison of the policies of two companies, A and B, will indicate the range in all-risk livestock coverages now available from a few companies. Both cover range cattle as well as show animals and racehorses. The insurance also covers transit losses. Rates are higher for animals less than about 3 months old and animals more than 7 or 8 years old.

Coverage on specifically described young cattle increases automatically by 10 percent of the original coverage per month—for 5 months in the case of company A, and for 12 months in the case of company B. Coverages of both companies during the fifth month are 140 percent of the original coverage. But the coverage of company A remains at 140 percent, while the coverage of company B during the 12th month has increased to 210 percent of the original amount of insurance. For company A, the premium is 4.9 percent of the average coverage for the year; for company B, it is 5.8 percent.

Insurance on specifically described mature animals, under which the coverage remains constant, may be obtained from either company. For dairy or beef cattle, company A charges a premium equal to 5.5 percent of the insurance, and company B charges 6 percent.

Both companies offer herd insurance on cattle. Not fewer than 10 animals may be insured. The policy of company A will pay not more than one-fourth of the insurance for any one animal. The maximum for company B is 50 percent for one animal. The premium is 3 percent of the insurance. Claims are subject to a deductible equal to the amount of the premium.

Forest fire (and lightning) insurance

is available in Southern States from at least two companies. Young planted stands and merchantable timber may be insured. Such insurance makes loans on standing timber more readily available at lower interest rates and encourages the replanting of trees in areas devastated by fire. The company prefers large holdings that are in the care of qualified foresters, although they will consider applications from owners of small tracts.

The basic rate in one Southern State is 56 cents per 100 dollars of insurance—subject to certain debits and credits.

Credits, or reductions from the basic rate, of 15 percent are given for forest protection; 5 percent for a tree size of 12 inches or more in diameter, breast high; 5 percent for fire-resistant species; 2 percent for heavy density of growth; and 2 percent for light underbrush.

Debits, or additions to the base rate, are as follows: Lightning, 2 percent; naval stores, 20 percent; railroads, 5 percent; recreation, 10 percent; paved State roads, 5 percent; no fire protection, 50 percent; tree size of 0–5 inches at breast height, 50 percent; steep terrain, 10 percent; heavy underbrush, 10 percent; and other recognizable hazards, 5 to 100 percent.

The premium rate includes a charge equal to 80 percent of the annual premium for the additional hazard incurred from February through June.

Under this plan, the insurance coverage on young trees increases by 4 dollars an acre for each additional year of age of trees up to about 20 years of age. For example, coverage on 2- to 3-year-old trees might be 4 dollars an acre; age 3 to 4, 8 dollars; and 15 to 16 years, 56 dollars.

FLOOD INSURANCE for most types of farm property generally has been unavailable. (All-risk Federal crop insurance, multiple-peril crop insurance, and some types of livestock insurance are limited exceptions.)

Private insurance companies have had little success in this field. A company organized to sell flood insurance at St. Louis, Cairo, and New Orleans after floods in 1895 and 1896 was ruined financially by a flood in 1899.

Several factors have prevented the successful operation of flood insurance. The necessary information about frequency of flooding and resulting losses is not available for many areas. Because losses are limited to flood plains, only persons who have a high probability of loss would take the insurance, and consequently the premiums would be high.

The chief stumbling block, however, is the need for huge reserves. William G. Hoyt and Walter B. Langbein, in their section on insurance in volume 3 of the Hoover Commission's Task Force Report on Water Resources and Power, June 1955, estimated that reserves for a nationwide flood-insurance program, based on a 25-year average, would have had to be 7 times the average annual loss. The necessary ratio of reserves to average annual loss would be even greater for smaller areas. Based on the same 25-year period, the Ohio Valley would have required reserves 14.5 times the average annual loss.

A company may be faced with a high-loss year before it can accumulate the necessary reserves. Because it may take a long time for premiums and losses to average out, flood insurance is not attractive as a business undertaking.

The Federal Government, however, can take a longer view. The American public is already investing large sums each year in flood-control and disaster-relief programs, both Government and private. Flood insurance, along with flood forecasting, zoning, and other adjustments in the use of flood plains, can be used both as a complement to and a substitute for flood-control structures. The only alternative in many areas is to live with the river. Flood insurance can make it easier to do that.

The Congress in 1956 provided for

an experimental program of flood insurance (Public Law 1016), under which real and personal property, both farm and urban (including property of State and local governments), could be insured against damage from flooding. The law provided for insurance in amounts up to 10 thousand dollars on dwellings and up to 250 thousand dollars on commercial property. Sixty percent of the "estimated" (actuarial) rates were payable by the insured persons: the other 40 percent was to be subsidized by the Federal Government. The law provided that after July 1, 1958, insurance could be offered only in areas where flood-zoning restrictions had been adopted and that half of the Federal subsidy must be borne by the States after July 1, 1959.

The program was to be operated on an experimental basis for 5 years. Considerable progress was made in 1956 and 1957 in planning and making tentative arrangements. The 85th Congress (1st session) did not appropriate funds, however, and the program became inoperative.

The planned program provided that for each claim there would be a deductible equal to the first 500 dollars plus 5 percent of the remaining loss. Policies for dwellings could be obtained with 80 percent coinsurance or no coinsurance requirement. Policies for commercial property could be obtained with 80 percent, 50 percent, or no coinsurance provisions. (Coinsurance means that any payment for loss will be reduced if the policyholder fails to have his property insured for the specified percentage of its value.)

Six zones, which included 14 river basins, were established. Base rates before deducting the subsidy ranged from 2 to 3.75 dollars per 100 dollars of insurance for 80-percent coinsurance, depending upon the zone. These rates were for either buildings and contents or contents alone and for construction of brick or stone. Policies were contemplated for buildings alone at 75 percent of these rates. Frame construction added 10 percent to the base rate. Rates on contents were reduced by one-third if they were kept above the first floor of the building. After the subsidy, the policyholder paid only 60 percent of the gross rates.

Under the planned program, premiums would have been doubled for property built over water. A surcharge of 10 percent was to be added for counties bordering on the Atlantic coast from Maine to the Virginia Capes. From the Capes south around Florida and the Gulf of Mexico, 20 percent would have been added in coastal counties. Rates for policies with no coinsurance provision would have been 3 times those for 80-percent coinsurance.

If a building, excluding contents, of frame construction were insured "flat"—with no coinsurance—and if this building were not located over water but in a coastal (10-percent surcharge) county in a zone carrying a 3-dollar base rate, the policyholder would have paid 4.90 dollars per 100 dollars of insurance, calculated as follows: 3 dollars times 0.75 times 1.1 times 1.1 times 3 times 0.6 equals 4.90 dollars.

The program as planned would have classed service buildings on farms, as well as the house, as dwellings. Fences could be included in the policy. Total insurance coverage for one farmstead would have been limited to 10 thousand dollars. Thus a farmer would have had to decide just how to allocate this coverage among his house and other buildings, their contents, and fences.

Under the 80-percent coinsurance provision, the indemnity would equal the loss times a fraction consisting of (1) the amount of insurance carried, divided by (2) 80 percent of the value of the property; but any indemnity would be limited to the amount of insurance. On dwelling property, an 80-percent coinsurance requirement would be satisfied by 10 thousand dollars of insurance on property valued at 12,500 dollars. With that much insurance, partial losses (up to the insurance) would be payable in full, as far as co-insurance is concerned. On the other hand, as only 10 thousand dollars of insurance could be obtained, dwelling claims would not be scaled down, because of coinsurance, in the case of properties valued at more than 12,500 dollars that were insured at the maximum.

The deductible amount of 500 dollars plus 5 percent of the remaining loss (considering coinsurance) would then be applied.

The payment under an 80-percent coinsurance contract would amount to (1.1875 times amount of loss times ratio of insurance to value) minus 475 dollars. Under a "flat" coverage contract, it would amount to (0.95 times amount of loss) minus 475 dollars. These formulas combine the coinsurance (if any) and the deductible calculations. Minus results indicate that no indemnity is due.

The maximum payable was also limited to the amount of insurance or the amount of the loss, whichever would be less. For example, under 80-percent coinsurance on a building insured for 5 thousand dollars but valued at 12,500 dollars, nothing would be payable for a loss of 1,000 dollars and 1,900 dollars would be due on a loss of 5 thousand dollars. Under identical conditions, the flat-coverage contract would pay 475 dollars and 4,275 dollars, respectively.

The future of Federal flood insurance is uncertain. Any new program probably would differ from the one we described. The research and planning of the Federal Flood Indemnity Administration might provide a basis for some future program, however.

MISCELLANEOUS forms of insurance available on farm (as well as on urban) property include the personal property floater which covers personal property belonging to and used or worn by the insured person or members of his family. The policy is all risk in character. It covers loss by theft and damage by flood and even extends to house-hold goods. So a person with other insurance on the contents of a dwelling would have duplicate coverage against damage by fire, windstorm and related perils. Payment for any loss would be shared by insurers.

New forms and combinations of insurance are constantly evolving. A so-called "package" policy, now available to urban homeowners, may soon be made available to farmers. Under it, liability and minor perils are covered in the same policy with the property insurance.

THIS CHECKLIST may be helpful:

Be sure your fire insurance is adequate. Replacement costs have increased greatly. Household contents and personal property are most likely to be underinsured.

Do you have deductible wind (or extended-coverage) insurance? By bearing the small losses yourself, you save premiums.

Do you have personal liability insurance? It is almost as necessary as fire insurance. You also need employer's liability or workmen's compensation insurance if you hire workmen. Increased liability protection (higher limits) costs only a little extra. The liability on your car applies only to its operation.

Do you receive all rate credits due you because of fire-resistive construction, a central heating plant, lightning rods, and so on?

Are policies in your name? Are all buildings covered? Are some insured that have since been torn down? If property has been mortgaged, did you notify your insurance company? An insurance contract is a personal one. It does not follow the property.

Could you make out if you lost your principal cash crop? If not, you need all-risk crop insurance to cover production costs. It may be available in your county. Crop-hail insurance also can be obtained from private insurance companies to cover crop losses due to hail damage. This insurance can cover profits above costs.

How taxes affect the land and farmers.

Taxes are as important and sometimes as burdensome to farmers as they are to other citizens and, besides, have a vital influence on national policies pertaining to the use, tenure, and value of land. Faulty assessments, overtaxation, tax delinquency, taxation of farm income, and assessment of suburban acreage are some of the subjects treated in this informative chapter. By *Frederick D. Stocker*, Farm Taxation Unit, Farm Economics Research Division.

THE TAX SYSTEM has much to do with landownership and use. Taxation modifies the allocation of land between agricultural and nonagricultural uses and the pattern and intensity of its use in agriculture. It bears on the tenure of land, as between owner-occupants and tenants and between older and younger operators. It affects the balance between large holdings and the family-size farms.

Taxation has been used in some countries to break up large estates, discourage absentee ownership, or force idle lands into use. American tax policy generally has subordinated aims of this kind to the prime objective of raising revenue. But effects there have been nonetheless, and we cannot safely ignore them.

Of income taxes, levies on property, and death taxes, all of which have an effect on land, the property tax is involved most directly.

As used in the United States, the property tax is an ad valorem levy, a flat-rate tax according to value. It is the chief source of revenue for local governments, and it also supplies some State revenue. The base includes land and improvements and, in most States, various categories of personal property. Our concern here is primarily with the part of the tax that applies to land.

Generally accepted economic doctrine holds that the chief result of a land tax is to reduce land values. The tax is imposed directly on the land and becomes a legal claim against the property itself.

An owner can do little or nothing to escape it. If he sells the property, the price he receives is lower because of the tax. To realize a rate of return equivalent to that obtainable on other investments, any prospective purchaser must reduce his offering price in line with the reduction in return after tax. In effect, he buys the property free of tax.

If the tax is considered to be permanent, land values will fall exactly in proportion to the reduction in the net return—that is, the tax will be capitalized into the value of the land. If the tax is thought to be temporary, it will be capitalized only in part, and land values will fall less than in proportion to the reduction in net return to the land. The uncapitalized portion of the tax would then remain with the owner in the form of a lower-than-normal rate of return on his land.

The property tax is one of many forces at work in the market for land. Its effects are therefore obscure. Changes or prospective changes in tax levels nevertheless constantly contribute to readjustments in land values in the direction of an equilibrium, in which the after-tax return on farmland is comparable to that on other investments.

240

The effects of land taxes on prices of farm products must be considered jointly with the question of effects on the amount of land used in agriculture. If land is withdrawn from production as a result of a tax on land, farm output will ordinarily tend to fall and prices of farm products to rise. But if the supply of farm products is unaffected (assuming that demand is unchanged), prices will not change.

The supply of farmland is not absolutely rigid. New land is brought into agriculture through irrigation, draining, and clearing woodland, and other land is going into building sites, rights-of-way, and other nonfarm uses or is being abandoned. The question to be answered is whether and how land taxes influence these shifts.

A property tax tends to limit the development of lands or to cause lands to fall into a lower use only to the extent that the value and productivity of land depend on the owner's own efforts. If an individual can add to the value of an arid tract by irrigating it, a tax on land values will reduce the profitability of such an investment.

For example: Land that requires a permanent investment of a hundred dollars an acre to irrigate will in fact be brought into cultivation only if the value of this land in irrigation exceeds a hundred dollars. Its value, in turn, depends on the return after tax; with a given productivity, the value will be lower as the tax gets higher. As in this instance the property tax is based on values created by individual effort, it tends to discourage such efforts. When the margin of profit on newly irrigated lands is small or uncertain, the tax may well discourage the growth of agricultural output and contribute to higher prices of farm products.

This applies also to lands that require expenditure of effort or money to retain their value. Much farmland requires constant care to prevent erosion or ditches to prevent flooding. A tax on values that rest on certain activities on the owner's part may lead him to discontinue those practices and

445509°—58——17

thus may reduce the productive capacity of the land. Under modern agricultural methods, in which much money and attention are directed toward protecting and enhancing the farmer's investment in land, a tax on land values may produce noticeable effects on the acreage and quality of productive land.

It is still true, however, that much of the usable farmland has a value and a physical productivity that is derived mainly from the natural qualities of the soil rather than from personal efforts. The effects of taxation on these lands depend partly on how heavy the tax is.

As long as the tax is not so great as to absorb the entire net return to land, there is no reason to expect taxation to cause this kind of land to be abandoned or its use to be altered. As the tax is a fixed charge, it cannot influence production decisions as to either method or intensity of use. If it pays to farm a certain piece of land before the tax, it will continue to pay (although not so well) after the tax is imposed. If the land is used in its highest capacity before the tax, this use will not be disturbed by the tax. An exception occurs when land is not used in its most productive capacity. A property tax and the resulting squeeze on income will then place additional pressure on the owner to utilize his land more effectively.

But if the tax takes the entire net return to land or exceeds it, the owner will be inclined to abandon the property. This is an exceptional case, because the property tax is based on capital values, which depend in turn on the net return. A property that yields no net return (and has no prospect of doing so) has no value and should properly bear no tax. A tax that exhausts the net return—thereby, in effect, expropriating the owner—strongly indicates faulty assessment.

INACCURATE ASSESSMENT is another matter. Assessors commonly apply a more or less standard valuation per acre to broad categories of land. The result is that land with below-average yields often is overtaxed. When that happens, land that is marginal (in the sense that it yields no net return) bears a confiscatory tax. Unless the owner of such land expects improved prospects later, he will have no incentive to retain the land. Nor would any purchaser have reason to take title. The land therefore would be abandoned.

Abandonment of farmland for tax reasons occurs commonly in declining farming areas where production and returns are meager. Because this land is marginal, its withdrawal usually affects aggregate farm output and agricultural prices very little.

Either faulty assessment or taxation of manmade values therefore can lead to changes in the amount of land employed in agriculture. In addition, cultivation of new lands, land values, and net returns are influenced by the level of land taxes in relation to the tax burden on competing forms of investment—for while a land tax, properly assessed, does not affect land at the margin, it does depress the returns on intramarginal acreage and its value.

A truly general property tax, one that would apply equally to all categories of real and personal property, would have few if any discriminatory effects. There is some evidence, however, that the property tax as it is used in the United States discriminates against real property, and that farm buildings and land tend to be overtaxed relative to nonfarm real estate.

The property tax favors the owner of personal property over against the owner of real property. Real estate is always included in the tax base, but all or much of the personal property is exempt by law in some States. In other States, administration of the tax is such that personal property often is overlooked.

Intangible personal property, such as securities and bank deposits, are particularly likely to escape taxation. Some States have attempted to achieve more complete assessment by establishing special low rates of taxation for intangible assets. But even though it were completely successful, a policy of this kind would leave this class of personal property in a favored spot.

In view of this discrimination, it is safe to conclude that the property tax enhances returns on income-producing forms of personal property and the values of such assets relative to real property and that investment in personal property is stimulated accordingly as compared with investment in land.

Within the category of real property, farm land and buildings tend to be overtaxed. Studies by the Kansas State Tax Commission, for example, indicate that in 1956 rural real estate was assessed for an average of 25 percent of full value, compared with 19 percent for urban property, and that this general situation has held true for many years.

Another report shows that 73 Iowa counties assessed rural properties in 1955 at a higher average ratio than urban properties, and that the reverse was true in only 19 counties, while in seven the averages were the same. Many other studies have shown similar results.

Homestead exemptions in some States have contributed to the relative overtaxation of farmland. When they were first introduced in the 1930's, homestead exemptions were promoted by farmers and farm groups as a device to lessen the burden of real-estate taxes on owner occupants and to meet the threat of delinquency. But the exemptions have continued in effect, even though the problem of delinquency is no longer acute.

Moreover, the general rise in farm property values has reduced the significance of a limited exemption to a farm owner, while the increased prevalence of homeownership in cities has greatly enhanced its value to owners of nonfarm residences. As a result, farm property may bear a larger share of the real-estate tax burden than it would bear in the absence of a homestead exemption.

A study of homestead exemptions disclosed that in Minnesota and Oklahoma—two States for which such a breakdown is available—rural property has declined steadily since the 1930's as a proportion of the assessed valuation of all exempted homesteads. Rural property in Minnesota accounted for 40 percent of all exempt property in 1936 but for only 29 percent in 1950. The proportion in Oklahoma declined from 44 percent in 1937 to 25 percent in 1954.

Finally, an overtaxation of farmland comes about in some States from the practice of granting exemptions to attract new industry. A few States give this policy legal sanction. Others permit it in the form of an extralegal exemption. The result in either event is to place a disproportionate burden on the owners of nonexempt property, which in those States means largely farm property.

THE BURDEN OF TAXES on agricultural land is indicated by several comparisons, none of which in itself is an adequate measure but which together give a fairly complete picture.

Statistics compiled in the Department of Agriculture show that levies on farm real estate in 1956 averaged 91 cents an acre. They varied by States from a high of 6.52 dollars in New Jersey to a low of 9 cents an acre in New Mexico. The variations among States reflect partly differences in values of farmland. Expressed as a percentage of the market value of farmland, the range in 1956 was from a high of 2.23 dollars per 100 dollars in Maine to a low of 33 cents in New Mexico. The national average was 90 cents per 100 dollars of full value. Variations among States in tax levies per 100 dollars of value depend somewhat on the degree to which individual States rely on property taxes rather than other sources of revenue to finance State and local public services.

Taxes levied on farm real estate in 1956 were an alltime record in relation to the acreage of farmland in private ownership. Real-estate taxes per acre trended sharply upward after the close of the Second World War. They were more than twice as high in 1956 as in 1945. The rise in taxes per 100 dollars of full value was much less

TAXES LEVIED ON FARM REAL ESTATE IN THE UNITED STATES

		Taxes per acre		
	Total taxes	Amount	Index (1909–13 = 100)	Taxes per 100 dollars of full value
Year [1]	1,000 dollars	Dollars		Dollars
1890	81,866	0.13	64	....
1900	105,582	.13	62	....
1910	165,739	.19	91	0.47
1920	483,020	.51	244	.79
1930	566,839	.57	277	1.31
1940	401,087	.39	187	1.18
1945	464,810	.44	213	.77
1946	518,734	.49	237	.77
1947	605,380	.57	276	.83
1948	655,957	.62	298	.87
1949	706,152	.66	320	.95
1950	740,573	.69	335	.86
1951	772,785	.72	350	.81
1952	804,489	.76	365	.84
1953	838,873	.79	381	.89
1954	869,703	.82	394	.89
1955	928,361	.87	421	.92
1956	977,401	.91	440	.90

[1] Year of levy but not necessarily year of payment.

AVERAGE REAL-ESTATE TAXES AND NET CASH RENT ON CASH-RENTED FARMS IN SEVERAL STATES

States	Net cash rent per acre before taxes			Real-estate taxes per acre			Proportion of net rent absorbed by taxes		
	1937–41	1947–49	1952–54	1937–41	1947–49	1952–54	1937–41	1947–49	1952–54
	Dollars	Dollars	Dollars	Dollars	Dollars	Dollars	Percent	Percent	Percent
Illinois	6.97	9.51	13.10	1.14	2.06	3.20	16	22	24
Indiana	4.04	8.94	10.90	.74	1.40	1.65	18	16	15
Iowa	5.19	8.98	11.20	1.10	1.82	2.57	21	20	23
Kansas	1.92	3.91	5.17	.43	.64	.88	22	16	17
Michigan	2.50	4.93	6.56	.45	.73	.99	18	15	15
Minnesota	3.16	5.32	7.44	.80	1.46	1.97	25	27	26
Missouri	2.46	4.69	6.29	.37	.64	1.11	15	14	18
Nebraska	2.10	4.03	5.28	.45	.65	1.03	21	16	20
North Dakota	.78	1.94	2.65	.20	.31	.47	26	16	18
Ohio	3.16	5.57	6.50	.62	.87	1.33	20	16	20
South Dakota	1.24	2.23	3.77	.36	.31	.71	29	14	19
Wisconsin	3.00	6.35	8.65	.91	1.62	2.26	30	26	26

TAXES AND NET RETURN ON REAL ESTATE FOR 7 SELECTED TYPES OF FARM; AVERAGES FOR 1937–1941, 1947–1949, AND 1954–1956

Type of farm	Net return to real estate, before taxes [1]			Real-estate taxes			Proportion of net return absorbed by taxes		
	1937–41	1947–49	1954–56	1937–41	1947–49	1954–56	1937–41	1947–49	1954–56
	Dollars	Dollars	Dollars	Dollars	Dollars	Dollars	Percent	Percent	Percent
Corn Belt hog-dairy	363	1,783	378	147	235	375	41	13	99
Wheat-small grain	44	3,037	1,289	142	315	440	322	10	34
Winter wheat	602	6,868	2,121	186	346	576	31	5	27
Wheat-pea	1,611	8,267	8,129	291	529	730	18	6	9
Southern Piedmont cotton	149	391	417	34	40	55	23	10	13
Corn Belt cash grain	1,575	5,723	4,296	277	537	935	18	9	22
Northeast dairy	219	1,320	837	190	265	423	87	20	51

[1] Source: *Farm Costs and Returns* and unpublished data in the Department of Agriculture.

marked because of the rise in values of farmland during the period. The 1956 average of 90 cents compares with 77 cents in 1945 and a peak of 1.52 dollars in the depression year of 1932. The tax per 100 dollars of full value averaged 90 cents in 1954–1956, compared with 88 cents in 1947–1949 and 1.17 dollars in 1937–1941.

Additional light on the burden of farm real-estate taxes comes from a comparison of real-estate taxes on cash-rented farms with the net cash rent before real-estate taxes. Such a comparison for the 12 North Central States, where cash renting is common, shows that in 1952–1954 taxes took about one-fifth of the before-tax return to the landlord. In 10 of these States, according to this measure, the burden of real-estate taxes was greater than it had been in 1947–1949, but in only five was it greater than in 1937–1941.

A third indication is found in Department of Agriculture data on farm costs and returns, which provide a basis for estimating the proportion of the net returns to farmland that is absorbed by taxes. In this calculation, a certain portion of the total return to the operator is treated as a return to management and labor, and the residual amount as the net return to land.

A comparison of seven selected types of farms in 1952–1954 shows a variation in the tax, expressed as a proportion of the return, from a low of 9 percent for the Washington State wheat-pea farm to almost 100 percent for the Corn Belt hog-dairy farm. These farms all carried a larger tax "burden" in 1937–1941 than in 1947–1949, but for only 3 of them was the part of the return absorbed by taxes greater than in 1937–1941.

A comparison of real-estate taxes and the net income of farm proprietors from agriculture shows that taxes averaged 7.7 percent of income in 1954–1956, compared with 4.5 percent in 1947–1949 and 8.9 percent in 1937–1941.

Taken together, these data suggest that real-estate taxes in the past few years have become somewhat heavier than they were in 1947–1949, but that they are generally less burdensome than in 1937–1941. One should note, however, that real-estate taxes are slow to reflect changing economic conditions. Thus, if farmland values, incomes, or returns were to show any considerable decline, it is probable that the burden of real-estate taxes as measured by the indicators I have listed would rise sharply.

THE FIXED CHARGE that a land tax places on the farming enterprise has an influence that is not revealed fully in its amount.

Real-estate taxes are part of the overhead cost of doing business. Unlike outlays for seed, fertilizer, hired labor, and other operating expenses, this cost cannot be adjusted readily to a changing scale of operations. The tax must be paid regardless of output or income. It continues even though the land is idle. Only by selling his real estate can a farmer get out from under the real-estate tax.

This aspect of the real-estate tax causes it to be particularly burdensome in high-risk farming areas, where a farm owner may realize little or no income for several consecutive years while taxes continue. As long as long-run income prospects are unchanged, land values are unaffected and no adjustment in assessments is to be expected. Of course, if a succession of low-income years depresses market values, assessment should be reduced correspondingly. As the tax is typically administered, however, assessments are slow to adjust to changed market values, and farmland in declining agricultural areas often continues for years to be assessed and taxed on the basis of an economic potential long since lost.

Even with good assessment, however, the fact that land taxes are a fixed cost places an obstacle in the way of diversion of land to lower uses. For example, a transfer of substantial acreage in the Great Plains from cropland to grazing or other uses often is held to be desirable for conservation purposes as well as on grounds of long-run economic efficiency. Such a transfer would require shifting cropland into uses in which prospects for profit are lower, at least in the short run. Land values, however, are based on use of land in its most profitable capacity. As long as this potential is unchanged, assessed values would not decline. Although a heavy tax in itself would not affect the relative profitability of the various uses of land, the fact that taxes continue unabated may well lead the owner to utilize his land most intensively to avoid loss.

The rigidity of real-estate taxes based on land values works against such Government programs as the Soil Bank and the various restrictions on plantings, which are designed to reduce output.

For example, a farmer who is considering placing land in the Acreage Reserve part of the Soil Bank Program must consider the extent to which he can reduce expenses by curtailing output. The more he can reduce his expenses, the more attractive the program will appear to him. If his costs are inflexible, he will require a larger Soil Bank payment to compensate for the cut in production. His real-estate tax is one cost that will not decline. The levy is unlikely to drop as land is withdrawn from cultivation, for even if the market value should decline, the assessment would probably be unchanged. In fact, placing land in the Soil Bank may well enhance its fertility and potential productivity, thereby providing the basis for an actual increase in market value and assessment for tax purposes.

If real-estate taxes were keyed more directly to current earnings, farmers would be more responsive to Government inducements to reduce output.

A landowner who is faced with a choice between present returns from his land and a future but possibly larger return that might result from more conservative use of the land is likely to choose the immediate return. The discount that attaches to future returns encourages rapid exploitation of land even at the expense of future productivity.

Any Government program designed to encourage conservation or curtail current output must overcome this inherent preference for immediate profits. The real-estate tax accentuates this preference. It places an annual charge on the land, whether it is idle or in use. If it is idle, the land yields no current income from which to pay taxes. The owner of such land therefore is under some pressure to keep it in use so that it will yield the largest current profit, even though its future productivity potential may be impaired.

The experience of some of the Lake States in the late 19th and early 20th century illustrates the tendency of property taxes to bring on immediate exploitation of land to the detriment of its long-run capabilities. In those States were vast acreages, rich in timber resources, that were privately owned and therefore were subject to taxation on the basis of their market values. To cut the timber would provide the owners an immediate income and at the same time would reduce the basis for taxation. To allow the timber to remain uncut would give no current income with which to pay continued heavy property taxes.

As a result of these pressures, the land was quickly denuded of its timber, and it was then offered for sale as farmland. Much of this cutover land was bought up for farming but at prices based on unrealistic estimates of the physical capabilities of the land and optimistic expectations of the future course of prices of farm products and values of land. Assessments and taxes were also fixed according to these inflated values. As time passed, it became evident that the earlier optimism was not justified, and many of these small, marginal farms were abandoned. Much of this land eventually reverted to public ownership as the State or local governments took over tax-delinquent properties.

This and other instances of the over-rapid development of land and the overtaxation of marginal farmland result partly from the fact that the property tax as used in the United States is based on capital values rather than on current income from the land.

Capital values depend only partly on current income. They are influenced also by the income anticipated in future years. Some properties have market values that are fully justified by current earnings. Other properties that are valuable largely or entirely because of a hope for future income or for a speculative rise in prices may have values far out of line with current returns. Taxes on such values are an especially heavy burden in relation to income and often lead to delinquencies, especially if the expected income or rise in prices fails to materialize.

Some countries, notably Great Britain, tax not the capital value but the annual rental of property. Taxes are thus keyed to current income-producing capacity, and land that yields no rental bears no tax.

The market rental system of assessment has often been proposed in this country as a means of alleviating the problem of too hasty development of land. This method, despite its many merits, cannot be considered a likely replacement for the system now in use. The British system is not without problems of its own—estimating rentals on properties not actually being rented is one. Nor is it everywhere agreed that unproductive properties bought and held for speculative purposes should be tax free. Some persons would argue that vacant land near a city should be taxed heavily to force it into use. Finally, the adverse effects of capital value assessment do not stem entirely from the system as such but are due largely to overassessment of properties that have declined in value as expectation failed to materialize. Much of the answer, then, to such problems as premature development of land or the threat of tax delinquency and abandonment of marginal properties would seem to lie in better assessment of properties that derive their value in large part from expected income.

THE RURAL-URBAN FRINGE poses another problem of assessment—one that has become critical in recent years. Suburban communities are springing up all over the country in areas that only recently were farmland. Not only does this growth in population enlarge local revenue requirements. It also raises the value of nearby farmland and adds to the tax burden of farmers.

It often is difficult to distinguish the role that rising market values of farmland have in inducing a farmer to sell from the role of rising taxes. In theory, the two should move together, except for changes in tax rates. Assessments on some properties, however, lag behind the rise in market values, while assessments on others increase prematurely and excessively. In either event, influence is brought to bear on the pattern of land use.

The problems in valuing farmland in the rural-urban fringe are impressive. It may be clear that general land values in a certain area are rising, but it may be difficult to find when and by how much the true market value of any particular tract has increased.

Occasionally the price at which a neighboring tract was sold or knowledge of a firm offer to buy may be used as an index of value. But such indications are not always available. Nor are they infallible guides to accurate assessment. The demand for residential land in a particular area is often limited. One or two isolated sales of farmland for homesites do not necessarily indicate that all the remaining acreage has the same potential.

Here, again, the most practical safeguard against overtaxation of farm properties and premature development into building lots appears to lie in improved techniques of assessment. This task, however, is not easy.

Besides the complexities I have noted is the fact that pressure for additional tax revenue in growing suburban communities often works against conservative valuation of land that is in process of transition. As long as assessment of property is proportional to true market value, the tax burden does not affect the use of land. Movement of land into higher uses—for instance, as residential or industrial sites—would be the natural result of rising land values rather than of increased taxes as such. The process may be slowed, however, if taxes are not increased as the market value rises. The owner still stands to gain by selling, but he is under no immediate pressure from taxes. If assessments rise more rapidly than values, the pressure on the owner to sell for subdivision is intensified.

Many of the effects I have mentioned can be traced to the very nature of property taxation rather than to any defect in its administration. They would arise even if the property tax were perfectly administered.

Some effects, however, are caused by faulty assessment procedures. The property tax is based on valuations by local officials, few of whom have the training, facilities, or time to do more than a cursory job. As a result, property assessments commonly show substantial deviations from values realized in the marketplace. Even worse: These variations are far from uniform; some properties are assessed at a low fraction of their true market value, while others are assessed at a high proportion or even more than they would sell for.

Much aberration in assessment is sporadic and, although it may bear heavily on individual properties, it gives rise to no systematic effects on the use or tenure of land. But one can see definite patterns in assessment inequalities.

For example, properties having a low value per acre are commonly overassessed relative to land of higher value. This discrimination is a result of the widespread practice of assessing broad categories of land at a flat amount per acre and ignoring differences in value that result from soil characteristics, location, topography, or other such factors.

Another tendency is to assess properties having small total values at higher rates than more valuable properties.

The combination of these two influences operates to place the heaviest tax burden on the properties that are least able to bear it—that is, the small properties having a low value per acre. There is some evidence also that property of absentee owners is assessed more heavily than that of owner-occupants, a bias that in some States accentuates the tax advantage these properties already possess because of homestead exemptions.

PROPERTY TAX DELINQUENCY is a common result of an excessive tax burden in relation to the current income-producing capacity of the property. Individual instances of delinquency, especially in marginal areas, may indicate inaccuracies in assessment. When incomes and the property values fall sharply, as they did in the 1930's, however, the failure of property taxes to adjust downward may cause mass delinquency and a general breakdown of tax collections.

Delinquency leaves its mark on the tenure system. Failure of the owner to pay property taxes by the due date or within a certain grace period normally leads to sale of a tax lien on the property. The usual procedure is for the local jurisdiction to put the property up for tax sale. The successful bidder on a tax certificate is entitled to a tax deed on the property unless the owner redeems the certificate within a stated period. The tax-sale process usually gives the owner ample opportunity to regain clear title to the property by paying up his taxes. A large share of the tax-delinquent property is kept in private ownership through tax sales. The process often is so time consuming, however, that years may elapse before either the original owner or the purchaser of a tax lien obtains clear title to the property.

Tax delinquency, especially when it is widespread, presents both a challenge to land management and an opportunity to wipe out the errors of the past with a socially desirable policy of land conservation and development. For instance, Michigan has worked out a successful program for development of much tax-reverted land in forests and recreation areas in the cutover regions of the State. In many other States, however, procedures for administering tax-reverted lands often are lacking. The land may lie unused and vacant, or sometimes the former occupants may be permitted to continue on the land.

ANY DISCUSSION of land taxation must include a reference to what is probably the most thoroughgoing program of tax reform ever advanced—the single tax. The single tax, which was promoted in this country in the late 19th century by Henry George, the economist and publicist, is a proposal to substitute a heavy tax on the economic rent of land for the existing tax on capital values of land and improvements.

George and his followers argued that returns to land—economic rent—and hence land values were not created by individual efforts, but resulted from the natural qualities of the land and the pressures of a growing society or limited land resources. They reasoned that to tax this return would be eminently just, because what society had created rightly belonged to society rather than to private landlords. Moreover, there would be no adverse economic effects. As the owners had done nothing to contribute to its value or its return, they could do nothing to take it away. The supply of land would not be diminished. In fact, absorption of the economic rent would make it more costly to hold land out of use, so that additional land would come into use and production would increase.

Despite its apparent logic and social objectives, the single tax has not received wide popular support. Among the various reasons is the radical nature of the proposal, which no doubt has turned away many potential adherents. Second, the proposal represents a discrimination against owners of land, for elements of economic rent are now recognized to occur not only in the return to land but in returns to any other scarce or limited factor of production. The logic in the singling out of land for special treatment therefore is specious. Moreover, many landowners have bought land in good faith as an investment comparable to many other forms of income-producing property. To expropriate one class of investors, leaving others untouched, hardly appears to be just.

Finally, the single tax would probably be complex to administer. In a world where market values of land and buildings are hard to determine, the task of determining the annual rental value of the land alone might prove to be well-nigh impossible.

A graduated tax on land is another proposal that has been advanced occasionally as a means of achieving certain desired changes in the use and tenure of land. A rate that increased with the size or value of the property would give relief to owners of small or low-value properties. It would also contribute to the breakup of large ownership units and would make more land available to the small operator, who might otherwise be unable to buy farmland except at a very high price.

The principle of graduation found expression in the system of land taxes used for years in Australia and New Zealand. Rates were differentiated according to the size of property, the character of tenure, and the residence of the owner. The objectives were to promote small operator-owner farming units and to discourage absentee ownership of large estates. By 1931, when graduated rates were abandoned, these goals had largely been achieved.

Some European countries also have levied graduated land taxes. In the United States, however, proportionality has remained the rule, despite proposals to introduce progression. A few State governments at one time or another have considered introducing a graduated scale of assessments, but the proposals were rejected. Their aim was to favor the small farmer as compared with the larger operator and to help preserve the small family farm. The chief objection to them, apart from the added complexity of administration, was the greater efficiency that can be obtained in many farming areas by enlarging the operating unit.

THE INCOME TAX, once negligible to the average farmer, has increased greatly in importance since the start of the Second World War. Along with the rise in amount, the effects of income taxes on the use and tenure of land have become more pronounced. The larger farmer especially must weigh the income-tax consequences of each decision he makes, because his income tax, unlike his property tax, may be affected by the way he manages his affairs.

One effect of the income tax is discrimination against agriculture in high-risk areas. The graduated rate structure of the Federal income tax, and to a lesser extent of State income taxes, penalizes the taxpayer whose income is variable. To illustrate: A farmer with a wife and two children who nets 2,500 dollars each year would pay no tax under 1957 rates and provisions. But if the same farmer traded his regular income for a risky farming enterprise that yielded no net income for 3 years, but 10 thousand dollars of net income every fourth year, he would be liable for more than 1,300 dollars in taxes on the same 4-year total income. In such high-risk areas as the Great Plains, therefore, agriculture bears a greater tax burden per dollar of income than it does in the more stable farming areas.

A variety of effects stem from the capital-gains provision of the Federal income tax. A capital gain—that is, a rise in value of a capital asset—is taxed on realization at rates lower than those that apply to ordinary income. This special treatment encourages the holding of farmland for appreciation. Thus, when prices are rising, the tax system adds to the incentive to buy farmland as an investment and as a hedge against inflation. The rise in land values is accentuated, and land tends to move out of the hands of owner-operators who hold land for the income it can produce and into the hands of absentee investors, whose aim is to profit from buying, holding, and selling land.

Improving the productive capacity of land as a means of raising its sale value is another device for saving taxes through capital gains. Beginning in 1954, farmers have been permitted to deduct as expenses their outlays for soil or water conservation or for the prevention of erosion. The effect is to encourage such expenditures. A dollar spent for conservation this way can thus be used as a deduction to reduce ordinary income, which is subject to taxation at full rates. But the expenditure, assuming it to be economically justified, will increase the sale value of farmland by at least a corresponding amount, and the gain realized on sale of the land would be subject to low-rate taxation as a capital gain. The effect is to stimulate further the demand for farmland as an investment, particularly on the part of persons desiring farms as country homes, hobbies, or sidelines on which a current (but eventually retrievable) loss can be used to reduce taxable income derived from other sources.

Tenure arrangements, too, are influenced by the Federal income tax. An example is the provision whereby the tax on capital gains can be avoided if property is transferred on the death of the owner. Every farmer must consider as he grows old how and when to transfer his land. The matter can be especially important if he bought his farm a generation or more ago, when land values were far lower than at present. If he sells it, he realizes a capital gain, and a sizable tax may be due. If he gives it away, for example, to his son, the gain is not realized and therefore is not taxed. But the basis of the property—that is, the value from which the capital gain is calculated—remains the same as it was for the father. If the son subsequently disposes of the property, he must pay the tax on the capital gain.

If the farmer holds the property until his death, however, and then bequeaths it to his son, the basis for the property becomes the fair market value at the time of death. As the son acquires the property at the higher basis, if he should later decide to sell it, only the gain in value since he acquired it would be taxable. The appreciation from the time the property was originally bought to the date of the father's death escapes taxation completely.

Transfer of property at death involves consideration of State inheritance taxes, and if the estate is large, it may also involve the Federal estate tax. More is said later about the effects of these taxes. It is sufficient here to note that the method of taxing capital gains under the Federal income tax penalizes the farmer who sells and favors the owner who retains until his death property that has appreciated in value. The saving varies with the rise in value and is therefore likely to be largest for the farms that have been in the hands of one owner for a long time.

Income tax considerations enter also into the decision whether to incorporate a farming enterprise. The income of an unincorporated farm is subject only to personal income taxes. The income of the corporation is taxed as corporate income, and (to the extent that earnings are paid out in dividends) it is taxed again as personal income. The farmer who withdraws most of his earnings for personal use rather than putting them back in the business therefore is better off, as far as taxes are concerned, by remaining unincorporated. But if his income is large, it may pay him to incorporate.

At 1957 rates, a taxpayer whose business income is more than about 20 thousand dollars might reduce taxes by incorporating. Because normally part of the corporate income is paid to the owners as a dividend and is subject to personal taxes, a farmer's income must be somewhat larger than this figure before it pays to incorporate. But at some level of income, the tax system ceases to be a barrier to incorporation and becomes an incentive.

Starting in 1955, farm operators have been both subject to social-security taxes on their farm income and eligible to receive benefits. The long-term influences of social-security taxes on land tenure are too complex to be considered here, but some immediate, and probably temporary, effects have become apparent.

The social-security law has made it possible for many farmers of retirement age (65 or older) to receive benefits after only a year and a half of taxable earnings. These retirement benefits are so large in relation to the modest tax payment required that older farmers had an incentive to continue farming long enough to establish their eligibility. For several years after 1955, therefore, land that otherwise would have become available to younger operators was retained and farmed by older operators. As time passes, however, a larger and larger proportion of farmers reaching the age of 65 will have established eligibility. Then the prospect of a retirement income from social security may well quicken the transfer of farms from older to younger hands.

DEATH TAXES—the estate tax of the Federal Government and the various State taxes on inherited property—have complex and varied effects. These taxes have been used in some countries as a device to break up larger estates, with far-reaching effects on the use and tenure of land.

Death taxes in the United States may have had some slight tendency in this direction, but rates have been generally low and opportunities for legitimate avoidance have been plentiful.

The most common problem farmers face as a result of estate or inheritance taxes is that of assembling the necessary cash with which to meet the tax-payment. If a valuable piece of farm property is transferred on the death of the owner, the cash required for taxes may be sizable. Often the estate is composed mainly of land, buildings, machinery, and other relatively fixed assets and includes little cash or near-cash items. To obtain the necessary cash, the heirs may even be forced to sell part of the farm or to mortgage the farm or otherwise borrow funds.

These difficulties can often be averted if the problem is anticipated and plans are made. The estate may be designed so that insurance, cash, and other liquid assets are sufficient to meet estate and inheritance taxes without forcing the breakup of the farm as an operating unit.

The problem is less easily avoided when the owner's death is unexpected, but even then much can be done to minimize adverse effects or tenure by wise planning. A number of bulletins have been published on various ways in which farmers can plan for death tax liabilities. One of the best of these is Estate Planning for Farmers, Circular 461, of the California Agricultural Experiment Station.

THE POTENTIALITIES for using taxation to achieve certain land-policy objectives are limited in this country by the separation of tax sources of the various levels of government as well as by the division of powers between the Federal Government and the States and between the States and their local subdivisions. Appropriate taxing authority does not always reside in the unit of government that originates land policy.

The effect of this arrangement is virtually to rule out the use of taxation as a means of implementing Federal land policies. The Federal Government has no control over the most direct and obvious tax device for accomplishing such an aim—that is, the property tax.

Any deliberate Federal influence on land use in all likelihood would have to be exerted through the income tax. But this method has limitations.

The income tax is a general law written to apply to a wide variety of taxpayers. Special provisions designed to accomplish nonrevenue objectives usually have been rejected unless they could be shown to be consistent with the basic principles of income taxation. There are exceptions to this rule, such as the allowance of rapid amortization to encourage construction of emergency facilities (although this provision was rationalized on the ground that these facilities declined in value more rapidly than other assets) and the exemption of interest on State and local securities. But provisions of this kind are rare.

Tax devices, moreover, must always be weighed in relation to other methods of achieving the same objectives.

Finally, a tax provision designed to influence land use can be effective only on persons whose incomes are large enough to be taxable. Tax deductions are of no consequence to a farmer who pays no tax. Special income tax provisions (many of which may be termed "gimmicks") thus must be regarded as a weak and unlikely tool of Federal land policy.

State and local governments are in a more favorable position to use taxation for objectives of land policy. Property tax rates and assessments are largely controlled by local governments under general conditions provided in State law. However, State and local land policies are likely to be narrower in scope than those of the Federal Government. Many States and localities, indeed, have nothing that can rightly be called a land policy.

The growth of suburban communities is one matter on which States and municipalities often have more or less explicit policies. In some circumstances, taxation can contribute to these policy objectives, for example, by bringing about the sale of land for subdivision. Although rising land values ordinarily provide the incentive, increased assessments may be the immediate source of pressure to sell farmland near cities.

The proper policy, of course, would be to increase assessments in proportion to increases in true market value. Then taxes would have no separate influence, apart from that of the rise in values. But it is difficult at any point in time to value lands in these zones of transition, so that the use of increased assessments to drive land into residential or industrial uses commonly leads to conflict between owners of farmland and those who favor more rapid development.

The chief danger in a situation of this kind is that taxes may be increased too rapidly. Land would be forced thereby into premature development, with results that would be unfortunate not only to the owner who is forced to sell, but for the community in which subdivision of land proceeds more rapidly than economic conditions warrant. The opposite error, that of increasing assessments too slowly, leads to undertaxation of property and reduces the incentive to sell, but the consequences appear less dangerous.

Use of property taxation to encourage conservative use of land is potentially effective, but most States have done little along this line. Property taxation can be a powerful incentive to conservation, if taxes are reduced on properties that are handled according to certain prescribed policies.

Several States have adopted special tax provisions to encourage conservative management of forest lands. Presumably, favorable treatment could be devised also for agricultural lands that are diverted to a use that is socially more desirable. The obstacle is that State and local governments, which administer the property tax, seldom have a stake in conservation. The benefits of land conservation are so widely diffused and so long in materializing, in contrast with the immediate and apparent gains from exploitation, that such a policy is seldom considered to be in the interest of local or State governments.

It is conceivable that Federal land policies, such as withdrawal of land from crop production for economic reasons or encouragement of certain conservation practices, could be furthered by giving State and local governments some financial incentive to reduce real-estate taxes on these lands. The incentive might take the form of a Federal grant to replace revenues lost through the abatement of taxes.

Safeguards would be required to insure that the tax reduction was offered only to the landowners who complied with the stated conditions, and the reduction continued only as long as the owners complied. Care would need to be taken also to see that taxes were reduced by the full amount for which the State or local unit was recompensed and that a rise in rates or assessments was not used to offset the reduction, thus defeating the aim of the grant.

Against this proposal would need to be considered the inevitable charge of undue Federal interference with an essentially local matter—property taxation. The gain from such a grant scheme must be balanced against that obtainable simply by making direct payments to landowners, as under the Soil Bank.

Apart from a plan of this kind, the role of State and local taxation in land policy appears to be confined largely to the rather negative one of reducing inequalities in property taxation. But this role is not unimportant. The property tax, as it is commonly administered, results in much random discrimination between individual properties. Some systematic tendency has been noted for the property tax to favor owners over tenants, properties of high value over those of low value, and good land over poor land. Inequalities of this kind cannot fail to affect land use and land tenure to some extent.

In an economy that places primary reliance on market forces as a means of allocating resources to their most efficient use, reduction or elimination of these distortions cannot be considered unimportant.

Getting started in farming is hard.

Young people can get jobs in cities with no outlay of capital, but farmers must have several thousand dollars before they can start their life's work. The money may be borrowed or inherited or gotten from relatives, but in any event there is a high hurdle in front of them at the very beginning. By *Don Kanel*, associate professor, Department of Agricultural Economics, University of Nebraska; *Franklin J. Reiss*, associate professor, Department of Agricultural Economics, University of Illinois; and *Charles L. Stewart*, professor, Department of Agricultural Economics, University of Illinois.

A STRIKING difference between opportunities in farming and most nonfarm occupations is the need for capital in order to start. To become farm operators, young families must accept the risks and responsibilities of acquiring and using enough land and capital to have efficient employment and to return enough money for decent living.

Beginning farmers are in a poor position to compete with established operators for control of land. The beginners are faced with high requirements for operating capital and managerial skills. The established operators have had a period in which to accumulate savings and skills.

The operation of farms by owners and families, which has long been held to be a desirable objective of land policies in the United States, depends largely on how successful young families are in making a good start on family-scale farms and progressing toward ownership of the land.

Concern over these problems led to research on the subject in the North Central States. The project is coordinated by a North Central Technical Committee, and the work is being carried on by agricultural economists and others in State universities.

Much of this discussion is based upon findings from that study. The results we cite are drawn from research done in a few States, but the problems of young farmers occur throughout the region and elsewhere.

Farms in the North Central States are large. Land is dear. The investment in farms large enough to employ fully an average farm family is substantial—quite often it is more than 50 thousand dollars in land and of 12 thousand dollars in operating capital. Competition for the ownership and operation of such land has been keen. These conditions increase the difficulties facing beginning farmers.

Insights afforded by research in these areas apply to every part of the Nation's agriculture in which commercial family farms predominate. Rather different problems face young people who enter agriculture in areas employing large numbers of hired workers, in plantation agriculture, and in areas of small farms, in which a large share of the production is used for subsistence of farm families and in which cash costs are small.

A decline in the number of farms, changes in farm technology (which have enabled each farm family to operate a larger acreage), the nearly unchanging total of cropland since 1920, and increases in production per acre (which have been more than enough to satisfy increases in demand for agricultural output) have brought a drastic drop in opportunities for beginning farmers.

The drop in the total number of farms means that fewer young farmers are needed to replace older farmers who retire from farming or change to other occupations. Much the same thing happens in a factory when workers are laid off. The management might decide not to replace the employees who retire or who quit to take other jobs. If no new workers are hired, total employment drops and the average age of the employed workers goes up.

Young people continue to enter farming—but in smaller numbers. The Census of Agriculture indicates that between 1920 and 1954 the number of farm operators in the United States dropped 25 percent but the number under 35 years of age dropped 59 percent. These young operators accounted for 27 percent of all operators in 1920 and only 15 percent in 1954.

Young people usually start farming when they are 20 to 30 years old. Thus the census count of operators under 35 years indicates the approximate number of young people entering farming in the 15 years preceding the census year. The data indicate that fewer young people entered farming in the years 1940–1954 than in the earlier period 1905–1920.

The decline in total numbers of farmers thus has occurred largely through a reduction in the opportunities for young people in farming.

WHEN THEY are getting established in farming, young people form new family farms by taking over opportunities and responsibilities released by older farmers. In the main, older people are in control of farming opportunities. While they are still farming they are the employers of hired labor-

ers. When they give up active farming, they often remain in farming as landlords, and eventually they or their heirs become the sellers of farmland. Parents and occasionally other older farmers often help beginning farmers to acquire machinery and livestock and to meet cash operating expenses. This help—credit or gifts—may be in cash or in kind.

Nonfarm landlords and credit institutions also control some farming opportunities.

Getting established in farming requires renting or buying land. Most beginning farmers acquire their initial land by renting. They get capital for machinery, livestock, and operating expenses through family assistance, their own savings, or loans from credit institutions. Loans from institutions are primarily available to beginning farmers who have enough savings and family assistance to provide security.

Credit for the purchase of land can also be obtained from financial institutions or from the sellers. Usually beginning farmers will need more savings and family assistance for buying land than for renting.

Land to enlarge farms also may be rented or bought. Credit institutions often assist. Enlargements of farms are made primarily by established farmers. Young people attempting to enter farming must compete with these established farmers for available land.

Established farmers have an advantage in renting land because landlords prefer the experienced tenants with enough equipment to do a thorough and timely job.

Furthermore, landlords may not rent land to inexperienced operators because they want to avoid the need to give detailed supervision to the tenant. Established farmers can get loans more easily because their accumulated capital serves as collateral and because they have an established credit rating.

These advantages of the established farmers are offset somewhat when landowners give preference to their own children and other relatives in renting farms and transferring the ownership of farmland and when family assistance enables beginning farmers to rent or purchase from non-relatives.

Young people generally are not too well equipped to compete for land. As a result, fewer of them succeed in becoming farmers. On the other hand, we have no evidence that farm enlargements are forcing increasing numbers of established farmers out of farming.

On balance, farm enlargements made by established farmers are taking up part of the land given up by older farmers who withdraw from farming, and the number of farms available to beginning farmers is reduced.

MOST BEGINNING farm families are better supplied with labor than with capital or land. Their problem is to get enough land and equipment to make full use of their labor.

That means more than fully occupying the operator's time. It means making that time productive by having enough land and capital to use labor efficiently.

The acreage of land required to provide productive employment for 12 months of labor (or more, if other members of the family work) varies with the type of farming.

Tobacco, cotton, vegetables, and other specialty crops require a relatively high amount of labor per acre. Feed grains and wheat require relatively little labor. Adding livestock to the crop enterprises can provide employment for unutilized labor.

Inexperienced operators, however, are usually reluctant to add livestock enterprises because livestock requires a broader range of managerial skills and increases the risk and the need for capital.

Results obtained in Iowa and Illinois from a new kind of budgeting technique called linear programing indicate that, when capital is the limiting factor, maximum returns can be secured from intensive grain rotations with little or no livestock.

Census data show that crop-share leases and cash-crop types of farming are more prevalent among tenants under 25 years of age than among older tenant operators.

Beginning farmers in Indiana, Illinois, and Missouri in the postwar decade who made a start other than through an operating arrangement on the home farm started on farms of 160 to 200 acres. Smaller acreages than this, if operated as general farms with little livestock, will not provide full or efficient employment for one man.

A sample of Illinois farmers who operated grain farms used 14 months of labor in 1955 on 170 acres of tillable land (cropped 80 percent to corn, soybeans, and small grains). Their average livestock inventory was 2 dairy cows, 100 hens, 9 animal units of beef cattle and sheep, and 7 litters of pigs. Their inventory of machinery and equipment (at used-machinery prices) was about 4,800 dollars.

AN AVERAGE INVESTMENT in livestock and feed inventories brings the capital requirements on such units to about 8 thousand to 10 thousand dollars for a tenant operator.

Beginning farmers who started farming in Corn Belt counties of Illinois and Indiana between 1946 and 1953 began with capital assets of 5 thousand to 6 thousand dollars, to which they added 2 thousand to 3 thousand dollars in borrowed capital in a year or two.

Most urban salary and wage positions available to young people seeking their first employment, be it remembered, require no capital at all.

Under the standard type of cash, crop-share, and crop-share and cash leases, the tenant usually provides all the working capital, part of which he may borrow.

Under other arrangements, the landlord provides part of the working capital, so that the beginner can start farming with smaller savings and less reliance on borrowing. These arrangements include livestock-share and labor-share leases and the father-son agreements and partnerships.

The characteristic of these arrangements is that the landlord, or an older operator, furnishes the land, owns part or all of the machinery and livestock, participates in managerial decisions, and may continue to work on the farm. Only rarely are these arrangements used among nonrelatives.

A study of veterans who began farming after the war in southeastern Minnesota showed that the landlords supplied 45 percent of the working capital under livestock-and-crop-share leases, 88 percent under partnership arrangements, and practically none under cash, crop-share, and crop-share and cash leases. The partnership plan was used by 37 percent of this group of beginners and the livestock-and-crop-share lease by 11 percent.

Despite the difficulty of getting started in farming without substantial family help, most new farmers in the Corn Belt in 1954 did not take advantage of a partnership or operating agreement with their parents to make their start in farming. The proportion who did not ranged from 67 to 90 percent in samples of beginning farmers in Illinois, Indiana, and Missouri.

Many home farms are too small to provide employment and income for two families. Besides, both fathers and sons tend to place a high value upon freedom and independence of operation. "To be my own boss" is a reason often given for choosing to farm.

Renting the home farm or another farm owned by relatives on terms of standard cash or crop-share leases is more important than the use of special father-son agreements. More than half of beginning farmers in Indiana rented land from relatives, although only one-tenth had partnership agreements. A third of the beginners in Nebraska and one-half in Minnesota rented from relatives. In addition to the one-third who started with father-son agreements in Illinois, one-fourth rented from relatives.

Renting land from relatives is important to beginning farmers who find it difficult to compete with established farmers in renting land from others.

Young related tenants under standard leases often use parents' machinery or obtain the needed equipment with family assistance. Because of this help, the dividing line between father-son partnership agreements and renting from relatives is not clear. Beginning farmers renting from relatives would tend generally to be more independent than those who have father-son pacts.

Parents often aid beginning farmers by providing working capital. The use of parents' machinery (often in exchange for the labor of the beginning farmer), loans made within the family, and cosigning on commercial loans are among the ways of making capital available. This aid often involves gifts in unpaid services or loans and sales at less than going rates and prices.

When land is not available through kinship ties, the effect of such family help is to place the beginning farmer in a stronger position to bid for land in the competitive market. The beginner's father or father-in-law may influence a landowner to decide in favor of the young man by promising help when it is needed.

Loans provided by credit institutions for operating capital mainly supplement the savings of the beginning operator and the family assistance extended to him. Commercial loans are usually not available to young men interested in farming who do not have savings or family backing because of the usual collateral requirements.

Only the operating loans of the Farmers Home Administration (and also, in the past, Government-insured commercial bank loans to veterans) make a start in farming possible for a few young people without savings and without family assistance. Funds of the Farmers Home Administration comprise but a small portion of the credit funds available to agriculture; thus the aid is limited to only a small number of farmers.

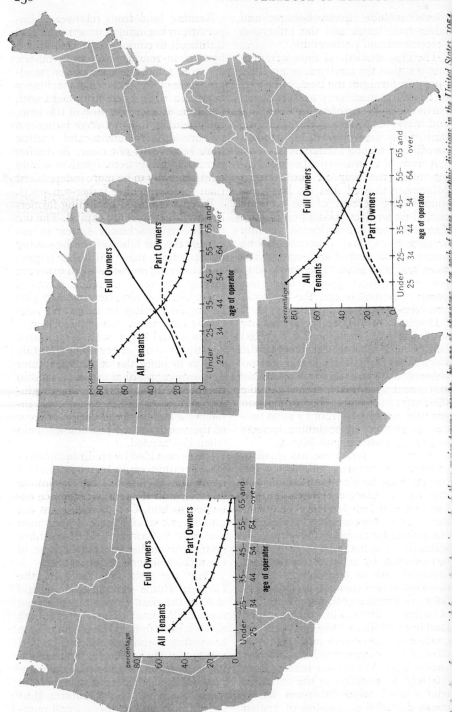

Commercial banks, the production credit associations, and merchants supply much of the credit to eligible beginning farmers for operating capital and production needs. Banks are the most important among these three sources. Almost all loans from these lenders are payable within 12 months. Some banks make a few loans with maturities beyond a year. Production credit associations have begun to offer some 3-year loans. Usually, though, credit from commercial sources and cooperative organizations has been strictly short-term.

Beginning farmers need intermediate-term loans to finance operating capital. One cannot expect to amortize the cost of a tractor in a year. An investment in heifer calves for breeding will not return an income until 2 or 3 years later. Furthermore, beginning farmers usually start with a low operating inventory. They want to use initial earnings to accumulate an inventory of machinery and operating goods rather than retire their debt. Except for the 5- to 7-year operating loans by the Farmers Home Administration, beginning farmers have depended heavily on family credit, which often is extended on a long-term or no-term basis, for their starting capital.

Beginning farmers without adequate savings (particularly those without family help) are apt to get the poorer, smaller, and less improved farms that become available. Their problems in getting established therefore are harder, because substandard land resources tend to be associated with inadequate capital and managerial resources.

Land and capital acquired by inheritance are not ordinarily important means for getting started among the younger beginning farmers. They are important, however, to advances up the tenure ladder. Unless a young man delays a start in farming until he is more than 30 years old, he is not likely to make a start on inherited land. The fact that most fathers have many active years ahead of them at the time their sons are ready to start farming is a major problem in transferring farm operatorships from one generation to another. This is why renting land outside of the home farm is so important among beginners.

Resources made available to younger beginning farmers may come with some mixture of blessings.

A clearcut inheritance may give a boost as can nothing else, but inheritance often is not a matter without strings. Installments of cash to coheirs who need to be bought out or be given subsidies for school or other agreed purposes may restrict the farming heir in the proportion of his net farm income available for the programs of progress he wants to achieve on the land. In a period in which shifts to a larger scale of operation and larger inputs per acre in the form of fertilizers, mechanical equipment, and so on, are essential, the heir who takes over from coheirs often may make less headway than on some other farm.

A MAJOR PROBLEM of beginning farmers is to improve rental terms and to achieve a greater security of tenure.

Farms lacking in improvements present special problems. The young farmer short of capital cannot afford to pay customary rents (in cash or in shares) and make real-estate improvements at his own expense. If capital is available, he should protect such investments by obtaining reimbursement guarantees from the landowner. Fertilizer may be the most profitable investment for the farm as a whole, but not for the share-tenant unless the landlord pays his share of the cost.

A young man, who had just completed his first year in farming as a tenant on a relatively poor Nebraska farm, was asked what he would do with the money if he were offered an additional loan of 2 thousand dollars. His reply was, "Buy more machinery." The answer can be justified in view of his 1-year lease and difficult rental terms, even though the farm as a whole needed fertilizer more than machinery.

Sharecroppers in tobacco, cotton, and other specialty crops have relatively easy access to land through landlord financing, but their labor share of the crop does not afford easy or rapid progress up the tenure ladder.

To escape the uncertainties of tenant operation, beginning farmers are prone to invest limited savings in the purchase of land, often with the result that they are short of operating capital. The farms they can buy may be too small for efficient operation or may require a heavy additional investment in fertilizers to make them productive.

Conventional mortgage financing, requiring a 50-percent downpayment of the purchase price plus debt-free operating capital, does not provide ready access to land for beginning farmers or ranchers.

A study in Virginia indicated that such purchases of land to make a start in farming usually were based on inheritances or on savings from an extended period of nonfarm employment.

A timely start in farming by buying land requires a low-equity means of financing for most young men. Such credit has been a significant contribution of the Farmers Home Administration farm-ownership loans and of guaranteed loans to veterans. An important policy in Farmers Home Administration lending has been its refusal to finance units that are too small, too unproductive, or otherwise inadequate to yield an income that will amortize the loan and provide for family living needs.

A land transfer device that serves as a low-equity financing device is the land purchase contract. It is a form of credit extended by the seller of land. Usually only a small downpayment is required under a land contract, but the seller retains ownership of the land. Ownership does not pass to the buyer until the contract is fulfilled.

Educational work on the advantages and limitations of this arrangement and some State legislation are needed to make land contracts a safer and more useful financing device for young farmers. Much standardizing and improving of land contracts must precede the development of a rediscount market for such obligations, a result that might extend their use.

Kinship sources of credit also provide credit with low downpayments for beginning farmers.

A GROWING NUMBER of young farmers close to cities avoid part of the high first requirement of land and capital by combining farming and city jobs. Some use part-time farming as a stepping stone to full-time farming. A survey in Ohio showed, however, that many who start as part-time farmers find it difficult to give up the steady income from off-farm work to make the transition to full employment in farming.

Others who start as full-time farmers on certain units find their farms too small for efficient operation or too small to yield enough income for a satisfactory level of living. Rather than give up the satisfactions of rural living, they take on some kind of off-farm work and become part-time farmers.

A small but significant proportion of beginning farmers fail in their attempts to become established and have to change to other occupations. A study in central Illinois indicated that 19 percent of farm boys who made a start in farming gave up their attempt after an average of 7 years.

The failure of a young family creates an opening for someone else just as much as the retirement of an older operator. The failure of a farm family, whether young or old, however, is more wasteful socially than the inability of a qualified young farm boy to enter farming.

The change to a nonfarm occupation by a family that had made its start in farming involves quite often loss of savings in attempts at establishing or continuing in farming, the cutting of community ties, and entry into the nonfarm labor market at a later stage in life and with fewer opportunities.

Education and training and vocational guidance and counseling can help farm youth adjust to an urban way of life. Lack of education and training was cited by Illinois farm boys holding nonfarm jobs as the greatest obstacle they met in finding satisfying job opportunities. Experience with tractors and other machinery and equipment leads many farm boys into jobs as truckdrivers, mechanics, servicemen, or machine operators.

Many opportunities for employment with marketing agencies, agricultural supply firms, and in agricultural service work give boys and girls chances to apply basic farm experience, but they require high school or college training.

Few individuals are limited to only one road to happiness. Education allows the individual to find a useful and happy life in many different ways.

Without ample and varied nonfarm employment opportunities for farm boys and the means to get farm boys established in such work, opportunities in farming will be less attractive, less remunerative, and more difficult to attain than they are today. Migration of farm boys out of agriculture makes possible the enlargement of farms, and it can help eliminate rural poverty in places where too many families depend on the limited agricultural resources for a livelihood.

Farm youth have been migrating in large numbers, particularly just after graduation from high school. Census data for the United States for the decade 1940–1950 indicated a heavy net movement from farms of young people who were 10–14 (54 percent) and 15–19 years of age (56 percent) at the beginning of that decade. Only 15 percent of persons 35–39 years old at the beginning of the decade left farm life.

That the rural population is becoming more urbanized is a truism now. Better roads, better transportation, consolidated schools, urban church affiliations of farm families, and the other forms of rural-urban social intercourse have led farm couples to expect more urban conveniences in their standard of living.

More young farmers are marrying nonfarm girls. Forty percent of the young farmers' wives in samples in Illinois and Ohio came from nonfarm homes. They brought urban standards of living with them. They influenced their husbands to farm on an adequate scale or to seek nonfarm employment so as to attain those standards. And why not?

Today young people are apt to base their decisions about starting farming or continuing in farming on the attractiveness of opportunities open to them in agriculture or in other occupations.

MANAGERIAL COMPETENCE cannot be taken for granted among farm-reared boys who remain in farming, which is a competitive, complex business.

One who would be a farmer must be familiar with the most efficient production techniques, and he must be skillful in their application to a farm. A high school education, including training in vocational agriculture, is almost a necessity for one to be successful in organizing and operating a modern farm business.

A successful farm operator, responsible for decisions that determine the course of his business, must have a knowledge of farm crops, tillage operations, fertilizers, tractor care and operation, machine adjustments, adapted crop varieties, sources of seed, herbicides and pesticides, drainage, irrigation, crop storage, mechanical crop drying, electricity and electric motors, automatic controls, livestock rations, feed additives, hormones, animal diseases, vaccines, bloat, artificial insemination, and many other items related to the physical inputs and outputs from the farm business.

As a business manager, he must also decide on the economic feasibility of any operation to be done and any tool, equipment, or product to be used. He must have knowledge of rates of physical input and output, uncertainties in prices and production, diminishing and marginal inputs and returns, effects of volume, and problems of investment, credit, marketing, and other phases of the financial side of the farm and household.

Despite the growth in size of farm and the value of assets per farm, there has been no important change in the tenure and credit arrangements used by farm families to gain control of land and other resources. As we said, farm families still have to provide sizable amounts of owned operating capital to begin farming, and they continue to aim for the acquisition of land ownership during their working lifetime.

Because land-owning farm families control opportunities in farming desired by the younger generation and few farm boys without savings or family backing can start in farming, American ideals, which favor both the family farm and equality of opportunities, are in conflict in the present situation of American agriculture.

Possibilities for public action to increase equality of opportunities are limited. Attainment of greater equality might be attempted by enlarging credit programs that can help farmers with small savings. An increase in credit available to beginning farmers without family assistance, however, will not enlarge the total number of openings, unless at the expense of causing more established farmers to quit farming. More likely it will cause an increase in land values and rents and have little effect on the total number of openings for beginning farmers.

Increase in credit available to agriculture might better be used to reduce failures of established farmers. Such credit can help people already in farming to increase their size of farm and volume of production. If measures like this were successful they would probably reduce even more the openings available to beginning farmers.

The important issue in the future might be whether family assistance will be sufficient for the needs of beginning farmers. It is possible that the need for changes in tenure and credit arrangements is hidden at present, because replacements are being recruited primarily from families with enough money to help their youngsters get started in farming.

It is difficult to see how in the future farm families can provide the beginning operating capital and achieve ownership under present tenure and credit arrangements in the emerging agriculture of larger family farms. If farm families should not be able to do this, they would also not be able to extend the assistance that the younger generation would need to get their start in farming.

It would seem that there would be need in the future for aid to farmers, extended through nonfamily credit and tenure arrangements that would resemble the terms on which family assistance is provided. This means that resources would have to be made available through leases or loans with a low downpayment, intermediate terms on operating capital, a sharing of risk, elimination of the necessity of attaining complete unencumbered ownership, and security of control.

Agriculture is the only major industry in America that has continued successfully to recruit, train, and employ many thousands of new commercial entrepreneurs and business managers annually. These men in their performance have demonstrated their ability to apply new techniques.

As farms grow larger and investments in land and capital mount, the managerial requirements also increase. This raises the question of further difficulties in access to farming opportunities. Training replacements for farm operators is a twofold problem that involves the question of which kind and how much basic training and the question of how new farm operators can be brought to a point of operating competence.

The fate of the family farm may well depend on continued success in finding and developing large numbers of such competent individuals.

Major Uses of Land, 1954

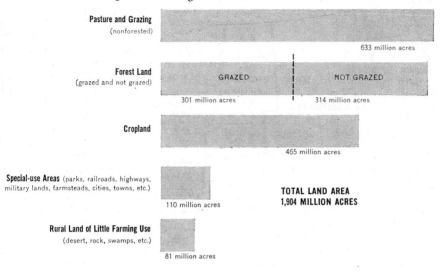

Pasture and Grazing (nonforested)
633 million acres

Forest Land (grazed and not grazed)
GRAZED   NOT GRAZED
301 million acres   314 million acres

Cropland
465 million acres

Special-use Areas (parks, railroads, highways, military lands, farmsteads, cities, towns, etc.)
110 million acres

**TOTAL LAND AREA
1,904 MILLION ACRES**

Rural Land of Little Farming Use (desert, rock, swamps, etc.)
81 million acres

A fourth of the land in the United States is cropland. One-third of it is grassland pasture and nonforest grazing land. Nearly one-third is woodland and forest, about half of which is grazed to some extent. The rest is in special and various other uses.

Of the cropland, about three-fourths is used for crops each year, and much of the remainder is pastured in rotation with crops. All cropland is in farms, but the acreage of pasture and grazing land not in farms comprises two-fifths of the total pasture area.

About 70 percent of the grazing land not in farms is publicly owned. The grazing land, both open and forested, that lies outside farms supplements land in farms.

Altogether, more than 80 percent of the total land area was used in the production of food and fiber in 1954. Urban areas, residential and industrial sites, farmsteads, highways, roads, railroads, airports, parks, and other special uses are high in value.

Finally, several million acres of semidesert, bare rock, marsh, and sand dunes are worth little for agricultural use, but they have utility for wildlife and recreational use.

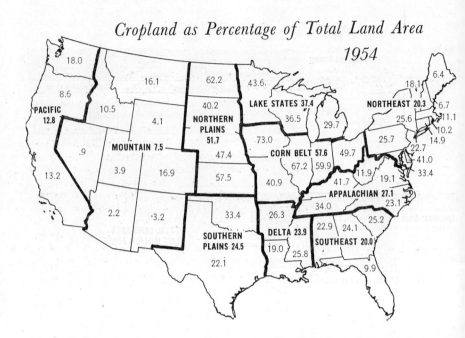

Cropland as Percentage of Total Land Area
1954

This map shows the general distribution of all cropland. More than 40 percent of the cropland was in the nine Corn Belt and northern Great Plains States in 1954, the year to which the latest census of agriculture pertained.

More than half of the total land area in Iowa, Illinois, Indiana, North Dakota, and Kansas was used for crops.

The Western States occupied two-fifths of the land area but contained only slightly more than one-seventh of the land used for crops. Texas, although it had the largest acreage of cropland of any State, used less than a fourth of its total area for this purpose.

The total acreage of cropland varies greatly among regions. Pasture and grazing land are inseparable from arable farming over immense acreages. The arable pasture and cropland are readily interchangeable. For example, much of the reduction in crop acreages 1954 to 1958 has gone into pasture. When there is need for a greater acreage in crops, some of this pasture may be plowed up again for cultivation.

Uses of Cropland Harvested

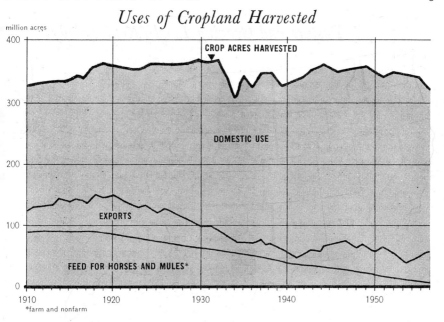

Of the 326 million acres of crops harvested in 1956, about 16 percent was used to produce exported products; 3 percent, feed for horses and mules; and 81 percent, food, fiber, and tobacco. Farm output for human use increased at about the same rate as the United States population until just before the Second World War, when it began to rise faster. Much of the grain has come from an increased output per acre. The acreage of cropland in 1957 was slightly less than in 1940, but higher yields raised total production 24 percent. Increases have been marked for such crops as wheat, corn, cotton, and tobacco.

Production per Harvested Acre

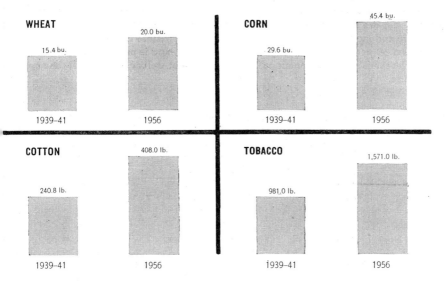

Pasture and Grazing Land (Nonforested)

AS PERCENTAGE OF TOTAL LAND AREA
by States and Regions, 1954

Pastures and grazing land (including plowable and nonplowable grassland) account for the largest acreage of land use in the country—633 million acres, or nearly one-third of the land area.

Many types of pasture and grazing land are included, such as the highly productive pastures in the Northern and Central States, the irrigated pastures and natural grasslands of the Great Plains and the Western States, and the improved grazing areas of the South and West.

Besides grassland or nonforest pasture, more than 300 million acres of forest and woodland are used for grazing to some extent. Nearly 75 percent of the grassland pasture and more than 40 percent of the woodland pasture is in farms.

About 30 percent of the total pasture and grazing land is publicly owned. Much of it is in the semiarid and mountainous areas that are not well adapted to full-time agricultural use.

Acreages in Food Grains, Feed Grains, Oilseed Crops, and Cotton   UNITED STATES, 1879–1954

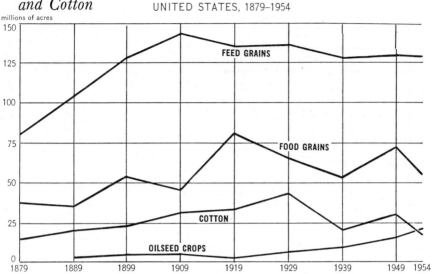

The acreage used for food grains—wheat, rice, rye, and buckwheat—became more than 19 million acres smaller between 1949 and 1954 and declined another 12 million acres from 1954 to 1957.

The total acreage of feed grains—corn, oats, barley, grain sorghum, and mixed small grains—occupied about the same acreage in 1954 as in 1949 but decreased by 5 million acres between 1954 and 1957. Some important shifts occurred. Corn harvested for grain declined. The acreages of sorghum harvested for grain, barley, and oats increased.

The acreage of cotton declined 7 million acres from 1949 to 1954 and another 6 million acres from 1954 to 1957. The acreage in soybeans and other oilseed crops increased about 6 million acres from 1949 to 1954 and 4 million acres from 1954 to 1957. Diversion of acreage from allotment crops to soybeans was a reason for the increase.

As a result of these and other shifts, the number of acres from which crops were harvested declined by about 19 million between 1954 and 1957. The drop was related to the existence of large stocks of certain crops and the resulting acreage controls and to the Soil Bank Program.

Fluctuations in the acreages used to produce the major crops in response to demand have been common in much of our agricultural history.

The Trend in Land Utilization

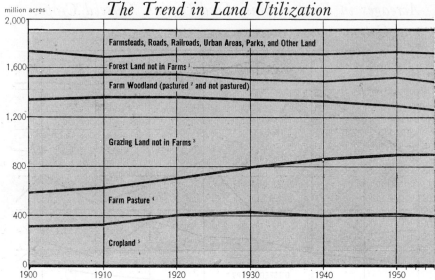

million acres

¹ Excludes forested areas reserved for parks and related uses and arid woodland, brushland, and forest land used for grazing.
² 121 million acres were reported pastured in 1954.
³ Includes grassland, arid woodland, brushland, and forest land grazed.
⁴ Open pasture in farms, including cropland used only for pasture and other plowable pasture.
⁵ Includes soil improvement crops, summer fallow, and land seeded to crops for harvest the succeeding year.
Cropland acreages are for the year preceding the date of the census except for 1954.

Notable shifts have occurred in the use of land since 1880. The total acreage in farms, crops, and pasture has increased generally in the West, the Corn Belt, and the Lower Mississippi Alluvial Valley, but the acreage in farms and crops has decreased in many parts of the East. The acreage occupied by cities, towns, rural residences, industrial plants, highways, airports, reservoirs, recreational areas, and other facilities has increased enormously with the growth in population, especially in the Eastern and West Coast States and around the Great Lakes.

A leveling off in the use of land for crops has occurred in the East since 1920, but the downward trend apparently is slowing down. The incorporation of grazing land into farms and ranches in the West has not always resulted in changed use, but abandonment of cropland in the East usually has meant a shift to pasture and eventually to woodland. In some areas of the Piedmont and other hill sections of Virginia, the Carolinas, Georgia, Alabama, and Mississippi, large acreages of cropland have been converted to pasture and large tracts have returned to forest. These regional shifts in cropland, pasture, and forest have been partly in balance, and so are not fully apparent in the national picture.

Land in Farms, Agricultural Land* and Cropland Harvested

BY REGIONS 1880–1954

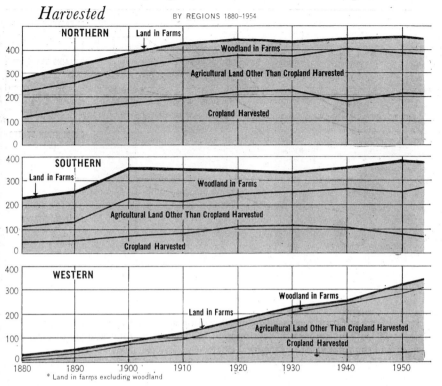

* Land in farms excluding woodland

Land in farms, agricultural land (not including farm woodland), and cropland harvested increased generally until 1940 in the Northern, Southern, and Western States. Harvested cropland reached a peak acreage in the North and South in 1930 and in the West in 1950.

Several important contrasts in trends exist among farm production regions within these three groups of States. Cropland and pasture acreages in the Corn Belt and Lake States have not changed greatly in recent years. In the Northeastern States, the downward trend has continued but apparently is becoming stabilized. In some parts of the South, such as the Mississippi Delta and eastern North Carolina, the area used for farming has increased because of the clearing and drainage of new land and in Texas through irrigation, plowing up of grassland, and land clearing. In other sections, such as hill sections of the Southeastern States, large acreages of cropland have been converted to pasture and large tracts have reverted to forest.

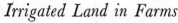

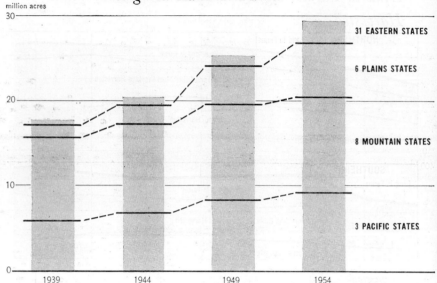

Irrigated land in farms increased from 18 million acres in 1939 to nearly 30 million acres in 1954. This important development influenced the total volume of farm production and the total value of farm real estate.

Several Western States have large acreages of irrigated land. Large investments in farm real estate improvements have been made to provide irrigation facilities.

Crop yields and income per acre generally average much higher on farms with irrigated land than on farms that have no irrigated land. Consequently many additions are being made in extent and location of irrigated acreages as new projects are developed and old ones are enlarged in various drainage basins of the West. Irrigation is increasing also in the rice areas of the South and in the eastern truck crop sections.

Agricultural Land in Drainage Enterprises

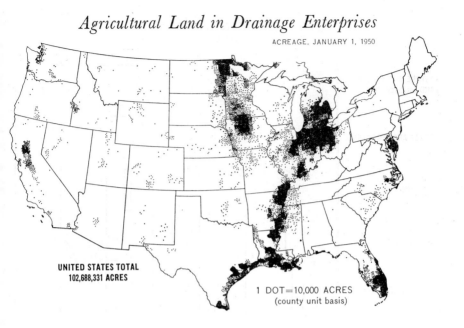

ACREAGE, JANUARY 1, 1950

UNITED STATES TOTAL
102,688,331 ACRES

1 DOT=10,000 ACRES
(county unit basis)

Farmland in organized drainage enterprises increased from 87 million acres in 1940 to nearly 103 million acres in 1950, or more than 1.5 million acres a year. About four-fifths, or 82 million acres, are improved. Of the unimproved land, 4 million acres are classified as suitable for development. Besides the land in organized drainage enterprises, there were an estimated 50 million acres of farmland drained by private or farm drainage—a total of 153 million acres of artificially drained land.

Many drainage improvements have been made since 1950. Records of local district and conservation programs show that large individual farm investments, as well as public investments, have been made to provide tile drains, farm ditches, and main outlets for excess waterflow. Drainage improvements have added greatly to farm production, income, and values in the Corn Belt, Lake States, Mississippi Delta, and Southern Coastal Plain.

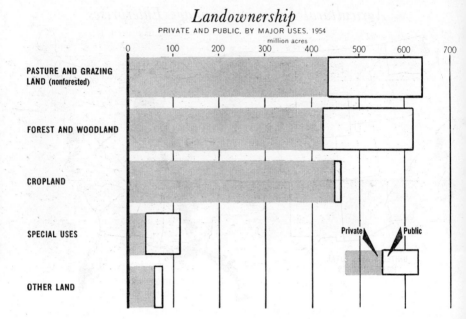

Landownership
PRIVATE AND PUBLIC, BY MAJOR USES, 1954

Nearly all cropland is privately owned. Only small areas are publicly owned—among them some State school lands and land held temporarily for a specific public purpose.

About a third of the grazing and forest lands are publicly owned. Much of it is in arid and mountainous areas that are not well adapted to full-time agricultural use. Special-use areas—parks, highways, reservoirs, and military posts, which are on land that has slight surface value for agriculture—make up a considerable part of the publicly owned land. Such special-use areas as highway rights-of-way, reservoirs, parks, and wildlife refuges are increasing. The acreage of public land, however, as a whole has shown a small decrease in recent years.

Ownership of Land and Land in Farms, for the United States, 1954

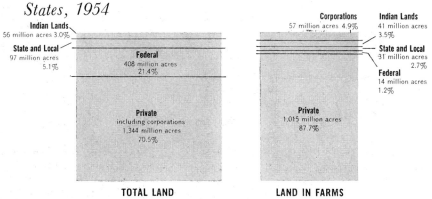

TOTAL LAND   LAND IN FARMS

Private lands comprised 70.6 percent and Indian lands 2.9 percent of the land area of continental United States in 1954. Title to more than one-fourth (26.5 percent) of the land area of the United States rested with Federal, State, or local governments. Much of it is in the West. Only 3.9 percent of the land in farms was publicly owned. Most of the land in farms owned by government was devoted almost entirely to grazing. Grazing land used by ranchers on a permit basis was not included as "land in farms." Private individuals owned 87.6 percent of the land in farms in 1954; corporations owned 5.0 percent; and Indian lands made up 3.5 percent.

Of the public land area, 407.9 million acres were owned in 1954 by the Federal Government; 80.3 million acres were owned by States; and an estimated 17 million acres were owned by local governments. The Federal land is mostly forests, parks, wildlife refuges, and range which was not homesteaded. The States also have large acreages in parks, forests, and wildlife refuges.

Distribution of Forest Land

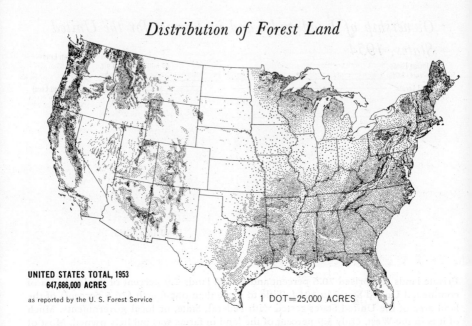

UNITED STATES TOTAL, 1953
647,686,000 ACRES
as reported by the U. S. Forest Service   1 DOT=25,000 ACRES

Included in the total forest and woodland area in the continental United States (exclusive of Alaska) of 648 million acres are 484 million acres of commercial forest land and 164 million acres of noncommercial land.

The noncommercial forest and woodland includes 138 million acres of unproductive forest and 26 million acres reserved for special purposes such as parks and wildlife refuges.

The total forest area is considerably larger than the area devoted to cultivated cropland, but about the same as the grassland pasture and range area. Of the total acreage of forest and woodland, about 35 percent is in the Southern States, including Texas and Oklahoma. Nearly 12 percent of the forest is in the Northeastern States; 16 percent in the Lake and other North Central States; and 37 percent in the Western States. Nearly a fourth of the commercial timber acreage and more than two-thirds of the sawtimber, however, are in the Western States. One-third of the sawtimber alone is in Oregon and Washington.

Seasonal Use of the Western Range

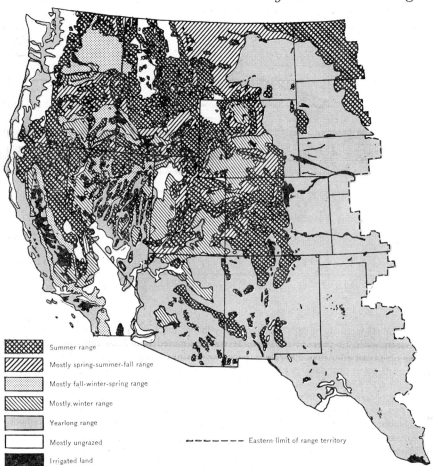

- Summer range
- Mostly spring-summer-fall range
- Mostly fall-winter-spring range
- Mostly winter range
- Yearlong range
- Mostly ungrazed
- Irrigated land

– – – – – – – Eastern limit of range territory

Feed for All Livestock

Percentage of All Feed from Pasture and Grazing
1949–50

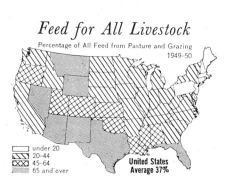

- under 20
- 20–44
- 45–64
- 65 and over

United States
Average 37%

Pasture furnished 37 percent of all feed for livestock in 1949–1950. Corn supplied 26 percent and hay 14 percent. Oats, barley, and other grains accounted for 9 percent. Animal protein feeds, oilseed meals, other high-protein feeds, and other byproducts also supplied 9 percent. Silage, beet pulp, skim milk, and seeds made up the remaining 5 percent of the feed for all livestock. Differences in climate and land in the Western States mean differences in season, type, and value of grazing. Higher areas furnish 3 to 6 months of summer grazing. Foothills and plateaus ordinarily do not carry animals more than 6 to 8 months without change of pasture.

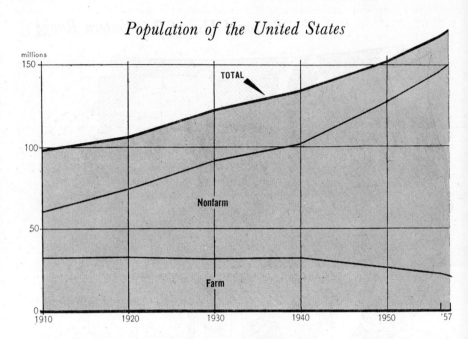

Population of the United States

millions

150

TOTAL

100

Nonfarm

50

Farm

0

1910   1920   1930   1940   1950   '57

The farm population in 1957 was 12 percent of the total United States population, compared with 23 percent in 1940. It was estimated that 20.4 million people were living on farms in April 1957, compared with the total United States population of 170.5 million at that date. A year later, April 1958, the total population was 3 million greater, or 173.5 million. Although farm population has decreased, the importance of the average farm family has increased in terms of farm production per farmworker.

The growth in population is one of the important long-time trends that affect the demand for farm products. The uptrend in food consumption per person combined with the increase in population boosted total food consumption 39 percent from 1940 to 1957. Nearly 39 million consumers were added to the United States population from 1940 to 1957. Looking ahead, we may expect an increase of 25 million in the next decade—almost as many as now live in New York and Pennsylvania combined.

Rights, ownership, and tenure
— How our rights in land came about—
What do we mean by "ownership"?—Farm tenure and the use
of land—Trends in kinds and sizes of farms—Land and one of
the farm programs

How our rights in land came about.

Our tenure system—the relationships established among men regarding their varying rights to own, use, and control land—evolved in the slow, painful struggle from feudalism toward equality and freedom, a glorious historical development but one that may need adjustment because of today's technology. By *Marshall Harris*, agricultural economist, Farm Economics Research Division, and research professor, Agricultural Law Center, State University of Iowa.

THE LAND-TENURE system of the United States has undergone fewer changes since the establishment of our Government than our Federal Constitution has.

The Constitution has been amended 22 times. The first 10 amendments, known as the Bill of Rights, followed soon after its adoption. Other significant amendments have been added as crucial problems have made clear the need for them.

Adjustments in our tenure system have been few and comparatively unimportant. Nothing comparable to the Bill of Rights has been inserted in our tenure "constitution." Its basic structure is similar to the structure that existed when Washington became our first President. Minor adjustments have strengthened the system in a few places.

Most actions to affect the developing tenure situation have been taken outside the tenure system because it lacks the conciseness and specificity of a formal statement and because its growth has been gradual and evolutionary, in contrast to the revolutionary change in the form of government when the Constitution was adopted.

The tenure system is not spelled out in a single basic document. It depends heavily upon the common law and court decisions, rather than concise statutory enactments. It evolved slowly before and during the colonial period. Most of the breaks with the Mother Country's tenure system were formalized in statutory enactments or were developed in practice by the time of the Constitution.

By and large, changes in the tenure system were within the province of each of the Thirteen Colonies. This responsibility remained in the States following the Revolutionary War. Each of the 48 States continues to be responsible for its own land-tenure laws.

Basic tenure principles were agreed to among the Original Colonies in the process of forming a Union. Some were put on paper in the Ordinances that outlined the conditions under which new States could enter the Union.

Although latitude is thus provided for minor variations among the several jurisdictions, it is accurate to speak of our land-tenure system, for we do have one basic system.

OUR TENURE SYSTEM is concerned with all of the relationships established among men regarding their varying rights in the control and use of land. It should not be confused with a second type of relationship between man and land—land utilization, which is concerned with man's dependence upon land for raw materials, food, shelter, and standing room. All men share this dependence on land, but tenure rights vary widely from country to country, and they vary from place to place even within a country.

There was no tenure in Robinson Crusoe's economy. Until Friday appeared on the scene, no problem of holding rights in land existed. The question of who would occupy and enjoy the produce of the land did not arise. Possession, exclusion, rent, trespass, and similar ideas did not bother Crusoe. Even after Friday arrived, there was no reason for him to be concerned with such complex land-tenure arrangements as deeds and mortgages, recording of titles and conveyances, inheritances and wills, and leases. Yet Crusoe was as fully dependent on the land for food, clothing, and shelter before Friday came as afterward.

To keep these fundamental differences straight, we speak separately of land tenure and land utilization.

The complete quota of rights to the control and use of land is frequently referred to as "property" in land. So numerous and complex are these rights that we speak of land tenure as a "bundle of rights." The bundle is made up of many separate yet complex sticks—rights. Many of the sticks may be assigned to several persons.

All tenure rights attach to specific parts of the earth's surface. The acreage of land to which rights may attach thus is relatively fixed and generally immovable—which is not true of many other economic resources with which we fulfill our needs.

If land were freely reproducible and movable, the tenure system would be less crucial in the growth and well-being of our economy.

An illustration: When the Louisiana Territory was purchased from France in 1803, the United States Government acquired complete sovereignty over the territory. Inherent in the sovereignty was the entire bundle of rights in the land. The first division of this bundle of rights was among those who settled in the territory. The Federal Government deeded, subject to restrictions, most of the sticks of the bundle to private parties. It did not transfer all of the rights, as many owners of farmlands traditionally assume.

The Government retained so few rights, at least on first sight, that many farm owners believed they owned their land from the heights of the heavens to the center of the earth to do with as they pleased. But this was not true; the Government retained several substantial rights.

Once a part of the territory was ready to join the Union as a State, many of the public rights held by the Federal Government were either transferred in toto or divided with the State. Or, if the opposite theory is preferred, the sovereign people entrusted to the State some of the rights in the land, and the States in turn accorded specific rights to the Federal Government. In any case, the primary division of rights in land is between public and private.

THE PUBLIC HOLDS FOUR RIGHTS in all farmland, not only in the sovereign States of the Louisiana Territory, but throughout the country. These four rights are the rights of escheat, eminent domain, police, and taxation. A fifth right—the spending power—may also influence tenure conditions.

The right of escheat arises in the United States only in the absence of any individual competent to inherit the land. The deceased cannot carry rights in land with him to the grave. Nor can rights exist without a holder—they must reside somewhere, in some person or unit of government. Society therefore has said that if privately held rights find no person in which to reside, they shall be held by the public.

The right of eminent domain is the power to take private land for public use. It is exercised as directed by the Federal and State Constitutions and the laws of the State and Federal Governments. The "due process" and "just compensation" clauses are fundamental considerations when the public takes private land.

The police power is less specific and more difficult to define than escheat and eminent domain. It is the power of government to establish laws, statutes, ordinances, and regulations to secure generally the comfort, health, safety, morals, and the welfare of the citizenry. Under the police power, government can establish many different tenure laws and regulations. Requirements for recording of deeds and mortgages, statutes as to inheritance, standards of surveying, laws on landlord and tenant relations, and liens for the collection of rents and debts are among rights outlined under the police power.

The right retained by society with which most people have become familiar is the right to tax. The land or real-estate tax is levied upon the assessed value of the property. If the tax is not paid, the land may be sold for taxes by the Government under specific procedures outlined in law. The right to tax originally was conceived as usable only in the raising of needed revenue. The power to tax, more recently, has been used for regulatory and other purposes. It has been said that the power to tax is the power to destroy; it should be used wisely.

The spending power of the Government may well have as great an impact on the tenure situation as adjustments under the police power or changes brought about by taxation. For example, publicly sponsored credit has been widely used to encourage ownership of land by the tillers of the soil. Public funds have also been used for research and education to improve the conditions of tenure under which farmers hold their land. The spending power, like the police power, is a broad general power that may be used in many ways to bring about adjustments in condition of tenure.

Thus society has reserved important rights in all private land. Society can take private land by eminent-domain proceedings. It can also have land thrust upon it through escheat and possibly by tax delinquency. Tenure relations among men can be regulated and controlled under the police power. The right to tax and to spend may also affect the conditions of tenure under which private persons hold their land.

PRIVATE RIGHTS are those that are not reserved to the Government. They are concerned with relationships between or among private parties. They include the rights to possess, occupy, hold, transfer, buy, sell, mortgage, lease, subdivide, consolidate, use, abuse, waste, exploit, conserve, improve, bequeath, give, and many others. Even these private rights are subject to controls by society. The laws that govern these rights are essential parts of our farmland tenure system.

They are complex and sometimes vague, but they are designed for specific purposes.

THE ROLE of our farm-tenure system in establishing relations among men is to expedite the use of land in satisfying human wants, since farmland serves chiefly to produce the food, fiber, and vegetable oil we need. It may be looked upon also as security, particularly during old age. Prestige and status are associated with landownership. Recreational services and esthetic values are also considered as want satisfying. A basic question is: How does the tenure system help to satisfy human wants?

The tenure system is designed to prevent conflicts among people in the control and use of land. If a conflict does arise, the rights of each party are subject to legal determination under wellestablished procedures. The reduction or elimination of conflicts in interest adds security to economic endeavors and minimizes risks related to economic activities in satisfying human wants. It would thus seem that a rigid, fixed, concise tenure system would minimize conflicts. That may be true. Our tenure structure, however, is reasonably flexible.

Flexibility in the tenure system permits and encourages the establishment of new conditions of tenure to meet modern change. For example, the size and value of farms have increased in recent years. New "labor-share" leasing arrangements therefore have come into use. Credit arrangements have been changed to meet the increasing costs of getting started in farming. The Torrens system of title registration—under which properly registered titles are guaranteed by the Government—is being introduced to facilitate the transfer of rights in land. Rural zoning and land-use ordinances are used more frequently to make land of greater service to all the people.

Flexibility also permitted the enactment, on short notice, of foreclosure moratorium law to meet conditions arising from lower income during the early 1930's. Father-son operating agreements and transfer arrangements came into common use as adherence to the old laborer-tenant-owner agricultural ladder diminished. Partnerships and farm corporations are sometimes formed to meet the demands for increasing capital requirements. Many other changes permitted under the flexible tenure system facilitate the fashioning of new arrangements to encourage growth in our dynamic economy.

THE FOUNDING FATHERS were largely responsible for this excellent system of land tenure. The development of our democratic Government and the development of our free land system paralleled each other in many ways. Although development extended over many centuries, our tenure system came into full fruition during the Revolutionary period.

Before the Norman Conquest of England in 1066, the land-tenure system was developing adequately to meet the needs of a free people. But the conquerors changed the tenure system to fit their requirements and foisted the feudal land system immediately on an unsuspecting population. The king held all land of the realm and parceled it out in large holdings to his military aides and court favorites, under whom lesser persons held rights in the land.

The feudal land system provided for a fairly clear-cut hierarchy of successive groups according to rank, from the king to the lowest worker. Naturally there were many persons between the king and the worker, each of whom exacted a payment of some kind from the person below him.

The feudal land system at its height was burdened with nine separate charges, or incidents, upon the land—fealty, homage, wardship, marriage, relief, primer seizin, aids, fines for alienation, and escheat.

The only incident that we recognize today is escheat, and it has been modified to apply only on failure of heir. Originally, land reverted not only for "failure of blood," but also for "corruption of blood," such as treason, murder, robbery, and arson.

Fealty—the oath of allegiance—is still a mark of citizenship, assumed for native-born Americans and "taken" by naturalized citizens.

Homage—the oath of personal subjugation—has disappeared.

Wardship—the power of the lord to reap profits from a minor's estate—we no longer have.

"Marriage"—a payment for the lord's permission to marry—has also been done away with.

Relief was a payment for admittance to the estate made by the heir upon his father's death. Our "relief" is the inheritance tax.

Primer seizin was basically a procedural method of enforcing the king's right to a relief. Aids were finally restricted to three payments—to ransom the lord if he were captured, to pay expenses for knighting the lord's son, and to provide a dowry for the lord's eldest daughter at marriage.

A fine for alienation was a payment made for the privilege of transferring rights in land. We no longer have aids and fines.

These charges on the land were burdensome. When measured in terms of farm income or ability to pay, many of them were heavy. Usually the charges were variable. They depended on the exigencies of the situation or the whim of the lord. Some of the payments were irregular—several of them might fall due within a single year. Even worse, they were poorly related (or not at all) to services rendered.

Before feudalism had attained its fullness, successful endeavors were made to reduce the severity of parts of the system. Magna Carta, the great charter of English freedoms without which our Constitution might not have been possible, started the process. Other adjustments were made in feudal tenures before Jamestown and Plymouth Rock. The English Statute of Tenures of 1660 sounded the death knell to the feudal system as such.

The most significant characteristics of feudal tenure that the colonists brought with them to America and which were essentially eliminated from the system were quitrents—fixed rents payable by freeholders to their feudal superiors in commutation of services—primogeniture, and entails.

The colonial quitrents were the aids of that period. For all practical purposes, the farmers in the New England Colonies never paid quitrent. In the other Colonies where quitrents were important, the collection process became so difficult that quitrents had largely disappeared before the Revolution.

The colonists drifted into the idea that the Mother Country could not tax them legally. This is not unrelated to the later idea that the Federal Government would not levy a land tax, and that such taxes would be reserved chiefly for local purposes. Through legislative action, some Colonies specifically stopped the collection of quitrent. Others either were not accustomed to such collections or observed the disappearance of rent collectors and ceased to bother about the matter.

The backbone of the feudal system was the idea of primogeniture and entails—that is, the idea of keeping the landed estate in the same family from generation to generation. Common

practice was that the entire estate would be inherited by the eldest son (primogeniture) and that he could not alienate it (entail). Both practices were in process of decay during the colonial period.

The barring of entails was made easy by provisions in many original grants to private parties, by private action in providing for equal division in wills, and by special acts of the colonial assemblies in individual cases upon request.

The decline of primogeniture was witnessed by granting to the eldest son a double portion rather than all and permitting daughters to have a half share. Equal devolution eventually prevailed.

Several States took action during the Revolutionary period to prevent entails and to outlaw primogeniture. The process was not easy. Wealthy families contended for the privilege. But the idea of equality and the trend toward free enterprise and individual initiative were too strong in Revolutionary America.

The arguments against primogeniture and entails were many and varied. Among them were: Perpetuation of property in families is contrary to good public policy; it tends to deceive businessmen who give credit on visible possessions; it discourages the holder from caring for and improving the land; it injures the morals of children by rendering them independent of and disobedient to parents. It was held also that perpetuities and monopolies were contrary to the idea of a free state and that the perpetuation of landed estates in the same family in effect would be subscribing to the idea that honesty could be bought with money and wisdom was hereditary.

Landholding and officeholding were closely associated in the feudal system. The new democracy held no brief for hereditary officeholding. By analogy, it was suggested that hereditary landed estates should be eliminated. Small landholders were already practicing equal division among their heirs. So were the rising merchants, who found that equal devolution induced intermarriage within the class, multiplied business contacts, and broadened financial resources in time of need. The stage was set for the outlawing of entails and primogeniture before the Revolution. The issue was settled in heated debate when the contours of the new democratic government and tenure system were outlined.

THE NORTHWEST ORDINANCES spelled out the new land-tenure system in general terms. In a way, they are our land tenure "constitution."

They described the kind of tenure that would be fostered as new States joined the Union. These conditions of tenure were similar to those in the Original Colonies.

The major provisions may be summarized as follows: The land would be surveyed under the rectangular survey rather than the metes and bounds system. It would be allocated first to the Revolutionary soldiers, as promised, and the remaining land would be sold to settlers and speculators. Land would be reserved for educational purposes.

The private owner would hold his land in fee simple. The land would be subject to transfer by sale among private parties. Deeds would evidence transfers and would be recorded. Land could be bequeathed by will; in the absence of a will it would be divided equally among heirs of equal degree. A land tax could be levied uniformly on the basis of assessed valuation within each taxing jurisdiction. All privately held land would be subject to taking for public purpose under due process with just compensation.

The holding of land under fee-simple tenure meant that: All rights in land resided in society except those alienated to private parties; society did not transfer the right to tax and the concomitant right to spend, to condemn for public use, and to police, and the right of escheat; the police power and right to tax were reserved largely for State and local governments, while the

rights of eminent domain and of spending resided in various levels of government; all private rights were held under rules laid down by society and were subject to change as society from time to time deemed desirable, but Government regulations were to be kept to a minimum; private rights were always qualified, never complete; and primogeniture and entails were looked upon with some disfavor and as against public policy. The rule against perpetuities prohibited entails.

It was accepted as basic policy also that all land, except the small amount needed to carry on the functions of government, would be alienated to private parties. The rules of common law would govern all tenure relations in the absence of specific constitutional or statutory provisions. No controls were imposed upon fragmentation or engrossment. Either resident occupancy or absenteeism was permitted.

These principles were never formalized in a single document, but they formed the core of our land-tenure system. The basic system left the private holders of rights relatively free to fashion tenure arrangements to suit their own needs. It provided for flexibility and not rigidity, for heterogeneity and not homogeneity.

ALIENATION of the public domain began soon after the close of the war. Land was sold until about 1800 in 640-acre sections and 36-section townships for a minimum of a dollar an acre to be paid within a year. The Federal Government needed ready cash, but revenue from sales of land came in slowly. To speed up disposition and increase revenue, the minimum acreage was reduced to 320 and the price was increased to 2 dollars an acre. Sales were made on credit payable within 5 years. The minimum was reduced in 1820 to 80 acres and the price to 1.25 dollars; credit was eliminated. Impatient, penniless settlers, however, swarmed into the Northwest Territory. Many of them settled upon the land as squatters. They demanded land free of charge and were restive over delays for surveying. The sales system fell into disrepute and disuse.

The Pre-emption Act of 1841 acceded to the wishes of the squatter settlers by formalizing the current practice into law. The squatter was given first opportunity to buy his claim up to 160 acres.

The Homestead Act of 1862 ended the sales and preemption era. Land became free to settlers in 160-acre tracts upon 5 years' occupancy and cultivation. As settlement moved westward, the alienation scheme favored private irrigation developments, increased the size of the homestead fourfold, and finally included publicly financed irrigation and reclamation.

The better agricultural lands of the public domain were alienated by 1934.

The rapidly growing conservation movement resulted in withdrawal of the public domain, particularly the grazing lands, from private settlement, for all practical purposes. Many other acts, which covered more than three-quarters of a century of the land-granting period, were concerned with use and conservation of our forest, coal, and mineral lands and with development of other lands for parks, monuments, and other public use.

The basic characteristics of the tenure system established by the end of the Revolution, coupled with the disposition of the public domain over the next century and a half, left in the United States a land-occupancy pattern of family farming. The policy was that the land should be owned and operated by those who tilled the soil. It was to be held by the freest tenures ever devised by modern man. Tenure relations were adjustable to meet the exigencies of unique situations that existed in various sections of the country and at different periods of time.

THE CONCEPTS OF EQUALITY, freedom of religion, and the democratic spirit, coupled with isolation on the frontier and plenty of free land, were forces that influenced our free-land system.

Perhaps the most powerful idea of the Revolutionary period was equality. Equality before the law, equal access to the ballot, and equal opportunity in the world were basic considerations. An inheritance law that provided for primogeniture and entails could not meet the criterion of equality, particularly of equal opportunity. The double portion for the eldest son and half portion for daughters could not be tolerated. So equal devolution for those of equal kinship became a basic principle in our tenure system. Equal access to the ballot could not be met so long as landholding was a qualification for suffrage. So this, too, was gradually done away with.

Another potent force that influenced the new land system was freedom of religion. The connections may not be so obvious and direct as with the concept of equality, but they were about as forceful. The religious bodies that fled European economic and religious oppression left an imprint on the free land-tenure system, no less than on the whole system of free enterprise.

European feudalism has been described as a system of government based on the organization of society upon the land. Political status depended heavily upon tenure status. Both economic and social status were determined in large measure by political and tenure status. During the Revolutionary era, democratic government could neither be attained nor maintained without a free land system—a wide distribution of land in the hands of those who worked the soil.

In his celebrated Plymouth oration, Daniel Webster said that the political situation of New England was determined by the fundamental laws respecting property. Some persons now take the position that the nature of society was to a great extent determined by the land policy.

Two types of isolation existed in colonial America—separation of the Colonies by 3 thousand miles of water from the Mother Country and individual isolation on the frontier. The former made it hard to adhere strictly to English land laws and made adjustments in the laws that governed the local tenure situation easy. The latter fostered the development of indigenous institutions and encouraged distrust for absentee landowners.

The breakdown of quitrent collection on the frontier and the lessening of dependence on earlier associations provided added incentives for freedom in various tenure relations—freedom to buy and sell or to alienate by will or gift, freedom from burdensome charges upon the land, and freedom to mortgage, lease, subdivide, and aggregate land.

The overabundance of free unsettled land made impossible the establishment of English feudal tenures in America, even though it was tried in several Colonies. Attempts to establish manors in the valleys of the Hudson and Potomac Rivers and in the Carolinas, although pursued with vigor for a time, were relatively unsuccessful. Even the Dutch patroonships that had the strength to survive the Revolution were eliminated during the rent wars of the 1840's. Land could not be monopolized in America as in England, for anyone dissatisfied with local conditions could move westward and take up new land, usually without paying for it. The abundance of free land on the frontier expedited the development of our land system.

THE BASIC CHARACTERISTICS of our tenure system, unlike our political system, were not marked departures from our English heritage. But many features were uniquely American.

The new land system was characterized by freedom of action. Private owners were almost completely free to buy, sell, transfer, contract, will, give, use, or leave idle their lands. Land could be held in many ways—publicly by Federal, State, county, municipal, and other units of government, and privately by individuals, partnerships, corporations, and cooperatives or in unsettled estates or trusts. The private holders of rights in land could be resident upon the land or absentee, whether owner, tenant, or a holder of a lesser estate.

No limit was placed on the acreage that one person could hold, and the acreage could be held in a single parcel or in noncontiguous parcels.

Rights in land could be split between surface, above-surface, and subsurface rights. Various rights could be definite or indefinite; they could be held for varying lengths of time or for an indeterminate period.

The land-tenure system provided the owner with quiet and peaceful possession and enjoyment. His neighbors could not trespass upon his private property or damage it. Nearby owners also were required to use their land so as not to create a nuisance.

Rights in land were held to be created by man, for use by man, and subject to change by man. The concept of inalienable rights, such as characterized our system of government, did not exist in our land-tenure system.

The system tended to emphasize rights and to ignore responsibilities. The wide disparity between immediate private self-interest and longtime public welfare was not considered adequately. Man was given almost full freedom to contract regarding his land as he pleased.

The freedom accorded private holders of land rights was subject to the authority of State and local political units to adjust tenures to suit varying conditions. A flexible system of land tenure thus was provided.

THREE PILLARS have been developed to undergird and strengthen the tenure system: Research, education, and credit.

The settlement of the public domain was still in process when it became evident that farmers needed public assistance. Each one of several million farmers could not conduct his own research. So they joined through Government to discover ways and means of producing more and better agricultural products at less cost. This publicly sponsored research program had as its roots the first congressional appropriation of 1 thousand dollars in 1839 for agricultural improvement. The real impetus, however, came several decades later when Federal land was given to the several States for the development of agricultural research and education in land-grant colleges and when public funds were appropriated to establish State experiment stations.

Soon after the turn of the century, it became increasingly evident that the results of research were not utilized by most farmers in a reasonable period. The Federal-State cooperative extension program came into being in 1914 to remedy this situation. Its chief purpose was to bring new ideas and improved methods to farm families at the earliest possible date. Educational techniques have improved greatly.

To strengthen a weak link in the farmer's publicly sponsored service chain, the agricultural credit system was improved, beginning in 1916.

An attempt was made to supply farmers with the kind of credit they needed at rates that they could afford and under repayment plans which provided a reasonable opportunity to liquidate the debt. Long-term loans, free of renewal charges, and at low interest rates, were introduced under public sponsorship. The introduction of the amortization of principal—repaying part of the principal each year—fitted repayments to farmers' needs. Insurance companies, banks, and other lending institutions accepted the new principles.

The new credit arrangements, however, were not sufficiently prevalent or strong to withstand the depression years. Publicly sponsored credit was expanded greatly, with the Federal Treasury standing behind loans to many thousands of farmers. Foreclosure moratorium laws extended to farmers an opportunity to put their financial houses in order. Other public aids—rural rehabilitation and submarginal land purchase, for example—

were called on to prevent a breakdown in the family-farm, owner-operator tenure structure on which American agriculture was founded.

For some reason, the benefits of these programs did not reach farm wage workers, sharecroppers, tenants, or small owners. Additional action was planned by 1937. The rehabilitation program was expanded greatly, and a new type of public credit developed.

Five features were added to the farmers' credit structure. Loans up to 100 percent of the value of the land and buildings were made. The period of the loan was extended to 40 years, and the interest rate was reduced to 3 percent. Repayment of principal could vary from year to year, depending on farm income. Technical assistance was supplied to the borrower. Loans were extended on the basis of personal characteristics of families, rather than accumulated equity.

Research, education, and credit have been used effectively under public sponsorship, but also with great private assistance, in making more effective our free land-tenure system. The strengths of individual initiative and free enterprise have been amplified and inherent weaknesses have been minimized by these three pillars.

OUR TENURE CONSTITUTION was amended only slightly while research, education, and credit programs were being brought to fruition.

Many observers now sense that our tenure system has not kept pace with modern technology, and legal adjustments are needed in order that our tenure system may better fulfill its function. Although it may have served admirably when land was free for the taking, our land system does not meet our present needs adequately, as land is a scarce and valuable resource.

Adjustment in the system should be based on research, discussion, and public understanding. Our tenure system, like our Constitution, provides opportunity for significant amendments without destroying the system.

What do we mean by "ownership"?

Ownership links land and man, but the meaning of the word is not always clear. In practice, we have no absolute property in land; society limits the use of land, just as it limits the use, say, of an automobile. All interests in land are held at the sufferance of society. Titles, leases, and mortgages show man's desire for orderliness. By *Gene Wunderlich* and *Russell W. Bierman*, Farm Economics Research Division.

OWNERSHIP is the important connecting link between man and land: It is ownership that fixes responsibility for the way the land is used.

No study of land is complete without knowledge of the qualities and dimensions of the ownership pattern. Let us first outline the overall dimensions of the ownership picture with types of owners and their characteristics. Then we can shade in the nature, origin, and functions of property and supply the third dimension of ownership—mortgage debt of farmland.

Our data on ownership are taken primarily from two sources: A cooperative study on types of farmland owners made in 1956 by the Agricultural Research Service and the Bureau of the Census and projections based on a study of owner characteristics, method of holding land, tenure, inheritance, and concentration, completed in 1949 by the Department of Agriculture.

Of the total acreage in farms and ranches in the United States in 1956 (1,158 million acres), individuals, partners, or heirs of estates owned 1,015 million acres (88 percent). Other private owners—insurance companies, banks, railroads, the few incorporated farms, and other corporations—owned about 57.5 million acres (5 percent). Thus nearly 93 percent of the land in farms (not including Indian lands, which are largely federally administered) was privately owned.

Of the 408 million acres of land the Federal Government owned in 1956, about 13.5 million acres, or 3 percent, were used partly or entirely for farming and ranching. However, 77 million acres of grazing land were administered by the Forest Service and 176 million acres by the Bureau of Land Management, primarily on a permit basis. Usually these Federal grazing lands are not regarded as "land in farms," but they do represent a considerable acreage devoted at least partly to agricultural production.

Notable regional differences in ownership of public lands stem largely from the historical formation of our land policy, growth pattern, and variations in the productivity and use of land. For example, almost 12 percent of the land in farms in the Mountain States was publicly owned in 1956, whereas the Federal Government owned less than 1 percent of the farmland in New England.

Except for the lands in the Thirteen Original Colonies and what is now the State of Texas, almost all land in the United States has been in Federal ownership at some time. Yet today scarcely more than 1 percent of land in farms (not including the grazing lands) is in Federal ownership.

State and local governments in 1956 owned 97 million acres of land. Slightly more than 31 million acres of it was farmland. Most of it was leased to private operators. Some State and local government farmland, however, was operated by managers who represented the Government. Among these were experiment stations, State farms, and penal institutions.

About 48 million acres of the 56 million acres of Indian lands in 1956 were used for farming or grazing. Much of it is of rather low productivity. It was operated by both Indians and others. Not all land operated by Indians is considered Indian land.

Corporation-held farmland is a relatively small proportion of total farmland, but it has increased in extent. The Bureau of the Census estimated that corporations owned 7 million more acres of farmland in 1954 than in 1950.

The proportion of corporate owners was much greater in the West than in the East. In the West, where 11.5 percent of the land in farms in the Pacific States and 25 million acres (about 10 percent) of the land in farms in the Mountain States were owned corporately, large ranching operations, timber companies, railroads, and fruit growers accounted for much of the high proportion of corporate ownership.

Corporations owned less than 2 percent of the farmland in New England and the North Central States.

We note, however, relatively high proportions of corporate ownership in Florida and Texas, where the large financial outlay and the long growing cycle required for citrus fruit favor corporate ownership. Large ranching and cotton enterprises, too, often are well adapted to corporate ownership and operation.

About 4 percent of our land in farms is publicly owned, and about 5 percent is owned by corporations. By far the greater part of our farmland is owned by individuals, most of whom operate their own farms or ranches. Others have little or no connection with farming.

WHEN WE SPEAK about the structure of farmland ownership, we speak of a multitude of interests and a diverse collection of individuals. Even to speculate as to the effect of landownership on production, distribution of income, and political or social status, we must know something about these individuals.

Nearly 85 percent of the owners of farmland are farm operators. Two-thirds of them own all the land they farm and farm all the land they own. The rest of the operator-owners rent additional land to farm, or rent out some of their own land, or do both.

Landlords—persons who operate none of the land they own—constitute about 15 percent of the owners. They own more than one-fifth of the acreage of land and nearly one-fourth of the value of farmland.

Although most of the estimated 5.5 million to 6 million owners are men and most of the farmland is owned by men, the interest of women often is understated. Much farmland in joint ownership by husband and wife is reported as ownership by the husband. Even the individual holdings of the wife are occasionally included with land held by the husband. It is probable that at least a one-fourth interest in the farmland is held by women.

Not all owners hold full, unconditional rights in their land. Nearly one-fourth of the individual owners of farmland hold their land in undivided interest—estates and partnerships—and life estates, or under purchase contract.

Aside from the general types of ownership, many qualifications, conditions, and combinations go into the pattern of holdings of an owner.

WHAT DO WE MEAN by "ownership"? A legalist who wishes to be precise speaks about forms of "estates." He does not use the general term "ownership." Each form of estate places certain duties, responsibilities, or limitations upon the owner.

What is important when we ask whether an estate may be classified as ownership is the type and quantity of rights and their duration. The person (or group of persons) with the greatest number of rights for the longest duration is usually called the "owner." Most so-called "leasehold estates" ordinarily are not classified as ownership.

Here are the principal forms of estates listed in the approximate order of the degree of rights held by the owner:

Fee simple is the estate with fewest limitations. It is the nearest to absolute ownership. It attaches no conditions on possession or use and endures without end or limit. Uses must not be illegal, and they are subject to government regulation.

Fee tail is similar to fee simple, except that inheritance is limited by statute to particular heirs. It is used rarely in the United States, and in most States it is not legal.

Life estate is an estate that endures for the life of one or more persons (usually the person holding the estate) but terminates upon the death of the specified person.

Conditional estates are estates that take effect or terminate upon the happening of some uncertain event. Many of these may be for a term of years. Some conditional estates, but not all, would qualify as ownership.

Several common forms of coownership should be mentioned:

Estate in common is held by two or more persons and provides separate and distinct (although undivided) shares for each. This estate may be indefinite or for a term of years.

Joint tenancy is an estate held by two or more persons, in which each has an undivided interest in the whole; that is, no particular share is assigned to any one person. Such estates may be indefinite or for a term of years.

Estate by entirety is an estate similar to joint tenancy, usually between husband and wife.

"Future interests" in property may be of various types. They often are created by a will, in contrast to estates that afford the holder a present possessing right.

445509°—58——20

In its purest sense, ownership means complete dominion, title, or proprietary right in a thing or claim. As we know it, however, ownership is a rather loose aggregation of human relationships that provides maximum, though limited, use and possession of property objects.

In practice, we have no absolute property in land. Just as society places restrictions on the use of an automobile, so it limits the use of land. Land, for example, cannot be used to grow opium poppies without Federal license (none of which has ever been issued).

THE ORIGINS OF PROPERTY are basically economic in nature. Usefully shaped stones, carrion, fires, and caves could have been property objects in the early Paleolithic Age, as they had value in satisfying basic wants of the early human beings. It is questionable, however, whether these early men had a sufficiently refined means of communication to make property relations understood.

The institution of property could only develop as man's comprehension, reason, memory, and powers of communication grew. Property rights at first were established with clubs, fists, and teeth. Habits and precedents later formed guidelines for property relationships and partly replaced the bloodier forms of violence. Fraud, duplicity, and courts of law marked the dawn of civilized property rights.

Now, with the intricacies of nearly 50 thousand years of experience with property, we have a property structure so complex that special segments of law are devoted to the otherwise simple matter of where man may place his feet.

Our property relationships, complex though they may be, provide us with the stability of possession and use of resources necessary for our highly integrated economy.

The objects of property give off certain services required in our economic processes. These services may be used by the owner, leased to others, or left idle.

Ownership is the mechanism that associates final responsibility for resource use to individuals.

In the development of American agriculture, the ownership of land to the farmer was more than a means for assuring a continuous flow of the services of land for production. It was a goal in itself. It meant security in old age, social status, and an estate to pass on to heirs. Ownership of land was the top of the agricultural ladder, on which a young man began as a laborer, passed through a stage of tenancy, and eventually became the owner of his own farm.

Large-scale commercial agriculture, however, has had within it forces that have made and will continue to make the traditional agricultural ladder less useful in trying to explain the goals of farm ownership.

The goal of the modern farmer is less clearly that of farm ownership. Instead, he seeks a larger cash income for himself and his family. Security in old age is increasingly provided for by a wide variety of private and Government insurance programs. The movement of persons into and out of agriculture is a two-way street, with rural residences and hobby farms operated by retired people as an emerging tenure class. Then, too, for an important number of young farm operators, inheritance rather than the agricultural ladder will be the route to ownership.

A third of the acreage and a third of the value of farmland held by individuals is acquired, wholly or partly, by gift or inheritance.

To the one-fourth of the farm owners who acquired at least part of their farmland by gift or inheritance, the boost in getting a larger unit, either for operating or renting out, can be important. Owners who have inherited at least part of their holdings have more land per owner and a higher value of holding per owner than those who do not inherit land.

Farm operators buy their land more frequently than landlords do. More than a third of the landlords acquire at least a part of their holdings through inheritance or gift. But three-fourths of the farm operators buy part or all of their holdings.

As farms become larger and the price of land rises, the investment required for farms becomes a growing obstacle to beginning farmers, and inheritance probably becomes even more important as a means for acquiring land.

Inheritance may involve the land directly and entirely. It may be a part interest in land, which permits one heir to buy out the others; or it may be other property or money that can be used in the purchase of land. According to one survey, the latter method was used by 14 percent of the individuals who owned land.

Inheritance is important, first, as it affects the distribution of income from land and the supply of farming opportunities and, second, as it may affect production.

The net effect on distribution and production will depend partly upon the relative strengths of the forces of fragmentation and the forces of consolidation in our inheritance system. A study in Michigan in 1954, for example, disclosed that, in the sample tested, the inheritance structure resulted in a net consolidation created by settlements of estates and recombination with adjoining units. On the other hand, there is a built-in tendency toward division of holdings by the excess population in agriculture since we do not have the system of primogeniture—inheritance by the oldest son.

The ownership of farmland is widely distributed. We have estimated that in 1956 there were at least 5.5 million owners of farmland. Many of these owners involved more than one individual. When one considers the multiplicity of ownership interests that arise, for example, from corporations, partnerships, and estates, one could reasonably estimate that 8 million or 9 million persons have interests in the agricultural land of our country. If one were to include mortgages as a form of interest in land (as it seems reasonable to do), the estimated number of persons with ownership interest in our farmland would be 10 million.

Despite the large number of owners and their wide distribution, the acreage owned is distributed rather unevenly. Our most recent estimates of the concentration of ownership are that at least 40 percent of the farmland owned by individuals was held by 5 percent of the owners.

Part of this imbalance is due to large holdings of grazing land in the West. Corporate holdings, which tend to be large, also concentrate ownership.

With the increases in size of farms and the reduction in the number of farms, the concentration of ownership probably is increasing.

Is this degree of concentration contrary to our precepts of equal opportunity and equality? If so, what can be done to encourage wider distribution of ownership and yet permit the necessary degree of incentive to grow? As population increases and space becomes dearer, these questions may have growing importance in our land policy.

THE OWNERSHIP INTEREST of a person in his land is not explained entirely by the nature and duration of the rights we have described. Ownership has a third dimension, which is represented by the owner's equity.

An owner's equity means essentially the difference between the value of his interest in the property and his liabilities assigned to the property. Thus the debts, evidenced by mortgages, on a tract of farmland are reductions in the equity owned by the owner-borrower. The mortgage to the creditor, on the other hand, is a contingent claim to, or interest in, the land.

Owners of farmland can pledge their land as security for debt. They incur debt not only when they buy land but also when they borrow to buy machinery and livestock, make improvements in buildings, pay operating and living expenses, and refinance debts.

Whenever an owner borrows and pledges his land as security, he reduces his equity according to the amount and terms of the loan and the rate of interest.

The exact form or legal instrument by which the owner of farmland pledges the land as security for debt varies according to the State, the nature of the transaction, and the type of lender. But all debt for which farmland is the security may be called farm-mortgage debt.

FARM-MORTGAGE DEBT usually is represented by mortgages and deeds of trust if the borrower has title to the land. The borrower secures the debt by giving the lender certain rights in the land. If the debt is not paid according to the terms of the mortgage or deed of trust, the lender may require that the land be sold and the proceeds be used to pay the debt.

Money owed for farmland bought under a purchase (sales) contract is also considered farm-mortgage debt. These contracts are agreements to buy (and sell) farmland, but the buyer does not obtain title to the land until he has made the contracted payments to the seller. Purchase contracts often are used when a buyer of farmland makes only a small downpayment or no payment at all.

Other legal instruments that pledge farmland as security for debt include deeds to secure debt, vendor's liens, and bonds for deed. They are not commonly used for this purpose, however.

The purposes and terms of farm-mortgage loans vary. These loans are often thought of as long-term loans used only to finance purchases of farmland and similar long-run outlays. Many, however, are made for fairly short terms to secure loans for annual operating and living expenses and other short-run needs. To refinance debts rather than to purchase land is the most frequent purpose for which the longer term farm-mortgage loans are made.

The Agricultural Research Service,

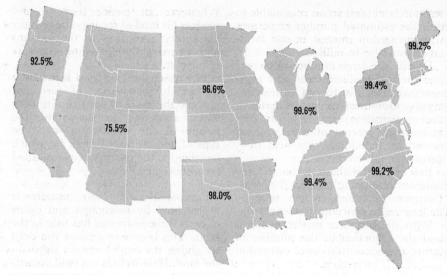

Private ownership of farmland in 1954.

in cooperation with the Bureau of the Census, estimated the amount of farm-mortgage debt in January 1956 to be 9,066 million dollars. This represented a 62-percent increase since 1950 and was well on the way to the 1923 peak of 10,786 million dollars. Farm-mortgage debt represents about 9 percent of the total value of land and buildings.

The increase in farm real-estate values, the increased proportion of real-estate sales that involve credit, the higher ratio of debt to consideration in these credit-financed sales, and readily available credit appear to have been the factors in the 1950–1956 rise.

An estimated 1,278,000 owner-operated farms—35 percent of all owner-operated farms—carried mortgages in 1956. The proportion of owner-operated farms mortgaged was 30 percent in 1950. It was 45 percent in the peak year of 1930. The proportion of tenant- and manager-operated farms under mortgage has been consistently lower than that of owner-operated farms. Only 21 percent of the tenant and manager farms were mortgaged in 1950.

We can divide farm-mortgage lenders into six major groups.

Individuals are the most important type of farm-mortgage lenders. This group held 32 percent of the total of 9,066 million dollars of outstanding loans in January 1956. Life-insurance companies held 25 percent; Federal land banks, 16 percent; commercial and savings banks, 15 percent; Farmers Home Administration, 3 percent; and all others, 9 percent. Interest rates, size of loan, and length of term vary among types of lenders and regions.

Individuals are important lenders in every region. Many of the farm mortgages they hold arise from sales of farmland in which the seller took back a mortgage for part of the sales price. Others often are simply investments of local people.

Individuals ordinarily hold loans of slightly larger amounts, at lower rates, and for longer terms than commercial and savings banks, but the amounts are smaller, the rates higher, and the terms shorter than those for loans held by Federal land banks and insurance companies. The proportion of the total loans held by individuals in 1956 ranged from 17 percent in the West South Central States to 52 percent in the Pacific States.

Life-insurance companies are the largest institutional farm-mortgage lenders. They hold some farm mortgages in each State, but they are most important in areas in which they can develop a large volume of long-term amortized loans of relatively large size that can be made and serviced efficiently by standardized procedures. The proportion of the total mortgages held by life-insurance companies in the various regions in 1956 ranged from 2 percent in New England to 40 percent in the West South Central States.

The Federal land-bank system is a federally sponsored cooperative long-term, farm-mortgage credit system that operates in all counties in the country. Borrowing is done from the land banks through local national farm loan associations, which are owned by their borrower members. Land-bank loans are made for long terms on an amortized basis, and they furnish an important part of farm-mortgage credit in every region. The proportion of the total loans held by Federal land banks in 1956 varied from 11 percent in the Pacific States to 20 percent in the West North Central States. Of the total amount of land-bank loans outstanding, 45 percent was in the North Central States.

Commercial and savings banks usually make relatively small farm-mortgage loans for short terms. They held only 4 percent of the 1956 total in the Mountain States and 8 percent in the West South Central States. In the New England, Middle Atlantic, South Atlantic, East North Central, and East South Central States, commercial and savings banks held from a fifth to a fourth of the farm-mortgage loans.

The average size of farm-mortgage loans varies between lenders and between regions. Loans are smaller in the South and Northeast, where farms are smaller, than in the North Central and Western States. The average size of farm mortgages in 1956 was 7,900 dollars; it ranged from 4,800 dollars in the South Atlantic States to 13,100 dollars in the Mountain States.

As larger loans tend to have longer terms, the South Atlantic and East South Central States have the shortest terms (an average of 5 years) and the West North Central States have the longest terms (an average of 13 years). The average term of all farm-mortgage loans in the United States is about 9 years. Interest rates follow the same pattern; they are lowest in the North Central States and highest in the Southeastern States. Farm-mortgage debt outstanding in January 1956 carried an average rate of 4.7 percent.

Now that we know something about the nature and size of farm-mortgage debt and the type of lenders to whom it is owed, let us see what kind of farms carry most of this debt.

Mortgaged farms are usually larger than farms without mortgages, are worth more per acre, and have a higher value of land and buildings per farm. Their operators have higher gross incomes from their farms. Similarly, a higher proportion of farms in the better, more commercial farming areas are mortgaged than in other areas. Owner-operated farms are more likely to be mortgaged and to be mortgaged for a higher proportion of their value than are farms operated by tenants or managers.

Possible explanations are that the larger farms require more capital investment and consequently their operators need long-term borrowed money and can use it profitably. Also, on the larger farms, the margin of farm income above necessary living and operating expenses is likely to be greater.

Owner-operated farms may be mortgaged oftener than tenant farms because owner-operators must supply all the capital needed to operate their farms. At least a part of the capital is supplied by the tenant on tenant farms. Some tenant farms are acquired by their owners as investments, and borrowed money is not needed for their purchase. Some are owned by corporations or Government units whose obligations are not considered to be a part of farm-mortgage debt.

We may demonstrate some of the differences between farms with mortgages and those without mortgages by utilizing the 1956 information on full owners (farmers who own all the land they operate). Part owners (farmers who own only part of the land they operate) are similar to full owners in mortgage characteristics.

Mortgaged full-owner farms are usually larger and have higher values of land and buildings per acre than those not mortgaged. Mortgaged farms had an average of 164 acres, compared with 135 acres for farms free of mortgage. Mortgaged farms had an average value of 19,400 dollars; mortgage-free farms a value of 14,400 dollars. The value per acre was 118 dollars for mortgaged farms and 106 dollars for those not mortgaged.

Most full owners with mortgaged farms had substantial equities in their farms. Of the average value of 19,400 dollars, the full owner's debt was 5,200 dollars, leaving him with an equity of 14,200 dollars. Ordinarily farms with low ratios of debt to value were larger and more valuable than those that were heavily indebted.

Farms from which the larger quantities of farm products are sold are more likely to be mortgaged than those from which smaller quantities are sold.

Only 21 percent of the smaller commercial farms (those selling less than 1,200 dollars' worth of farm products) were mortgaged in 1956, but 40 percent of the farms selling 2,500 dollars' to 4,999 dollars' and 47 percent of those selling 25,000 dollars' or more worth of farm products were mortgaged. The value per farm, value per acre, total debt per farm, and the owner's equity increased as the value of farm products sold increased.

The ratio of mortgage debt to the value of the farm was lower for the larger mortgaged commercial farms than for the smaller ones.

Apparently, therefore, the larger commercial farmers require greater amounts of farm-mortgage credit and make greater use of it. The data suggest also that lenders are more willing to make loans to the larger farms. Although these loans are larger, they are likely to be lower relative to the value of the land mortgaged as security and lower relative to the proportion of the farm income that must be used for repayment than loans on smaller farms.

Many farmers start out as tenants. After farming for a while they buy farms with substantial mortgages. As they grow older, they reduce or pay off the mortgages altogether and enlarge their farms. About 31 percent of all tenant farmers were under 35 in 1954, but only 13 percent of the part owners and 9 percent of the full owners were as young as this.

Fifty-seven percent of all full owners had mortgages in 1956. But as farmers grow older and continue to farm, they pay off mortgages. Only 16 percent of those full owners over 65 years still owed any farm-mortgage debt.

In the whole United States, mortgaged farms operated by full owners under 35 years averaged 122 acres, and the total value was 15,300 dollars per farm, but for those 55 to 64 years old the average size was 194 acres and the average value was 21,000 dollars.

The amount of mortgage debt per farm declined from 5,900 dollars for mortgaged full owners under 35 to 4,600 dollars for those 55 to 64 years old. The ratio of debt to value also declined, and the value of the owner's equity increased. This probably means that farm-mortgage credit is used by younger farmers to become established in farming and that many farmers achieve ownership of debt-free farms.

WE HAVE PRESENTED and examined some of the types of interest in land.

Society transcends these individual property interests by expressing itself through courts of justice, custom, and economic forces. All interests in land, therefore, are held at the sufferance of society. A title, a lease, or a mortgage manifests not an inherent right of an individual but a proclivity of mankind for orderliness.

Farm tenure and the use of land.

Tenure means the holding of rights to use land. Tenure arrangements embrace many agreements. The function of the tenure system is to distribute rights to the use of land among individuals so that land can be used in an orderly way. It provides both social and economic stability, and it in turn can be stabilized through continued traditional usages, which are discussed in this summary of farm sizes, incomes, and types of tenure. By *Gene Wunderlich* and *Walter E. Chryst,* agricultural economists, Farm Economics Research Division.

TENURE TOUCHES the way every farm is run. All farming operations require land. All farming operations require time. Hence, if production is to be achieved, the farmer must know he can use the land long enough to complete any production process he undertakes.

That is, each farm operator must have some rights to the use of some land for some period of time, or planning is impossible. If planning is impossible, production is impossible.

It is the function of the tenure system to distribute rights to the use of land among individuals so that the land can be used in an orderly way.

The distribution of rights in land is highly important to the individual because it establishes the size of farming operation that is feasible to carry on; the period for which crop rotations and livestock enterprises can be planned; the amount of labor, tools, and livestock the farmer can use; and to some degree the extent of such permanent fixtures as housing, buildings, fences, and soil conservation measures that can be used.

No less important to the individual is the effect of the tenure system on his share of the fruits of production.

The word "tenure," from the French "tenir" (to hold), has come to mean the holding of rights to use land. One's tenure rights in land specify the conditions of possession and use over time.

The time aspect of the tenure pattern is composed of two main classes of estates (that is, types of interest)—freehold and leasehold. Freehold estates are of indefinite duration. Leasehold estates are for a certain term. Duration, plus the degree of interest and location of the final proprietary right, determines the exact type of estate, which we classify loosely as ownership or tenancy.

These two broad classifications of tenure—ownership and tenancy—are used separately and in combination to identify most of the arrangements that follow.

In practice, tenure arrangements contain a multitude of written, oral, and implicit agreements. Variation in the statutes of each of the 48 States multiplies the number of possible tenure arrangements even more.

If a common denominator, say a measure of "interest in land," could be developed, tenure might be viewed more appropriately as a scale, rather than as separate and distinct classes. Such a scale might run from agricultural labor, with no legal interest in the land, to full and unqualified ownership, such as the interest held by the public in public lands. Pending refine-

295

ment of such a scale, however, the classes of tenure as given in the 5-year censuses of agriculture are useful.

In the census system, the tenure of a farm or ranch operator is prescribed by his legal interest in the land he operates (not necessarily the land he owns).

A full owner owns all the land he operates.

A part owner owns part of the land he operates and rents part from others.

A manager operates a farm for someone else on a salary basis.

A tenant owns none of the land he operates.

Tenants are further classified by the type of rent paid.

Cash tenants pay rental in cash as a lump sum or on a per acre basis.

Share-cash tenants pay part of their rental in cash and part as a share of the crop or livestock.

Crop-share tenants pay a share of the crops but not of the livestock.

Livestock-share tenants pay a share of the livestock or livestock products and perhaps also a share of the crop.

Sharecroppers ("croppers") provide labor only, are supplied workpower and management supervision by the landlord, and are paid a share of the crop.

The relative strengths of the tenure classes are both the cause and effect of the production patterns in agriculture. The tenure structure determines how the total agricultural income is to be divided, and yet tenure arrangements are themselves developed to divide income in a particular way.

The tenure structure is the framework within which resources of production are combined, but the tenure arrangements in turn are especially adapted to meet the peculiar requirements of each type of production.

The tenure system provides both social and economic stability, and it in turn can be stabilized through continued traditional usages.

The relative importance of each tenure class may serve as a measure of two important aspects of the organization of agriculture: What it is and what it may be in the future.

Let us look first at the current situation, then examine the important trends, and from them suggest what the next few decades may hold.

THE MOST RECENT DATA on farm numbers, the 1954 Census of Agriculture, showed a total of 4.8 million farms. Of them, 57 percent were operated by full owners, 18 percent by part owners, 24 percent by tenants, and fewer than 1 percent by managers.

Compared with the number of farms, the proportion of land operated under each of these tenure forms is quite different. Of the 1,160 million acres of farmland in the United States in 1954, 34 percent was in full-owner farms, 41 percent in part-owner farms, 16 percent in tenant farms, and 9 percent in manager farms. Thus the average full-owner farm contained 145 acres; the part-owner farm, 544 acres; the tenant farm, 166 acres; and the manager farm, 4,786 acres.

From this alone, however, one cannot conclude that owner and tenant farms are small and that part-owner and manager farms are large. There are other measures of farm size.

The value per acre of full-owner and tenant farms is 101 and 116 dollars, respectively; the acre value of land operated by part owners is 62 dollars; and the value per acre of manager farms is 49 dollars. The relatively high acre value of owner and tenant lands does reduce the disparity in farm size between tenure groups but not enough to eliminate substantial differences in the average value per farm of the various tenure groups. The average full-owner farm was worth about 14,500 dollars; the part-owner farm, 35,800 dollars; the tenant farm, 19,500 dollars; and the manager farm, 165,800 dollars.

Farm income is a measure of farm size that is better suited to measure the farm enterprise than acreage or value.

By this standard, too, manager-operated farms are largest. A third of them reported gross value of products sold of 25 thousand dollars or more in 1954, while only 3 percent of the commercial owner and tenant farms and 6.8 percent of the part-owner farms had gross sales of 25 thousand dollars or more. Many of the full owners are at the lower end of the income scale, where 44 percent of the operators of commercial full-owner farms sold farm products with a gross value of less than 2,500 dollars. Of the tenant farms, 36 percent of the operators, of the part-owner farms, 24 percent, and of the manager farms, only 10 percent sold less than 2,500 dollars' worth of farm products.

One may conclude from the relative income positions of the various tenure groups that the goal of full ownership is attained at the sacrifice of farm income. Fewer than one-half of the commercial farms are operated by full owners, but 64 percent of commercial farms reporting a value of farm products sold of less than 1,200 dollars are operated by full owners. Tenants, except for the sharecroppers of the South, are in a favorable income position as compared with full owners.

The forms of tenancy associated with different types of farming and with geographic areas show a considerable range in income positions.

Farms operated under the livestock-share arrangement common in the Corn Belt have relatively high incomes; 75 percent of commercial livestock-share farms sold at least 5 thousand dollars' worth of farm products in 1954. Only 10 percent of the sharecropper farms, which are found ordinarily in the South, reported sales of farm products of 5 thousand dollars or more. More than 60 percent of the operators of sharecropper farms reported less than 2,500 dollars' worth of farm products sold.

The rather marked differences in the characteristics of farms of the four main tenure types suggest that there may be important relationships between tenure and other aspects of farm organization worth investigating.

THE TENURE STRUCTURE encompasses agriculture as an industry and as a way of living.

The first distinction between tenure types therefore should be between farms that are commercial units devoted primarily to production for cash income and other noncommercial farms that provide only supplementary cash income and employment or are used as rural residences.

Part-time, residential, and other noncommercial farms account for 30 percent of the farms and 11 percent of the land in farms. As security of tenure may be relatively important to persons who use their farms as residences or as sources of subsistence income, owner-operatorship of these noncommercial farms is more common than tenant or part-owner operatorship.

About 42 percent of the full-owner farms are noncommercial. Only 13 percent of the part-owner and 16 percent of the tenant farms are noncommercial. Seventy-nine percent of the noncommercial farms are operated by full owners.

The large share of the 1.5 million noncommercial farms operated by full owners helps partly to explain why full-owner farms are smaller in acreage and value than part-owner and tenant farms.

For purposes of relating tenure to production, it is preferable to deal only with the 3.3 million commercial farms, as they account for 98 percent or more of the total value of farm products sold. We shall use only commercial farms therefore in characterizing the various forms of tenure in terms of their advantages or disadvantages for various kinds of production.

Each form of tenure exists in all major types of production. Certain characteristics of a particular tenure, however, sometimes make it more desirable than other forms of tenure for certain types of farming.

Some of the important attributes of a type of farming that affect tenure are the proportion of the total value of investment that land represents, the length of the production cycle, the importance of labor in the operation, the risks involved with hazards to production, the possibility of mechanization, flexibility in management practices, the quality of management, and the location of the owners of land and equipment.

Full ownership offers a relatively secure length of tenure and thus is used to greater degree than other types of tenure when the production cycle is of long duration. An example is orchards; full owners operate 82 percent of the commercial fruit and nut orchards.

Ownership of all the land by the operator tends to be more prevalent also for farms in which the value of land represents a relatively small part of the total investment in the farm. Of the 549 thousand commercial dairy farms, for example, 338 thousand, or 62 percent, are operated by full owners.

Part owners, the middle group between full owners and tenants, are somewhat more difficult to identify with particular farming conditions. They often are related to the more extensive types of farming, which require flexibility and much equipment. Part owners, who represent 23 percent of all commercial farm operators, for example, operate 31 percent of the commercial cash-grain farms.

Managers operate farms for which a high degree of management skill is required and on which ownership of the farm resources is separated, as in the case of absentee employers. Managers are also used to a large extent on noncommercial institutional farms. Only large enterprises can afford a manager, and the total investment on manager farms usually is large. Nearly 40 percent of the commercial manager-operated farms are livestock operations other than dairy or poultry. Many of the managers operate cattle ranches in the West.

Tenancy affords flexibility in combining resources. Tenancy also permits spreading the risks of production. Tenancy is greater when a short pro-

duction cycle requires less security of tenure as, say, in cash-grain production. When the value of land represents a relatively large part of the total investment in farm resources, tenancy tends to be high. Tenancy tends to be relatively more important in places where land values are high, as they are in the fertile areas of the Corn Belt and the Mississippi Delta.

The types of tenancy arrangements vary with the production pattern.

Cash rents often are used if the landlord is dissociated from the management or if he contributes little except the land to the enterprise. The number of cash-rented farms is relatively small—3 percent of commercial farms. Compared with other types of tenant farms, however, the average size of cash-rented farms is large—349 acres per farm—mainly because of the greater use of cash rents in the grazing areas where large acreages predominate.

Share arrangements, particularly the livestock-share leases, involve close working arrangements between landlord and tenant. Not infrequently in livestock-share arrangements, the landlord and the tenant are related. Livestock-share tenancy is used oftener in the livestock-feeding and dairy areas of the north-central region than in the grazing areas of the West, where manager and cash-tenant farms are relatively more important.

Sharecropping is closely identified with cotton and tobacco. Sixty-two percent of the commercial cropper farms were classified as cotton enterprises, and another 33 percent were classified as "other field crop," most of which was tobacco. Croppers accounted for about 28 percent of the commercial cotton farms and about 15 percent of the cotton acreage harvested. They also harvested about 25 percent of the tobacco acreage.

As the different forms of tenure on commercial farms develop to accommodate the methods and conditions of production, regional patterns of tenure on all farms are affected.

In the Northeast, for example, where

dairying and poultry are important and where farmland represents a relatively small part of the total investment, 77 percent of all farms and 65 percent of all farmland are full owner operated. Tenancy accounted for only 6 percent of both the 339 thousand farms and the 41 million acres of farmland in the Northeast. In the South, 29 percent of the 2,317 thousand farms and 17 percent of the 387 million acres of farmland were operated by tenants.

The north-central region, which is dominated by Corn Belt agriculture, has been generally responsive to technological changes that call for farm expansion. The growth in farm size has been faster than could be accomplished by farm purchase under the pressure of high land values and large investments in machinery and equipment. The rental of additional land—one way of expanding farm size—may be part of the reason why in 1954 more farmland was operated by part owners than by any other tenure class in the north-central region. Part owners there operated 22 percent of the farms and 40 percent of the farmland.

The influence of large ranching operations is reflected in the relatively high proportion of manager-operated farmland in the West. The number of farms operated by managers is small; only 1.1 percent of the 422 thousand farms in the West were manager operated in 1954, but they included 20 percent of the 337 million acres of farmland in the region. As a tenure class, part owners also have large holdings. Part owners operated 53 percent of the farmland in the West in 1954.

Efficient farm operation depends sometimes on a relatively long period of secure tenure, but in other circumstances it may be important for the operator to change his type of operation or to move if he can make either change with little inconvenience and financial loss.

The choice between secure tenure and flexibility is relevant to the selection of a tenure arrangement. Ordinarily the owner-operator is assured greater security of tenure than the tenant is. The owner, however, is usually less mobile. The owner-operator may or may not have opportunity for flexibility in his operation, depending on his debt position and the possibilities of renting additional land.

The decision a farmer makes between security and flexibility will depend on the type of production and also on personal preferences and available farming opportunities.

Owners apparently occupy their farms longer than tenants do.

Owner-operators in 1954 had occupied their farms an average of 16 years, but tenants averaged 7 years. Of the commercial farms operated by full owners, only 2 percent of the operators began farming their present farms in 1954; 50 percent had begun in 1940 or earlier. Only 14 percent of the tenant farmers, however, reported that they had operated their current farms since 1940, and 12 percent reported that they had worked their present farms less than a year. Sharecroppers in the South reported even shorter tenure. Only 11 percent had operated their farms for 15 years or more and 17 percent had been on their farms for less than a year. The pattern for part owners is similar to that of full owners. About a fifth of the managers had been on their current farms since 1940 or earlier.

Preferences for security or mobility do not account entirely for differences in the length of time operators were on their farms. Part of the difference was due to their age.

Farmers accumulate equipment, livestock, and land as they grow older. Through purchase, gift, and inheritance, the tenants acquire ownership in land and are reclassified as full owners or part owners. On commercial farms in 1954, fewer than 14 percent of the farmers younger than 25 years were full owners, 10 percent were part owners, and 76 percent were tenants. In the age group 45 to 54, 48 percent were full owners, 27 percent were part

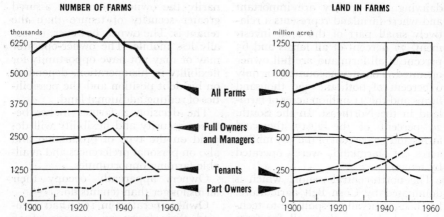

Farm tenure in the United States.

owners, and 25 percent were tenants. By the time farmers had reached 65 years or more, 76 percent were full owners, 14 percent were part owners, and only 10 percent were tenants.

The transformation of tenant to owner and then to landlord is called the agricultural ladder. The tenure process we are witnessing today, however, shows movement both ways on this wobbly ladder; men jump on and off at each rung.

The increasing integration of agriculture with other industries has made the stages of the ladder process less clear and perhaps less useful in explaining how individuals get into any one tenure class. A new model that would account for lateral as well as vertical movements would be more descriptive.

JUST AS THE PATTERN of production has changed, so has the tenure structure changed. Tenure arrangements have had to be adjusted to accommodate such critical economic factors as the migration out of agriculture, the expansion in the size of some farms, the increase of farm mechanization, improved production techniques, and the shift toward a livestock economy.

The farm population remained at about 31 to 32 million between 1910 and 1935. The farm population had declined by 1954 to 22 million, with no accompanying retirement of land. The reduction in number of farms from 6.8 million in 1935 to 4.8 million in 1954 resulted in an increase in average size of farm from 155 to 242 acres. The changes were much greater in some areas. This meant that labor had to be moved out of agriculture, and land, labor, and capital had to be recombined into new operating units. These economic shifts took place during a period of prosperity, which made ownership easier. The proportion of farms operated by full owners and part owners consequently has increased relative to the proportion operated by tenants.

Four in 10 farms in the United States were operated by tenants in 1935. Fewer than a fourth were operated by tenants in 1954. A substantial part of the decline in the total number of farms is due to the reduction in number of tenants from 2.9 million in 1935 to 1.2 million in 1954. A third of the farmland was in tenant farms in 1935, but only a sixth of the farmland was in farms operated by tenants in 1954.

From about 1920 to 1930, while tenancy was going up, the number of full owners was going down. In the early thirties the depression had the effect of slowing off-farm migration. The number of full-owner farms increased to 3.2 million in 1935, but again declined to 2.7 million by 1954. Farmland operated by full owners increased until

1950, when it reached 418 million acres, but it fell to 395 million acres by 1954.

Part owners have increased almost continuously in number of farms and acres of farmland operated since they were first differentiated in the Census of Agriculture in 1900. This is the only tenure class that shows such an increase. From 1945 to 1954, the total number of farm operators declined by 1.1 million, while the number of part owners rose from 661 thousand to 857 thousand. Part owners are the only operators who, as a group, showed an increase of land in farms between 1950 and 1954. Part owners have accounted for a larger part of the farmland than any other tenure class since 1945.

Only for 1950 and 1954 are data available on the proportions of farmland rented and owned by part owners. The average part owner in 1950 owned 302 acres, rented 238 acres from others, and rented 28 acres to others; in 1945, he owned 319 acres, rented 244 acres from others, and rented 20 acres to others. Growth in the size of part-owner farms, therefore, is more or less balanced between owned and rented land.

Managers account for only a small number of farms, and the number in 1954—21 thousand—is the smallest recorded since data became available. The largest number of manager-operated farms was 68 thousand in 1920. Land in farms operated by managers, however, increased until 1945, when more than 106 million acres were managed. The acreage of manager-operated land dropped by 5 million acres between 1950 and 1954.

Corporation farms are included under manager farms. The decrease in manager farms suggests that the corporation as a form of tenure is becoming less important. From 1950 to 1954, when the average size of all other commercial farms was increasing, the average size of manager farms declined slightly. Although the average value of all farms increased, manager farms increased by a smaller percentage than those of any other tenure class. Except possibly for the poultry and fruit enterprises, there is little indication of widespread factory farming, which is generally associated with corporation farming.

Managers are currently important in the beef cattle industry. If consumers continue to prefer more meat products in their diets and if new techniques permit further expansion in farm and ranch size, managers may become even more important in the total of land they operate, if not in number.

THE IMPORTANCE OF TENURE and the adjustments required in the future will depend on the number of people who seek livelihoods in agriculture and the complexity of the agricultural production process. The number who seek rights in land will be determined by the number and relative profitableness of nonfarm employment opportunities. To the extent that well-paying nonfarm jobs exist in abundance and attract farm youth, the pressure on the tenure system to distribute rights in land is lessened.

The tenure system will have a large part in years to come in either facilitating or retarding adjustments in size of farms to accommodate new techniques of production.

The time element associated with the growing complexity of agricultural production will have an important bearing on the future role of tenure.

IN GENERAL, modern farming requires fairly long crop rotations, the use of more livestock, and a heavy investment in such durable items as livestock facilities, soil improvement, and water-control structures. They can be utilized fully only if the operator has stable and secure tenure. If our agriculture is to be efficient, increasing emphasis must therefore be placed on tenure arrangements that provide for a long period of expectations on the part of the operator and means of effectively reimbursing him for the unused value of these permanent improvements.

Trends in kinds and sizes of farms.

Technology has brought many changes to farms, farming, and farmers, and people are concerned about what is happening to family farms, which Americans traditionally have regarded as the seedbed of American life. In the broad perspective, there seems to be little evidence that efficient family farms cannot survive with larger farms. By *Kenneth L. Bachman,* head of the Production, Income, and Costs Section, Farm Economics Research Division, and *Jackson V. McElveen,* agricultural economist in that section.

MANY PERSONS have been worried about the changes that have been coming fast in the kinds and sizes of American farms.

As a Nation, we grew up believing in the values of farm life; in farming as a small, family enterprise; in the farmer's independence, self-sufficiency, and mental and physical strength.

Now, in less than a generation, we have seen the changes a technological revolution has made in our agriculture. Farms have become bigger and fewer. Fewer boys grow up on farms. Fewer families live on farms.

Farmers now produce primarily for the market and buy from the store much of their eggs and milk.

Many wonder whether family farms are giving way to large-scale employer units. Some fear that "factories in the field," which separate management and labor, and accumulations of land in relatively few, large holdings may be a result of the revolution in farming.

Others question whether the increasing investment needed and the larger cash costs that are associated with modern, highly specialized, commercially oriented agriculture will make it impossible for operators of family farms to compete in the adoption of new techniques.

In short, can the family farm survive? We cannot answer that question, for the answer depends on developments whose outcome we cannot foresee and on forces that we cannot or are unwilling to change. All we can do is to describe the forces.

They are part of the great social and economic change in the Nation. More jobs in nonfarm industries, trades, and service have led to shifts from farm to nonfarm occupations and have thereby facilitated the combination of farms. Shifts in concentrations of population and markets, changes in eating habits, and developments in processing and transporting farm products have affected the types of farming.

Present trends in the sizes of farms became evident before the First World War. By 1910 the settlement of western lands was virtually complete—the climax of a historical marvel in mass migration. Although the number of farms continued to increase until 1920, land frontiers were giving way to even greater technological frontiers.

The 1920's marked the beginning of the long and continuous transition from animal power to tractor power. The number of farms has declined steadily since 1920. Farming has moved toward greater specialization. Integration of production with financing, supply, or marketing functions has risen. Nonfarm employment has grown in importance: More than a fourth of all farm operators worked at off-farm jobs 100 or more days in 1954. That is more than twice the proportion of operators who worked off the farm in 1930.

In looking at the trends that have taken place since 1920, we will need to distinguish between the commercial farms—those operated primarily for income—and farms that serve mainly as part-time farming and residential units.

We estimate about a third of all farms were operated as part-time or residential units in 1958. These farms have increased both in number and as a proportion of all farms. The number of commercial farms has declined substantially. There were 4.7 million commercial farms in 1930—fewer than 3 million in 1958.

The Census of Agriculture provides the only source of comprehensive data on trends in kinds and sizes of farms. While 1954 is the most recent year for which census data are available, the indications are that the trends have continued since 1954.

We here deal primarily with commercial farms, which account for practically all—about 98 percent—of the market sales by farmers and for most of the farmland, machinery, and other capital investments.

As COMMERCIAL FARMERS shifted from animal to tractor power and began making use of a steady stream of improved farm machines, they and their families found they could handle larger acreages of crops and care for greater numbers of livestock. This is the essence of the process of consolidation of land into fewer commercial farms, which has progressed through depression and prosperity.

The commercial farms, although fewer in number, are larger in acreage—half again as large on the average in 1958 as in 1940—and in volume of products they sell. Not all are large farms, of course. Their average acreages range from a few acres to several thousand acres. What has happened is that there are now more farms of larger acreages and fewer farms of small acreages.

Among certain types of farms, however, acreage is becoming a minor factor in determining the size of operation. A large poultry farm, for instance, may have few acres, and a relatively small acreage of irrigated land may produce much more than a large acreage of dry rangeland.

The volume of farm products sold probably is the best indicator of the change in size. In terms of 1954 prices, the average volume of sales of commercial farmers has more than doubled since 1940.

During the 25-year period that ended in 1954, farms with a volume of farm products sold of 5 thousand dollars or more (in terms of 1954 dollars) grew in number. They comprised fewer than one-fifth of the farms in 1930 and about two-fifths in 1954. Farms that sold products worth at least 10 thousand dollars more than doubled in number.

Nearly all the commercial farms that did decline in number were those that produced less than 2,500 dollars' worth of products. This drop occurred both under the depressed economic conditions of the 1930's and during the prosperous postwar years. The rate of change has been much faster during the later years. Very likely these small farmers left for better jobs outside agriculture or else seized the chance to enlarge their farm business.

Much of the current concern about larger farms stems from the fact that increased mechanization of farming tends to induce larger operating units. The salient effect of mechanization on agriculture has been to cut the amount of work. Machines enable a given farmwork force to handle larger acreages and more livestock. It paves the way for increasing the size of farms.

Changes in the size of a farm have been closely related to mechanization of farm operations and improvements in technology. In wheat farming, significant increases in the size of farm occurred largely during the 1930's and early 1940's. Back of this increase was the development of the modern tractor and combine. In work capacity, the tractor could easily do the work of 20 to 25 horses. As the combine replaced horse-drawn binders, two men could do the harvest work that had previously required 12 to 15 men.

In the Corn Belt there was a steady stream of improved machines during this period, including the tractor, cornpicker, and now the picker-sheller, which picks, husks, and shells the corn. Added to this are the technical developments that have increased yields, such as hybrid corn and fertilizer. These developments have enabled the farmer in the Corn Belt to expand his operations in two directions—to handle more acres and to get a larger production per acre.

More recently, mechanization has become widespread in the Cotton Belt. The use of cotton strippers in Texas and Oklahoma and cottonpickers in the Delta and irrigated areas and the mechanization of preharvest operations have permitted a marked expansion in the production and acres of cotton that can be handled by one person. A 1-row cottonpicker can cover as much as 8 acres a day and harvest as much as 10 bales of cotton.

The evidence we have, however, does not indicate that the wage-operated, industrial type of farm is increasing. The rate of growth in size of commercial farms has been geared closely to the pace of invention and farmers' adoption of laborsaving and yield-increasing innovations.

THE AVERAGE FARMWORKER today produces 2.5 times more than his counterpart of a generation ago did. If we use this increase in a worker's output as a reflection of the difference in farm techniques in the two periods, we can view changes in size of farms over time in terms of today's farming techniques.

Such a measure has been applied to farms grouped by the value of the products they sell. Farms are classified as large scale, family scale, and small scale. Large-scale farms, as shown by this measure, are those that would produce a volume of products of more than 25 thousand dollars, with today's techniques and prices.

Small-scale farms would be those that would have a volume of sales of less than 2,500 dollars. The large-scale farms in general can be viewed as the farms that have a greater volume of business than could ordinarily be handled by the farm operator and members of his family. Small-scale farms can be viewed as those having a volume of business too small to employ a full-time worker who uses average farming practices.

Family farms, considered in this way, appear to be holding their own. The number of operations that are larger than family size has gone down. Although their number declined along with the overall decline in the total number of commercial farms, family farms and large-scale farms make up about the same proportion of commercial farms in 1958 as they did a quarter century earlier.

There has been no tendency toward increasing concentration of farmland or market sales in the larger units. Farmland and market sales since 1930 have been divided in approximately similar proportions between the large-scale and the family farms. There has been evidence since 1940 that operators of family farms have made a slight gain over those of large-scale farms in controlling land and market sales.

The much larger scale of operation on our commercial farms has not meant any significant tendency toward a general development of an industrial type of organization in agriculture. Estimated requirements for hired labor per commercial farm in 1958 were at approximately the 1930 level.

A problem in farm management— and one that has ordinarily been a limiting factor in the size of farm operations—is the supervision of labor in a variety of different farm tasks. These tasks are usually dispersed both within and without the boundaries of the farm. They vary with the seasons as well as the enterprises, and day-to-day modifications are the rule rather than the exception.

Mechanization has not appreciably reduced the number of specific farm tasks to be performed. Thus it has not increased the capacity of management for supervision of more farmworkers. Rather, it has reduced the need for so many farmworkers and enabled farmers to supervise a greater quantity of other farm resources.

The number and importance of family farms have been affected largely by the many adjustment problems that are found on the smaller units in commercial agriculture rather than by the encroachment of large-scale farming.

Operators of the larger farms have more nearly kept abreast of new machines and techniques. Their more favorable financial situations afforded greater freedom of choice. Because they depend mainly on hired labor to operate their farms, the rising farm wages that have resulted from the competition of nonfarm jobs stimulated the adoption of mechanical equipment as a substitute for labor.

Technological improvements in production practices have been associated with increasing disparity between the largest and smallest sizes of commercial farms. The substantial shift of farm families from commercial to part-time farming and the migration of others from agriculture to nonfarm occupations have resulted in no appreciable improvement in the farm organization of many small units that remain in commercial agriculture.

Operators of the smaller farms have been faced with the reality that mechanization could not increase incomes unless it was accompanied either by increases in the size of farm or reorganization of the farm. There was no strong economic incentive to substitute

445509°—58——21

machinery for labor as long as family members remained at home.

Small-scale farms—those with a volume of business too small to employ a full-time worker using average farming practices—have apparently grown in importance as a proportion of the commercial farms. Apparently a more serious problem than the threat of domination by large-scale farms exists in the failure of many farmers to take full advantage of developments in mechanization and technology.

CHANGES IN KINDS OF FARMS also are significant.

American agriculture has always been and will probably remain an industry in which individual units commonly carry on several enterprises. Diversification of enterprises makes for fuller use on most farms of land and labor resources. But the increase in the size of farms since 1930 has not meant more enterprises. Farmers instead have tended to concentrate on fewer enterprises.

During the depression and the production-control programs of the 1930's, little change occurred in the average number of enterprises on each farm. A definite trend has been evident since 1940, however. The number of major enterprises dropped by about a fourth during and since the war.

Many farmers since 1940 have eliminated small home-use enterprises, such as a family milk cow, a small flock of chickens, or the home orchard.

Other farmers have stopped producing feed for workstock and other livestock. The number of farmers reporting production of corn, for example, has reduced by about two-fifths since 1940. Increased purchases of gasoline, more use of tractors, and purchase of larger amounts of feed have replaced the feed enterprises on many farms.

At the same time, some farmers have found it profitable to specialize in commercial production of a few enterprises. Specialization in cotton farming, dairy farming, fruit and vegetable farming, and poultry farming has increased significantly.

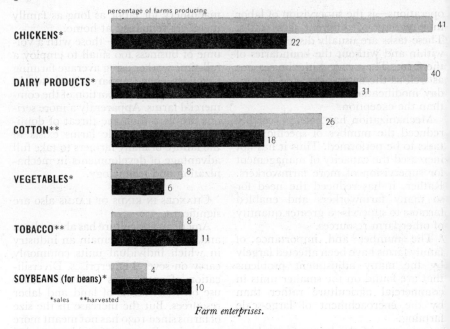

percentage of farms producing

CHICKENS*   41 / 22

DAIRY PRODUCTS*   40 / 31

COTTON**   26 / 18

VEGETABLES*   8 / 6

TOBACCO**   8 / 11

SOYBEANS (for beans)*   4 / 10

*sales   **harvested

Farm enterprises.

What has happened to the poultry enterprise is a good illustration. Only two-fifths as many farmers sold chickens in 1940 as in 1958. But during this period the number of farms with flocks of 400 or more chickens more than doubled.

As farms have become mechanized, farmers often are in the position of either enlarging an enterprise to permit efficient utilization of buildings, machinery, and equipment, or of cutting it out entirely. Modern machinery costs so much that it encourages farmers to develop enterprises on a scale that permits relatively full use of the machinery and equipment.

Most farm machines encourage some degree of specialization. An instance is in the Great Plains, where many farmers found that the use of a tractor increased the advantage in growing crops rather than in, say, dairying. New harvesters encourage production of small grains in some areas rather than the production of small grains and row crops at the same time. Milking machines and bulk tanks encourage larger

herds of dairy cows, but they do not increase directly the advantage of raising the feed on the farm.

Not all trends have been in the direction of increased specialization, however. Soybeans have become an additional crop on many farms in the Corn Belt. A greater percentage of the farmers grew tobacco in 1958 than in 1940.

Certain factors in buying supplies and in marketing also work in the direction of farm specialization. Farmers who produce large amounts of such products as broilers, milk, and vegetables can buy and sell more economically in quantity. The cost of assembly often can be reduced. A more uniform product may be possible. Feed may be bought more cheaply.

Changes have occurred in both costs of farming and the structure of the market for farm products. These have affected the organization of production and marketing functions, and, in turn, may influence both the sizes and kinds of farms in the future.

The use of such things as modern machinery, commercial fertilizers, and scientifically mixed feeds increases the farmers' cash outlays. This intensifies problems of finance. Markets for farm products have become highly specialized, demanding products of more exacting quality and in more uniform quantity throughout the seasons.

These and other developments in some situations have encouraged supply and marketing organizations to make contracts with farmers. These contracts usually involve agreements with respect to financing and purchase of supplies and sale of the product. Integration of production with related functions sometimes has meant that the operator gives up some management functions with respect to production methods, size of enterprise, and markets that used to be associated with the farmer.

The tendency toward vertical integration is most evident in some of the fruits and vegetables and in broiler production. Much of our fruit, vegetables, and poultry is produced on large, highly specialized farms. From class I farms—those that sell more than 25 thousand dollars' worth of farm products—we get about one-third of our poultry, more than one-half of our fruit, and one-half of our vegetables. In appraisal of this trend, however, one should bear in mind that the number of farmers who specialize in poultry, fruit, and vegetable production is not large. Only about 6 percent of the farms are classified in these types, and they account for about 15 percent of the value of farm products sold.

WHAT IS THE MEANING of these changes in the sizes and kinds of farms? Do they have implications for the future?

We need first to summarize and explain some of the basic reasons for the trends that have characterized farming since 1940.

Of first importance has been the availability of the technological innovations that increased a worker's output. Especially significant to the en-

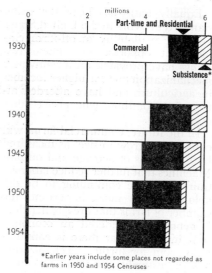

*Earlier years include some places not regarded as farms in 1950 and 1954 Censuses

Farms in the United States.

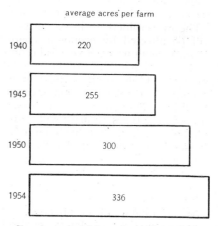

Size of commercial farms in the United States.

largement of the family farm were the mechanical inventions that encourage replacement of labor with capital. Many of the larger farmers found that they could reduce their hired labor considerably when they shifted to tractor operations and bought a combine, a cornpicker, or a milking machine.

Equally basic has been the rising standard of living in the United States and the availability of off-farm employment opportunities. These two things have provided an incentive for mechanization and for higher incomes in agriculture and have afforded alternatives for those who prefer other occupations.

In the future, commercial farms will continue to grow in size, as measured both in terms of acreage and output. Machines that further reduce labor requirements are continuing to be developed. Even more important, the number of farms that are smaller than is generally considered an economic unit indicates that there is considerable room for further mechanization and adjustments in farm size. The chances for the survival of small, low-income farms in a high-wage, full-employment economy are not bright. Family farms that are large enough to utilize modern machinery can be expected to continue to hold their own.

The rate of increase in size of farm will be affected by economic conditions. Agriculture each year is becoming more closely tied to the general economy. Opportunities to enlarge farms will be related to employment conditions in nonfarm occupations. Shifts in the types of farms will be related closely to the relatively large increases in the demands for livestock and fruit and vegetable products we foresee. That in turn may affect the trends toward specialization and vertical integration.

An additional aspect affecting the changes in sizes of farms revolves around the types of technological development that are forthcoming.

Some people believe that in the coming quarter century, innovations that increase crop and livestock yields may be more important than those that further reduce labor needs. These may provide more opportunities for development on small farms and encourage family farm operation. On the other hand, irrigation and other changes in methods of production in

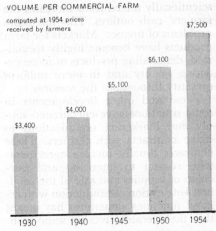

VOLUME PER COMMERCIAL FARM
computed at 1954 prices received by farmers

Farm products sold—volume per commercial farm.

some situations may greatly simplify management decisions, reduce the problems of supervising hired farmworkers, and work to the advantage of large-scale operations.

Getting into farming may be more difficult for the young man of tomorrow. Problems of financing and ownership take on increased significance.

Capital investments in agriculture have gone up greatly. In the past quarter century, the average investment per worker in agriculture more than trebled. In 1958, more than 18 thousand dollars of capital is associated with the average farmworker, as compared with less than 5 thousand dollars in 1930. A question of real concern is whether able young men with limited funds can get the capital needed for modern mechanized farming.

In the South, changes in the size of farms will be more closely tied to changes in the number of management units. With only a quarter of a million sharecropper units now classed as commercial farms, a further reduction will not be as large a factor in the next quarter century as it was in the past quarter century.

If the trends toward vertical integration continue, for example, they may exert a pull in the direction of larger farms in order to retain producer bargaining power and management responsibilities. Or, with other arrangements, a greater integration of production with the financing, supply, or marketing functions could bring some of the advantages of technical efficiency to small operations. Cooperative financing, marketing, and purchasing of farm supplies and products are being tried in some areas.

In the broad perspective of our whole agriculture, there appears to be little evidence that efficient family farms cannot survive with larger farms. Trends indicate that the scales to date have probably been tilted in the other direction. For the future, much will depend on the developments in institutions, educational services, financing, and farm policies.

The trouble seems to have been that we have assumed the idea of operator ownership of our farm lands to be synonymous with just private ownership. We have interpreted the freedom and opportunity of an individual to be master of his own farm to include not only his right to operate his farm by his own decisions, but to include the right of anyone to have pretty near 100-percent rights to encumber the property with debt, to sell it in whole or in part, to transmit it to others under all sorts of arrangements, to place whatever value might be set upon it.

In other words, having established the right of the individual farmer to operate his land as he pleased, we find that we also have established the right of moneylenders to write mortgages with terms that can never be met. We have also established the right of all and sundry to transfer lands at prices which can only mean misery and squalor for the family of the farmer who is going to have to pay those prices. We have also established the right of landlords to rent and farmers to lease land under terms which we now can only result in impoverishment both of the soil and of the farm family.

We have established the right of people to retire on the value of their farm like they would on the value of a bank-book, drawing not only on its annual income but also if necessary on its capital or asset value, as though the disappearance of a section of land were comparable to the disappearance of a bank-book balance. We have established the right of people to pulverize land titles and to complicate them so that the sheer burden of keeping the records straight becomes an unnecessary expense of our land system. Isn't it obvious that these so-called freedoms of our land system are something other than that freedom of private ownership of our farm land which our American ideal has always encompassed?

The real question is whether or not we can devise ways and means not to weaken but actually to strengthen and give assurance to the people who work our farms their right to find economic opportunity and equality and security in the holding of their land; and at the same time to find and to put into operation devices that will protect our land and the people who work it from these cumulative and self-destructive tendencies which operate when private ownership of the soil is interpreted to mean the right to use land titles as financial play-things, as though the title to an American farm should be just as much a pawn for commercial manipulation as a share of wildcat stock.

If we have the ingenuity to devise these ways and the courage and the interest to put them into effect, we need not abandon the idea of giving our farm people individual security and freedom in the operation of their farms. Nor will we jeopardize our sources of supplies of food and fibre; nor will we risk the deterioration of our natural resources. To attain the Jeffersonian ideal of rural democracy, we need not give up the whole idea of individual freedom, but we will have to keep individuality from running riot.—LEONARD A. SALTER, JR. The conclusion of an address presented at the Seventy-sixth annual meeting of the Wisconsin Academy of Science, Arts and Letters, April 1946, and published posthumously in the JOURNAL OF LAND & PUBLIC UTILITY ECONOMICS, November 1946.

Land and one of the farm programs.

Government adjustment and price-support programs are designed to help farm people. In which ways do the programs help big farmers, little farmers, tenants, sharecroppers? This chapter explains the operation of one program and gives part of the answer, without trying to influence opinion one way or another about this controversial issue. It leaves out several vital points, such as effects on consumers, costs, surpluses, and policies, because we are too close to the program to have the historian's objective, long-range view. By *Frank H. Maier*, Farm Economics Research Division.

How THE LAND is owned and operated determines which farms and farm people may come under one or another of the Government programs for agriculture. Tenure—the legal and the customary rights and obligations that say how, when, and by whom farmland is used—also may influence the ways that the benefits of public farm programs are distributed.

We speak in general terms about a farm program or the farm program. Actually, there are many farm programs, and they differ in several ways, because each was set up to deal with a problem that involves particular products or geographic areas.

Some of the programs influence the market prices of agricultural commodities by stabilizing prices or by increasing their average level or by doing both. Others provide direct cash payments to farm operators for reducing their production of certain products, for increasing their production of other products, or for employing certain desirable practices that conserve or increase soil fertility. Some programs pay for part or all of specific long-term capital improvements that increase the productivity and value of the farms. Some restrict the production of certain products. Others encourage greater production of specific products.

The only one I shall discuss here is the price-support and production-control program as it applies to the six so-called basic commodities—corn, wheat, rice, cotton, peanuts, and tobacco—each of which is handled in a somewhat similar, but not identical, way.

I single out this one because of its importance, the attention given it and the discussions it has evoked, its bearing on land tenure, and its value as an example of the influence farm programs may have on the prices of land.

THE PRICE-SUPPORT AND PRODUCTION-CONTROL PROGRAM was set up under the Agricultural Adjustment Act of 1938, whose purpose was ". . . to provide an orderly, adequate, and balanced flow of such commodities in interstate and foreign commerce. . . ."

The program affects the prices of each commodity by having the Government buy (or make a loan on) part of the crop and put it in storage when its price falls below a certain level and by inducing individual growers to comply with the restrictions the program sets on production of each commodity.

The idea of limiting agricultural production and supporting agricultural prices through Government action was tried in the depressed 1930's. The Agricultural Adjustment Act of 1938 made it mandatory to support—bolster—the prices of certain commodities and increased the importance of production controls in the improvement of agricultural prices and income. By the time the United States entered the war, we had surplus stocks of some basic commodities despite the controls over production.

The program was turned around during the Second World War and the Korean conflict and was used to increase production by guaranteeing farmers higher minimum prices. Wartime price controls also imposed ceiling prices, however. Heavy production of many price-supported crops since the Korean conflict has caused stocks to increase. Production controls and expanded price-support activity became necessary again.

Under the price-support and production-control program in 1958, five of the six basic commodities—wheat, rice, cotton, peanuts, and tobacco— may be put under a strong type of curb on production when surpluses of the commodity threaten. One commodity, corn, may be put under a mild type of check on production.

Farmers who receive allotments to grow a specific crop vote in a special referendum on whether they prefer the strong type of limitation on production. If they give their approval, individual farmers are subject to both acreage allotments and marketing quotas. Cooperators—farmers who plant only their allotted acreage—are eligible for price support on their entire crop. A farmer who plants more than his allotted acreage loses the price support on his entire crop. Such a noncooperator must also pay a penalty on production from the acreage in excess of his allotment.

The mild type of limitation on production involves acreage allotments without marketing quotas. If a farmer who is subject only to acreage allot-

ments chooses to plant in excess of his allotment, he merely loses the price-support privileges available to cooperators and does not have to pay a penalty on excess production. Acreage allotments without marketing quotas may be used for any crop, but actually they have been used only to a limited extent. This mild type of check on production was used only for corn in the mid-1950's.

Let us consider first how the price-support program operates for commodities that may be put under acreage allotments with marketing quotas—the strong type of limitation on production.

When surpluses of a basic commodity reach a specified level, the law requires that the Secretary of Agriculture proclaim marketing quotas for the commodity and announce a reduced rate of national production as a goal for the country. The national acreage from which such a reduced national production may be expected is then apportioned among the various growers of this crop. The acreage allotted each farm depends on its past production and, to a lesser degree, on such other considerations as soil, topography, crop rotation, and number of tillable acres.

Farmers with allotments to grow the crop then participate in a secret vote to approve or disapprove marketing quotas for the crop during the coming year. If more than a third of the farmers disapprove of quotas, the only benefits available to those who comply with their acreage restrictions are price supports at a low level—50 percent of parity. No penalty payments are imposed on marketings from acreage in excess of a farmer's allotment.

(The parity price of a farm commodity measures the commodity's purchasing power. It is the price at which the commodity would have to sell at a particular time to have the same purchasing power in buying what farmers purchase at that time as it had in an earlier base period.)

If at least two-thirds of the farmers vote approval of a program, its most liberal price-support benefits become available to all farmers who plant within their acreage allotments during the year. For such farmers, the Government, through the Commodity Credit Corporation, supports prices by purchasing their crops at support prices or by lending the farmers the full value of the crop at support prices. A grower who receives a loan may repay it or give to the Government the crop that was collateral for the loan, whichever he prefers.

Growers who plant more than the acreages allotted to them under the program lose price-support benefits for their entire crop. They must also pay a penalty on marketings from acreage planted in excess of their allotment—45 to 75 percent of the value of such production, depending on the commodity.

Wheat is handled differently. Every farmer in the commercial wheat area may grow 15 acres without being subject to a marketing quota, but some wheat growers may have smaller acreage allotments: A farmer whose acreage allotment is less than 15 acres can get price support only if he plants within his allotment. If he exceeds his allotment, he must pay a penalty only on the wheat produced from acreage in excess of 15 acres.

Farmers in States outside the commercial wheat area are not subject to curbs on production of wheat. They may plant as much wheat as they like, as long as too many of them do not increase production enough to bring their State into the commercial wheat area. All such wheat grown outside the commercial area is eligible for price support at a level somewhat lower than that available to cooperators within the commercial wheat area.

A mild type of production control—acreage allotments without marketing quotas—is applied to corn. Legislation in 1949 specified that corn cannot be put under quotas. Farmers in the commercial corn area who plant corn on acreage in excess of their allotments give up the price-support privileges

available to cooperators and are not subject to penalties on excess production. In 1956 and 1957, however, even noncooperators were given price support but at a lower level than cooperators.

Farmers in counties outside the commercial corn area are not under acreage allotments. They may plant as much corn as they choose and are eligible for price support at a somewhat lower level than that available to cooperators in the commercial corn area. If many farmers in a county outside the commercial corn area increase their corn acreages, they may cause their county to be declared a commercial corn county for the following year; as a consequence, they would then be under acreage allotments for corn.

THE PROGRAM of price supports and production controls influences farming in two ways.

First, it tends to raise the average level of the prices of the six commodities over the years because limitations on the volume of production tend to keep supplies lower than would otherwise be the case.

Second, the supports and controls tend to stabilize the prices of the six products by reducing year-to-year fluctuations. When the price of a basic crop begins to fall below a certain point, the Government bolsters its price by purchasing and storing some of the commodity. The Government later disposes of its stocks of such stored commodities as best it can.

Who benefits from the price-support and production-control program for the basic commodities?

An important part of the price-raising benefits appears to go to the persons who acquire the "rights" to produce each crop.

A program has to try to limit production of a crop if it is to raise the long-run average price of the commodity (above what it otherwise would have been) and still not accumulate surpluses.

Such restrictions on production take the form of limitations on the number of farmers with acreage allotments and on the acreage each farmer grows. The greater the price-increasing benefits of a program, the wider will be the gap between the quantity of the crop that farmers would like to produce at the higher price and the quantity that is consumed at that price.

Under a program that raises the price of a crop by limiting its production, the right to grow the crop really becomes a production license, or franchise, created by the program. In order to be able to grow such a controlled crop and receive the price-support benefits while avoiding the payment of whatever penalties are imposed on noncooperators, a farmer must possess the intangible license to produce it under the program. A good part of the price-raising benefits of the program therefore is likely to be obtained by farmers able to get these rights to produce—the acreage allotments.

As the program for the six crops was operating in 1958, the right to produce those crops was coupled with the control and use of land. The advantage of such an arrangement is its ease of administration. Because it is not hard to determine who has the use of land, it is a simple matter to decide who can grow a crop under the program. Land on which a basic crop was produced during a particular past base period is given an acreage allotment. The size of a person's allotment is roughly proportional to production of the controlled crop in the base period.

Persons who own farmland with an allotment may be expected to obtain for themselves an important part of the price-raising benefits of the program because the allotment for a particular farm is "owned" and its use is controlled by the person who owns the land. Landowners can obtain part of the price-raising benefits in various ways under different farm-tenure arrangements.

When a landowner does not use the allotment by operating the farm himself but instead rents out the farm, as the landlord he will tend to be in a stronger bargaining position and may be able to demand a higher rent than if there were no program limiting production and raising the prices of the crop under the program. While the tenant is likely to get a part of the price-raising benefits, an appreciable part is also likely to go to the landlord in the form of larger rental receipts.

The exact proportions in which the benefits are shared on a particular plot of land depend on a number of things—the "stickiness" or flexibility of customary rental arrangements, how well farm people are informed about rental opportunities, the way a program is administered, and the opportunities in farming in a community.

A landlord can increase the rent by insisting on some change in the rental arrangement, because he is the one who has the acreage allotment and is therefore in a stronger bargaining position. He can press the tenant to accept changes in the terms of the lease that are favorable to him. A tenant under a crop-share lease might be asked to pay a share of costs that the landlord formerly paid in full. A landlord might ask the tenant to pay for the milk, meat, or other farm products that formerly he had been furnished free. Under a crop-share-cash lease, the cash rental on pastureland might be increased, or, with a cash lease, the rent could be increased.

A farmer who had title to the land he farmed when such a program was set up gets most of the price-raising benefits that flow from the program. The farm family owns the land and with it the acreage allotment, furnishes most of the labor, and provides the management. The family therefore receives all returns except those to hired labor, borrowed capital, and purchased operating items. Since the type of farm program we are discussing is unlikely to increase appreciably either hired wage rates, interest rates to farm borrowers, or the prices of purchased farm inputs, the owner-operator who already had his land when the program was initiated will receive most of the benefits from the long-term rise in crop prices.

Over a period of time, however, a shifting of program benefits between sellers and buyers of land is possible. Landowners who bought their land after a program began probably do not get so large a share of the price-raising benefits of the program as persons who, when the program was first set up, happened to own land that received acreage allotments.

When a program is expected to continue into the future, the right to receive future benefits is a valuable right in the form of an acreage allotment that is transferred from one individual to another as a tie-in with the sale of farmland. When such farmland is sold, its selling price will probably be somewhat higher than it would otherwise have been, so as to include at least some part of the expected future benefits.

The person who owned farmland when the land was assigned an acreage allotment therefore will receive a windfall gain when he sells the land with its allotment. He will profit in this way to the extent that expected later benefits of the program are capitalized into the prices of such land. Probably only a part of the price-raising benefits of the program will be reflected in higher selling prices for land having an allotment, because the future of the program is not certain.

Persons who buy such land after some of the future price-raising benefits of the program have been capitalized into farmland prices must therefore pay higher prices than would prevail without the program. These later purchasers—owner-operators or landlords, as the case may be—are paying in advance for a part of the future benefits of the program. To this extent a program that raises the long-run average level of crop prices increases the amount of capital that later owners must put into their farms.

Thus it is not always obvious which persons actually benefit from a long-term increase in prices of crops under a price-support and production-control program.

The tobacco program illustrates how a price-support and production-control program may push up the price of land that has an acreage allotment. The view is widely held in flue-cured and burley tobacco regions that the value of a tobacco allotment in the mid-1950's averaged more than 1 thousand dollars an acre. A farm with a 4-acre tobacco allotment may sell for about 4 thousand dollars more than it would have brought without such an allotment. Buyers of land with a tobacco allotment thus pay in advance for at least a part of the later benefits to be had from the right to grow tobacco.

THE PRICE-STABILIZING aspects of the program even out short-run fluctuations in crop prices by making season-to-season price changes smaller than they would have been without it.

Who gets the price-stabilizing benefits? Whereas an important part of the price-raising benefits of the existing program tends to go to land, the other production factors seem to share more fully in its price-stabilizing features.

Less uncertainty about future prices makes more efficient production possible because when crop prices are more stable it is easier for operators to employ practices that reduce cost of production and to risk the investment necessary for adoption of the new farming methods. More stable prices also tend to make the returns of operators, farmworkers, and sharecroppers less changeable from year to year than these would otherwise be.

One final aspect should be mentioned. People come to expect the continuance of a program that has existed for a number of years. The sudden end of a program would disrupt the economic life of many agricultural areas, and would mean sudden capital losses for persons who had purchased farmlands with acreage allotments at prices that reflected the expected future benefits of the program.

Taking care of what we have
—The wise use of our resources—Where farmers can get the help they need—Technical assistance for landsmen—The uses and values of soil tests—Some new jobs for irrigation—Wanted: Partnership to manage water—Protecting watersheds: Ways and whys—The classification of rural land—Group action to develop and protect land—A new program for better living—Information on land from airphotos

The wise use of our resources.

Conditions require that the United States maintain a strong resource base to meet whatever the future brings. Our population is growing about 1.7 percent each year. The drain on our land, forests, and water grows greater each year. The demand per capita for water, for example, has been increasing 3 percent a year. Our resources should be used—but used wisely. By *John F. Timmons*, professor of agricultural economics, Iowa State College, and *Elmer L. Sauer*, research liaison representative, Department of Agriculture, Urbana, Ill.

CONSERVATION means the wise use of resources. It includes several elements: Economical output of goods and services from land and water in accordance with needs; the particular goods and services that people want; and a continued flow of products and services indefinitely into the future.

This idea of conservation means that resources should be used—but used for the maximum benefit of man both now and in the future. The use of land resources must be geared to the demands of consumers in terms of the kinds, amounts, and qualities of goods and services forthcoming from our lands. Costs of units of goods and services must be rendered as low as technology and continued productivity will permit.

Land resources include all the attributes that go with a particular space of the earth. Soils, water, climate, vegetation, wildlife, and location are all resources of land.

The use of land and water takes place within three dimensions—physical, economic, and legal. Each dimension is interlaced with the others.

The physical dimension is concerned with what is possible in terms of land uses. It deals with kinds of plants, yields of various plants, yields of specific plants with different seeding rates,

cultivation methods, applications of water, and fertilizers and the rates of applying them.

It also includes effects of various practices, such as contouring, stripcropping and mulching, and land investments, such as terracing and water-retention structures and their effects upon runoff, erosion, siltation, infiltration, crop yields, and the like.

The physical range of possibilities of conservation is being extended constantly through research and developments in technology.

Before recommendations about the use of land may be made, we must consider the economic dimension, which includes the prices of products, costs of productive factors, and relationships between and among products and the labor and capital needed to get them.

The economic possibilities of conservation are constantly changing through prices, which reflect changing demands of consumers, and through costs or profits, which reflect scientific developments and other conditions.

Finally, attention must be given to the legal dimension, which tells us what is legally permissible.

Suppose a river is big enough to supply 5 inches of water on 5 thousand acres of a crop. That is the physical possibility of the water available. The costs of applying the water in relation to the prices of the products grown, however, may mean that only 3 inches of water can be used profitably. That represents the economic feasibility. The river, though, is in a State where the use of water is governed by the riparian doctrine and irrigation is considered an artificial use. The natural uses of water for people and livestock, sanitary purposes, and the like do not permit any water to be used for an artificial use—irrigation. Therefore it would not legally be permissible to use any of the water for irrigation, according to the legal dimension.

The legal dimension consists of a set of rules, customs, and laws that were made by man and may be changed by man to fit the needs of conservation of land and water resources. But the laws in the example must be changed before any of the water could be used for irrigation of crops.

Land and water resources vary in their origin, availability, and nature. That is particularly true of soils, water, and plantlife—the principal agricultural land resources.

Two groups of land resources are basic—flow and fund.

Flow resources—like rainfall—become available in certain amounts each year.

Fund resources are stored-up productivity available for use. Certain soils and forests fit this characteristic.

Fund and flow are based on the amount of resources available, the amount of resources becoming available periodically, and the possibilities that the resources may be renewed and restored.

Inexhaustible resources include certain soil elements and underground water reservoirs that appear sufficient to meet all future demands. We have no reason now to be concerned about conservation of inexhaustible resources. That does not mean that demands at some distant time may necessitate a reclassification of these resources—only that their conservation is not important

at the moment. Water in humid areas has been in this class, but we are reclassifying them because of rapidly increasing demands.

Flow resources become available periodically regardless of use. If they are not used when they are available, they—like rainfall—disappear through evaporation and streamflow. Flow resources may be used either as they become available or, within limits, may be stored for future use.

Exhaustible but renewable resources may be depleted currently, although they may be renewed by human action. An example is forests. Trees may be cut, and the forest may be used up— or the forest may be renewed through replantings. Some elements in soil, such as nitrogen, phosphate, calcium, and humus, may be exhausted through use, but they may be added again in fertilizers and amendments.

Exhaustible but nonrenewable resources may be exhausted through current use and may not be renewable through human action within economic limits. An example is a shallow soil underlain by hard rock, wherein the soil is permitted to erode. Severe gullying on deeper soils may bring exhaustion.

Composite resources include characteristics of each of the classes. Certain soils have several characteristics, some of which are inexhaustible, some are flow in nature, and some are exhaustible—while other characteristics are exhaustible but nonrenewable.

Thus the important classes for conservation purposes are the exhaustible but renewable resources, the exhaustible but nonrenewable resources, and exhaustible elements of composite resources.

As to the exhaustible resources, we can identify two limits of conserving use. The limits apply to both renewable and nonrenewable exhaustible resources.

A lower limit of use is the point where renewability cannot be achieved economically. For example, excessive erosion should never be permitted to proceed to the point where the productivity of the soil cannot be regained through an economic investment of resources.

An upper limit may be identified as nonuse or investment in improvement beyond what appears to be justified by present and potential demand for products and services coming from the resources. An example would be not to use virgin soils.

The desired levels of use might be well within these two limits at any particular time.

Within the two limits, three choices are available: Investment, the expenditure of funds on land and water resources in order to increase their future productivity; maintenance, the expenditure of funds on resources in order to maintain their current productivity indefinitely; and disinvestment, the mining of the resource so that current production reduces future productivity.

Whether we should invest, maintain, or disinvest in particular land resources depends on whether one or the other is economic or uneconomic. The criterion is the maximum output of the products and services people demand and will demand at the least cost per unit of product.

THE ECONOMICS of investment, maintenance, and disinvestment varies with the interests of the individual users of the resource, groups of users, and the public. The interests may or may not be in conflict.

Problems arise when the individual's interests conflict with group and public interests. A tenant with a 1-year lease, for example, may want to plant intertilled crops and disregard conservation practices because he feels his profits will be greatest, regardless of whether he may cause water and silt damage to farms lower in the watershed and damage to the farm he operates.

Another example is a farmer who may plow a steeply rolling meadow because he can realize more profit for a few years from that land in corn or cotton than in meadow, although farmers and public interests farther down the watershed are damaged from more runoff and siltation.

A third example of levels of economic interest is a large water-retention structure on a subwatershed of the Little Sioux River in western Iowa. Neither the individual farmer nor the farmers in the subwatershed could afford to build and maintain the structure, but the public might afford the investment because damages from flooding downstream would be less.

FARMERS ARE INTERESTED in conservation as a means of obtaining larger future incomes. Most farmers are interested also in increasing current incomes. Present farming systems often need to be changed. To do so may require the outlay of additional capital and a temporary reduction in current income. The fact is, however, that in most sections this reduction in current income soon is more than offset by increased production and income resulting from the conservation measures.

A random sample of Illinois operators of cash-grain farms who followed recommended soil-conserving rotations and other appropriate conservation practices in 1955 spent about 50 percent more for fertilizer and land improvements than farmers with similar land who did not follow a recommended conservation program. Net returns were 32 dollars an acre for the conservation farms, compared with 2? dollars an acre for the others.

High-conservation farms in northeastern Illinois in 1950–1955 earned ? dollars to nearly 8 dollars an acre a year of net income more than comparable low-conservation farms. The total capital expenses for conservation and related improvements were about twice as great on the high-conservation farms. As an indication that farmer are convinced that investments in land improvements and fertilizers pay, the high-conservation farms more than doubled their expenditures for these improvements in the 5 years.

A study of the Crab Orchard Lake watershed in Illinois in 1954 showed that total cost of establishing the recommended conservation programs would amount to an average of 38 dollars an acre for the watershed. The average annual total value of crops would be boosted from 11 dollars to 21 dollars an acre by applying recommended conservation programs. Thus, in this relatively low-income area, only 4 years of increased production resulting from the conservation program would pay for the cost of establishing it.

A survey in Illinois in 1954 showed that contour farming should increase net returns by 5.45 dollars an acre because it would permit a more intensive rotation while holding soil losses to a minimum. Stripcropping should increase net returns by 6.66 dollars an acre and terracing by 10 dollars.

For sloping land, farmers may choose to keep a high proportion of land in hay and pasture crops or use terraces, stripcropping, contouring, and other conservation practices and put a higher proportion of land in intertilled crops. Livestock farmers may choose the first alternative because they have a market for their forage crops. Grain farmers may rely more heavily on terracing and other conservation measures.

A 10-year study in three Midwestern areas demonstrates that higher farm production and better earnings were the measurable results of soil conservation practices. Longtime benefits of soil conservation were significant in each area studied. Conservation and improvement practices generally increased production and income the first year. If the land was badly eroded and depleted, however, much effort, money, and time had to be expended to build productivity to a high level.

On the individual Illinois farms studied, the total costs of conservation practices were 20 to 50 dollars an acre. At 1954 prices, the 10-year average net earnings of farms with conservation plans were 6 dollars an acre higher each year than those on matched farms not having such plans. This difference

was about 1 thousand dollars a year for a 160-acre farm, or about 1 hundred dollars a month more net income for a farm of average 180-acre size in the area studied.

A 10-year study in southwestern Illinois disclosed that high-conservation farms had almost twice the total expenditures of low-conservation farms with similar land resources and types of farming for items such as machinery, buildings and equipment, livestock, and direct conservation expenses. The high-conservation farms had a 10-year average annual expenditure of 7.09 dollars an acre more than the low-conservation farms, or 1,219 dollars more per farm. They also had an average annual net income of 8.36 dollars per acre more than the low-conservation farms, or 1,438 dollars more per farm.

Thus, although more conservation may boost total expenses, returns from the additional farm production are usually large enough to offset the added cost. The economic use of capital must be determined on an individual farm basis. Improved management is needed along with the use of more capital.

Changes in income on the farms studied varied with the condition of the farm when the program started, the speed at which the program was applied, the kinds and amounts of fertilizer used, the weather, and the quality of management of the owner and the operator.

Landlords and tenant farmers frequently overemphasize quick returns. Landlords who do this, however, often find their farms disinvested and their income in later years reduced. Tenants, too, find that their abilities to succeed as farmers and to rent highly productive farms depend on their acceptance of systems of farming that insure longtime high production.

Some conservation measures may not work out as expected because of adverse weather or because they are poorly adapted to the individual farm. Farmers need to get the best advice available, and they may also need to do some experimenting. For this reason, it is probably best to work gradually with the conservation plan rather than make a heavy investment all at one time. This is particularly important to farmers who may be in debt.

Data on the costs and benefits of conservation on farms in other Midwestern States and other areas of the United States indicate results similar to those shown in the studies in Illinois.

Dollars and cents alone do not always determine what farmers can and will do about conservation. Insofar as they can afford it, farmers with a sense of stewardship take broader values into account when they make decisions regarding conservation on their farms.

THE SUCCESS OF SOIL CONSERVATION programs often depends on local responsibility and leadership. Good decisions and application of sound conservation programs on individual farms result in progress in soil conservation in those communities. Soil conservation districts provide an opportunity for local leadership to be effective in soil and water conservation programs. Watershed programs are a means of using group action to get complete soil and water conservation on the land combined with supplemental mechanical measures that will help to reduce flood and sedimentation damages both on and off the watershed.

Farmers often can solve their conservation problems by working together. Erosion does not stop at farm boundaries—neither does the flow of water.

There are many examples of group activity that have resulted in conservation—the community approach program in two Illinois communities (Odell and Rankin) was particularly effective in soil conservation and farm improvement, through youth work, vocational agriculture and 4–H, community fairs and demonstrations, and the working together of churches, schools, local organizations, farmers and businessmen.

Numerous parish groups, such as Island Grove, Ill., Villa Ridge, Mo., and Westphalia, Iowa, are examples of where leadership, vision, and understanding on the part of local ministers have made the communities "oases in the desert" in soil and water conservation and farm improvement.

The expanding watershed and other approaches to our problems of conserving resources intensify the importance of soil surveys to determine land capabilities, conservation farm and ranch planning, conservation education, and treatment and use of all lands within their needs and capabilities.

Further studies are needed to provide a complete and reliable survey of United States soil and water resources, and long-term plans and investments for the conservation and use of these resources. In developing and carrying out these studies, we need continued teamwork among all agencies and interests, including private and governmental; local, State, and Federal; research, technical, and educational.

FARMERS alone cannot assume the national responsibility for conservation. That must rest on all of the people if the public wishes to achieve the conservation of land and water.

Conservation must be supported as a basic national policy just as defense, public health, education, roads, and other measures for the benefit of all.

The national inventory of soil and water conservation needs under way in 1958, which includes every county in the United States, will provide some of the basic facts about the amount and kind of measures needed to protect and improve our resources.

As an indication of the concern of the Congress with the conservation of our national soil and water resources, the House passed a bill on April 17, 1957, to put the Agricultural Conservation Program on a permanent basis. Under the program—now scheduled to expire December 31, 1958—farmers receive partial reimbursements (a total of about 250 million dollars annually) from the Government for carrying out approved conservation practices.

Where farmers can get the help they need.

Modern land management and the public interest call for skills and resources that some farmers do not have. Several programs have been developed to assist them. By *Virgil D. Gilman,* extension economist, Federal Extension Service; *James M. Hunt,* director, Program Analysis Division, Agricultural Conservation Program Service; and *D. Harper Simms,* director, Information Division, Soil Conservation Service.

THE LANDSCAPE of farmed and forested America has been undergoing its greatest change since the prairies and forests first yielded to the plow and ax.

Perhaps we can even say that the day of exploitation, when the soil was mined, water was taken for granted, and forests were despoiled, is past, that the day of conservation has come, and people know how to take care of Nature's bounty.

Water storage is an example. Talk with any 10 farmers, and the chances are that one or more of them will have a new farm pond to talk about. (Farmers and ranchers in 1957 built more than 80 thousand ponds to provide water for livestock, fire protection, erosion control, and recreation.)

And if not a pond, most of the 10 farmers will have other improvements to tell about. They will show you land actually reshaped in one way or another for better farming—leveled for more efficient irrigation, terraced to hold rainfall, and contour plowed and stripcropped to save soil and water.

They will show you poor or wornout cropland being converted to pasture or trees. They will point out acres of good rangeland, wrested from worthless scrub and brush, reseeded, properly grazed, well fenced, and watered.

They will point to tile or open drains, which have improved pasture or cropland. They will show you thickets, ponds, and marshes developed for wildlife, a farm crop that yearly assumes more importance.

They will show you meandering streams that are being straightened and held in place by streambank plantings or masonry revetments. They will take you to detention dams that catch and release safely what would otherwise be runoff of flood proportions in the upper watersheds.

They will show you tree shelterbelts and stripcropping for the control of wind and water erosion. They will show you these singly and in combinations according to the needs of the land and the opportunities to put modern techniques of land management into operation.

Ask why this is done, and you hear about one aspect or another of the changes in agriculture in the last 50 years—changing patterns of farming, startling developments in machinery, rising requirements of capital investment, cost-price squeeze, the evolution of the modern commercial family farm, pressures of increasing competition, and other factors that affect output and income.

One fact stands out clearly: Today's successful farm or ranch operator has to take advantage of every possible development in soil and water conservation, land improvement and management techniques, as well as new varieties of crops, new fertilizers, pesticides, new marketing techniques, and other advances not directly related to land improvement.

Stay with the subject a little longer and you will find that these are technically sound practices on which farmers get information and help from county agents, conservation technicians, other agricultural representatives, and publications. They are installed scientifically. Modern land management calls for many skills the farmer has not time to acquire, the large and growing number of college-trained farmers notwithstanding. It calls also for a rapid, effective means of keeping up with new developments in technology and management.

Because of this need for help in various aspects of land treatment and management, a number of programs of assistance have evolved that are available to the farmer and the rancher. Indeed, knowing how and where to get such specialized help is an important requisite of farming today.

Some of the services are available from local professional consultants, management companies, and similar commercial sources. A growing number of State government agencies, such as State forestry departments and State game and fish departments, are providing technical services free of charge to farmers. Farm-equipment companies, commodity organizations, and other commercial firms sometimes offer free services to their customers.

Most of the help farmers get on land improvement and management measures comes through the United States Department of Agriculture and the land-grant colleges. Programs of research, education, cost sharing, credit, and technical assistance bring to the farmer information, consultive, and facilitating services that enable him to improve the efficiency and quality of his farming.

These advisory and technical services are provided primarily from public funds. Participation is voluntary, and the aim is to assist the individual in doing parts of his job that he cannot do entirely by himself. At the same time, however, the programs work for the public good. For example, the costs of installing the practices are borne mainly by farmers, but cost-sharing provisions of certain conservation programs may be used by farmers to help defray the cost of practices which have widespread benefit but which would be seriously delayed if Government aid were not available.

Price-support programs, crop insurance, marketing services, other general economic programs, and programs of livestock and crop improvement are other forms of assistance that affect farm income and are important features of American agriculture.

THE HELP AVAILABLE in land use and treatment from the Department of Agriculture and the land-grant colleges is of three general types.

General educational assistance is a function carried on primarily by the county agents of the State extension services working with farmers. Their information comes largely from the State agricultural experiment stations and the Agricultural Research Service.

Technical assistance in conservation of soil and water is provided mainly by technicians of the Soil Conservation Service through local soil conservation districts, watershed protection projects, and the Great Plains Conservation Program.

Cost-sharing and credit facilities are provided from several sources in the Department of Agriculture. Cost sharing for certain land-use adjustments and conservation practices is available through the Agricultural Conservation Program, the Great Plains Conservation Program, and the Soil Bank.

Loans for soil and water conservation are available to farmers through the credit program of the Farmers Home Administration.

Educational assistance is available to farmers and ranchers for their use with specific techniques of soil and water management, crop and livestock improvement, and problems of business management.

The amount of scientific information on land-use practices has itself become something of a problem. Not only is it voluminous; much of it is fairly technical and not ready for use in specific situations without further interpretation or adaptation. The educational program of the Department and the land-grant colleges was designed to meet this problem. The program includes counsel on technical land-use practices such as fertilizer use, crop rotations, irrigation, drainage, contour cropping, terracing, and developing water supplies, as well as on general farm and home management, crop varieties, animal husbandry, marketing, family nutrition, and the study of public policy problems.

Farmers work with county agents in observing what the experiment stations and the research branches of the Department have learned. Farmers also work with one another in observing one another's experiences and in adapting these land-use practices to their individual situations. This educational process of observing and making comparisons provides the vital link between research and farm operation.

A great part of the research work and a still greater part of the educational programs are set up on a local basis, with offices and representatives readily accessible to farm people. Farmers themselves take an active part in working with representatives of the colleges and the Department in determining the land-use problems to be studied in the educational program. Farmers also assist in planning a county program of educational activities that brings the results of scientific research and the experience of farmers to bear on local problems.

An important phase of the educational assistance available to farmers is information on business problem questions for which they often want counsel: How much and what kind of land is required for the different purposes; whether to own or to rent land; the selection of machinery; planning layouts of fences and buildings; and the capital and labor requirements and returns from alternative types of farming. Young men beginning to farm and townspeople thinking of a home on the land can get guidance that may prevent mistakes.

All farmers can obtain information on methods of planning a farm business so as to compare costs and returns to be expected from different combinations of crops. Similar assistance is available for comparing different kinds of livestock as to land, feed, and water requirements, and possible costs and returns to be expected.

The various agricultural programs are described in order that farmers may know of them and consider the alternatives for participation.

In using information of this type, farmers can consider and work out major changes in land use. Depending on the area, this might include the development of substantial feed-crop acreages and feed reserves to meet drought. It might involve the development of new cropland through irrigation, clearing or drainage, or the more intensive use of present cropland. It could lead to an analysis of the possibilities for going out of farming by shifting all cropland to grass or trees or the sizing up of possibilities for enlarging the acreage of an existing unit that is too small.

This cooperative educational program is centered in a local agricultural extension service, which is part of a statewide and nationwide Cooperative Extension Service, organized and operated by the land-grant colleges in cooperation with local county governments and the Department of Agriculture. The county agent is the local representative. His office, usually in the county seat, is a source of information on many types of land-use problems.

THE GREAT GROWTH of technology in the use of soil and water and in the management of plants has brought a need for specialized technical services to help landowners and operators plan and carry out the more difficult conservation practices.

Problems of land improvement and conservation usually cannot be solved by generalized techniques. Problems differ from farm to farm. The solutions often require the combining of information from two or more fields such as soils, engineering, agronomy, range management, forestry, biology, hydrology, geology, and economics.

They often require the propagation and testing of new or improved plants for use in conservation and a planned sequence of practices and land-use adjustments.

Thus the role of the soil conservationist is to provide technical data about soils on a particular farm or ranch and about alternative uses and treatments which the land user can choose in light of that basic information. The technician also helps to plan and apply the combination of practices that is determined by the needs and capabilities of the land and the farmer's or rancher's desires and decisions.

Technical services of this type are furnished to about 2 million farmers and ranchers in connection with soil and water conservation programs they carry out in cooperation with the Department of Agriculture.

The Soil Conservation Service was established in 1935 to provide these services. Its technicians give aid in accordance with individual farm or ranch conservation plans primarily through some 2,780 soil conservation districts, which comprise about 93 percent of the Nation's farm and ranch land. (The Soil Conservation Service also has leadership for a nationwide watershed protection and flood-prevention program, which is discussed later. Similarly, another chapter provides detail about soil conservation districts.)

The development and application of a typical plan involves four steps.

First, from soil survey data that have been gathered on an acre-by-acre basis, a land-capability map is prepared for the farmer who has asked his soil conservation district for help. The map is superimposed on an aerial photograph of the land surface of the farm or ranch. After the soil survey data have served to identify soil types, slope, extent of erosion, and similar characteristics, an interpretation is made that classifies each parcel of land as to the uses to which it may be put safely and productively and the intensity of treatment required.

From this a conservation plan is developed by the farmer. It provides for the use and treatment of the land within its needs and capabilities. In developing his plan, the farmer or rancher considers various alternatives of use and treatment of the land. It includes what he plans to do with his soil and water and what he hopes to accomplish in conservation and use of his cultivated land, grassland, and woodland.

A third step is application of the uses and measures called for in the plan. One or more conservation technicians assist in laying out the drainage and water disposal systems, irrigation systems, farm ponds, terrace systems, diversions and waterways, and contouring and stripcropping. Help is given as needed in the establishment of improved pastures and good range use; in the use of crop residues, cover crops, grasses, legumes, trees, and shrubs for erosion control and moisture conservation; in improvement of wildlife habitat; and in woodland management, as each of these practices fits into a well-rounded conservation program.

Since conservation practices need to be maintained, a fourth type of aid to conservation-program cooperators comes in the form of guidance and help in keeping the conservation plan in operation once it is applied.

Similar help—to insure that practices installed are both feasible and soundly applied—is provided farmers and ranchers who receive cost-sharing aid under the Agricultural Conservation Program, the Great Plains Conservation Program, and the Conservation Reserve Program of the Soil Bank.

Many of them are cooperators of soil conservation districts, but that is not a requirement to receive this help. Help is provided by field technicians of the Soil Conservation Service on planning and carrying out certain of the more permanent practices, such as construction of dams, terraces, and drainage systems on which they are receiving cost-sharing help in these programs. Borrowers from the Farmers Home Administration can get similar technical help on soil and water conservation practices for which they have obtained loans.

COST SHARING in the application of conservation practices is another type of assistance. It helps to improve the level of conservation, including land-use adjustment. It also is a recognition by the public that it shares with the farmer the responsibility for the wise use and conservation of our resources of soil and water.

One might ask why all farmers do not use their land in a wise and conserving manner. It would be easy to say that the farmer is morally obligated to use his land in such a way that it will be passed on by him in as good or better condition than it was when he started using it. But under our American system of free enterprise, landownership is a treasured tradition and the private owner is not compelled to protect or conserve the land.

Many factors tend to deter farmers from applying the needed conservation treatments and measures—perhaps lack of information as to the proper way to manage the land; customs and traditions so strong that even with adequate knowledge the proper methods of farming are not followed; or a greater investment of funds and labor than a farmer can readily provide.

Sometimes the farmer has to sacrifice a part of his income while he is in the process of making needed adjustments.

Although proper treatment and use of the land generally increase its future productivity, there is usually a temporary decline in the level of use of the land or in its productivity before the increase can be realized. These types of obstacles, coupled with the many different tenure and ownership arrangements, account for the lag in the farmer's desire or ability to use safely the acres in his care.

Nearly all conservation measures require initial outlays in materials, power, and labor. Recovery of the investment may be slow, compared to investments in measures necessary for the production of things to sell and produce income. One of the problems in carrying out conservation measures also is that the more enduring ones usually are more costly and require a longer time before a return on the additional capital investment is realized. Some projects with the greatest permanence will not of themselves return to the farm operator the capital he invests in them. The sole benefit may be of an off-farm nature.

Sharing the cost of applying conservation measures that are needed in the public interest helps to overcome the economic barrier to carrying out conservation measures. The basic purpose of conservation cost-sharing programs is to help farmers to protect the public interest in the Nation's soil and water resources by carrying out more conservation measures and at a faster rate than would otherwise be done. Sharing the cost of conservation complements the other kinds of assistance offered farmers. It helps them make better use of research results, technical assistance, and credit facilities.

The Department of Agriculture therefore offers to farmers and ranchers cost-sharing aid under three programs. Participation is voluntary.

The Agricultural Conservation Program is authorized in sections 7–17 of the Soil Conservation and Domestic Allotment Act and is implemented each year by applicable appropriations acts. The maximum annual program authorized by the Soil Conservation and Domestic Allotment Act is 500 million dollars. In the early years of the program (1936–1942), conservation through adjustment of land use and the application of conservation measures was emphasized. The average annual amount of assistance to farmers was about 420 million dollars in 1936–1943.

Beginning with the 1944 program and through the war period, the emphasis was changed to encourage conservation measures that could be applied at the same time that intensive crop production was being encouraged. All of the assistance to farmers after 1943 was used to help them carry out conservation measures. None was used for land-use adjustment or payments for shifting land out of intensive cropping. The average annual amount of Agricultural Conservation Program assistance to farmers was about 240 million dollars in 1944–1952.

Since that period and especially for the 1954 and later programs, the longer lasting types of practices have been stressed.

As in the war period, assistance under the program consists entirely of sharing the cost with farmers of carrying out conservation practices. Measures to control erosion, water-saving practices, and the establishment of permanent vegetative cover are especially emphasized. Rates of assistance generally amount to 50 percent of the cost of carrying out the practice, although they may represent a somewhat higher percentage (not more than 80 percent) under certain conditions. The authorization for the 1958 program was 250 million dollars.

The development of the Agricultural Conservation Program for each year begins at the local or county level. The county agricultural stabilization and conservation committee, the county agent, and representatives of the Soil Conservation Service, Forest Service, and other agencies interested in conservation make recommendations to the State agricultural stabilization and conservation committee.

The recommendations are summarized by the State committee and are used as the basis to formulate joint recommendations by the agencies interested in conservation to the Agricultural Conservation Program Service in Washington. From the recommendations, it and the Commodity Stabilization Service, the Soil Conservation Service, and the Forest Service develop and recommend to the Secretary of Agriculture a national program. After the national program is approved, State and county committees develop their programs within its provisions.

The provisions of the national program for each year are contained in the National Bulletin of the Agricultural Conservation Program. State program provisions are contained in a similar State handbook. Provisions of a county program are included in a county handbook.

The State program includes authorizations for cost sharing in practices for which assistance is most needed in the State and contains the basic standards of performance that must be accomplished under the various practices as a condition of cost sharing. A maximum degree of control at the level closest to the farmer is emphasized, and the program is kept flexible so that local needs may be met.

The Agricultural Conservation Program is administered locally by agricultural stabilization and conservation committees, which are composed of farmers, who are elected by the farmers they serve. County committees are supervised by agricultural stabilization and conservation State committees composed of farmers appointed by the Secretary of Agriculture. The county agent is an ex officio member of the county committee, and the State director of extension is a member of the State committee.

A farmer who wants Agricultural Conservation Program cost-sharing assistance makes a request to the county agricultural stabilization and conservation committee before he starts the practice. The committee considers his request and the relative need for conservation on his farm, and determines the extent of the practice on which cost shares are approved and the amount thereof. The Soil Conservation Service or the Forest Service must determine the need and practicality of certain designated practices.

When the farmer has performed the practice, has filed a claim for the cost share due, and received certification by the county committee and the authorized certifying officer, the payment due him is paid by check direct from the Treasury Department field disbursing office. If, however, a farmer wishes to obtain certain available conservation materials or services from an approved vendor, as a grant-in-aid in lieu of a cash payment, he may do so.

When a conservation problem affects more than one farm, several farmers together may get approval of Agricultural Conservation Program cost sharing for the entire project through a pooling agreement, an arrangement that permits the solution of community conservation problems which farmers otherwise could not undertake.

Farmers who wish to participate in the Agricultural Conservation Program or get information about it should see their local agricultural stabilization and conservation committee, which administers the program in each county. County agents and other representatives of State and Federal agricultural agencies and services also can supply general information about the program.

The Great Plains Conservation Program was authorized by Public Law 1021 of the 84th Congress. It was approved by the President on August 7, 1956. It provides both cost-sharing and technical assistance for farmers and ranchers in designated counties of the ten Great Plains States to help them undertake longtime adjustments planned to meet the climatic hazards of the area. The authorization provides that the total cost of the program (excluding administrative costs) shall not exceed 150 million dollars and that payments for any program year shall not exceed 25 million dollars.

Farmers in the area may enter into longtime contracts (up to 10 years) and receive cost-share payments for installing eligible conservation practices as specified in a conservation plan. Maximum cost-share rates do not exceed 80 percent of the average cost of the practices. General responsibility for administration of the Great Plains Conservation Program has been assigned to the Soil Conservation Service. Farmers in the designated counties who desire assistance under this program or who wish more information on it should see the county representative of the Soil Conservation Service.

The Conservation Reserve Program is authorized in title I of the Agricultural Act of 1956, which established the Soil Bank Program. The Soil Bank is supplementary to the production adjustment programs (acreage allotments and marketing quotas) provided by the Agricultural Adjustment Act of 1938 and is designed to help farmers attack the surplus problem and to retire and build up land not presently needed for crops.

The Soil Bank consists of two parts, the Acreage Reserve and the Conservation Reserve. The Acreage Reserve is aimed at a temporary cutback to reduce surpluses of the six basic crops—corn, cotton, peanuts, rice, tobacco, and wheat—by adjusting acreages below established allotments, while the Conservation Reserve is intended to obtain a more lasting shift of crops to conservation uses.

All farmers are eligible to take part in the Conservation Reserve. Producers enter into contracts with the Secretary of Agriculture for periods of 3 to 15 years. In return for removing designated cropland from production and establishing long-range conservation practices, the producer may receive two types of payments: An annual cash payment for the period of the contract—averaging about 10 dollars an acre nationally but varying on the basis of the value of the land for producing crops, land rent rates in the locality, and other factors; and a payment either in cash or conservation materials and services for carrying out a conservation practice on the designated conservation reserve acres. The latter payment may represent up to 80 percent of the cost of establishing the practice.

The conservation practices eligible for cost-sharing payments under the Conservation Reserve Program include those for establishing a permanent vegetative cover crop for soil protection, including land treatments necessary for the use of legumes and grasses for soil improvement; establishing trees and shrubs; building dams, pits, or ponds in order to protect cover crops or to hold irrigation water; and protecting wildlife through cover, water and marsh management, or dam and pond construction.

Farmers who wish to get information about the Conservation Reserve Program should see their local agricultural stabilization and conservation committee, which administers this program in each county. County agents and other representatives of State and Federal agricultural agencies also can supply general information.

Farmers are familiar with mortgage credit for the purchase of land. This is long-term credit for which the farmer gives a mortgage on the farm as security for the loan and may take 20 to 30 years to repay. They also know about short-term credit to take care of farm operating expenses, such as the purchase of seed, fertilizer, and labor, which generally must be repaid within a year or less. These kinds of credit have long been available to farmers and used by them. There are many sources, but only in recent years has it been recognized that a special kind of credit, different from any of the types already available, is needed to help finance conservation practices.

Usually the kind of credit needed for conservation work is one that will make funds available to carry out that work a step at a time. Rarely can all of the conservation work needed on a farm be carried out all at once.

If a lump-sum loan large enough to carry out all of the needed work is obtained, the farmer would be required to pay interest on funds before he actually needed and used them, yet it would not be feasible to arrange separate loans each time he needed to carry out additional conservation work. A single loan, covering the entire amount of funds required, with provisions to use it only as fast as needed to carry out the conservation work, is desirable. Another aspect is that interest be paid only on the unpaid balance. Repayment of the loan should be fixed over a long enough period and in accordance with a time schedule that is feasible for the kind of work done and income possibilities of the farm.

Farmers can obtain this type of credit from a number of private and governmental sources. Loans are made by the Farmers Home Administration to finance various types of conservation work, including erosion control; the development, conservation, and use of water, and drainage.

Farmers Home Administration offices are generally located at county-seat towns and are under the direction of a county supervisor. A three-man county committee, of which two are farmers, determines the eligibility of applicants, passes on the value of farms to be bought or improved, and reviews the borrower's progress.

COUNTLESS ADDITIONAL sources of assistance are available to American farmers and ranchers. A full listing would be difficult.

These services and information as to where they may be had are as near to every landowner and operator as his telephone or his county courthouse. Employees of the State agricultural extension services and Department of Agriculture agencies can provide many of them and are informed as to all other sources of help that may be needed.

Technical assistance for landsmen.

This chapter, the second on the Government services available to farmers and ranchers, deals with a far-ranging development. Technical assistance offers them individual help in planning the use and management of soils and land and in laying out practices that require specialized skill. By *Raymond W. Heinen,* Soil Conservation Service.

TECHNICAL ASSISTANCE is a fundamental ingredient in the programs of the soil conservation districts, which are local units of State government, organized and managed by local people, under State law, in a partnership operation for protecting and improving their soil and water resources.

As its part in the partnership, the Government furnishes technical assistance to help individual district cooperators in developing and applying a program fitted to their individual holdings.

Technical assistance is relatively new in comparison with other Government services to landowners and operators. It had its beginning in 1935.

The Congress in 1935 enacted the first broad national soil conservation act adopted by any country. The act recognized that waste of soil and water resources menaces the national welfare and established the Soil Conservation Service as an agency that devotes its major effort to the control and prevention of soil erosion.

It became a task in the Department of Agriculture to develop a means to administer this new authority. An interbureau committee was established to do that. Through its deliberations the soil conservation district idea was conceived.

The committee recommended that on and after July 1, 1937, and sooner wherever feasible, all work to control erosion on private lands be undertaken by the Soil Conservation Service through legally constituted soil conservation districts.

A model State soil conservation district law was developed and presented by the President to the governors of all States for their consideration.

State legislatures in 21 States in 1937 enacted soil conservation district laws. By 1947 such laws had been enacted by all States, Alaska, Hawaii, Puerto Rico, and the Virgin Islands.

Each law is designed to fit conditions within the State or Territory. No two States have laws exactly alike, but all provide common principles of exercising local initiative and responsibility.

The laws establish soil conservation districts as local subdivisions or instrumentalities of the States. The districts are responsible only to the people within the district and to their State government. They are operated by governing bodies consisting of local people, usually elected landowners or operators.

Each soil conservation district has the legal responsibility for developing a districtwide soil and water conservation program and for carrying it forward by helping landowners and operators to plan, apply, and maintain technically sound conservation measures.

Each of the State laws established a State soil conservation committee (board or commission) as a State agency to make statewide determinations on district creation, to consult with and advise the district governing

329

bodies, and to facilitate the work of soil conservation districts in the State. The agency manages the State funds that are available for district operations.

In memoranda of understanding with the districts, the Soil Conservation Service agreed to make available the services of technically trained conservationists and to supply the facilities necessary for the planning and application of sound conservation measures. The assistance is made available in accordance with an annual schedule presented to a district after joint review of district needs and Soil Conservation Service resources.

During the decade that State soil conservation district laws were being enacted, a changing concept evolved as to the conservation objective. The original objective was to overcome the menace of erosion to American land. Today the objective is to use each acre of agricultural land within its capability and to treat it in accordance with its needs for protection and improvement.

Modern soil conservation includes proper land use, protecting the land against all forms of soil damage, correcting deficiencies of lime and plant nutrients, rebuilding eroded and depleted soils, protecting and improving forests and farm woodland, improving grasslands, conserving moisture for crop use, reducing flood and sediment damage, improving the quality and regularity of water yields, installing proper agricultural drainage and irrigation, and increasing crop yields.

IT HAS BROUGHT into focus the need for planning the use of land according to its capability. To sustain efficient production, management of land and water must be related specifically to the pattern of soil and water resources on the individual farm or ranch as well as to the resources, aptitudes, desires, and needs of the family.

Soil conservationists are assigned to soil conservation districts to provide technical assistance to cooperators in fitting available technology to the specific soil and water resources of their land. Any farmer or rancher may become a cooperator with his soil conservation district by agreeing to conserve and use his land properly.

The soil conservationists are trained in soil science, agronomy, range management, biology, forestry, engineering, and farm management.

A farmer or rancher starts his conservation plan as soon as he becomes a cooperator with the district. His plan may take several months or years to complete, depending mainly on how fast he wants to proceed and on how soon the district can furnish him technical assistance.

The cooperator starts by using the conservation measures his land needs most urgently. He may be able to apply a part of the work without help, but often may need technical help before he can go very far with his program.

The soil conservation district sends a soil scientist to make a soil map of the farm as soon as possible. Soil maps are already available in some districts. Eventually the farm surveys are consolidated and published to serve as a guide for many agricultural programs.

The soil map is interpreted in terms of land capability. It is given to the farmer, along with a conservation guide. The map shows him what kinds of soil he has in each field and the capability of each for agricultural use. The guide gives general information on different ways each kind can be used and treated. By following the map and guide, the farmer can plan many of the needed changes in land use and conservation.

In range areas, the conservationist helps the rancher identify his range sites and judge the condition of his range. The information helps him to balance his livestock operation with his forage resources.

If there is woodland, the conservationist helps evaluate the condition of the stand and plan for wood crops.

The district provides a Soil Conservation Service technician to give help with details as soon as possible after the soil and land map has been made.

The cooperator and technician make the basic conservation plan together. They go over the farm or ranch acre by acre. They study the kind of soil they have to deal with on each field, pasture, or woodlot. They check with the map. They discuss possibilities and alternatives for each field and for the farm as a whole. Then the farmer or rancher decides what he will do on each acre of his land.

The plan is put in writing after all decisions and plans have been made. It becomes a part of the cooperative agreement between the landowner or operator and his conservation district.

Most cooperators are able to apply a great many of the conservation measures called for in their plans. Usually some conservation work, however, requires more technical skill than the operator has—to locate and lay out a terrace or drainage system, a stripcropping system, or contoured orchards; locating and designing a pond or an irrigation system; constructing ponds, waterways, flumes, and diversions; leveling or smoothing land; designing and building gully-control structures; developing improved pastures and rangeland; planting woodlots and shelterbelts; determining cropping systems; and improving areas for wildlife. Most farmers get technical assistance from the conservation technicians in applying such practices.

District cooperators can also get help from the conservation technicians in maintaining the conservation system after it is applied to the land.

LANDOWNERS AND OPERATORS had organized 2,770 soil conservation districts throughout the United States by 1958. Most of them have the same boundaries as counties. The districts cover more than 1.5 billion acres in almost 5 million farms and ranches. About 90 percent of the Nation's farms and ranches were in such districts.

Eighteen States—Alabama, South Carolina, Delaware, Rhode Island, New Hampshire, Vermont, New Jersey, Massachusetts, Nebraska, Mississippi, Iowa, Connecticut, Kansas, Kentucky, North Carolina, Arkansas, Wisconsin, and Georgia—the Virgin Islands, and Puerto Rico were completely covered by districts. Twenty-four other States had 90 percent or more of the total farms and ranches in districts.

In the governing bodies of the conservation districts are nearly 14,000 supervisors, directors, and commissioners.

More than 1.7 million farmers and ranchers were district cooperators by 1958 and had signed cooperative agreements with soil conservation districts. More than 1 million of them had basic conservation plans covering all their lands. The Soil Conservation Service had assembled soil survey data for nearly 540 million soil acres and more than 2 million farms and ranches.

The results of this effort are evident on the face of the land. On millions of acres, crops are being grown in contour rows that follow the curves of the hills. Green waterways reach back into fields to carry the excess flow from heavy rains. Miles of terraces slow down the water and guide it to waterways. Many sloping fields are farmed in contour strips where gullies once were eating their way up the hillside. Livestock graze on green pastures or on ranges restored to productivity.

Major soil and water conservation practices applied by soil conservation district cooperators to the end of 1957 are given:

Cropland: Contour farming, 35 million acres; conservation crop rotation, 60 million; cover cropping, 21 million; stripcropping, 15 million; stubble mulching, 20 million; crop residue utilization, 48 million.

Grassland: Conservation use, 101 million acres; rotation grazing, 22 million; pasture planting, 27 million; deferred grazing, 37 million; range seeding, 4.2 million.

Woodland: Improvement cutting, 11 million acres; tree planting, 4.4 million acres; windbreak planting, 29 thousand miles.

Wildlife areas: Hedgerow plantings,

7 million rods; fish pond improvement, 315 thousand; wildlife area improvement, 4 million acres.

Drainage operations: Farm drainage, 19 million acres; open drains, 221 thousand miles; closed drains (tile), 280 thousand miles.

Irrigation improvement: Irrigation reservoirs, 20 thousand; sprinkler irrigation systems, 45 thousand; land leveling, 5 million acres; improved water application, 8 million acres; irrigation water management, 3 million acres; water spreading, 600 thousand acres.

Practices for one or more land uses: Terracing, 1 million miles; water diversions, 64 thousand miles; ponds constructed, 842 thousand; waterway development, 970 thousand acres; land clearing, 5.8 million acres.

Many of the practices were applied with cost-sharing assistance through the agricultural conservation program.

A new development came in 1954, when the Congress enacted the Watershed Protection and Flood Prevention Act. The purpose of the act was to help meet the needs of people who are faced with problems on small watersheds.

This new authority gives landowners and operators a means for grouping together to get technical assistance to work out both the land management and the water management needs of small watersheds. It also provides for Federal cost sharing on small waterflow-retarding dams and other flood prevention and water management measures. It places responsibility on local organizations to initiate projects, adapt plans to local requirements, share in the costs, and make provisions for the plan's application and maintenance. The administration of this authority has been assigned to the Soil Conservation Service.

Some 712 local sponsoring organizations had made application for assistance on watershed protection projects by 1958. In almost every instance a soil conservation district was one of the local sponsoring organizations. Assistance in planning was being given on some 268 of these projects. Work plans

had been approved for 42 projects where works of improvement were being installed with assistance from the Soil Conservation Service.

Publications available from the Department of Agriculture indicate the variety of subjects encountered in the technical phases of the soil and water conservation program. They also indicate the variety of services farmers and ranchers seek from the Soil Conservation Service through their soil conservation districts. The subjects range from the production and harvest of grass seed in the Great Plains to farming terraced land and from managing farm ponds to land leveling for irrigation. These publications are available free from field offices of the Soil Conservation Service. Where districts have been organized and have requested help from the Soil Conservation Service, a local office usually is located in the county seat. State offices usually are in State capitol or State college towns.

Among the publications are: Our Productive Land—We Can Conserve and Improve It While Using It, AIB–106, 16 pages; First Things First—Know Your Land and Have a Plan Before Starting Conservation Farming, PA–69, 8 pages; Strip Cropping for Conservation and Production, FB–1981, 46 pages; Farming Terraced Land, L–355, 14 pages; Wood Chips for the Land, L–323, 8 pages; Your Soil—Crumbly or Cloddy? L–328, 8 pages; Making Land Produce Useful Wildlife, FB–2035, 29 pages; Lespedezas for Quail and Good Land Use, L–373, 8 pages; More Wildlife Through Soil and Water Conservation, AIB–175, 16 pages; How to Build a Farm Pond, L–259, 8 pages; Managing Farm Ponds for Bass or Bluegills, FB–2094, 20 pages; Conservation Irrigation, AIB–8, 15 pages (For Western States); Conservation Irrigation in Humid Areas, AH–107, 52 pages (For Eastern States); and For Insurance Against Drought—Soil and Water Conservation, FB–2002, 22 pages.

The uses and values of soil tests.

Land management usually is considered to include appraisal of alternative treatments relative to the use of land for specific purposes, selection of practices to be used, and direction of the use of desired practices. In determining the alternative treatments, it is essential that as much information as possible be obtained about the land in question. Soil tests should be one of the first steps in a good land-management program. By *J. W. Fitts*, head, Department of Soils, North Carolina State College of Agriculture and Engineering.

You can use the information from soil tests in many ways. They give a basis for classifying soils for the purpose of suggesting lime and fertilizer practices. They help you predict the probability of getting a profitable response to the application of plant nutrients and evaluate soil productivity. They furnish data by which to determine specific soil conditions that may be improved by the addition of soil amendments or cultural practices. Soil acidity, alkalinity, or saline conditions can be detected by soil tests.

A good soil-testing program has several aspects. They include:

Representative soil samples should be obtained for testing. A poorly taken sample may be worse than none at all.

Laboratory analyses should be conducted accurately by skilled technicians. An adequate volume of samples is essential to make a laboratory test worth while.

The interpretation of the results of the tests and recommendations for liming and fertilizing the soil can best be made by an agronomist who is familiar with the testing procedures, the soil types, and field results.

Personal contact with farmers after a test has to be made to be certain they understand the results and the recommendations is important. Soil clinics or meetings for farmers who have their soils tested have been successful in many States.

Interest in the tests and an understanding of their uses need to be developed. Soil tests alone are not the whole answer to problems connected with fertility and lime. They merely point out where problems exist.

Taking the samples is an important phase of soil testing. No matter how accurate are the analyses and the procedures for interpreting them, the results are meaningless if the samples are poorly taken.

Instructions for taking samples, containers for the samples, and information sheets to be filled out and submitted with the samples may be obtained from the county agents. The samples should not be sent to the Department of Agriculture in Washington, which has no soil-testing service.

Routine soil tests are concerned largely with testing the soil zone, or layer, that reflects past management practices relative to fertility and lime. The zone may show an accumulation of an element not present in the virgin soil if much fertilizer or lime had been applied periodically. It may also show

333

a decrease if fertilizer practices were inadequate.

The sample should be taken from the proper depths. The nature of the soil profile below the layer that is plowed influences the growth of plants. Aside from the plow layer, however, the fertility of the soil profile does not change very much from one year to another under most farming conditions.

Neither phosphate nor lime moves much in the soil. Studies in North Carolina indicated that the greatest accumulation of phosphate and lime is in the upper 3 inches of soil and declines gradually to plow depth or slightly below. The methods, frequency, and rates of application of materials and the frequency and depth of soil disturbance through plowing or cultivation have a bearing on the distribution of lime and phosphate. The lime and phosphate accumulate in the upper 2 or 3 inches of soil when they are broadcast on the surface of, say, permanent pastures and lawns.

The depth at which you should take the sample depends on the depth of soil to which you want to increase the fertility (particularly as regards phosphate or lime).

A sample taken from below the zone where phosphate has accumulated may show a deficiency of phosphorus, but the addition of phosphate to the upper part, which already is high in phosphate, is not likely to result in much crop response. On a cultivated field, therefore, the generally recommended depth at which to take samples is the plow zone or an inch or two below the plow zone. The best depth for sampling pastures where lime or fertilizer is to be broadcast and not worked into the soil is the surface 2 or 3 inches.

If you want to investigate a special soil condition, you should take samples at the depth at which the condition occurs. Because soluble salts may accumulate at the surface, for example, you should get a sample from the first inch. To ascertain the distribution of salts through the profile, the samples should be taken at 6-inch intervals below the surface inch. "Alkali" conditions may occur at the surface or may be buried several inches below the surface. You usually can recognize such conditions by digging a pit and examining carefully the layers of soil. You should sample the sticky, plastic layers separately.

Most laboratories recommend taking a composite sample for testing. The composite sample is composed of 10 to 20 borings—cores or slices—of equal volume of soil from the place to be sampled. You put the borings in a clean pail, mix them thoroughly, and remove about 1 pint for the composite sample.

The number of borings is related to the possible variabilities that may be due to past practices, like the distribution of lime or fertilizer. Soils may vary greatly within a few feet because of residues from burning or uneven distribution of soil amendments. The number of borings to take is not related, therefore, to the size of area to be sampled. In sampling a lawn, garden, or eroded hillside, the composite sample should come from 10 to 20 borings—the same as a sample from a 5- or 10-acre field.

Most instructions for taking soil samples designate the area to be sampled as a "field." That implies an area confined to one crop or bounded by a fence, stream, road, or some other line. The size of an area for a composite sample often is given as 5 to 10 acres.

Usually it is not practical to lime or fertilize a plot smaller than 5 acres differently from the way you would the rest of the field. You might treat a problem area, however, in such a way that it can be corrected and then handled the same as the remainder of the field in the future.

It is conceivable that a 20-acre field may be more uniform than a 5-acre field, and it would be justifiable to take only one composite sample from the field. You do not know the variabilities in the field before you test it, and it is better to have several samples (indicating a uniformity of soil) than to attempt to include too large an area in the sample.

Borings should not be taken from unusual areas, such as dead furrows, back furrows, terrace channels, old fence lines, marshy areas, eroded spots, areas near a lime rock road, and the boundaries between slopes and bottom lands. If you want information about an unusual area, you should sample it separately. You should take a composite sample from the unusual area in the same way as you would the remainder of the field.

When the 10 to 20 borings are taken for the composite sample, it is generally assumed the locations will be selected at random. A completely randomized sample would mean that every boring has an equal chance of occurring anywhere in the field regardless of where any other boring is placed. In actual practice, that is not done. The borings are taken in a stratified random design or a zigzag procedure, which assures a distribution of the cores over the area to be sampled.

Satisfactory samples can be taken equally well with a number of tools, such as a soil tube, spade, trowel, and auger. But whatever the equipment, you must be careful to get a uniform slice of soil from the surface to the depth the tool is inserted; equal volumes of soil must be taken from each boring.

Usually the soil tube is the tool that is easiest to use correctly. If a spade is used, a V-shaped hole should be dug to plow depth and a slice of soil one-half inch thick should be removed from one side of the hole. The slice should be of uniform thickness. The soil is trimmed from each side, so that a ribbon about 1 inch wide is left at the center of the spade. It should be placed in a clean pail with 10 to 20 other slices for the composite sample.

If you use an auger, you are apt to lose the surface inch of soil, especially if the soil is dry—an important loss, because phosphate and lime accumulate in the surface.

Most laboratories recommend taking samples when the soil is in a good physical condition for plowing or cultivation because the soil then is easier to mix for the composite sample.

Variations in acidity, available phosphorus, and potassium occur at different times of the year, but the specialist who interprets the test results usually is aware of the variations with season and allows for them.

Sampling to determine soluble salts is best done after a dry period, when the salts accumulate near the surface.

After you have taken the samples, you should number them and prepare a record of the areas from which each was removed. A map or sketch of the field is useful for this purpose. You should fill out information sheets about conditions in the field and send them to the laboratory with the samples. It is wise to check the numbers on the containers with the numbers on the record sheets to avoid mistakes.

Under ordinary management practices, the fertility and acidity level of soils do not change rapidly. Sampling a field once every 3 to 5 years or once a rotation usually is enough. This should indicate the trend in fertility and acidity levels and furnish the information needed to develop a good soil-management program for the cropping system you follow.

BOTH CHEMICAL AND BIOLOGICAL methods are used in soil-testing laboratories, but the chemical methods are faster and easier.

For the chemical tests, a portion of the element in the soil—the available fraction—is removed by an extracting solution. The solution may be a strong acid, distilled water, or an alkaline solution.

The amount of the element that is removed varies with the extraction solution, the characteristics of the soil, and technique used for extraction. The elements occur in different forms in soils, and many factors (such as acidity or the presence of free lime) influence the amount and rate of their release. No universal extracting solution has been developed that will apply to all soils and conditions and give equally reliable results. The results of each test must be interpreted in view of the conditions involved. Many field and greenhouse studies therefore are necessary to interpret results of the soil tests.

Tests for pH, available phosphorus, and potassium are commonest and are made in almost all soil laboratories.

About half of the laboratories determine the organic matter, calcium, and magnesium. A few laboratories determine boron, manganese, soluble salts, and nitrate on special samples but not as routine analyses. Soluble salts may be determined routinely in some of the western laboratories where saline conditions frequently occur.

The determination of soil acidity was one of the first routine soil tests and still is the most widely used determination. Two general methods are used to determine soil reaction—electrometric (glass electrode pH meter) and colorimetric (dye solutions).

The glass electrode has made the measurement of pH a simple one. It is standard in most laboratories. Some laboratories and some field kits use color indicator dyes, but they must be used by experienced operators for best results. The values obtained should be checked periodically with a glass electrode pH meter. A few county laboratories use the thiocyanate test for lime requirements.

In a complex mixture like soil, the hydrogen ion concentration indicated by pH often is a small fraction of the total acidity. Since the ions responsible for soil acidity are concentrated at the surface of the soil particles, the relationship between pH and total acidity is not a simple one. In most of the soil-testing laboratories, the amount of organic matter and clay is considered, along with the pH, in making recommendations about liming. Buffered solutions have come into use for determining lime requirement, and almost a third of the laboratories use a lime-requirement test in addition to determinations of pH.

Soils with a pH above 8.3 usually have considerable exchangeable sodium, which is largely responsible for "alkali" conditions. A determination of excess free lime, exchangeable sodium, and soluble salts usually is made on samples having a pH of 8.5 or higher to ascertain the presence of a saline or alkali condition.

Some laboratories determine phosphorus and potassium from the same extraction. Other laboratories use different extractants for each element. Phosphorus is determined colorimetrically with a photometer in most laboratories, but a few make comparisons visually. In soil-testing kits, the color comparisons have to be made visually. The flame photometer has become popular in determining potassium. It affords an accurate and rapid method of analysis.

Because many complex factors influence the rate of field nitrate production, a meaningful determination of nitrogen is not simple. Biological mineralization of nitrogen during controlled incubation of soil samples has received much attention in Iowa and is used in some soil-testing programs. The results obtained from the incubation studies are a good guide to the potential nitrogen-supplying power of the soil in the Midwest.

The percentage of organic matter and the exchangeable calcium and magnesium are used in determining the lime requirement. The organic matter is used also by some laboratories as a guide to nitrogen availability.

Tests for trace elements are tedious, and the answers are difficult to interpret. A test for the total amount of the element is no guide to the amount available. Sometimes a given amount of a trace element may be satisfactory for plant growth but may be toxic under other conditions. Likewise a given amount may be satisfactory in some conditions but deficient in others.

Biological tests have been developed to measure the amount of available nutrients in the soil. Rapidly growing plants are produced in the greenhouse or laboratory in small amounts of soil.

Such plants as small grain, lettuce, or sunflowers sometimes are used. The Neubauer procedure utilizes sprouting rye or barley seeds to measure the uptake of nutrient elements from small quantities of soil. Lettuce and sunflower plants are grown in small pots; various fertilizers are applied, and the responses are noted. Lower plants, such as bacteria and fungi, also are used, as in the incubation procedures for available nitrogen. *Aspergillus niger* and *Cunninghamella* are used for potassium and phosphorus tests.

The problem of biological procedures is much the same as with chemical procedures. Do the rapidly growing plants remove the same proportion of nutrients from the soil under the controlled environmental conditions that field crops will obtain? The biological procedures must be calibrated with field studies in the same manner that chemical procedures are calibrated. Research studies indicate they are no more reliable generally than the chemical procedures and require much more time to perform.

AFTER THE SOIL TEST ANALYSES are obtained, the results must be interpreted in terms of fertility levels or possible responses, and recommendations must be made accordingly. For them, as much additional information as possible is needed.

Almost all laboratories have blanks that the landowner should fill out and submit with the soil samples. An accurate location of the field is desired. A legal description is best if it is available and can be presented briefly. A glance at a soil survey map tells the specialist the soil type of the field and gives him information about the characteristics of the profile. If the subsoil in a particular soil type is low in available nutrients, such as phosphorus and potassium, it may be necessary to apply larger amounts in the plow zone. If the subsoil is high in the nutrients, only enough fertilizer will be needed in the plow zone to get the plants started.

Drainage and aeration influence the

availability of nutrients. This usually refers to internal drainage of the soil rather than surface drainage—that is, how fast water passes into the soil after a rain and how quickly it can be cultivated. Recently applied lime usually will not have had time to react with the soil, and the effect of liming will not be shown in the test. Fertilizer applied the past year may not have been evenly distributed in the soil sample taken. Therefore it is important to list the fertilizer, lime, and other amendments recently added to the soil in order to avoid confusion and erroneous recommendations. The specialist gets all such information from the properly completed information sheets.

Information about crops grown during the past 2 or 3 years and the yields plus the crops that are planned for the next 2 or 3 years gives the specialist a good picture of the cropping system and the level of productivity and helps him in making the recommendations.

In reporting soil tests, the results frequently are classified as very low, low, medium, high, and very high. Sometimes the results are given in terms of pounds per acre of elements like phosphorus and potassium. Differences exist in the meaning associated with the very low to very high classification in the various sections of the country. Some laboratories regard soils classified as "high" as those on which no fertilizer should be applied. Soils requiring only a maintenance application are classed as "medium." The "low" soils need larger amounts of fertilizers. Other laboratories regard the "high" classification as the one at which optimum production is attained and recommend the addition of maintenance fertilizers on these soils.

USUALLY RECOMMENDATIONS for fertilization are given in terms of pounds per acre of nitrogen, phosphate, and potash. Fertilizer grades and materials usually are suggested that can be used to meet the recommendations. A survey of prices of various fertilizers and materials available locally that can be used to obtain the desired rates may result in a considerable saving.

Soil tests may indicate the fertility status of the soil, but the predictions of crop responses to lime and fertilizer must be made in terms of productivity, of which fertility is only one part.

The problem of proper use of fertilizer and lime includes not only determining what nutrients are needed for the best growth of plants as related to local soil conditions but also making sure the recommendations are understood and can be followed. Recommended materials must be obtained and adequate machinery must be available for correct application.

Copies of the soil test results usually are sent to the county agent or some other local agricultural leader. In many States, the county agents are taking an active part in making recommendations based on soil tests. The practice is a good one, for the individual help given by someone who is familiar with local conditions and is trained in soil fertility problems is of untold value in soil-testing programs.

Several laboratories have prepared summaries of the results of the tests they have made. Such information is of value to educational and research agencies and to commercial companies. They are helpful in making general fertilizer recommendations. Summaries prepared on the basis of two-way tables that show the range of two elements, such as phosphorus and potassium, indicate the futility of attempting to predict the fertility level of a given field from the summaries. To gain the knowledge that is necessary for a good management program, every field on the farm should be sampled separately.

State-operated or controlled soil-testing services are available in all States. Most of the laboratories charge a small fee to cover the costs of materials and equipment and a part of the salaries of technicians. In several States, especially in the Southeast, the soil-testing services are free to all residents of the State. All States but one

have a central laboratory. Ten States have regional laboratories, and nine have county laboratories. The county laboratories are primarily in the Midwestern States, including Illinois, Missouri, Kansas, Oklahoma, Michigan, Wisconsin, and Kentucky.

The interaction between essential elements in respect to soil and climate conditions is one of the major problems in interpreting soil tests and in making recommendations. This interaction is particularly noticeable in the minor elements and is one of the stumbling blocks in testing for elements such as iron, copper, molybdenum, manganese, and zinc.

Research in soil fertility generally is concerned with factors affecting the availability of nutrient elements and the response that is likely to be obtained from the use of soil amendments. In making recommendations for use of lime and fertilizers based on soil tests, thought should be given to the economics involved. Development of economic response data in respect to rates of application of nitrogen, phosphorus, and potassium is important. The desirable level of soil fertility and residual effects of fertilizers must be considered. Studies that should give valuable information on the subject have been started in several States, including Iowa, Mississippi, Michigan, Virginia, and North Carolina.

There are almost 20 percent more farms today than business firms in the United States, and the physical assets of these farms have about the same value as manufacturing corporations. The principal physical asset of agriculture is the land that is farmed. To increase the efficiency of production, as much knowledge as possible must be obtained about the soil. The greatest advances in soil testing have been made since 1945. During the coming years, greater advances are anticipated. As more information is gained through research concerning the factors influencing the availability of nutrient elements, improved testing procedures will be developed.

Some new jobs for irrigation.

We tend to link irrigation with dry conditions in the West, where it has shaped the pattern of use of much of the arable land and influenced size of holdings and tenure arrangements. More and more land is being irrigated in the East, where it widens the uses of land, insures higher yields, upgrades other factors of production, and perhaps enhances quality of crops. By *Elco L. Greenshields*, in charge, Water Utilization Unit, Farm Economics Research Division, and *William I. Palmer*, chief, Division of Irrigation, Bureau of Reclamation.

EVER SINCE the Mormon pioneers in 1847 diverted the waters of City Creek to their parched lands to assure the harvest on which their survival in Utah depended, the hunger for land and the favorable results from irrigation have made an epic of irrigation in the West.

Perhaps because of the experience in the West we have become accustomed to link irrigation with aridity. The greatest potential of irrigation in the United States, however, lies not in reclaiming the deserts but in correcting the seasonal deficiencies of moisture in the sections where we used to consider rainfall to be adequate.

Irrigation there broadens the usability of the land, insures a high level of yield, and upgrades the efficiency of the other related factors of production—soil, topography, and temperature. The pressure for opportunities to extend the agricultural plant is manifested in the intensification through irrigation farming in the humid areas.

The map on page 342 shows three great agricultural regions, which are preponderantly one-crop regions—all production centers around and supports one major enterprise. The main crops of these areas—corn, wheat, and cotton—have received a major share of the efforts of our programs of research and Federal assistance.

Irrigation can be seen now as a major instrument to relieve these large areas of their one-crop economies. A vast field for development of new agricultural crops lies ahead.

Without being unduly visionary, it appears certain that we will have immense new markets for many oilseed plants, resinous plants, special fibers, and the specialty foods, such as sesame, safflower, sunflower, flax, soybeans, avocados, dates, hops, and olives.

It also may be practical soon to attain a high finish on livestock by a system of periodic and progressive grazing on new, highly nutritious forages. Thus we might go far in eliminating the present wasteful steps of harvesting, storing, handling, and feeding the grain rations.

We are now on the threshold of these new possibilities, and irrigation may open the door to them.

We recognize now that crop production in principle is only a factory process—a process of creating from the inputs, such as seed, fertilizer, water, and labor, which are introduced and controlled by man and must be replenished. This agricultural factory is regenerative, self-replenishing. In this respect it differs from oil and minerals, which, once taken from the earth, are irreplaceable in kind.

339

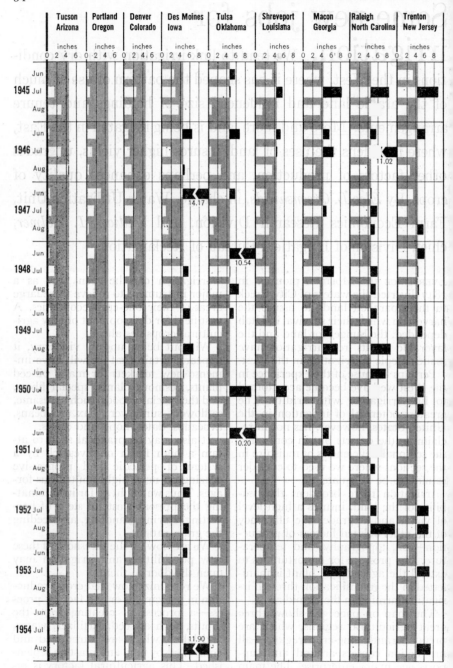

Normal monthly requirement of about 4½ inches per month or 1 inch per week

Irregularity and deficiency of rainfall during three critical months of the growing season.

Our irrigation in the United States until two decades ago was largely confined to lands that required the application of 12 inches or more of supplemental waters, commonly called the full irrigation supply. These semiarid lands mostly were west of the 100th meridian and received less than 20 inches of precipitation a year.

The eastern border of the irrigation province gradually has pressed into the semihumid zones of the Middle West. In the prairie States of North Dakota, South Dakota, Nebraska, Kansas, Oklahoma, and Texas, irrigation once was common only to the western counties, but now it is practiced throughout this prairie belt.

Each year sees the march of more and more irrigation into humid zones where farmers generally have never before seriously contemplated its use. The extension of irrigation into areas of marginal benefit follows the pattern of progress in the intensification of other input factors that augment the productivity of land.

Its pattern of growth resembles that of the use of fertilizer, for example, which first became common where it was needed most, then gradually became accepted, and now is demanded throughout the country. The expansion in the use of fertilizer has been the reverse, however, of irrigation. Fertilizer was used first in the humid areas and later in the drier areas; while irrigation is moving from the drier areas to the humid areas.

The value of both fertilizer and irrigation is most clearly seen where the need is greatest. Results prove their value as use penetrates farther and farther into the zones formerly thought to be marginal.

A total of 29.6 million acres were irrigated in 1954—27 million acres in the 17 Western States and 2.6 million acres in the 31 Eastern States.

In Arkansas and Louisiana, where large acreages of rice are grown under water, the latest census reported a total of 1.5 million irrigated acres. In Florida, where citrus and truck irrigation is practiced on a large scale, 500 thousand acres are under irrigation. In the other 28 Eastern States, only about 600 thousand acres are irrigated, but the potential is great.

An estimate published in 1957 in the magazine Irrigation Engineering and Maintenance is that farmers irrigated about 36 million acres of crops and pasture in 1956. They are equipped to irrigate several million more acres if the need arises and if water supplies are sufficient. Since the 1954 census, scattered surveys indicate that farmers, particularly in the humid States, have continued to equip their farms for irrigation.

The acreage under irrigation in 1954 represented an increase of 10 percent over the preceding 5 years in the West and an increase of 70 percent in the East. The relative rate of growth in the West now is slower than in the East and may be expected to continue so, because we are getting closer and closer to the maximum area of irrigable land and available water supplies in the West.

UNLIKE THE OTHER PHYSICAL factors that contribute to the utility of land, water is seldom naturally supplied in the full and even amounts needed for greatest production. This elusive factor—different from fertility, depth, texture, location, or topography, all of which can be seen and measured—has to be anticipated.

One of the most uncertain factors of farm production is the supplies of water. If the farmer is fortunate in his forecast of the water supply he needs, he is a successful producer, but if the next year proves him wrong, he fails. It is the degree of variation in rainfall in the annual growing season that makes it hard to determine the need for irrigation.

The need is clear in the West, where the total annual precipitation is too little for crops. But in places where the total annual precipitation is almost enough but is undependable, one has to appraise irrigation needs in terms of marginal returns versus marginal costs. To some extent, irrigation, therefore, in humid areas can be looked upon as an insurance policy.

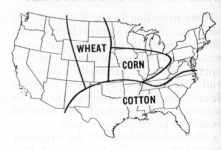

Growing-season droughts, minor or major, occur almost every summer in every State where crops are grown. The average annual precipitation is enough in the 31 Eastern States to mature a crop, as it is in many sections of the 17 Western States. The problem, however, is that of distribution over the growing season. Often 2- to 4-week droughts occur during the most critical time of the growing season. A drought usually may be considered to exist if not more than one-fourth inch of rain falls in 2 weeks. The water-holding capacity of the soil and the type of crop determine whether the crop will suffer seriously from a 14-day dry spell.

Crop requirements average about 1 inch of moisture a week, or 0.14 inch a day, throughout the growing season. There may be periods of greater or smaller requirements according to the stage of growth and the specific crop. Over a 6-month growing season, this requirement averages 4.33 inches a month. Because crops frequently require 0.25 inch or more a day on windy days and in the peak of the warm-weather growing season, the monthly rate of water consumption may exceed 7.5 inches in the latter part of July and in August. These requirements do not exist continuously over long periods, but the highest possible yields depend largely on meeting the moisture demands during the critical periods of plant growth.

Our chart of precipitation at nine places in the three growing-season months illustrates the frequency of harmful summer droughts. The data indicate that cropping would be extremely hazardous or impossible without irrigation in many areas. In other areas, particularly in the Midwest and East, there is a better than even chance of getting through the season without critical droughts. All places on the chart, however, have had drought months—an indication of a need for supplemental irrigation if high production is to be attained.

Full irrigation service is needed near Denver, Colo. Supplemental irrigation near Des Moines, Iowa, could probably be justified on the basis of the shortages that were experienced there 4 years out of 10 in June, 9 years out of 10 in July, and 5 years out of 10 in August. One moisture-deficient month followed another 35 percent of the time. In 1 year of the 10, all 3 of these important growing-season months were deficient in moisture.

Eight of the nine locations had at least 1 month in which shortages occurred 80 percent of the time, and 2 of the 3 summer months were deficient 50 percent or more of the time. Every station had 1 or more years of 3 successive months of deficient moisture conditions.

The data are inadequate for determining exact irrigation needs. For that, one would have to determine the amount that would be required to balance weekly precipitation against weekly water requirement for each location. Carryover of soil moisture, efficiency of precipitation, temperature, and wind movement also must be related to the water requirements in a specific cropping system.

As important as the severity and frequency of the drought itself is the rate at which water is lost to the atmosphere from plants and through soil. As a dry period progresses, evaporation and transpiration losses may become greater and aggravate the effect of the drought on the crop.

The total rainfall in the Midwest is sometimes made up of violent rains, from which most of the water is lost in runoff, and light showers, which do not penetrate the soil to any depth and is dissipated in the air without helping plants very much.

Fertility or moisture can limit gross yields even when all other factors are optimum. The response of crops to irrigation up to the maintenance of optimum moisture in the root zone depends on the fertility in the soil. Further increases in yield depend on increased fertility. Good fertility therefore insures maximum efficiency of use of water.

THE RESPONSE OF CROPS to irrigation in the section once considered to be the "Great American Desert" is outstanding. Once it produced nothing of commercial value. Now it supplies an abundance of high-quality fruits and vegetables. In fact, irrigation in this section, plus modern transportation and marketing facilities, has changed the eating habits of the Nation.

The section also produces abundant yields of other field crops. For example: 142,483 acres produced 290,958 bales of cotton (average yield per acre was 2 bales); 249,291 acres produced 965,669 tons of alfalfa (3.9 tons an acre); 144,808 acres produced 8,559,-714 bushels of barley (59.1 bushels an acre); 49,845 acres produced 9,798,222 crates of lettuce (196.6 crates on an acre); 9,539 acres produced 107,955 tons of carrots (11.3 tons an acre); and 26,819 acres produced 3,324,941 crates of cantaloups (124 crates an acre).

Production under irrigation in the semiarid western border of the Great Plains contrasts sharply with the production achieved in nearby dry-farmed sections. The high average yields obtained at one irrigation project near Scottsbluff, Nebr.—potatoes, 342 bushels an acre; dry edible beans, 1,620 pounds an acre; corn, 61 bushels an acre; barley, 32.5 bushels an acre; and alfalfa, 2.5 tons an acre—illustrate its great margin of productivity and ver-satility beyond the yields of 20 bushels of wheat an acre obtained on dry land.

THE POTENTIAL CONTRIBUTION of irrigation in expanding the frontiers of agriculture, in increasing production, and in making possible greater diversification of crop enterprises remains its chief justification. Another contribution of irrigation will gain in importance in the future: The scientific application of irrigation to improve the quality of foods.

Agricultural experiment stations have started to investigate the effects of irrigation on the quality of many kinds of crops. The effects are not always good. Studies at the University of Florida, for example, disclosed that the injudicious use of irrigation can impair the quality of grapefruit.

Fruitgrowers in the East, however, have concluded that the gain in the size and quality of fruit more than pays the cost of irrigation.

Results of tests on peach irrigation by the Maryland Agricultural Experiment Station in 1955 showed that fruit growth increased much faster under irrigation. Elberta peaches during a dry spell between July 22 and August 8 gained in volume 7 cubic centimeters (cc.) on nonirrigated blocks while on irrigated blocks the volume gain was 26 cc.; the final increase in size of irrigated fruit was about one-third greater than that of the nonirrigated. In a test with Sunhigh peaches, the irrigated peaches showed an increase 50 percent greater than that of peaches from blocks that had no supplemental irrigation. These tests did not specifically cover a measurement of improved quality, but the increased size of the peaches produced under irrigation would result in upgrading in market quality.

Irrigation of slicer cucumbers in Arkansas increased the yield of marketable cucumbers by 277 bushels an acre when 1 inch of water was applied every 10 days. Increasing the application to 1.5 inches every 10 days resulted in an additional increase of 282 bushels an acre.

Yields of fancy grade were increased proportionately more than any other grade. Yields of fancy grade were tripled by use of 1 inch of water and increased fivefold by use of 1.5 inches every 10 days.

A few tests show important differences in quality between irrigated and nonirrigated cotton.

John R. Carreker, of the Department of Agriculture, in a report in the Plant Food Journal, summarized 18 cotton-yield tests with and without irrigation. Losses in yield resulted in two of the tests. No increase was shown in two. Slight to large increases were shown in 14 studies.

Research workers in Georgia found that irrigation improved the weight of seed, the weight of lint per 100 seeds, and the length of fiber. This test and studies at the Clemson Agricultural College, however, showed a slight reduction in ginning percentage for cotton grown under irrigation. Irrigation increased the oil content of the cottonseed by 2 percent.

Scientists at the Georgia Experiment Station in a report on 4 years of tests of irrigation of flue-cured tobacco observed that irrigation tends to reduce the percentage of nicotine and total nitrogen of the cured leaf, raise the percentage of sugar and chlorine, and improve the burning quality. All these effects, except the increase in chlorine, are favorable to good smoking. Tobacco grown under irrigation, according to the report, matures earlier and more evenly than nonirrigated tobacco, and thus can be cured to better advantage.

The research workers also learned that 10 growers got yield increases of 232 to 1,100 pounds an acre from irrigation. The average was about 400 pounds an acre. Seven of the growers reported an improvement in grade that gave them 8 to 32.5 cents more a pound. One grower reported a lower grade under irrigation, and the price he got was 7.5 cents a pound less.

Irrigation of soybeans at the Missouri Agricultural Experiment Station increased yields from 17 to 31 bushels an acre. The beans were 50 percent larger and had 11 percent more oil. A rough measure showed less loss in refining the oil of soybeans grown under irrigation. Additional research is needed on the response of soybeans to irrigation, as soybeans stand drought better than many other field crops, and can resume growth after short dry periods.

Irrigated plots in Missouri had substantially higher yields of corn. The average weights per ear and shelling percentage were higher. The protein content of irrigated corn was a little less than that of nonirrigated corn.

Irrigation of sweetpotatoes at the Arkansas Agricultural Experiment Station increased the yield of marketable sweetpotatoes by 336 bushels an acre.

MANY PROBLEMS must be met in order to establish and expand irrigation on a permanently sound basis.

One problem has to do with the acidity or alkalinity of soil, either of which may affect the availability for plant growth of nutritional elements in a soil. Soils in arid climates often develop heavy concentrations of harmful salts. In the West, therefore, new lands being subjected to irrigation for the first time should be tested to insure that conditions are favorable for plant growth. The alteration of excessive acidity or alkalinity conditions is frequently accomplished by applying soil amendments, such as gypsum, or leaching out the harmful concentrations, or both.

Another problem is how to dispose of unused irrigation waters. Conditions of soil and topography occasionally contribute to excessive runoff, ponding, seepage, and salt accumulation. Highly important is good management by a farm operator and by his neighbor, whose mismanagement may cause an adverse condition. In certain areas, the very water that brings land into its full fruitfulness can be its bane if allowed to collect as excess water.

Associated with the problem of controlling excess water is the need to conserve water. In many of our gravity irrigation systems, no more than one-third of the diverted water finds its way to the plant root zone. The rest is lost en route through percolation, run-off, and evaporation. Such losses can be reduced by the use of closed distribution systems, ditch linings, and better management practices.

Location is important when land is considered for irrigation. If land is located where it can be irrigated, it is said to have site value for irrigation. Throughout the country are lands that are otherwise productive but have no site value with regard to the possibility of artificially supplying water. Laws have been developed in many of the Western States that permit the diversion of streamflow for irrigation whether or not the property to be irrigated is adjacent to the stream. This is called the appropriation doctrine. It contrasts to the riparian doctrine of water rights of most of the humid States, which in effect restrict the use of water to lands immediately adjacent to a stream. Potential irrigation from flowing streams therefore is restricted in the States with riparian water rights. But irrigation in those States is being expanded by farm storage of diffused surface runoff and through the use of ground water.

Irrigation from wells is an important share of our total irrigation. Productive value of land is greatly enhanced by an irrigation well. More than a third of the total supplies of irrigation water were obtained from ground-water sources in 1958.

The development of much of the gravity irrigation in the West has necessitated group effort because of the scope and scale of the project works to be built. Mutual associations were first organized to construct and operate the systems. Irrigation districts, organized later under State laws, had broader powers to deal with dissenting landowners, levy assessments against benefited lands, and so forth.

The conservancy district, the latest development, differs from the irrigation district in the scope of taxing authority. In the irrigation district, only lands that benefit directly from project works are assessed. The conservancy district, in recognition of the benefits to all segments of the community, may tax all types and kinds of property. Irrigation districts or conservancy districts now are the preferred forms of organization for large projects.

Individual irrigation systems are the rule only in places that use wells for irrigation or where individuals irrigate from small headstreams in the West or from streams and ponds in the Eastern States.

The appropriative system of water rights in the West has become well established after years of legal battles.

The English common law, which is the root of our legal system, embodied the riparian principle and was not well adapted to our arid regions.

The few Western and Prairie States that cling to vestiges of the riparian system while attempting to adhere to the doctrine of appropriative water rights have created for themselves a paradoxical situation. Statutory water law in the humid States has not developed because of lack of need up to recent times. It now appears that a doctrine is needed that will serve and facilitate irrigation use of the streams along with domestic and industrial uses.

Rational development of irrigation from streams in the Eastern States will likely require some modification of current riparian tenets. These States need to develop suitable statutes that will encourage the full development of the beneficial uses of streamflow while affording adequate protection against the future loss of water rights for those making the necessary investment.

THE ALLOCATION and regulation of use of underground waters has become a major problem because of the over-expansion in the use of wells in several areas. The intrusion of salt water into underground reservoirs has become serious in some places. State laws are needed to regulate the withdrawal of subsurface water.

One difficulty is to ascertain which subterranean water is tributary to a stream. A moot point is whether pumping such waters is subject to the appropriative surface controls of the stream to which they are tributary.

Another thorny question is the extent to which a well depletes the supply of another well. The immediacy of the problem of ground-water legislation perhaps overemphasizes its magnitude relative to overall water law, but it is nonetheless highly important.

A special contribution of irrigation in the West is that it makes locally accessible livestock feeds that could not be shipped in economically. By having locally produced feeds at lower cost than if they were shipped in from the crop areas to the eastward, markedly greater use is made of millions of acres of rangeland that would otherwise be ineffectively utilized. The total volume and value thus achieved is many times greater than merely the value of irrigation-produced feeds. This integration enhances the utility of the agricultural lands of the entire West and results in a more efficient system of production on dry-farmed lands and rangelands.

Irrigation in the West is flexible in quickly shifting to production of commodities most in demand. This is possible because control is maintained over the factors of production and contrasts with single-crop systems of the

semiarid areas. Versatility is demonstrated in the offseason production of highly desirable fruits and vegetables, flowers, and specialty crops.

Irrigation in the East will not be a panacea for all problems, but it does hold promise for multiplying the productivity of millions of acres of favorably situated lands. By insuring high crop yields and products of uniformly higher quality and by promoting intensification and upgrading of cropping systems, it will go far toward meeting the increased demands of our country's growing population.

Economics will dictate the future extent of irrigation in the United States. From a purely physical and engineering standpoint, we are limited only to the extent of water supply. How much more and how rapidly irrigation will be developed is largely a matter of economics. Only if it creates a product at lower cost than is possible by other methods, or insures a harvest each year or one which would not otherwise be produced, can irrigation be justified.

The future size of the irrigation enterprise cannot now be estimated. Based on attainable benefits alone, a high percentage of the Nation's farming plant could gain from irrigation. Whether or not this country will have 50 million or 100 million or more acres under irrigation depends on future requirements for crops and upon the emphasis science and Government will place upon the attainment of required production through irrigation.

Estimated Increase in Irrigated Acreage, 1949–1956

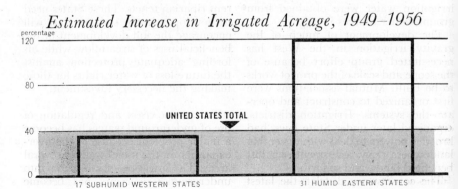

Wanted: Partnership to manage water.

Water often determines the value and use of land. So do floods and poor drainage. The problems of setting up programs to control and manage water involve the ownership, tenure, and management of land. This chapter, which deals particularly with stream-channel flood control and with drainage, calls for a "full and equitable sharing of costs and responsibilities and a genuine partnership effort among local, State, and Federal agencies." By *J. T. Sanders*, agricultural economist, Farm Economics Research Division, and *N. A. Back*, Corps of Engineers, Department of the Army.

MAN has not devised effective controls of the amount of rain that falls or the time and place it falls.

The control and management of water is practicable only after the water strikes the earth, and from that point on the major limitation on its conservation and its control usually is economic rather than physical.

Too much rain may bring floods. The control of floods is essentially the process of slowing down or stopping the destructive streamflows, confining them to the normal capacities of stream channels, and keeping them from doing damage.

Too much rain also may cause water to collect in places and make them unsuitable for several uses. That land may have to be drained. Drainage is the process of moving standing water from places in which it does damage to places in which it does little or no damage.

The elevation of land above the ocean level has a bearing on its productive use, but elevation also may mean that heavy rains acquire great destructive powers. Temperature, mass air currents, convection, and other forces of distribution of moisture to the land are practically unpredictable and uncontrollable.

Nature's distribution of water on the land varies greatly in intensity, volume, and time. The extreme variation in storm patterns is the genesis of the flood problem: Long, heavy, widespread storms usually are the cause of floods on the main stems of rivers. Concentrated local storms usually are the source of damage in headwater areas. Both of these aspects of flood damage are of great importance to land and people.

There is no hard-and-fast dividing line between main-stem or downstream areas and upstream flood-control areas. In this chapter we refer mainly to the work of the Corps of Engineers as downstream or main-stem flood control and to the work of the Department of Agriculture as upstream control.

Because man's control of water on the land begins only after its first impact, the earlier he takes control the more complete will be his control. Land-treatment measures or structures that are put on upland channels to give the soil greater absorptive capacity or to slow down runoff therefore become the first line of defense against floods and sediment for the drainage areas farther downstream. Sediment damage, which consists mainly of the depositing of sand, gravel, clay, and debris on productive lands in stream channels and reservoirs, is especially important in upstream flooded areas.

BUT EVEN GOOD UPSTREAM cover and structures fail to provide effective control when the land already is saturated and an unusually intense storm occurs.

Even when an ideal mantle of forest and grasses covered our humid areas, great floods ravaged the land. DeSoto saw what may have been one of the greatest floods on the Mississippi River. Two of the three largest floods on record at Pittsburgh occurred in 1762 and 1763, when the native cover on the land above the present site of the city was as yet undisturbed.

Effective flood control therefore requires not only upstream watershed protection. It requires, as well, flood-prevention facilities on the channels of main rivers and their bigger tributary streams.

We need to bear in mind that the control of floods is only one part of our efforts to put to wise use the water and related watershed lands. The growing need to conserve water was brought out by the 1955 report of the President's Policy Committee on Water Resources. The committee estimated that by 1975 Americans would need and use 90 percent more water than they used in 1950. Reservoirs therefore must be more than flood-control structures; they are needed more and more for the full development of land and water.

That requires some knowledge of the nature and frequency of floods.

HYDROLOGISTS designate floods on the basis of the number of years that are likely to elapse between storms and floods of a given size. Within reason, they can tell us over a long enough period, say 500 years, the number of storms of different magnitudes that are

likely to occur. They know that storms of given magnitudes do not occur at equal intervals or even at a semblance of regular intervals. In the nearly 200 years of flood records at Pittsburgh, two of the three largest recorded floods to date occurred in successive years, 1762 and 1763. The flood of 1763 was not exceeded until 1936, 173 years later.

A small, intense storm usually does little damage if it occurs over a large flood plain of a main river because it is not likely to cause a flood that exceeds the capacity of the river channel. But small, intense storms over small tributaries can tax the limited capacities of the channels and, because of high gradients, can cause inundations and generate damaging velocities in local flood plains.

No public or private agency in the Nation undertakes a systematic and complete collection of flood damage soon after it occurs. Estimates of both upstream and downstream flood damage are only approximations. They must be pieced together from estimates of the United States Weather Bureau, the Department of Agriculture, and the Corps of Engineers.

DAMAGE FROM EROSION, sedimentation, and floods is caused by excess water either standing or in motion, but chiefly by the movement of water on the land. We give a summary of the estimates of damage from floods and sedimentation to complete the picture of the total damaging effects of excess standing or moving water on the land.

When a part of the productive constituents of soil is dislodged and carried from its productive location by excess moving water, this is clearly damage from erosion. If the moving mixture of water and sediment also smothers and damages the productive life of plants, the damage cannot be classified as strictly erosion, flood, or sedimentation damage: As the excess water moves, the three forms of damage cannot always be separated. The totals of erosion, sediment, and flood damages are given with these qualifications in mind.

The Soil Conservation Service has estimated that erosion damage in the United States amounts to about 750 million dollars annually. The total yearly damage from sedimentation was set at 160 million dollars, of which 132 million dollars is in upstream areas and 28 million dollars is in downstream areas. Annual upstream flood damages alone were said to average 545 million dollars.

Potential downstream damage from floods and sediment was estimated by the Corps of Engineers to average 911 million dollars annually. This estimate was based on anticipated flood-plain conditions without protective works; it did not take account of damages prevented on properties added to the flood plain as a result of protection.

Thus the potential downstream damage and upstream flood and sediment damage that might occur annually from floods if no protective works were installed were estimated to be 1,588 million dollars. According to this measure of relative importance, downstream damage amounts to 57 percent of the total flood damage.

Much of the downstream damage has been corrected, but correction of the upstream portion, 43 percent, has scarcely begun. When the total damage from erosion of 750 million dollars annually is added to the total damage from floods and sediment, we have a total of potential damage of 2,338 million dollars caused mainly by moving water. That amounts annually to 1.23 dollars an acre of land surface.

The flood-plain area on which flood damage occurs has never been estimated accurately. From data derived from 52 upstream watershed plans, we estimate that the flood plain is slightly less than 8 percent of the total area of the watersheds.

This percentage may represent the proportion of upstream watershed land in agricultural areas that is subject to flood damage, but it is not indicative of the flood-plain land for the entire country. Vast areas of mountains and semidesert lands contain only small acreages of flood plain. Also, the proportion of flood plain to the total drainage of major rivers is doubtless less than 8 percent.

William G. Hoyt and Walter B. Langbein, in their book *Floods*, published in 1955 by Princeton University Press, estimated the flood plain for the Nation at 2.5 percent of the total land surface, or 50 million acres. That probably underestimates the total area, as it does not account adequately for upstream areas of flood plain.

Our total of land in flood plains probably is about 5 percent of the total land surface, or 95 million acres, a figure intermediate between the two estimates.

Using this estimate of the floodable area of the Nation, we find that the total flood damage of 1,588 million dollars in the rural and urban areas amounts to 16.72 dollars an acre for the 95 million acres of flood-plain lands.

Agricultural damages are estimated roughly at about two-thirds of all upstream damage. Nonagricultural damages, including indirect damage, comprise about a third of the total upstream damage. Downstream damages are divided in reverse proportion, about one-third agricultural and two-thirds nonagricultural. On the basis of these relationships, we can conclude that agricultural damages average about 7 to 8 dollars annually per acre of flood plain in the United States.

Upstream flood-control programs therefore are necessarily agricultural flood-control programs with respect to their beneficiaries as well as the location of works of improvement and consequently are programs applied to farmland, largely to benefit farmers.

Downstream programs are primarily works of improvement that benefit largely nonfarm interests. At least two-thirds of them are intended to give protection to urban people or to nonfarm properties in urban and rural districts. Nonagricultural damage in rural areas is largely damage to roads, utilities, and other industrial property. Indirect damage includes loss of wages and profit, injury to health, and increased transportation costs.

Some farmers are opposed to major installations to control floods, particularly when they include downstream programs with large main-stem reservoirs. The large reservoirs often flood out farmlands and destroy farm homes. Rarely are reservoirs placed on urban lands where homes must be abandoned. These works largely benefit nonfarm interests, but they may have serious impact in rural areas.

A desirably complete and sound national flood-control policy and program therefore must take into account and deal with a conflict of urban and rural interests.

SOME SECTIONS of the country have more floods than others.

Almost two-thirds of the country's downstream flood damage occurs in the drainage system of the Mississippi, Ohio, and Missouri Rivers. If we use potential damage (as we described previously) as the basis for showing the patterns of downstream damage, we find that 13 percent of the total damage occurs on the main stem of the upper Mississippi and 24 percent on the lower part of the river—together, 37 percent of all potential damage. The Ohio contributes 12.3 percent, and the two rivers cause a little less than half of all downstream damage in the United States.

The Missouri, Red, Arkansas, and White River drainages together contribute a relatively small part—12.6 percent—of the total flood damage of the Mississippi Basin. The total for the Mississippi River and its tributaries thus is 62 percent of the total potential downstream flood damage in this country.

The Colorado River drainage area contributes only 0.5 percent to downstream flood damage, because the acreage of flood-plain land is small and there is little property in the area that is subject to damage. The Great Lakes area, with 1.3 percent of the Nation's downstream damage, is unimportant in the aggregate of the flood problem.

The Atlantic seaboard contributes a relatively light burden of damages to the national potential total—only 11.1 percent. That is less than that of the upper Mississippi above Cairo, the Ohio, or the coastal drainage area in California, which has 11.7 percent of the Nation's total damage. This relatively heavy damage in California is due to high concentration of property values in exposed alluvial areas and the intensity or high risk of floods.

The Columbia River and other streams in the Pacific Northwest may add 7.4 percent to the potential downstream damage, even though the total volume of flow of the Columbia is second only to that of the Mississippi, and it carries more melting snow—a source of floods—than any other river in the country. The Columbia does not have extensive flood plains or heavy concentrations of properties exposed to flood hazards.

The factors that determine downstream damage are principally the extent of the flood plains, the number and the extent of properties concentrated near rivers, the capacity of the river channels, and the pattern of the storms over the drainage areas.

PATTERNS OF DISTRIBUTION of flood damage in upstream areas deviate markedly from downstream patterns.

Upstream damage is linked closely with the extent of agricultural properties and operations in the thousands of smaller upstream flood plains.

The heaviest upstream damage occurs in nine States south of Kentucky and Virginia and east of the Mississippi. They contain slightly less than 15 percent of all farm values, but they have 29 percent of all upstream flood and sedimentation damage. Their downstream damage is probably less than 8 percent of the national total. Probably close to a third of all the needed upstream flood-control work should be done in these States.

Three other groups of States, the North Central group, the four States of the Southwestern group, and six States of the northern Great Plains receive an almost equal proportion of the total upstream damage—that is, 19, 18, and 20 percent, respectively. The North Central States have about 26 percent of the farm property. The three groups of States have 60 percent of the Nation's farm values. They bear about the same proportion of upstream damage. Crude as this comparison of flood intensity is, it indicates generally that these States, which have uniformly concentrated farm resources, sustain only normal upstream flood damages.

The northern part of the Great Plains corresponds closely to the Missouri River drainage area. The six States in it sustain 6.9 percent of the downstream potential damage, but they suffer 20 percent of its upstream damage. Summer flash floods are frequent. About 75 to 80 percent of the rainfall here falls in the spring and summer.

In the four southern Rocky Mountain States—Colorado, Utah, Arizona, and New Mexico—upstream flood damage amounts to only 2 percent of the national total and downstream damage to 0.05 percent, mainly because of the Colorado River.

The Pacific drainage group of five States sustains 5 percent of the upstream flood damage and 18.1 percent of the downstream damage. Their agriculture, which largely is irrigated, generally is concentrated in the broad alluvial valleys downstream. Consequently it represents heavy concentrations of wealth and income. Many of the areas of the heaviest urban concentration are in the downstream flood plains. The upstream areas have relatively small proportions in flood plains, and agriculture is not important.

A full half of all downstream damage in these States is agricultural damage. When it is noted that urban properties and other nonagricultural properties are also concentrated in the downstream valleys, this equal proportion of agricultural damage serves to emphasize the extraordinary concentration of farm wealth that is exposed to downstream damage.

Conservation of water is no less important than flood control in these States. In no other part of the country does water in all its aspects play such a direct and vital role. The proper combination of land and water reaches its climax in the economic life.

FEDERAL PARTICIPATION in flood-control activities began with the establishment of the Mississippi River Commission in 1879.

The Rivers and Harbors Act of 1917 authorized flood- and debris-control work in the Sacramento-San Joaquin Rivers in California and specified that examinations and surveys for flood control should be comprehensive in scope and should include consideration of the development of water power and such other uses "as may be properly related to or coordinated with the project." As clarified and expanded in subsequent legislation, this language has provided the basic authority and directive for comprehensive studies by the Corps of Engineers for flood control and related purposes.

In the Rivers and Harbors Act of 1927, the Congress authorized the Corps of Engineers to prepare comprehensive studies of the major river basins of the United States. Studies were completed and reports were prepared on 191 river drainage areas.

The Flood Control Act of June 22, 1936, established for the first time a national integrated flood-control policy. It recognized the importance of watershed lands and protection as well as main channel works in the total flood problem. This new responsibility for watersheds was placed in the hands of the Secretary of Agriculture.

It was amended in 1944 to broaden the concept of flood control to include provision for major drainage improvements in programs of the Corps of Engineers. The Congress authorized the Secretary of Agriculture to carry out programs on 11 watersheds. No additional programs were initiated by the Department of Agriculture under the 1936 act, and its application to the Department of Agriculture was repealed in the Watershed Protection and Flood Prevention Act of 1954.

The 1954 act, as amended by Public Law 1018, 84th Congress, in the following year, authorized the Secretary of Agriculture to assist local agencies in planning and carrying out programs for flood control, drainage, irrigation, and other specified water-use purposes on watersheds not exceeding 250 thousand acres in extent. Assistance may be provided for both land-treatment and structural measures, but reservoirs, if included, are limited in size to 25 thousand acre-feet of total capacity and to 5 thousand acre-feet of flood-detention storage. Through these limitations on the size of watersheds and structures, the Congress sought to minimize conflict with the overlapping authority for engineering structures of the Corps of Engineers.

The flood-control program of the Corps of Engineers has been directed primarily toward the major river channels because of their high population and potential productivity of land.

Studies by the corps have ranged from investigations of the water resources and problems of major river basins to flood problems of communities. Several studies have been carried out in cooperation with other Federal agencies that also have responsibility for development of water resources.

The Congress has authorized the Corps of Engineers to carry out 817 projects in which flood control is the primary or a major purpose at a total investment of 9.2 billion dollars. (Converted to an annual cost basis, that sum is equivalent to 324 million dollars at 2.5 percent for 50 years.) Appropriations for these purposes through fiscal 1957 totaled 4.2 billion dollars, 2.6 billion of which was for flood-control projects only.

The added cost of completing the authorized flood-control projects has been estimated by the Corps of Engineers at 5 billion dollars and the authorized projects in which flood control is a major purpose at 1.3 billion dollars.

The generation of hydroelectric power, an important feature of completed multiple-purpose projects of the corps, has accounted for roughly two-thirds of the cost of the projects. Although the importance of hydroelectric power in new projects of the corps has been declining as the better sites for this purpose have been taken up, increasing recognition is being given in these projects to water supply, recreation, and other multiple uses.

The Corps of Engineers has estimated that 391 projects, which were built at a cost of 3.2 billion dollars and on January 30, 1954, had been in operation an average of 11 years, had prevented damages totaling 7.3 billion dollars. This estimate was based on the degree of development of the flood plains when the floods actually occurred. Part of this development has taken place after, and because of, the protection provided by the projects. In determining the economic justification for the construction of a project, however, benefits are limited to the damages that will be prevented on the basis of flood-plain development anticipated without the projects, plus any increase in the net value of flood-plain property as a result of the projects.

ZONING OF FLOOD PLAINS should be considered as an alternative means of reducing losses from floods.

Zoning calls for restricting the use of flood plains in accordance with the frequency of anticipated flooding and damages that cannot be prevented economically. The imposition of such restrictions, however, is a police power of the States and their subdivisions. Zoning holds little political appeal at the local level, however, especially when it must compete with programs of flood protection that are paid for wholly or largely with funds provided by other than local sources.

Little use has been made of flood-plain zoning. Known instances of limited applications of such zoning include Keene, N. H., Los Angeles County, Calif., Jefferson and Milwaukee Counties in Wisconsin, and Duval County, Fla. Even in these few instances, however, it appears that the impetus has come more f om difficulties of drainage and se verage than from the need to adjust t) the hazard of floods.

It is the policy of the Corps of Engineers to require assurance from local governmental units against forms of encroachment on flood plains that would endanger or make ineffective the protection provided by its remedial works. Wider use of all available means to regulate the use of flood plains could mean significantly lower public expenditures for flood control.

ORIGINALLY about 275 million acres, or about 1 acre in 7 in the United States, were poorly drained. Much of it was in flood plains.

Much land in the South Atlantic, gulf coast, and Mississippi Delta areas is poorly drained. Some of the good agricultural lands in northern Ohio, Illinois, Wisconsin, Iowa, and Minnesota need drainage.

Based on trends before 1950 which are projected to 1958, organized drainage districts in 1958 covered 107 million acres, of which 86 million were highly improved and productive agricultural lands. Some 55 million acres of wet lands outside organized districts have been improved by farm drainage. We estimate that about 133 million acres are unimproved wet lands (an area approximately equal in size to Iowa, Kansas, and Missouri combined) and that proper drainage and flood control could make about 44 million additional acres physically suitable for crops and pastures. Whether all such lands should be drained for pastures and crops is debatable, of course, since their use for wildlife

propagation and recreational purposes is often more desirable than their use as reclaimed farmlands.

The advisability of draining additional lands during periods of surplus farm production is sometimes questioned. The problem is not whether these lands will add more to our surplus, but whether, when drainage cost is included, these lands will supply food at a lower cost than lands already tilled. It is largely a matter of relative productivity in terms of the costs. If drained lands have an advantage in this regard, sound policy might require that other low-income lands used for crops be abandoned or changed to a less intensive use.

These low-lying lands generally are less subject to erosion and drought than adjoining lands at a higher elevation. Their potential productivity is relatively high. They are mostly in areas of adequate and dependable rainfall and near markets. To the extent that development is feasible within limits of present costs and benefits, drainage of some lands could facilitate soil-conserving adjustments on lower quality lands in use elsewhere.

DRAINAGE AND FLOOD CONTROL often are interrelated. When set in motion, static water can help to swell a flood flow in a lower area. Waters from upstream areas cannot be classed as controlled, however, if they are managed to avoid damage in one area but become excess and damaging in lower areas of a watershed.

Much of the drainage undertaken up to 1957 has been planned and financed locally. Consequently drainage projects all too often have reduced local damage but have increased drainage and flood problems lower in the drainage area. Furthermore, many locally financed projects have been inadequately planned and built and so have failed. The lesson they teach is the growing and urgent need to coordinate drainage and flood control in the plans of a sufficiently large watershed to take into account all major consequences and returns from both means of water control.

Federal assistance in drainage before 1934 was limited to work of the Department of Agriculture primarily in the fields of research and planning. The Congress took note in the 1944 Flood Control Act that flood control and drainage are closely related by providing that the words "flood control," as used in the declaration of policy in the 1936 Flood Control Act, should be construed to include "channel and major drainage improvements." Under this authority, the Corps of Engineers has included in flood-control projects such measures as are needed to provide improved major drainage outlets. Secondary drainage works and needed improvements on private lands, however, are still the responsibility of private owners and non-Federal interests.

Drainage problems existed on 55 percent (about 23.9 million acres) of the gross agricultural area affected by the authorized Federal flood-control program of the Corps of Engineers. The corps estimated that the increased production from flood protection and drainage on these projects is equivalent to adding 8 million acres of new productive land. These lands are interspersed with and added to 43.6 million acres of farmland that are already in a high state of production. In effect, they are thus net additions to going farms at a time when improved techniques and new machinery are causing farmers in general to take every practical measure to enlarge the size of their farm units.

INCREASED FEDERAL DRAINAGE assistance is available through the watershed-protection and flood-prevention program of the Department of Agriculture.

The basic act, Public Law 566 of 1954, was amended in 1956 to broaden the program by authorizing (in addition to flood control) drainage, irrigation, water supply, and other purposes. Financial assistance was made available for the installation of drainage measures to provide more efficient land use on existing farms and ranches. The Federal share of the costs allocated to drainage is limited to 45 percent of the total drainage cost. Under the Department's policy in 1957, drainage of land not presently in agricultural use must be incidental to—not a primary purpose of—the measures for which assistance may be provided.

The extent of Federal participation in the watershed program under Public Law 566 is greater for flood prevention than for other purposes, as the Federal Government pays the full costs of constructing flood-prevention works. But for drainage and other purposes, non-Federal interests are required to share the cost of installing measures, as determined by the Secretary of Agriculture on the basis of direct identifiable benefits.

As drainage benefits are largely identifiable with specific tracts of land, non-Federal interests and private owners would pay the major share of the cost of drainage. Under Public Law 566, however, they would contribute relatively little to the cost of flood-control installations. Works that can be financed with Federal funds do not meet with as much local resistance or lack of interest as those requiring the raising of funds locally. These provisions of the law tend to lead to lopsided planning and development not only with regard to flood control and drainage but also with regard to flood control and water conservation for irrigation and other water needs.

Among proposals of local watershed groups submitted to the Secretary of Agriculture are requests for assistance to install "flood-prevention" measures primarily for drainage improvement. As yet, the amount involved in these requests is not large, but granting them could cause the Federal Government, under the interpretation of "flood prevention" to embark upon a large program of expenditures for local drainage. If it is to be the policy of the Federal Government to bear the major share of the cost of local drainage improvements, the same standard should apply to the programs of all Federal agencies.

FURTHER COORDINATION of upstream and downstream work is a great need in present and future programs. The development of standard procedures for planning and for the evaluation of costs and benefits acceptable to all agencies can do much to bring about more effective coordination. Such procedures are needed to implement uniform principles and criteria for the planning, evaluation, and cost-sharing of Federal project proposals under present programs.

The need for improved coordination will increase as work goes forward under the Watershed Protection and Flood Prevention Act for upstream areas above downstream projects. The problems and needs of the larger basin may not always coincide with those of the small watershed, or vice versa. For instance, they may conflict, as when the prior installation of a number of small headwater reservoirs reduces to an unfavorable status the economic feasibility of downstream works needed to control floods in densely settled main-stream reaches. The institution of small watershed programs, together with programs of the Corps of Engineers, has focused attention on the importance of improved coordination in all major river-basin programs.

ONE PROBLEM that arises in accomplishing effective coordination of development of resources is the diverse and often contradictory cost-sharing provisions that are applicable to projects of different sizes and kinds developed by an agency, and to similar projects developed by different agencies. These differences may arise from diverse provisions in the several acts under which development of resources is carried out and in the administrative rules and procedures under which the work is done.

The fact that the Federal Government pays for all flood-control measures is a temptation to omit other worthy and serviceable features from programs under present watershed-development laws and programs. Under this provision, the tendency is to get maximum development for only one of a number of useful purposes required for complete use of water resources. The omission of feasible and needed multipurpose works may be regretted in later years, in view of the widespread recognition of the growing national need for more water for uses connected with supplemental irrigation, wildlife, recreation, industry, pollution abatement, and ground-water replenishment.

Impairment of full development of resources and future uses of our water supplies may well be a consequence of such partial development.

WE BELIEVE that the remedy lies in two basic changes.

One is the devising of legal and administrative means for improving coordination of upstream and downstream programs of development of resources.

The other is a requirement that all upstream and downstream watershed plans include a complete analysis of all feasible uses of water resources involved, whether all are recommended for construction or not, and that costs of all features recommended be equitably shared by individual, local, State, and Federal beneficiaries.

In short, we must have full and equitable sharing of costs and responsibilities and a genuine partnership effort among local, State, and Federal agencies and identifiable beneficiaries.

Without this effective partnership, more and more responsibility will in time center in the Federal Government. This centering of responsibility may bring undesirable consequences that transcend incomplete development of resources—the gradual undermining of a truly Federal union with balanced responsibilities and powers.

Protecting watersheds— ways and whys.

We have started—none too soon!—a big program to improve and develop watersheds because we have come to realize more fully how the care of watersheds determines whether we are to have floods or usable water, erosion and sediment or productive land. By *M. L. Weinberger,* Farm Economics Research Division, and *Erwin C. Ford,* Planning Division, Soil Conservation Service.

THE DEPARTMENT of Agriculture began in 1946 to install measures to protect 11 watersheds — about 30 million acres—from floods and erosion. It was the start of a national, coordinated program to improve land and water.

Federal expenditures for the improvements to June 30, 1957, totaled about 70 million dollars. Other expenditures, including those for labor and materials, amounted to 47 million dollars.

Under authority of the Flood Control Act of 1944, conservation plans were prepared for 51,268 farms containing more than 11,600,000 acres, or about 39 percent of the total area of the 11 watersheds. The practices installed included contouring of 1,756,- 000 acres, seeding 1,185,000 acres of pasture and range, and making 58 thousand miles of terraces.

About 431 floodwater-retarding structures, 5,962 gully-stabilizing and sediment-control structures, 244 silt and debris basins, and 788 miles of stream-channel improvement were constructed under contract. Grasses, legumes, and trees were planted on more than 189 thousand acres where runoff and silt were serious.

The Congress in 1953 appropriated 5 million dollars for pilot projects in small watersheds. This program was designated to find out the best ways of planning and developing upstream watershed protection and flood pre-

vention through cooperation of local, State, and Federal governments and to demonstrate the benefits to be derived from such improvements.

The planning and installation of improvements were undertaken in 58 small watersheds in 34 States. The recommended measures are expected to cost 69 million dollars. The Federal Government will bear half of the cost, and non-Federal interests will contribute a like amount in labor, services, materials, and money.

Experience in these projects has indicated how watershed projects can be developed successfully.

Two of the pilot projects were completed during the first year of operation. Work plans were completed for all of the 58 watersheds, which contain altogether about 3 million acres. These projects range in size from about 2,500 acres to more than 200 thousand acres. Contour farming was begun on more than 16 thousand acres, 938 miles of terraces were built, 35,800 acres of range improvements were made, 1,142 acres of trees were planted, 113 stabilizing and sediment-control structures were installed, and 34 miles of stream channels were improved in 1956.

By December 31, 1956, 197 floodwater-retarding structures with a total capacity of 97,600 acre-feet had been installed. This represents an average capacity of about 495 acre-feet per structure. Apparently a total of 450 floodwater-control structures and 1,900 stabilizing and sediment-control structures will be required.

The Watershed Protection and Flood Prevention Act, Public Law 566, passed August 4, 1954, and amended by the act of August 7, 1956, provided a new Federal authority for carrying on water-resource developments. This act established arrangements under which local organizations and States may obtain help from the Federal Government through the Secretary of Agriculture in planning and carrying out works of improvement for watershed protection.

Provisions of this legislation require that application for assistance to the Secretary of Agriculture must come from a local organization having authority under State law to carry out, maintain, and operate the works of improvement. The local organization may be a State, a political subdivision of a State, a soil or water conservation district, a flood-prevention or flood-control district, or combinations thereof. Under the laws of most States, soil conservation districts are qualified to act as the sponsoring organizations for projects.

Assistance by the Secretary of Agriculture can be provided only after the State in which the watershed is located has approved the local application or has not disapproved it within 45 days from the date it is submitted.

This act limits the size of the watershed on which assistance can be provided to 250 thousand acres. When the local organization so desires, however, several watersheds that are parts of a larger watershed may be planned for. The act also limits the floodwater-detention capacity of any single structure to 5 thousand acre-feet and the total capacity to 25 thousand acre-feet.

Public response has been impressive. The Governors of all States have provided administrative machinery for carrying out the States' responsibilities in reviewing and approving applications from local organizations for Federal assistance. Up to March 1, 1958, 826 applications for assistance on specific watersheds, representing 63,-508,000 acres in 47 States and Hawaii, were received in Washington. They range in size from 2 thousand acres to 250 thousand acres. Planning has been approved for 330 watersheds, which contain altogether 24,700,000 acres. Installation of works of improvement has been approved for 71 of these watersheds—3,493,000 acres.

THE BENEFITS from watershed protection are many. They vary in kind and amount among the owners and operators of watershed lands. Provision of these benefits depends on acceptance of a remedial program by all participants, each of whom must contribute an amount that varies in kind and extent. Management practices applied by one farmer and water-control structures built by others affect the economy of still others.

These relationships set up different degrees of interest among the beneficiaries in installing and maintaining a project. Because of the nature of the improvements, group action is essential. It requires in turn an understanding by all members of the plans and objectives involved.

A representative organization therefore must sponsor the project. Its responsibilities include development of local interest, cooperation with technicians in deciding upon remedial measures, obtaining easements and rights-of-way for construction of water-management measures, awarding contracts for the installation of structures, collecting the funds necessary to meet non-Federal expenditures, and maintaining and operating the program. To meet these responsibilities adequately, the organization needs legal authority to exercise powers of eminent domain, levy taxes and assessments, borrow money, and carry on other functions ordinarily delegated to local governments.

Legal powers of local organizations generally are adequate to meet minimum requirements of the project sponsors, but they may require some revision. The grant of additional legal powers to districts or the establishment of new districts may be needed.

Soil conservation districts, which have had long experience in soil and water conservation, act as sponsoring organizations in most States.

Several States have passed legislation to authorize establishment of special-purpose districts.

Another problem is the selection of measures that are best suited to the objectives. Selection of the appropriate means falls to the lot of the technicians responsible for making and evaluating the watershed plan. The planners recommend to the sponsoring organization the measures that seem to meet the desires of the local people most economically. Feasible alternative measures may produce slightly different benefits, however, and so may affect different property owners. These differences must be reconciled by the sponsoring agency, and give and take is essential if the work is to be done.

Allocating costs equitably among beneficiaries will become more difficult as the projects develop multiple purposes. No particular problem is involved in allocating the costs of land-treatment measures—farmers generally are willing to bear these costs under the sharing arrangements established by the Agricultural Conservation Program.

Structural measures for the control and management of water produce benefits to downstream owners of property; they may be of relatively little value to the owners on whose lands they are located. Most of the measures of this type so far have been installed for flood prevention. All costs except easements and rights-of-way were paid by the Federal Government. Costs of maintaining and operating the measures are to be borne by local interests. Experience in watershed-protection projects has been too short to demonstrate the most appropriate method of providing funds for these purposes.

Future projects are expected to include additional features for such purposes as water storage for domestic and irrigation uses, recreation, and drainage. Installation of these features will require contributions from non-Federal interests toward the cost of construction. Although the sponsoring organization will be responsible for raising the funds, the way in which that will be done poses several problems.

Each investor must be convinced that the investment will pay. Each participant considers his cost in relation to his anticipated returns. The project measures must be economically feasible, and the costs must be shared in such amounts that they will be profitable to each investor.

Justification of some watershed measures depends on the accrual of benefits over long periods. Investors therefore must consider the future needs for products supplied by the measures and must make allowances for uncertainties. An unfavorable outlook for future conditions may limit the scope of the projects in some watersheds.

Many of the measures desired for watershed protection require little cash outlay, and farmers may apply them in a rather short time with their regular equipment and normal labor force. Other measures may require high cash outlays; some may temporarily curtail current income; some may take years to become effective.

The Watershed Protection and Flood Prevention Act authorized the Secretary of Agriculture to make long-term loans to local organizations to finance watershed improvements. The adequacy of available credit for future needs will be indicated as further experience is gained.

BENEFITS OF WATERSHED protection may be classified into two broad groups—onsite and offsite. The first includes the benefits to the land that result when measures are installed.

Land-treatment measures (including terraces, contour farming, stripcropping, rotations, pasture improvements, range management, contour furrowing, and tree planting) protect the soil from sheet and gully erosion, retard runoff, conserve moisture, and increase yields. These benefits are examples of the onsite effects.

Land-treatment measures also help to reduce damages from floods and sediment and tend to stabilize stream-flows. It is mainly because of these offsite influences that so much interest in watershed protection is expressed by civic groups and governments and by farmers who till bottom lands.

The larger part of the offsite benefits of watershed protection usually is obtained from measures that retard floodwaters and enlarge stream channels. Floodways, levees and dikes, sediment-collecting basins, and gully stabilizers also are included. The maximum usefulness depends on application of land-treatment practices.

Some benefits and certain other effects of watershed protection are difficult to measure in dollars and cents. Prevention of loss of life, illness, and disruption of social activities are strong incentives for flood protection in some watersheds.

Greater use of land and water resources for recreation and stabilization of streamflow often result from watershed developments. Maintenance and expansion of the productive capacity of watershed resources have favorable impacts on the general economy of the surrounding communities. For example, greater stability of operations is assured to processors and handlers of agricultural products.

Reduced rates of erosion on upland fields are one of the major sources of onsite benefits to the farmer. Work plans for watershed protection indicate that installation of recommended improvements would reduce the average rate of sheet erosion by about 45 percent and the rate of gully erosion by 72 percent. The amount of soil saved through prevention of erosion varies by regions, depending on soil, slope, vegetative cover, climate, and the kind and number of conservation practices in use.

Typical reductions in soil loss from sheet and gully erosion attributable to watershed protection are 64 percent in the Southeast, 72 percent in the Great Plains, 43 percent in the central Southwest, 51 percent in the North Central States, and 26 percent in the Western States.

Watershed-protection measures usually required for prevention of erosion have other beneficial onsite effects. For instance, they increase the water-holding capacity of the soil and the rate of water infiltration into the soil.

Adjustments in land use may be a necessary part of watershed protection. Construction of terraces and water-ways, seeding of pastures and meadows, and changes in cropping rotations may require 5 or 10 years to become fully effective. Net income may be reduced during those years. Once the farming systems have become effective, however, incomes may be expected to increase substantially. Based on evaluations of the watershed-protection measures recommended for installation in pilot watersheds, annual farm income would increase by 550 dollars a farm as a result of increased crop and pasture yields, or an average of about 2.50 dollars an acre.

Soil transported by water from farm-lands, roadbanks, streambanks, and other sources creates additional damage when it is deposited on or in fertile bottom lands, roads and culverts, waterways, drainage and irrigation ditches, and water-storage reservoirs. Sediment carried by floodwaters adds to the damaging effects of inundation, especially in urban areas. Costs of water treatment for domestic and industrial uses are also affected by sediment. Annual damage from sedimentation on the 58 pilot watersheds has been estimated at 332 thousand dollars. This loss equals 14 cents an acre of watershed land and 1.80 dollars an acre of land in the flood plains. In terms of average soil erosion of all kinds, the sediment damage is 38.60 dollars for each thousand tons a year.

Sixty-one percent of all damage from

sedimentation in the watersheds occurred from overbank deposition on farmlands. Sometimes soil productivity is restored soon after flooding by removal of the deposits, but often the cost of removal is excessive. If the deposits are entirely sterile, full production may never be regained. Additional cropping practices, such as application of fertilizer and green manuring, may be applied in attempting to rebuild the topsoil. Frequently it becomes necessary to discontinue cropping and revert to grazing or to no productive use. Application of watershed-protection measures are expected to reduce these losses by 70 percent.

Losses from deposition in stream channels and ditches in 52 watersheds amount to 36 percent of all damage from sedimentation. The damages occur mainly through increased costs of maintaining drainage, irrigation, and roadside ditches and from swamping of farmlands. Swamping is caused by raising the level of the water table, thereby creating inadequate drainage for crop production. Swamping occurs frequently on streams that have low gradients and that drain areas with high rates of erosion. The problem is fairly common in the Piedmont and coastal areas of the Southern States. It is estimated that damages from sedimentation of waterways in the 52 watersheds would be reduced 84 percent by installation of protective measures.

In the watersheds we cited, average annual damages from floodwaters total more than 2.25 million dollars. This loss is equal to about 1 dollar for each watershed acre, or 12.30 dollars for each of the 183 thousand acres of flood-plain land that is subject to damage from floods. Planned watershed improvements would reduce this loss by 83 percent.

Agricultural benefits occur mainly from increased crop and pasture production, lower costs of repairing fences, buildings, and other fixed improvements. Prevention of scour and streambank erosion, although only a small percentage of the agricultural benefits, is important, because it maintains the productive capacity of the lands.

Land in the flood plains of many headwater streams is idle or limited to use as low-yielding pasture and meadows. This low intensity of use often is caused by frequent floods, swamping, poor drainage deposition, and scour. As many flood-plain soils are potentially high in productivity, farmers are anxious to utilize these lands in raising high-value crops. In several watersheds where flood protection has been provided by floodwater-retarding structures and stream-channel improvements, such changes in land use have been observed. Intensifying the use of lands protected from flood hazards may require clearing, drainage, and other improvements.

In 35 watersheds, including a total of 112,300 acres of bottom land affected by floods, we expect that 23,900 acres will be put to more intensive uses. The net value of the increased production would average about 15 dollars annually on each acre that is benefited. In these watersheds, a similar benefit is expected from improved drainage on 20,100 acres of bottom land. The net value of increased production made possible by drainage would average 7 dollars annually on each improved acre.

Planning watershed-protection projects offers an opportunity to consider needs for domestic use, irrigation, livestock, and recreation. Floodwater-retarding structures are planned for construction at the most favorable sites on the streams. Thus, if storage of water is desired at a later time, only the less feasible locations are left for construction of reservoirs. Incorporating all needs for water management in one watershed plan may cut the cost of construction. If a reservoir is built on a site so as to control floods, besides storing water, the cost assigned to each purpose would be lower than if separate single-purpose structures were built. Only a few watershed-protection projects planned so far include multiple-purpose structures.

In watersheds where flood and erosion damages are severe or where good sites for water-control structures are scarce, total costs of protection will be higher than in watersheds where floods and erosion are less troublesome and good sites for structures are plentiful. Costs of individual measures are more uniform, although they also vary with soil conditions, slope of the land, plant cover, stream characteristics, and land use.

The estimated average cost of installing land-treatment measures would average about 10 dollars an acre of watershed land.

Floodwater-retarding structures included in watershed plans prepared to date vary in size from only a few to 5 thousand acre-feet of storage capacity. In 33 watershed plans, 303 structures are recommended at an average cost of 50,150 dollars. This cost averages 67 dollars an acre-foot of storage capacity. Annual benefits produced from this initial investment are expected to reach 1.4 million dollars, not including those obtained from use of temporary water storage retained in the sediment pools.

When installed, these floodwater-retarding structures would inundate 7 thousand acres of land permanently and 15 thousand acres periodically. They would provide a substantial degree of flood protection on 98 thousand acres of more productive bottom lands. Nonagricultural properties also would be protected.

Stream-channel improvements provide flood-control and drainage benefits to bottom lands in the watersheds where temporary storage of runoff would be less effective. In 15 planned watersheds, including more than 516 thousand acres, 233 miles of recommended stream-channel improvement are expected to cost a little more than 3 million dollars, or an average of 13 thousand dollars a mile. Benefits from flood protection and drainage in the amount of 426 thousand dollars annually would average 14.06 dollars an acre on 30,300 acres of agricultural land. About 28 percent of this benefit would result from restoring lands to the use they had before they were flooded.

Drainage benefits account for 19 percent of the total benefits from stream-channel improvements. Increasing production through improved drainage and restoration of the former use helps to increase incomes on low-income farms.

Studies of 36 planned projects throughout the country indicated that the annual benefits of watershed protection exceed the annual equivalent of costs by 88 percent—that is, annual returns are expected to be 1.88 dollars for each dollar of annual costs. This comparison does not include the costs and benefits of the land-treatment measures; they would increase the amount of net gain. Corresponding comparisons of benefits to costs show that benefits exceed costs of floodwater-retarding structures by 70 percent and of channel improvements by 114 percent.

PRELIMINARY ESTIMATES are that about 595 million acres of eroding land contribute flood damage and sediment to about 45 million acres of farmland and property in small watersheds.

The treatment of about half of the impaired watershed lands would not be physically or economically feasible under existing economic conditions. On the rest—about 297 million acres—in about 4 thousand watersheds of less than 250 thousand acres protective measures seem to be warranted in the near future. We estimate that (on the basis of 1957 prices) the cost of such treatment would approximate 6 billion dollars.

The number of watersheds that will eventually be protected, developed, and improved depends on conditions we cannot foresee. As more flood plains are developed, the need for watershed protection will increase, but that need may be offset partly by zoning programs, which may provide guidance for new developments.

The classification of rural land.

This chapter takes our consideration of land values one step further and puts it in a broader frame. Tracts can be classified—typed, described, and grouped as to use and quality—to provide information for farmers, bankers, assessors, land buyers, officials, and others. By *Frederick K. Nunns*, director of the Land Study Bureau, University of Hawaii; formerly agricultural economist, Farm Economics Research Division.

WE CLASSIFY TRACTS of land for numerous reasons. Bankers want information on which to base loans. Assessors need data on relative productivity as a basis for tax levies. Farmers, land buyers, and agricultural agencies want information on probable yields and profits from adapted crops.

Classifications of tenure indicate the way in which land is owned and by whom it is used. Rural lands are classified periodically as to types of farming in order to show location and trends in size and type of farming enterprises.

Public grazing and forest lands are classified to help determine their most profitable uses and wise management.

Classifications are made to help communities that require systematic information when they consider development of irrigation, flood, and drainage projects.

Maps and tabulations are commonly used to help present and record the results of land classifications.

The best known classifications are those that deal with soils, erosion control, and crop yields. These are largely physical types, but classifications made according to tenure, use, financial returns, and market value are known as economic types.

Physical classifications of land may be used to make economic classifications by applying monetary interpretations. An example: The various land types of an area are classified as to tons of alfalfa they produce in a year. The classes are known as 2-ton, 4-ton, and 6-ton alfalfa lands. They are converted to economic classes by applying sales prices and costs to estimated yields, and thereby annual dollar returns per acre are obtained. In turn, a second form of economic classification may be created by converting the various classes of annual dollars of return per acre to classes of land values per acre. This is done by such devices as capitalizing the annual income and comparison with market sale prices.

The close links between physical and economic considerations require that both be included in this discussion of land classification.

Land is classified by many different methods. I discuss some of the established systems that illustrate the various techniques and objectives.

STANDARD SOIL SURVEYS bear closely on land classifications.

Their basic purpose is to furnish information on which to make predictions as to the behavior and capabilities of various soils. Defined ranges and combinations of physical characteristics are identified, mapped, and named as different soils.

The usefulness of a soil survey in contributing to various classifications of land is governed by several factors. One is the degree of detailed information required for a specific objective.

When detailed information is needed, a generalized soil survey cannot be expected to be as useful as a detailed soil classification.

Another factor is the planning of the soil survey toward a particular land-use objective. If a survey is made and interpreted under the assumption of dryland agriculture, for example, its usefulness for evaluations of irrigated agriculture may be limited.

A third factor is the ability of the technicians to produce absolute as well as relative estimates of productivity.

CLASSIFICATIONS OF PRODUCTIVITY made from soil surveys are useful in several ways. Crop yields on absolute and relative bases are predicted by soil types according to defined farming systems and levels of management. A classification may be presented in a table or map, as the users prefer.

This type of classification has been made over a broad area by various State and Federal workers. I give a few examples.

The University of Nebraska in Research Bulletin No. 98 presented a technique whereby estimated acre yields of corn, wheat, oats, alfalfa, and pasture were related to various types of soil and land.

L. F. Gieseker, of the Montana Agricultural Experiment Station, expressed productivity classes in terms of bushels of wheat per acre for nonirrigated farmland and in terms of the number of acres necessary to graze a 1,000-pound steer during a 10-month season for grazing land.

R. E. Storie, of the California Agricultural Experiment Station, developed a method of classification whereby the productivity of various soils was expressed in relative terms through an index. The technique appears best adapted to the evaluation of lands for irrigation.

The University of Maryland created a productivity classification of its various soil types by rating the estimated productivity of various crops in relative terms in indexes.

Two of these classification systems have somewhat broader uses because physical productivity is expressed in absolute as well as relative terms. The results can be converted to a form of economic land classification. The degree of convertibility depends on the adequacy of available data on costs that are pertinent to the crop-yield estimates. Supplemental economic studies of various kinds are necessary to arrive at classifications of net income. Classifications from these techniques have been used in connection with tax-equalization studies, production-control programs, land-use adjustment programs, and economic studies.

Certain imperfections are inevitable, but the results are becoming more precise and economically measurable. Absolute estimates of productivity are generally more useful than relative estimates, and estimates of productivity that are accompanied by information on costs and cultural practices are more useful than those that omit it.

These classifications go out of date in time, because of technological and economic changes, but the adjustments needed to make them current can be made because the basic source of information, the soil survey, is intact for reinterpretation.

CLASSIFICATIONS of land capability have become familiar to many farmers. They were designed by the Soil Conservation Service to focus attention on the need and place for conservation practices to reduce production losses from erosion, protect land from floods, and improve drainage.

They are a form of soil-survey interpretation. The results are recorded on maps. There are eight land-capability classes and many subclasses.

The first four classes of land are considered suitable for safe and profitable cultivation if specified management practices are observed. Class I land may be used for crops, pasture, range, woodland, or wildlife. No (or relatively inexpensive) conservation practices are necessary for accomplishing high-level production or soil protection. Classes II, III, and IV have progressively more limitations in use, or they require increasingly costly practices for soil protection or improvement of productivity.

Land classes V, VI, and VII are generally considered unsuitable for cultivation but can be used for grazing or forestry. As with the first three classes, limitations in use or in protective practices or reductions in productivity increase as the class number becomes larger. Land in class VIII is unsuitable for cultivation, grazing, and forestry but is suitable for wildlife, recreation, or watershed uses.

The subclasses provide additional information regarding the kinds of limitations within each class of land.

Land-capability classifications can be put to other uses, but those who use them should remember that the classifications were intended primarily for one purpose.

Those who would convert land capability classifications to an economic land classification are confronted with difficulty, as the system is more concerned with land use and conservation practices than with financial productivity as such. Economic considerations receive attention in this classification, but the indicators of physical returns or costs of management practices are not easily converted to quantitative measurement.

The term "land capability" is somewhat broad. Designers of the system probably intended the word "capability" to mean principally that certain lands can be put to broader uses with fewer conservation practices than others. It should be clear that this classification does not necessarily indicate relative or absolute capabilities of net returns from various uses. The term is probably here to stay, however, and most people seem aware of its intended meaning.

CLASSIFICATION OF FOREST LANDS has been performed by various agencies, but the principal responsibility for it is borne by the Forest Service. The Congress authorized the Forest Service in 1928 to perform a nationwide survey. Inventories had been made of 504.6 million of the 648 million acres of forest areas in continental United States and 10.4 million acres in coastal Alaska by 1957.

The immediate objectives of the nationwide forest survey included the location, extent, kind, availability, and ownership of timber supplies; present and potential productivity of forested areas; depletion and replenishment rates of timber products; and information administratively useful for using, protecting, and developing forest resources and industries.

The inventory classifies many items, which include: Ownership in various public and private forms; location and area of forest lands; commercial and noncommercial forest lands, types, and acreages; types and species of woody vegetation; size of stand; age of the growth; the type and volume of sawtimber; rates of annual growth; and rates of depletion.

The information is a supporting base for plans to meet our future requirements of wood products.

The classification is suited to the purposes intended, but sometimes the factors are not easily converted to precise amounts of income from land.

Public and private ownerships and such multiple uses as watersheds, recreation, commercial harvesting, and grazing complicate calculations.

Gross returns may be calculated with some accuracy from sales and use leases when timber or pulpwood harvests occur. Returns from wildlife, recreation, and watershed uses are less tangible. Costs of production, such as artificial restocking, protection, roadbuilding, and administration may be derived separately with varying degrees of success. Costs of harvesting are frequently dispersed among public and private sources. The larger private timber and pulpwood firms have had better opportunity to accumulate the economic facts of forest production.

The classification of publicly owned grazing lands is done principally by the Bureau of Land Management of the Department of the Interior and the Forest Service, which are administratively responsible for most of the publicly owned grazing land.

Each agency classifies its grazing lands as a means of planning full but safe utilization of the areas. The classification indicates the number and type of animals that may be grazed gainfully for a specified period on any tract without danger to the quality and supply of grasses or shrubs the next year.

Grazing permits are issued in accordance with the classifications that indicate the respective livestock-carrying capacities.

CLASSIFICATION of lands to determine suitability for irrigation is a difficult task, in which the Bureau of Reclamation became a leader when the Congress specified in the Fact Finders' Act of 1924 that lands proposed for irrigation development "shall be classified with respect to their capacity, under a proper agricultural program to support a farm family and pay water charges."

The Bureau of Reclamation has developed a system whereby technicians classify the suitability of various lands for irrigation agriculture.

Essentials of the method are summarized here. The system uses six classes of land. The first four contain lands suitable for irrigation agriculture. The fifth indicates temporary unsuitability. The sixth indicates definite unsuitability. The association of physical and economic considerations is evident in the basic definitions of the classes.

Class 1 lands have a relatively high capacity to pay charges under irrigation. Soil, topographic, and drainage characteristics are highly favorable, and a wide range of crops adapted to the climate may be produced with relatively high yields and at low cost.

Class 2 lands have intermediate payment capacity if irrigated. The ability to produce crops may be as high as that for class 1 lands, but production, land development, and drainage costs are higher. The payment capacity is somewhat less. Or production costs may be low, but the capacity of the soil for crop production is moderately lower than for lands in class 1.

Class 3 lands are suitable for irrigation, but they approach borderline qualification because of more extreme deficiencies in the soil or in topographic or drainage characteristics than are described for lands in class 2.

Class 4 lands are designated only after special economic and engineering studies have shown them to be suitable for irrigation. Some lands in this class may be costly to irrigate, but returns are adequate because intensive crop production can be carried on. In other instances, yields of adapted crops are low, but the costs also are low and the tracts may be operated profitably within certain farm units.

Class 5 lands are temporarily considered unsuitable for irrigation, but specific favorable conditions warrant further consideration. When special studies indicate that it is feasible to irrigate these lands, an appropriate arable class is assigned them. Otherwise they are put in class 6.

Class 6 lands do not have sufficient payment capacity to justify irrigation. A wide variety of physical and economic conditions may be the reason.

Before field classification is begun, a set of land-classification specifications is prepared. The specifications are based on information from preliminary inspections of the area and on comparison with data from similar areas.

The specified soil characteristics for each land class reflect an estimated range of gross returns from anticipated crop yields under described farming practices. As in soil survey procedure, the rated characteristics include depth, organic content, fertility, ability to absorb, store, and release moisture for crops, the ease with which excess moisture is drained from crop roots, salt content which might damage crop growth, response to fertilizers, erodibility, and ease or difficulty of tillage.

Similarly, the specified topographic and drainage characteristics for each class are intended to reflect a known justifiable range of development costs. The permissible land-development costs for each class come from a preliminary estimate of payment capacity under irrigation. Development costs include necessary land leveling, farm irrigation systems, farm drainage systems, and removal of stones and vegetation.

In addition, land slope also determines the class because it affects the range of crops and farming costs. The mapping technicians apply these specifications as they inspect the land areas. Refinements in the specifications are made if a need arises.

A field classifier has considerable responsibility as he weighs the factors that add or detract from the suitability of the land for irrigation, for it is he who maps the boundaries and records the land class for each tract investigated. Engineering and economic measurements supplement his work.

The classification system has the aim of segregating lands that appear to be suitable for profitable irrigation agriculture from those that apparently are not suitable for irrigation.

THE CORNELL SYSTEM of economic land classification is best known in the eastern part of the country.

Its primary objectives are to help buyers select farms that can give profitable returns and to get information useful for community planning, credit programs, farm management, and tax assessments.

Details of the present-day Cornell system are given in the publication, An Economic Classification of Farm Areas [in] Lewis County, New York; Cornell Economic Land Classification Leaflet 4. It is by H. E. Conklin and Broder F. Lucas, who point out that the classification represents income appraisals of farm areas extending into the foreseeable future and that the classes indicate relative probability of success rather than specific levels of dollar income.

In the Cornell classification, land in class I comprises areas in which the chances for success in full-time commercial farming are slight. Included are areas once farmed and later abandoned. Forest enterprise is dominant. Recreational interests are expanding.

Class II includes areas in which chances for success in farming are too slight for full-time commercial farming to survive. Much of the soil has low productivity. Abandoned land is common. Much of the farming is on a part-time basis. Some of the land is used successfully for pasture or crops by nonresident farmers, whose base operations are in better land-class areas.

Class III is occupied by farms on which chances for financial success are moderate, provided caution is exercised in expanding capital equipment, cash outlays are kept low, and debt loads are minimized. Buildings and equipment are maintained at about the minimum necessary for operation. Land resources and location limit the chances for success. Technical improvements in agriculture probably will weaken the competitive position of the farms on class III, but most farms will continue in full-time commercial farming in the immediate future.

Class III–X contains land of higher potentialities but is currently in this level because of undersized farm units or less profitable enterprises.

Class III–Y contains farms benefited by superior managerial skill but with land of inferior quality. In event of unusual losses or price declines, these farms probably will not survive.

Class IV consists of farms on which chances for financial success are good. Agriculture is well adjusted. Public facilities and social institutions are adequate and readily supported.

Class IV–X contains farms of class V incomes, provided moderate adjustments are made in size of unit and operations.

Class IV–Y contains farms benefited by superior managerial skill but of inferior land quality.

Class V includes areas in which land

resources are strong and farm size and organization are adjusted for large-scale operation. The land will support heavy investments in buildings, equipment, feeds, fertilizers, and labor.

Class VI is found only where operations are well adjusted on the strongest land resources. Cropping systems support much livestock. Buildings and equipment are adequate and are well maintained. Farms of these areas produce the highest standard of living and incomes among the land classes.

The land class or level of anticipated income for each farm is rated by field workers by a combination of two methods. Eighty percent of the farms are classified by rapid observation of the number, type, and condition of buildings, farm equipment, crops, and livestock near the farmstead. Plotting the farm boundaries is considered too expensive. Twenty percent of the farms are classified from information gained in interviews with the operators.

The resulting land-classification map is derived from classification of individual incomes from farming. Land-class boundaries might be expected to follow farm boundaries, but actually they do not, because the boundaries are not determined. All farmsteads, however, are plotted on the map, and any farmstead within a given boundary is the indicator of land class for the entire farm.

Income expectancies of the farm businesses are based on the "most probable operator." The method appears to assume an essentially stabilized situation with respect to size of farm, type of farm enterprise, tax assessment, and public services. Therefore the anticipated "most probable operator" would be expected to farm much as his predecessors farmed.

The attribute classified in this method is farm-unit income, but Dr. Conklin and Mr. Lucas express the various class categories in terms of the relative probabilities of farming success.

The Cornell system has been used a good deal in New York but hardly at all in semiarid and arid sections. Western agriculturists believe that the condition and number of buildings, equipment, crops, and livestock do not reliably indicate income accumulated from the local farm business and that types and sizes of farms are not necessarily stabilized.

LAND CLASSIFICATIONS made as a basis for tax assessments are of interest to rural taxpayers because nobody wants to pay more than his share of the public expenses. Equitable tax assessment is difficult.

Instances are known in which productive farmlands have been assessed at the same rate as poor farmlands. Grazing lands that have never been plowed have sometimes been assessed as farmlands because the original classification considered nearly level topography to be the essential qualification. Early classifications for tax-assessment purposes often were made under contract by persons who lacked training and experience for such work.

New advances in agronomy, soil science, and economics and records of crop yields now provide means for systematizing tax assessments.

Many States are overhauling antiquated assessment systems by using newer, more scientific methods.

Among them is Montana, which started to reclassify its rural lands for this purpose. The technique, which is explained in Montana Agricultural Experiment Station Bulletin 459, uses the services of agricultural technicians and information from farmers, ranchers, soil surveys, and records of crop yields to classify lands according to use and yields. Grades of productivity associated with each use are expressed in terms of average acre yields of a major crop. Bushels of wheat are the measure of productivity for nonirrigated lands. Tons of alfalfa are the measure of productivity for irrigated lands. The number of acres necessary to graze an animal unit for a specified time is the measure for grazing and pasturelands.

The classification provides the basis

for subsequent dollar valuation and tax assessment. A number of steps are followed. County commissioners review the nature and number of inequities resulting from existing classification for tax-assessment purposes. They determine the availability of specialists in soils, crops, economics, and other aspects of land classification and the availability of soil classifications, crop productivity and grazing-capacity maps, aerial photographs, county maps, and other materials. If a need for reclassification exists, meetings are held to inform the public and enlist support for the proposed program. The commissioners appoint the classification staff, and a plan of operation is developed that is acceptable to the State board of tax equalization.

The classification staff selects a few sample townships, which contain a cross section of the soils and types of farms or ranches in the county. Through soil studies, conferences with farmers, and reference to maps showing yields and productivity, levels of productivity are established for each land type within the sample townships. The classes of use and grades of productivity for each type of land are then mapped on work sheets, which also indicate ownerships. Work within the sample townships is carefully reviewed, because it is to serve as a model for the rest of the county. The results of the classification work in the sample townships are presented at public meetings for review and possible improvement. Finally the rest of the county is classified.

Results have been encouraging. Two salient factors are that the county staffs have professional assistance and that the use of soil surveys insures a basis for establishing the production possibilities of land, uncomplicated by differences in managerial skill, labor, and capital. They are more consistent than the proposals of local groups might be without such aids. Public participation helps to generate interest, add information, and increase acceptance of the completed product.

Precautions are taken to balance local opinions, which may reflect partisanship, and unconsidered differences in managerial skill against scientific information about differences in land.

A more comprehensive method for improving tax assessment of farm lands has been developed by the Nebraska Agricultural Experiment Station. Details of the system are presented in a publication, Valuation of Farm Land for Tax Assessment, Bulletin 427, by Howard W. Ottoson, Andrew R. Aandahl, and L. Burbank Kristjanson. It was published in 1954.

Whereas the Montana method, published in 1949, limits itself to estimates of actual and relative crop and pasture yields, the Nebraska method takes additional steps by converting estimated crop and pasture yields to net income per acre, which is converted to land value.

The steps of the Nebraska procedure are:

1. Make a soils map of the county if an adequate soil survey does not exist.

2. Estimate the proportion of various crops and pasture commonly grown on each soil.

3. Estimate average crop yields per acre for the soil-management system most commonly used on each soil.

4. Estimate a net income (economic) rating for each soil. This involves the application of assumed long-term prices and costs to the estimated yields of crop and pasture production. To obtain net income per acre, expenses commonly associated with the typical cropping system for each soil are subtracted from the gross income. These expenses include charges for labor and management as well as for equipment, seed, and miscellaneous cash expenses. Cropping expenses may be based on estimated custom rates for hire of various crop operations, plus cost of the seed. Care must be taken that estimated custom rates are not warped by unusual conditions of supply and demand for such services. If certain operations are seldom done by custom hire, it may be necessary to calculate a rea-

sonable rate. Custom rates are useful because they include charges for labor and management as well as expenses for operating the machinery. Custom rates also conform with tax assessment practices by using average costs per acre to arrive at net income, regardless of variations in cost that might occur from individual differences in farm size. The income estimate for each soil is supplemented by a relative economic rating. This is accomplished by assigning a rating of 100 to the soil determined to have the highest net income per acre, and assigning proportionate ratings to soils with lower net incomes per acre. If pasture appears to be a more profitable use than crop production on a particular soil, the rating or income level of pasture use will be selected unless the size and location of the soil tract indicate that such use is impractical.

5. Measure the acreages of each soil on each assessment unit. The assessment unit might be 40 acres, a fraction thereof, or a farm of whatever size.

6. Calculate a weighted economic rating for each assessment unit. This is done by multiplying the acreage of each soil by its economic rating (index). The sum of all the products is divided by the total acreage in the assessment unit.

7. Estimate the approximate sale value for each assessment unit, without buildings, on the basis of the economic rating. This requires a study of selected farm sale prices over a considerable period, and comparison of sales prices to estimated economic ratings. Farm sale prices are a check on accuracy of the relative economic ratings. They also provide a reference point to which the economic ratings can be tied to sale value. Further, farm sale prices can be used to convert economic ratings to sale values, in the case of tracts that have seldom been on the land market.

8. Calculate the adjusted sale value if there are farm buildings on the tract. This requires rating of types, adequacy, and quality of buildings and reference to farm sales.

445509°—58——25

9. Estimate the adjustment in sale value that is necessary according to location of the farmstead from schools, churches, market centers, recreational facilities, and roads. Opinions of farmers and information about farm sales are useful in making this determination.

10. Estimate the sale value of assessment units with buildings, according to economic ratings of the soil, with adjustments necessary for buildings, and location of the farmstead.

Originators of the method recommend that the county assessor enlist support from a volunteer committee of farmers, agricultural technicians, a school administrator, and a realtor. That assistance would be particularly helpful in review and criticism.

The Nebraska method is based on scientific information and the experience of the people affected. Public participation makes the results more accurate and better understood and accepted. Successive steps and techniques of the classification are presumably recorded and available for inspection or change if a need arises.

FEW SYSTEMS of land classification exist that completely cover large areas. The United States Census of Agriculture provides nationwide coverage of information classified as to land tenure, use, crop yields, value, and other items. Useful as this information is for many purposes, other systems, such as the ones I have discussed, are necessary for the study of certain problems.

The information from any system of land classification can become obsolete. Changes affect the physical as well as the economic productivity of land. Better crop varieties and improved farming practices sometimes have multiplied earlier crop yields. Prices and costs often change considerably and with short notice. The rapidity of economic changes emphasizes the need for economic classifications so designed that necessary revisions can be made quickly and efficiently.

Classifications of land income and value are quickly affected by fluctuations in prices and costs and by changes in crop yields and technology. Nevertheless, they can be systematically renewed if they are based upon classifications of crop yields that in turn are supported by soil surveys. It is essential that the original classifications preserve the identity of the various land or soil types and the supporting physical and economic assumptions. If the data supporting the original classifications are lost, there is no basis for adjustment, and the entire task must be done over.

A revisable system of this type is illustrated by the Nebraska method. If assumed prices and costs change materially, the classification could be adjusted by substituting new estimates against the acreages of anticipated crop and pasture yields. If improved farming practices or superior crop varieties significantly change yields, necessary adjustments could be applied to the recorded acreages of the various soils. In turn, the adjusted physical yields could be reconverted to income and land value. If the farm buildings and access to roads, markets, and other necessities change materially, adjustments in value could also be made because these items are separately recorded in the total valuations.

Land problems are so numerous and different that countless formalized systems of classification would be necessary to throw light directly on each.

Limited time, funds, and talent require compromise of aspirations as well as some methods that can be put, with care, to more than one use.

The scarcity of basic data on land and the high cost of gathering it make people search for information already available in completed land classifications. Any system of land classification is primarily planned for a single purpose, but its information invariably is used for other objectives, if it appears useful.

Additional uses of the information from a given system of land classification may be determined if the potential user can inform himself of the data, techniques, and assumptions that support the system. These items were discussed in connection with revisions of classification data. Given these data, the banker, buyer, farmer, or professional worker can determine whether the available information is usable, and if it is usable, whether it is suitable in unchanged form or whether supplemental information and modifications must be made.

To illustrate, the reader is again referred to the Nebraska method of evaluating farmland for tax assessment purposes. The primary purpose of this classification is obvious, but approximated sales value and land income per acre are also apparent although the original technique indicates that some adjustments might be necessary for farms of unusual size. Average acre yields of crops and pasture by various soils are also available to interested parties. The method has possibilities for supplementary classifications and uses other than its basic objective, if those who make it preserve the supporting information.

Unwary parties have occasionally been known to put existing classifications to uses for which they were not adapted. A simple illustration: A certain acreage was classified as to average tonnage of alfalfa that might be expected from the prevailing system of soil management and the nonirrigated farming. Plans later were made for irrigating this land. It was reasoned that if 3 tons of alfalfa were produced without irrigation, 6 tons per acre could be expected with irrigation. On this basis, cost and return calculations indicated profitable irrigation. Irrigation was introduced, but the nature of the land was such that an excessively high water table developed, alfalfa and other crops were damaged, and costs for a drainage system were prohibitive.

Part of the error may have been laid to the original classifier, who assumed that conditions of nonirrigated farming were evident in the classification. The user, on the other hand, did not check with him to determine whether the classification was accurate for irrigated conditions.

Group action to develop and protect land.

We have to protect our resources of land and water and, as need arises, develop them. Many measures to that end can be applied by individuals on single farms, but others can be undertaken only by group action on a wider basis. Often the engineering and economic factors are complex, and it takes group action to provide the necessary technical help. By *Fred A. Clarenbach* and *John Muehlbeier*, agricultural economists, Farm Economics Research Division.

PEOPLE THEMSELVES can organize to protect and develop land resources. How to organize and for what purposes are key points: The method selected for group action has to be based on what the group wants to get done.

Such action has a long history. Many groups have been highly successful. Some have failed because they did not understand the engineering or economics of the project or because they did not have appropriate organizational, administrative, or financial arrangements to do the job.

Although the Federal Government has had a growing part in the work, activities of State and local governments and private groups also have increased. Many of the major undertakings have involved cooperation among local, State, and Federal agencies and private groups. The processes of working together have not always been smooth. Different interests and jurisdictional disputes are bound to enter when many persons and agencies must get together.

Some of the private groups are small, informal neighborhood associations. Some are large national organizations. Some are concerned primarily with the conservation of soil and water. Others give attention to conservation as one part of their wider interests.

Among the national organizations are the American Farm Bureau Federation, National Farmers Union, National Grange, the National Association of Soil Conservation Districts, the Soil Conservation Society of America, Friends of the Land, the American Watershed Council, Inc., Izaak Walton League of America, the National Reclamation Association, the National Rivers and Harbors Congress, the American Municipal Association, the American Water Works Association, Conservation Foundation, Resources for the Future, Inc., the National Association of Manufacturers, the Chamber of Commerce of the United States, Citizens Committee on Natural Resources, Council of Conservationists, American Forestry Association, National Audubon Society, National Parks Association, Wilderness Society, and others.

Among the organizations that operate on a State or area basis are the Ohio Valley Improvement Association, Brandywine Valley Association, New York Council for Stream Improvement, Connecticut River Watershed Council, Inc., Southeast Sprinkler Irrigation Association, Georgia Water and Sewage Association, League of Wisconsin Municipalities, Feather River Project Association, Irrigation Districts Association of California, the Salt-Wahoo Watershed Associa-

371

tion, Stony Brook-Millstone Watersheds Association, Inc., Four Lakes Watershed Alliance, Mound Branch Watershed Association, Little Trappe Farm Improvement Association, Devil River Watershed Cooperative Association, and Trees for Tomorrow, Inc.

Many towns and counties are interested in water supplies for domestic, industrial, and recreational uses and in protection against floods. Special districts have been organized to deal with problems of drainage, irrigation, floods, and soil erosion.

Within State governments, many types of agencies administer land and water programs. Some are special boards and commissions set up to plan and administer the programs or to handle special segments, such as pollution control, development of small watersheds, or water rights. Often the agencies are part of a larger administrative unit—for example, a department of conservation. State utilities commissions sometimes have jurisdiction over hydroelectric installations and rates. State boards of health typically have responsibilities for abatement of water pollution. State departments of agriculture frequently have important duties with respect to drainage or irrigation. State colleges of agriculture conduct programs of research and education relating to conservation. Many States have formed forestry and park agencies.

The Federal Government maintains the largest groups of professional persons directly concerned with the conservation and development of land and water. Most are in the Department of Agriculture, the Department of the Interior, the Federal Power Commission, the Corps of Engineers, Department of the Army, and the Tennessee Valley Authority.

The chief agencies in the Department of Agriculture that deal with erosion control, watershed works, and land improvement are the Soil Conservation Service, Forest Service, Agricultural Research Service, Farmers Home Administration, Federal Exten-

sion Service, and Agricultural Conservation Program Service.

The chief agencies in the Department of the Interior concerned with similar activities are the Bureau of Reclamation, Bureau of Indian Affairs, Bureau of Land Management, National Park Service, Fish and Wildlife Service, and Geological Survey.

A PERSISTENT question is how best to fit the many related agencies into a working scheme of overall organization. In the face of divergent client-group and agency-group interests, this is not an easy task.

One problem is how to coordinate the activities of the various Federal agencies themselves. After the termination of the National Resources Planning Board, the major departments that have responsibilities in resource development organized a kind of clearinghouse originally called the Federal Inter-Agency River Basin Committee and later designated as the Inter-Agency Committee on Water Resources. In addition, regional committees were organized (for example, the Missouri Basin Inter-Agency Committee), made up of field representatives of Federal agencies. Governors of the States of the region also are invited to attend the meetings or to send representatives. These and similar interagency committees have performed useful services, but they do not yet function as a legal or practical coordinating device.

The primary conclusion reached by a Presidential Advisory Committee on Water Resources Policy was: The greatest single weakness in the Federal Government's activities in the field of water-resource development is the lack of cooperation and coordination of the Federal agencies with each other and with States and local interests. This has been occasioned by the fact that the Federal interest in water-resource development has been expressed in different laws that have empowered different agencies to pursue particular programs for different purposes.

According to the committee, there has been inadequate coordination of the program of one agency with that of another and inadequate consultation with and consideration of the interests of the States, local communities, and individuals most vitally affected. The close connection between the development of water and development of land makes apparent the significance of this conclusion.

Many proposals have been made for reorganization of Federal land- and water-resource agencies, but only relatively minor changes have been made. A persistent theme has been decentralization—a term with diverse meanings. Another persistent theme with variations has been cooperation or partnership.

The organization plan recommended by the Presidential Advisory Committee includes four elements.

First, a river-basin, water-resource committee made up of representatives of Federal Departments having water-resource responsibilities, representatives of the affected States (appointed by the respective governors), and a permanent nonvoting chairman of each committee (appointed by the President). These regional committees would be the principal and continuing means through which the State and Federal agencies would coordinate their development activities. Each committee would prepare and keep up to date a comprehensive plan for the development of water and related land resources. Each committee also would recommend an annual work schedule to be reflected in the budget requests of each cooperating agency.

Second, a permanent Inter-Agency Committee on Water Resources composed of the heads, or other major officials, of the chief Federal agencies with responsibilities in this field. This Committee would be the high-level medium for coordinating the interrelated activities of the several agencies. It would advise the President and also would be the channel for communication between the President and the Federal representative on the regional committees.

Third, a Coordinator of Water Resources, in the Executive Office of the President, to be permanent chairman of the Inter-Agency Committee. With a small staff, the Coordinator would cooperate with the Bureau of the Budget and the Council of Economic Advisers in the evaluation of departmental requests for appropriations. He also would help in reconciling water-resource policies with other Federal policies. He would seek to develop a long-range public works planning. He would take the lead in establishing principles, standards, and procedures to be used by Federal agencies in the development of water-resource programs and projects. He would prepare for the President an annual report on the development of the Nation's resources of land and water.

Fourth, a Board of Review for Water Resources Projects, to be established in the Executive Office of the President. The board would consist of three persons, appointed by the President, who would devote full time to duties of the board and would report to the President through the Coordinator of Water Resources. This kind of review board, which has been recommended frequently by other study commissions, would be expected to provide expert, objective advice on the engineering and economic feasibility of proposed major projects. The members would have had no part in promoting or planning projects under review, nor would they be involved in the subsequent construction of such projects. In addition to reviewing individual projects with the aid of a small staff, the board would evaluate all reports on basin or regional plans, in the light of congressional policies and the criteria established by the Coordinator. The review board would be empowered to recommend any modifications in proposed projects or programs considered desirable from a comprehensive national viewpoint, to recommend changes in criteria for planning and selection of projects, and to advise on other questions referred to it by the President or the Coordinator.

ANOTHER ASPECT is how to coordinate State and Federal activities within the State.

Within the State governments, problems of organization and coordination of agencies and programs are often similar to those encountered at the Federal level. Different and sometimes largely independent State agencies are concerned with collection of basic data, land-use inventories, and land classification, forestry, drainage, irrigation, flood control, water rights, pollution control, review of proposed Federal projects, and assistance to general local governments and to special units, such as soil conservation districts.

Some States have prepared comprehensive plans for development of their resources and to coordinate State activities. Efforts of this kind may require the reorganization or expansion of existing administration. At a minimum, they will necessitate setting up some kind of council of State agencies for natural resources.

The Council of State Governments in the publication, State Administration of Water Resources, in 1957 said: "Existing agencies in many States have a record of substantial achievements. But in the face of increasing demands and strains on present structures and arrangements, careful consideration should be given to proposals for agency organization conducive to a higher degree of program unification. Each State will need to decide which elements of such proposals will be useful and feasible in its particular situation."

Units of local government and many special districts often lack some elements of functional authority or financial power that are necessary if an adequate job of protecting and developing local land and water resources is to be done.

Many units cover areas that are too limited in size and seek to carry out programs that are not well coordinated with projects and activities in neighboring related areas. Cosponsorship of multiple-purpose projects by several units of local government often leads to difficulties in allocation and acceptance of the responsibilities. Frequently there is a tendency to rely heavily on Federal and State agencies for technical planning and for financing locally desired projects.

WE CAN PRESCRIBE no easy or universally applicable solutions for these problems. We can suggest several guidelines based on observations and experiences over the country.

An early step is to provide for widespread discussion of any proposed project—the physical and economic problems, remedial measures, organizational arrangements, and sharing of costs and administrative responsibility. The whole community should know and understand the proposal if the project is to be effective. All interested persons should have an opportunity to participate in the planning and making the decisions. Technicians of State and Federal agencies should make their contributions. All groups thus can help to develop or adapt proposed programs to local needs. This kind of procedure is especially important in programs administered in large areas.

Community groups can improve their chances for a successful project by forming an organization that can raise the funds necessary for planning, constructing, and maintaining the improvements. The funds available for construction often are adequate, but funds for operation and maintenance often are not.

Land-use regulations and zoning ordinances can be used to help direct the orderly development of land and water. Sometimes they can be used also to make unnecessary a large outlay of funds at a later date for protective works. Both can be used by local organizations to help direct private development along lines that are in the public interest. Only local people can apply these powers in most States. In a few States, zoning of flood plains may be initiated by the State. Ordinarily, however, these powers are provided by the State, through enabling legislation, for use by local people.

As more and more programs and projects are proposed, they may conflict with each other, overlap, affect one another adversely, or even damage adjoining areas. Here is an opportunity for the State to minimize difficulties by giving appropriate direction to local efforts. Only through effective State participation can serious problems be avoided.

Differences of opinion sometimes arise within a State over proposed Federal programs. The State government then has an opportunity to act as a relatively impartial agency, considering the desires of both those for and those against the proposal. The State can arrange for an independent study and make the findings available.

States are asked for their views in connection with proposed Federal programs. To the extent that they are prepared to take part in the planning process or are prepared to make a thorough analysis of proposed projects, they can help greatly in adapting Federal programs to local needs and in coordinating programs. To do these various jobs adequately, however, the State governments need to be organized effectively. They also need staff and funds that will permit them to act on an informed basis.

The States could stimulate the protection or development of land and water by sharing in the cost. Some localities do not have the resources to undertake needed work. Also, to the degree that sharing of costs appears to bring out better judgment in the use of public funds, States and local groups might pay more of the cost of the Federal programs they demand.

Inequities exist in cost-sharing arrangements. Local people bear almost all the costs of some public improvements. In these instances, they vote on the question before the improvements are made. Although the Federal Government makes little or no contribution to these improvements, the national public interest in some of them may be very high. The cost of other public improvements is borne largely, if not entirely, however, by the Federal Government. There is no direct control over these expenditures by either local people or the States. There may be limited national public interest in these improvements in some instances because the benefits are mainly local. In the interest of greater equity between those who benefit from proposed projects and those who bear the cost and in the interest of providing the people with more direct choice as to how public funds shall be spent, new arrangements for Federal-State-local cooperation in this matter may be desirable. This might include both the manner and the amount of cost sharing.

MANY OPPORTUNITIES exist for making local-State-Federal cooperation more effective and equitable.

One of these opportunities lies in the selection by local groups of the type of local organization best suited to their needs. The organization should have the powers needed to carry out the program chosen.

A second opportunity lies in active State leadership. This involves having a strong State agency with sufficient resources to be able to work actively with local, Federal, and other State agencies. It necessitates cost sharing in some instances.

A third opportunity exists in providing for greater and more uniform cost sharing in Federal programs. Private beneficiaries could be expected to pay more in relation to their direct benefits.

Working along the lines suggested, responsible groups could be expected to achieve more solid progress in the protection and development of land and water resources. The country also could expect greater discretion in the use of public funds, better coordination of programs, and fewer conflicts.

A new program for better living.

Can people in so-called depressed rural areas gain progress and stability using mainly their own resources? Can they—by taking thought and action—overcome obstacles rooted in old economic, cultural, and physical conditions— obstacles like traditional land-tenure systems, lack of resources, restricted opportunities off the farm that perpetuate an unbalanced man-land relationship, limited markets for new crops, and inadequate zoning? By *Joseph C. Doherty*, Office of Information.

THE RURAL DEVELOPMENT PROGRAM started early in 1955, when the Secretary of Agriculture issued a report that delineated nine areas in which farm income generally was low.

The report—"Development of Agriculture's Human Resources"—suggested changes in Government and private programs and activities to help improve the economic and social conditions of these areas on a permanent basis.

Representatives of Federal departments and land-grant colleges in 28 States met shortly thereafter to chart methods of implementing the Secretary's recommendations.

Their main recommendations were to form State committees to foster development projects in low-income rural areas; organize selected counties or areas for a systematic development program; to begin surveys in development areas, centering mainly on farm improvement, market potential, and needs for jobs off the farm; and to stimulate private initiative to contribute to development projects.

Several States subsequently formed advisory committees, which selected areas in which to begin rural development. Starting a local program generally followed this pattern: Organizing a citizens' planning committee, making a study of existing problems, and start-

ing projects that seemed to have some immediate possibility of success.

The program received further impetus in 1956 through a small appropriation in the Federal budget. Funds were earmarked for direct assistance to pilot areas.

The direct assistance has been mainly the time and skills of agency employees. State extension service staffs added workers for the program. They undertook meetings with small farmers, community groups, and development committees. The Soil Conservation Service stepped up its technical work in development areas, and in the first year of the program mapped nearly 450 thousand acres.

Other Federal and State agencies made special services available to the pilot areas to develop better methods of assisting rural communities in solving their chronic economic problems— limited land, a need for more off-farm jobs, and a lack of proper job training and guidance for rural people. The Farmers Home Administration enlarged its staffs in several counties. Agricultural Stabilization and Conservation Committees in several States increased the amount of money available for conservation work on small farms in these counties. Agricultural experiment stations provided technical aid for surveys and other research in pilot counties and the tabulation and publication of results.

SOME 100 RURAL COUNTIES in 30 States by early 1958 had been selected as "pilot or demonstration" areas in the Rural Development Program. (This includes single-county and multicounty areas.)

Economic planning groups were established in most of these areas. Called rural or resource development committees, they consisted of local citizens. Government workers had an advisory role.

A main objective of the Rural Development Program has been to help underdeveloped rural communities organize such planning groups that would consider the solution to important economic problems, including the use of land, as part of a unified program of development.

The aim has been to encourage local people to think about the long-term future of their areas. Also rural development committees would serve to keep up interest in development projects and gain communitywide support for difficult, often costly adjustments and improvements.

The committees have had three principal responsibilities in the program: To evaluate the resources and needs of their areas in the country and towns; develop plans for improved use of resources; and promote acceptance of area development as a unified, well-coordinated, and continuous community interest.

The rural development committees should not be confused with the county land-use planning groups that existed before 1942. Rural development planning committees have maintained pretty much a locally organized, informal character. They have usually included representatives of nonfarm agencies and interests. The problems they have taken up go beyond agriculture and land planning, although farm development, where possible, has had a central place in most programs.

Rural development nevertheless was envisioned as essentially a local program, organized and carried out by local leaders and resources.

The Under Secretary of Agriculture made this clear when he explained the program to a congressional committee soon after publication of the report on low-income farming areas.

"This will not be a program dominated, administratively or financially, from Washington," he said. "We intend that the program will be the catalyst which brings about the actions at the local level which the people themselves desire. For every dollar and every decision at the Federal level, there will be many decisions at the State and local level."

The term "self-help" fits the Rural Development Program exactly. Experimental by design, the program above all has been an experiment in bringing leaders in business, farming, and civic and community affairs into the guidance and coordination of service and education projects involving State and Federal agencies.

Obviously, the Rural Development Program is just one approach and one means of focusing attention on rural problems.

The improved use and management of land have been one part of a broader concern with the economic social and educational needs of rural people in pilot counties: Land, other natural resources, manpower, and community facilities and services are the raw materials of program planning.

By reviewing a typical county program, we can see a planning committee at work and the amount of interest in land use in a community.

Avoyelles Parish, in east-central Louisiana, organized a development program in January 1957. About half of its total acreage is in cultivation. The rest is forests and swampland. Of about 4,400 farms in the Parish, 70 percent were owner operated in 1954. Nearly two-thirds of the farmers sold an average of less than 2,500 dollars' worth of products. The average farm had 20 acres in row crops, chiefly cotton.

The Avoyelles development group early in 1957 set major goals for a program in a statement of objectives in which these ideals were expressed:

"Prepare soils map showing soils of various areas in Avoyelles.

"Seek to release acreage of land tied up by old folks on welfare.

"Encourage use of more fertilizer and adapted varieties of crops.

"Increase size of farms where requested and when possible.

"Get one or more communities to adopt intensive agricultural practices."

One community in the Parish was chosen by the development group to adopt intensive agricultural practices. Technicians prepared a soil map for the community and explained it to farmers. Technical advice and land-development tools, such as drainage equipment, were made available to farmers as part of the continuing projects in the community.

Farmers in one other community wanted to increase the amount of land available for cultivation. Discussion at regular community meetings brought out two men owned—but did not till— most of the land. The committee got the owners to agree to sell some of their land and arranged for credit so that small farmers could buy it.

A similar problem was to obtain release of tillable land owned by older people who received most of their income from such sources as old-age and survivors insurance.

Other projects in Avoyelles Parish were to develop industry, improve fishing and hunting facilities to attract sportsmen, and develop better health services.

THE RANGE of economic and social conditions or possibilities for improvement in farming, industry, and community development varies greatly among counties and areas.

In his second annual report on the Rural Development Program (September 1957), the Secretary of Agriculture mentioned that point.

"Dent County in the Missouri Ozarks," the report said, "has fewer than 1,500 farm families on farms that are half in timber. In Sandoval County, N. Mex., a majority of the Spanish-American farm families live on tiny plots of land and enjoy few health, education, and recreation facilities. Stevens County, Wash., produces mainly wheat, feed grains, and hay. Many farms in the county have a large acreage."

Despite the wide differences among pilot counties in climate, crops, resources, manpower, farm tenure, and size of units, members of local development committees have recognized land use as a basic problem and have devoted a number of projects to studying the subject and improving the land resources.

Some of these projects have strengthened work already underway. Others have marked a new interest in long-range planning as a way to augment income. County groups have studied or undertaken projects having to do with reforestation, new crops, demonstrations of fertilization, zoning, assessment of industrial sites, landlord-tenant relationships, development of recreation, and drainage projects.

County and community leaders also have shown interest in surveys, records, interviews, and other studies that can give planners, businessmen, and officials a better grasp of economic and social conditions in rural areas.

Some 80 surveys were reported in 45 counties in 1957. They included data on land use, land-treatment practices, land potential, and the ratio of people to land. Questionnaires in the Arkansas Rural Development Program, for example, contained such questions as: "How many acres of land do you rent?" and "Did you lime cropland this spring?" One section deals with "cropland use and yields."

I have mentioned an important initial project in the Rural Development Program: Completion by Soil Conservation Service of soil surveys and mapping in many development counties and areas. In the fiscal year 1957, the first year funds were available, Soil Conservation Service workers did 42 man-years of such work in 53 development counties. The usefulness of such surveys to county planning committees and to farmers themselves is great.

A REVIEW of typical projects that committees have inaugurated or sponsored indicates the wide range of interest in land use and its place in the Rural Development Program.

A group in Covington County, Miss., conducted a countywide campaign to encourage farmers to plant pine seedlings on their idle acres. Agricultural agencies in the county cooperated, and young people did much of the actual planting.

Expansion of production of grain sorghum was an initial aim in west-central Kentucky, where a county group reported that it is a crop well suited to soil in the county.

Extension Service people, working closely with a local produce association, started a commercial vegetable project in Franklin Parish, La. Farmers increased their production of peas, beans, and sweetpotatoes.

Vocational agriculture instructors in a Tennessee mountain community held classes to encourage farmers— who had never done so before—to grow specialty vegetables for market. The first results were the production of 200 acres of peppers, which were sold to a canner.

Traditional systems of land tenure have long been identified with low incomes and a lack of agricultural progress in some places. As one Louisiana Parish committee put it, "The tenant feels no responsibility to improve his place, and the landlord is satisfied to let it remain in a rundown condition." A North Carolina committee said flatly, "The existing tenure pattern does not lend itself to progressive farming."

Rural development leaders in several counties have recognized and tried to meet this problem in the face of many obstacles rooted in the economic, cultural, and physical situation of their area. One pilot county, as an example, reported that new agreements, worked out among some farmers, should lead to a more stable tenure and to better farming.

Another chronic problem is the lack of enough land on small farms to permit adequate production. Small farmers may have too little money to buy more land, and credit may not be available to them. Some counties have made plans to undertake this difficult phase of rural development possibly by farm consolidation; attempts to release land held by large-scale owners and older people who have retired from farming; special credit to help small farmers increase their holdings; and drainage and land rehabilitation.

Off-farm job opportunities, training in industrial skills, and other industrial projects have a direct bearing on this work. Money earned in towns can help pay for farms or enable some to farm part time and release land that will help to make up economic units for others.

Industrial development has held a central place in the thinking of rural communities. It was estimated that some 2,400 organized groups in the United States were competing in 1957 to get new plants and new companies to move to their communities.

Rural Development Program committees have had some advantage in this competition because they usually have drawn on a larger number of individuals who understand better the total county resources and have accurate information on sites for factories, access to water and power, roads and transportation, nearness to marketing centers and raw materials, zoning for industry development, and similar matters, all of which are important in industrial development. Besides, many of these committees have had the special technical services of the State university and the State industry development agency.

People in Kentucky reported considerable planning for long-range industrial uses in the State's program areas. For example, 20 acres had been leased for a new factory in one county. Businessmen in another county raised a fund to buy an industrial park. A major railroad had taken an option on some 400 acres in a third county looking to its use for industry. These activities did not come about as a direct result of the Rural Development Program, but they do indicate the kind of long-range industrial planning and site development that has been going forward in many rural areas.

A development committee in Cumberland County, Va., published a detailed study of available industrial sites in the county, including maps of the site location, information on available transportation and water, proximity to markets and sources of raw material, and site ownership. The study also included information on the labor supply.

The construction of a large industrial plant in an Ohio pilot county raised major issues of rural and urban zoning. The county previously was almost entirely rural, without even a railroad spur line. A subcommittee on planning and zoning was formed to inform citizens about the purpose and importance of zoning, establish a county zoning commission, carry out research on land use to provide facts for county officials, and develop land-use and zoning regulations.

IN THE SHORT TIME it has operated, the Rural Development Program has stimulated new interest in long-range, coordinated economic development in the pilot areas. Programs and research projects in some areas have generated an informed concern about such issues as trends in farming, improper land use, the need for off-farm jobs, and realistic training programs for youth.

In many areas, committees at the local level—informal, volunteer, and without legal or governmental authority—have planned and inaugurated sound development projects.

We cannot measure the exact value of their efforts to arouse an awareness of what economic improvement can mean to an area. We cannot measure exactly their importance in gaining community understanding. Without such an overall planning group, however, a broad program involving many community interests very likely would fail.

Some observers have raised questions regarding the ability of local development committees to accomplish fundamental objectives. They ask:

With no legal authority and little financial resources, can committees bring about significant farm consolidation, so important to efficient farming in many of these areas?

Are such informal, community-based planning groups in a position to advocate realistic, essential changes needed in some rural areas?

Can these committees make significant and permanent changes in tenant-landlord arrangements rooted in the social, economic, and cultural environment of certain areas?

If the large-scale production of new crops—vegetables or berries, for example—affects adversely an area market, will the development program have enough flexibility to encourage adjustment to these new market conditions?

These—and similar—questions deserve conscientious consideration.

We might sum them up in this way: Can immediate, local solutions to chronic problems caused by low income in some rural areas be reconciled with the need for broader, national solutions?

The answer must be yes, of course.

Henry Simons in his book, *Economic Policy for a Free Society*, said:

"Democratic process is an invention of local bodies. Free, responsible local bodies correspond, in the political system, to free, responsible individuals or families and voluntary associations in the good society. A people wisely conserving its liberties will seek ever to enlarge the range and degree of local freedom and responsibility."

Information on land from airphotos.

A method used to detect changes in enemy targets in wartime has been put to important and interesting peacetime uses. Photographs from the air, carefully compared, give basic data on changes in the use of land with savings in time, money, and effort. By *Henry W. Dill, Jr.*, agriculturist, Farm Economics Research Division.

To HELP us evaluate the changes in the use of land, we borrowed a leaf from wartime experience and developed a method of airphoto interpretation.

The method uses an adaptation of standard photointelligence procedures used during the Second World War.

In military practice, reconnaissance planes take airphotos of enemy target areas at frequent intervals—weekly, daily, or oftener. The newest ones are studied and compared with those taken previously to detect any change. Much information is obtained or can be deduced from knowledge of new installations, changes in gun positions, changes in numbers and types of ships, airplanes, and so on.

In a somewhat similar procedure, we use two or more sets of airphotos of an area to measure land clearing, reversion of cropland to idle or forest land, shift of farmland to urban use, rate of gully growth, the use of conservation practices, and so on. Examples of these changes are shown in the photograph section that follows page 384.

The changes in the use of land concern many people—farmers, businessmen, manufacturers, bankers, economists, real-estate developers, city planners, students, and Government agencies, all of whom are affected in one way or another.

Agricultural economists particularly must be able to answer questions about the costs and benefits of clearing land, shifts of farmland to urban development, and the progress of some farm programs. They need certain basic information about the type and location of the changes and their extent.

Detailed field surveys are a usual way used to provide location maps, acreage figures, and other information, but often too little time and money are available for adequate fieldwork, especially when it may need to be repeated at intervals.

The accuracy of sample coverage by survey methods often is not reliable because of sampling difficulties and insufficient basic data. Some shortcut method is needed therefore to provide certain information quickly, economically, and with reasonable accuracy. That is the reason for using airphoto interpretation to study changes in land.

UP TO ABOUT 1947 only one airphoto coverage was generally available for most agricultural areas. Most of these photographs were taken between 1938 and 1940 by commercial firms under contract to the Department of Agriculture. Copies of them can be obtained from the Commodity Stabilization Service.

Most of the farmland in the United States is now covered by two or more sets of airphotos made for the Commodity Stabilization Service, the Soil Conservation Service, or the Forest Service. The early photographs are for 1938–1940 and the later coverage is from 1952. The availability of photographs for two periods permits detailed study of the two sets for the purpose of identifying, locating, and measuring areas where land use has changed. An estimate of the rate of the changes also can be made.

THE AIRPHOTO METHOD we use involves several steps.

First, we select the two or more sets of photographs that cover the area under study. Ordinarily, contact prints with a scale of 1:20,000 (1 inch=1,667 feet) are used. These prints, made from the original negatives, usually have the best contrast and clearness for study purposes.

We use stereoscopic photo coverage—that is, each photograph overlaps the adjoining one by about 60 percent. This provides two photographic views of the same land area, each taken from a different position of the air camera along the flight line the plane is following. The two camera positions are comparable to the relative positions of the eyes of anyone who looks at the photographs. When the two photographs are viewed under a stereoscope, we get a three-dimensional representation of the surface of the land.

Then we establish the boundaries of the area under study on the more recent set of photographs. The area may be a township or county, or it may be a selected sample area or a watershed. Usually the boundaries have been established on topographic maps of the Geological Survey or other available maps. The boundaries are transferred to the photographs, and the stereoscope is used to locate those along ridges or other natural features.

When the area boundaries have been marked, match lines are put on each photograph to show the portion that is to be used. As the different photographs of the study area overlap each other in the direction of flight as well as on each side, lines must be marked on each to show the portion that is to be used. This is to make certain that no part of the area under study will be overlooked and to avoid duplication.

The actual interpretation can now begin. This is a detailed comparison of the two or more sets of photographs. In practice, we study the two sets, using a magnifying glass to locate all evident areas of change. The areas in which changes are suspected are then studied in detail; a stereoscope is used to make more positive identification. When changes are identified, the area is outlined on the photograph and is marked with an appropriate identifying or classifying symbol.

The details of identification and the amount of precision desired or developed vary with the requirements of the problem, the scale and time of year of the photographs, and the skill of the interpreter.

Some studies, for example, may require only data on major changes in land use, such as clearing forests for cropland or the acreage of cropland taken over for urban use. It is usually desirable to have more detail for most studies. In a North Carolina study, we identified forest land in three classes to aid in estimating the costs of clearing.

After changes in land use have been identified and the areas have been outlined on the photographs, the acreages of the various types of changes found must be estimated. To measure these areas, we use a clear acetate grid with a known number of dots—usually 40—to the square inch. This grid is placed over each area to be measured, the dots are counted, and the number is recorded. We also get the total number of dots within the match lines for each airphoto. The dot grid is used because it takes less time and is simpler and less expensive to use than a planimeter—a precision instrument for measuring area.

Theodore C. Tryon, Gerald A. Hale, and Harold E. Young, of the University of Maine, tested the dot grid and planimeter in comparative experiments. They found that the accuracy of the dot grid compares favorably with the planimeter.

When the dot count—made by using the transparent grid—is completed, we have the total number of dots for the area under study, as well as the number that represents each class of the changes in land use. From these data we can calculate the percentage of the study area in each class of change. The percentage figures can then be applied to the total acreage of the study area to obtain the acreage of each type of change.

Area data for counties and townships are available from the Bureau of the Census, Department of Commerce. Acreages in watersheds or sample areas can be measured from maps by using the planimeter. In some studies, we have found it desirable to identify and to measure the acreage of cropland as well as the acreage involved in land-use changes. For most studies, however, the extent of change has more meaning when compared with the acreage of cropland than when it is expressed as a percentage of the total acreage studied.

THE RESULTS obtained by using airphoto interpretation can be illustrated by some examples.

In Long Acre Township, Beaufort County, N. C., which is in the lower Coastal Plain, land clearing has been going on for several years. There were 11,758 acres of cropland in the township in 1938. From 1938 to 1954, 2,590 acres of cropland were cleared—297 acres from brush, 594 acres from brush and scattered trees, and 1,699 acres from forest. Clearing for cropland was in process on an additional 598 acres in 1954 when the photographs were taken. This was indicated by partial removal of the forest cover and the presence of felled trees pushed into windrows for burning. If we include the clearing already completed and clearing in process, 21 percent of the cropland in 1954 had been cleared during the previous 16 years. As a matter of further interest, only about 200 acres of cropland had reverted to forest during the period of study.

In Carlton Township, in Chicot County, Ark., in the lower Mississippi Valley, there were 10,631 acres of cropland and 4,663 acres of permanent pasture in 1944. Two later sets of airphotos were available for this area for 1951 and 1955. A study of the 1951 photographs showed that 469 acres of cropland and 33 acres of pasture had been cleared since 1944. We found that 2,219 acres of cropland and 753 acres of pasture had been cleared between 1951 and 1955. This included clearing in process shown on the 1955 airphotos. Clearing during these years amounted to 17 percent of the total cropland in 1955 and 9 percent of the pastureland in that year. We found that practically no cropland had reverted to forest in Carlton Township during the period of our study.

A different type of change in land use was studied in Moorestown and Chester Townships, Burlington County, N. J. Here we were interested in the urban impact on agriculture. The two townships had 6,225 acres of cropland in 1940. By 1956, 1,022 acres had shifted to urban or industrial use. On an additional 377 acres, the shift from agriculture to urban use was in transition. In this category were 243 acres of abandoned cropland, 97 acres of former cropland on which construction was in process, and 37 acres of cropland completely surrounded by housing developments. During the 16 years, 16 percent of the former cropland had shifted to urban use and another 8 percent was in transition. Some former cropland on lower grade land apparently was reverting to forest.

It should be emphasized that these data are the best estimates that can be obtained, given the scale and quality of available photographs. Errors are confined generally to types of land use that have the least distinct characteristics for identification. For example, it may be difficult to distinguish between idle or abandoned cropland and lightly grazed pasture that has not had proper management. In most of the areas we studied, however, the extent of the transition classes of land use has been relatively small.

WITHIN THE LIMITATIONS I mentioned, airphoto interpretation provides basic data needed for economic analysis. We can identify and locate the areas where changes in land use have occurred. The photographs may be used as field location maps for detailed study. We can measure the acreage of change in use, and by comparing it with the size of the study area or the acreage of cropland, we can estimate the rate of change.

The airphoto interpretation method is not a substitute for detailed field study, but we are getting suitable data in a relatively short time, at low cost, and with a minimum number of experienced workers.

The face of our land looks to the sky. To see its many features, we must get above it and look down.

The airphoto is our best chance to get a bird's-eye view of our farms and ranches; from an airplane we only get a fleeting view.

The photograph gives us the opportunity to study an area in detail, and we have a record of how things were at the time the picture was made. The natural red, green, black, gray, brown, tan, and yellow are black, white, and gray in an airphoto, but the story is there if we can interpret it. We can see a field partly plowed, shocks of grain, the new farm pond, and the other marks people make on the land.

Most of our agricultural areas have been photographed from above by private companies for the Department of Agriculture. Many have been photographed two or more times so that we can keep up with changes in the use of farmland. More than 6.6 million square miles have been photographed since 1938.

On the pages that follow are airphotos of typical farm regions throughout the United States. They were taken at a time when the characteristic patterns are most apparent. They give us another kind of tour, beginning in the Northeast and continuing generally southward and westward—more or less in the way our agriculture developed.

The well-drained sandy lands of Aroostook County in Maine (above) support intensive potato production. The wooded areas usually have poor drainage (September). The area shown in the picture below of a part of Hampshire County in Massachusetts is typical of the more intensive dairy sections. A sizable acreage is in grass; a minimum is in row crops. Much of the land is wooded, including some tracts that were once in cropland or pasture. The photograph was taken in June.

The farms shown in this picture (above) of a lake plain in Monroe County, New York, are typical of the orchard and truck-farming area along Lake Ontario. The gentle topography and climate favor the intensive production of vegetables and fruits (October). In Cumberland County in New Jersey, as in many coastal sections, truck crops to be sold as fresh vegetables and for canning are grown intensively on drained tracts that are adjacent to the tidal marshlands (September).

These farms (above) are in Lancaster County, Pennsylvania, in a section that has been intensively cultivated more than 200 years—with good management and careful attention to soil-conserving practices (June). This part of Rockingham County in Virginia (below) is similar to many other areas of the Limestone Valley, where general farming and live-stock raising predominate. Sloping land is stripcropped. Tracts near the streams are kept in pasture. This picture was taken in July.

The Bourbon County, Kentucky, area pictured above has a land pattern typical of the Kentucky bluegrass section. The gray areas with a scattering of dots (trees) are pastures. The round, black, white-rimmed areas are stock ponds. The cultivated fields look almost white in the picture. Much of the land is in pasture and hay (the black areas) (October). Pitt County in North Carolina (below) has many intensively cultivated tobacco farms. The buildings along the roads include many barns used for flue-curing the fine-leaf tobacco.

This part (above) of Beaufort County, North Carolina, is typical of many sections in the lower coastal plain of the Southeast, where drainage has been established by systems of ditch and tile lines.   Undrained swampland can be seen on the left; some land next to the cultivated fields is partly drained.   General farming is the major enterprise (February). Below is a part of Walton County, Georgia, which is typical of the Piedmont area where cotton was once the major crop.   Two sets of terrace systems for control of soil erosion are visible.   Those in operation appear in the white or cultivated areas.   The older systems show in the darker gray areas.   Some are idle and reverting to forest (April).

This portion of Tift County, Georgia, is like many other sections of the Coastal Plain. Terrace systems permit intensive cultivation of the low ridges between the many stream channels. The stream areas are in pasture and woods. The gray area near the center of the picture is a pecan orchard (March). This view of Polk County in central Florida (below) shows the usual pattern of citrus groves. The dark-colored round areas are small lakes, which are characteristic of this part of the Florida Peninsula (January).

This photograph (above), taken in Terrebonne Parish, Louisiana, indicates the intensive cultivation of land that has been drained between bayous. It has large sugar plantations. Farm buildings are visible in the lower left corner (March). This farm (below) in Sunflower County, Mississippi, exemplifies land patterns in the lower Mississippi Valley. The cultivated fields have been adjusted to the old meander channels formed when the river overflowed its banks in the past. The higher areas between the old channels now are the cropland (December).

This area (above) in Green County, Wisconsin, is typical of the Lake States dairy region. Terraces and stripcropping help control erosion. The pattern of land use is somewhat like that in the Corn Belt, but more of the land is in pasture (June). The picture below of Webster County, Iowa, in the Corn Belt, shows a complete section of land bounded by roads on all sides. The land is used intensively. The chief crop is corn. Some hay and other forage crops are grown. The photograph, made in September, shows the tone and texture pattern of crops just before harvesttime.

Wheat growers in Hill County, Montana (above), as in other parts of the wheat-producing sections of the Northern Plains, lay out alternate strips of wheat and fallow on the more level terrain and use rougher areas for range (September). Below is pictured a wheat-barley-flax area on the glaciated plains in Bottineau County, North Dakota. The depressions—potholes—occur in varying sizes. Trees form windbreaks around farm-steads, as in other localities in the Northern Plains (July).

Parts of the large operating units that are typical of wheat-producing areas in the Northern Plains are shown in the picture above of a part of Kit Carson County, Colorado. Near the top of the photograph, the units of wheat and fallow alternate in separate large fields. In the lower part, the strips of wheat and fallow are relatively narrow so as to control wind erosion (September). In Randall County, Texas, on the High Plains of the Panhandle, both dryland farming tracts and rangeland occupy adjacent areas. The white, roughly circular patches are depressions in the caliche soils developed on limestone. The wavy dark lines in the upper part of the photograph are ridges made to control wind erosion (February).

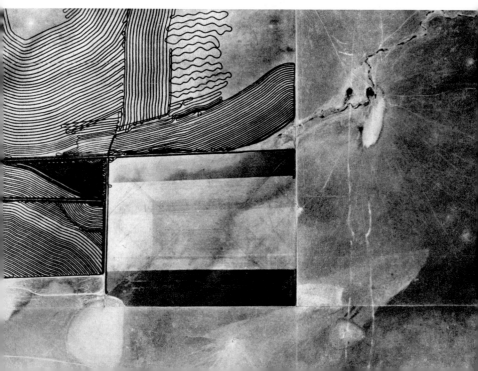

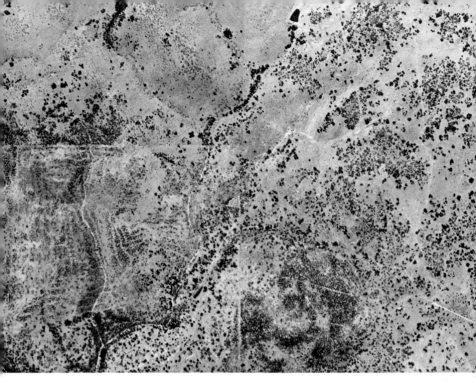

The area pictured above in San Saba County, Texas, is typical of the southwestern all-year range. In the lower left half of the picture, juniper and mesquite are being cleared off for range improvement. In the upper middle portion, a dam has been built to provide a pond for watering livestock. The ranch buildings are at the end of the road, which appears as a white streak in the lower right (February). Below is a part of Ellis County, Texas, in the Black Prairie area of the Southern Plains. The curving lines mark terraces used to control erosion in fields where cotton and feed crops are grown. In the upper corners of the photograph we can see pasture areas (December).

In Weld County, Colorado, in the Rocky Mountain region, are many contrasts between dry and irrigation farming. At the left of the picture above is a dry-farming area, which is mainly in wheat. The rest of the photograph shows general farming with irrigation from canals, which are marked by trees. Storage ponds are connected to the canals. The circular object at the top and the irregular white spot near the lower middle are ponds. The white lines in several fields show where oats have been harvested (September). The ranches (below) along the John Day River in Grant County, Oregon, typify a combination of irrigated cropland in the valley and dry range on high land.

Cache County, Utah (above), contains many relatively small irrigated farms, on which sugar beets, small grain, and hay are the main crops. Many of the farmsteads are grouped in villages at crossroads like the one at the right in the photograph. At the top is a dryland area (September). This area (below) of Tulare County, California, is typical of the more fertile areas of the Central Valley. Citrus and deciduous fruits, vegetables, and many field crops are grown. Some of the land is irrigated from one of the Central Valley Project canals that is seen in the photograph; at the left is an intensively farmed area; at the right is a nonirrigated dryland area (September).

The pattern of small and medium-sized farms along the Willamette River in Marion County, Oregon, is seen in the picture above. General farming is the main enterprise. The better soils are used for orchards and vegetables. Yakima County, Washington (below), is famous for its apple orchards, which flourish close to the dry mountain slopes that we can see at the bottom of the picture (June). Orchards have a distinctive pattern in airphotos.

The photographs above of the same area in Chicot County, Arkansas, reveal how farmland is developed by clearing and drainage. The picture on the left was taken in April 1951; the one on the right, in November 1955, when much of the cutover forest had been cleared. The white lines mark areas where felled trees were bulldozed into windrows and burned. The picture on the left below was taken in February 1938; the one on the right, in March 1955. Both show the same area in Robeson County, North Carolina. During this period, forest land had been cleared or was in process of being cleared. The black lines, roughly parallel to the roads (white lines), are trees pushed into windrows for drying.

The two photographs above of the same area near San Jose in Santa Clara County, California, illustrate the shift of land from farms to urban use. They were taken in January 1950 and June 1956. During this period, cropland and orchards became subdivisions for residences. This area (below) near Wilmington, Delaware, was photographed in 1937 (on the left) and 1954 (on the right). Housing developments are seen in the upper left corner and in the lower part of the 1954 photograph. The gray area with the white lines crossing in the left center of the 1954 picture is an airfield.

Our woods and
templed hills—Our vital private forest lands—The

care and use of national forests—Programs for forest management—Clearing land for different uses—The potential demand for timber

Our vital private forest lands.

A key factor in our national supplies of timber and water is the way we handle privately owned wooded lands, which comprise more than one-fifth of the land area of the United States. The public interest requires an increasing output from them and protection of the watersheds they cover. A major problem is how to provide that without infringing on private rights and privileges. By *John R. McGuire*, chief, Division of Forest Economics, California Forest and Range Experiment Station of the Forest Service.

MORE THAN one-fifth of the land area of the United States is privately owned forest land. Private individuals and firms hold three-fourths of all the commercial forest land and more than one-third of the noncommercial forest.

Half of the private commercial forest land is in the South. About 40 percent is in the North. Only 10 percent is in the West, but it carries a major part of the present stand of timber. Most of the forest land in the North and South is privately owned. Private holdings make up one-third of the commercial forest area in the West.

SMALL SIZE is the outstanding attribute of ownership of private forest lands in the United States. Not counting the thousands of holdings smaller than 3 acres, there are 4.5 million separate holdings of private commercial forest land. Some are larger than 2 million acres. The average size, however, is 79 acres, and forest properties smaller than 1 hundred acres number 3,875,000. About 633 thousand properties contain 1 hundred acres to 5 thousand acres. The remaining number—fewer than 3 thousand— are larger than 5 thousand acres. Of these, fewer than 3 hundred are larger than 50 thousand acres.

386

The operation of these private forest lands is a key factor in the national supplies of timber and water.

Nearly three-fourths of the private commercial forest land area is held in ownerships of fewer than 5 thousand acres. More than one-third of the area is in ownerships of 3 to 100 acres:

	Million acres
3 to 100 acres	121
100 to 500 acres	98
500 to 5,000 acres	46
5,000 to 50,000 acres	35
More than 50,000 acres	58
	358

Small holdings of fewer than 5 thousand acres are most numerous in the East, where they make up nearly all of the private commercial forest land area. Even in the West, however, half of the private commercial forest land is in small holdings.

Farm forests represent three-fourths of the number and almost half of the acreage in private ownership. Fewer than 1 percent of the owners belong to the forest industries, but they account for 17 percent of the acreage.

Other private owners of various kinds (city people, railroads, and retired persons, for example) number about one-fourth of the total, and their properties take up 36 percent of the private commercial forest area.

PRIVATE FORESTS long have supplied the major share of the Nation's requirements for timber products. Today they contain proportionately less sawtimber area—the area of trees suitable for sawing into lumber—than the public forests. One-third of their area is occupied by sawtimber stands, and two-thirds has stands of smaller trees or is nonstocked. Most of the sawtimber is young growth. Sawtimber stands in the East occur on less than one-third of the private commercial forest land. More than half of the land in the West supports these larger stands.

Farm forests over the country carry an average volume of less than 2 thousand board-feet of sawtimber per acre of commercial forest land. Forest industry ownerships probably average between 7 thousand and 8 thousand board-feet an acre. Other private holdings are somewhat higher than farm forests—perhaps an average of 23 hundred board-feet an acre.

Privately owned sawtimber volume totals slightly more than 1,000 billion board-feet—about 55 percent of all the sawtimber in the Nation. This volume includes 46 percent of our softwood and 88 percent of our hardwood.

PRIVATE COMMERCIAL forest lands usually are more accessible than public holdings. They occupy better sites and contain more than a proportionate share of our timber-growing capacity.

With the exception of most of the lumber company and pulp and paper company lands, and other forest industry holdings, however, private forest lands frequently are managed with relatively little attention to the principles of modern forest management. The intensity of management of most private holdings is low. This, in turn, is reflected in the productivity of the land.

The most productive lands are those on which the trees are carefully harvested. Seedling and sapling trees are preserved, seed trees are left, or other provisions are made for full restocking. Less desirable species and weed trees are removed so that the best species will have room to grow. If the stand is immature and is growing rapidly, harvesting is postponed, and cutting is done only where the trees are mature.

The Forest Service, in its nationwide Timber Resource Review, disclosed that about 65 percent of all recently cut commercial forest lands, both public and private, can be classified as relatively high in productivity—as measured by restocking and other conditions. Forest industry lands that had been recently cut average 77 percent in the upper productivity class. The average for all private holdings is 56 percent, however, chiefly because so much of the farm and other nonindustrial private acreage is left in an unstocked condition after harvesting. About 41 percent of the cutover land in farm forests and about 52 percent of the other private cutover land are classed as high in productivity.

The correlation between the area of recently cut private land in the upper productivity class and the size of holding is marked: 38 percent of the 3–100-acre tracts are so classified; 40 percent of the 100–500-acre tracts; 44 percent, 500–5,000 acres; 64 percent, 5,000–50,000 acres; 78 percent, 50,000 acres and larger.

Most of the larger holdings are owned by the forest industries. Most of the smaller holdings are farm or other private lands.

The operation of farm and nonindustrial forests generally is different from the operation of forests belonging to forest industry. Most farm and other owners operate their forest properties as an incidental occupation, but forest industries are interested primarily in the production of timber.

FOREST INDUSTRY ownerships number about 23 thousand and cover 62 million acres of forest land. More than half of this area is owned by 21 thousand firms in the lumber industry. Pulp companies own 23 million acres in some 160 different holdings. The remainder, about 4 million acres, is owned by 2 thousand manufacturers in the veneer, cooperage, pole and piling, turnery, and other forest industries.

Forest industry properties are generally larger than 50 thousand acres. Nearly all of the pulp industry's forest area, about half of the lumber industry's area, and about one-third of other forest industry's area are in holdings of 50 thousand acres of commercial forest land or larger.

Forestry industries have recognized the favorable timber-growing opportunities that exist in the South and have concentrated their land acquisition and management efforts there. More than half of the land owned by forest industries is in the South. The rest is about equally divided between the North and the West.

Careful harvesting so as to maintain the productivity of cutover land is one way in which the forest industries observe good forestry practices. Many of the companies conduct thinning or other stand-improvement operations in young forests and help public agencies control forest fires by providing manpower, equipment, and money. Many of the larger land-owning companies have their own fire-control organizations. Some go to considerable expense to provide for detection and control of tree diseases and insects. Forest industries do one-third or more of the planting of trees on private lands. Industry-operated forest tree nurseries exist in some States.

The forest industries have been intensifying forest management and protection on company lands, particularly since 1940. Mill capacity has expanded rapidly, and so has the need to assure future supplies.

Industrial forestry also has probably been stimulated somewhat by the growing competition for timber, by greater awareness of popular opinion, by the corporate tax situation, and by continuing prosperity. All of the larger firms in the forest industries employ staffs of technical foresters, and the highest proportion of recently cut private lands in the upper productivity class is in these ownerships. Small forest industry ownerships average lower in productivity. The acreage of forest industry holdings, however, is concentrated in large ownerships. Small sawmill firms and small pulp and paper companies own relatively little land.

The forest industries undoubtedly will continue to maintain their forestry programs, even if the economic climate should change. The goal of most industrial forest ownership is to maintain permanent production.

Some smaller firms, to be sure, have acquired land because they could not buy the timber separately, or because they saw opportunities for speculation in stumpage, or because they wished to keep accessible timber out of the hands of the competitors. Landownership for them usually is temporary, and they make no attempt to improve the productive condition of the timber resource.

But the great majority of firms in the forest industries exhibit an increasing responsibility in landownership. For the industry as a whole, cut and get out is a policy of the past.

A more pertinent issue is the extent of the responsibilities of the forest industries for cutting practices on the private lands that they do not own.

Forest industries seldom are entirely dependent on timber supplies only from their own lands. Most firms buy stumpage, logs, or bolts cut from farm and other private holdings or from public lands. They may have no direct control over the cutting methods employed on these other lands, but usually industry can influence cutting and other operations of woodlot owners and independent loggers: Industry foresters do so by example and demonstrations of successful techniques on company land and by technical advice and assistance on small private holdings. Many of the larger firms are coming to recognize the importance of maintaining the productivity of farm and other small private forests so that they will have adequate future supplies of timber in areas in which they operate.

A number of activities of the forest industries are directed to improving the management and the protection of nonindustrial private lands. One is the Tree Farm Program, which is aimed at encouraging more intensive forest land management and stimulating public interest in timber production. A large part of the acreage certified as tree farms is owned by forest industries, but the area of farm forests and other private forests in the Tree Farm System is growing. Another activity is the "Keep Green" program, which is a State-by-State educational campaign to prevent forest fires.

A number of firms and trade associations in the industry provide services of industrial foresters to assist owners— without cost to them—in managing timber on noncompany lands. Few firms have gone so far as to restrict their open-market purchases to wood harvested under technical forestry supervision, however.

OWNERS OF FARM FORESTS and other nonindustrial private forests belong to all walks of life. Farmers and ranchers are most numerous. The group also includes professional people, businessmen, wage earners, housewives, dealers in land and timber, speculators, retired persons, resort owners, banks, unsettled estates, churches and other institutions, and sportsmen's clubs.

Individual holdings are typical, but there are some partnerships and a few corporations. Corporate holdings include large farms, railroad lands, properties of mining companies, and forest areas owned by other large landholding concerns that are not part of the forest industry.

Some farmers and other nonindustrial owners operate sawmills, but such activity may provide only a secondary income. The owner's occupation usually bears little relation to timber growing.

The 3.4 million farm forests cover 165 million acres of commercial forest land. Other nonindustrial forests number 1.1 million, and their total commercial forest land area amounts to 131 million acres. Both types of ownerships are typically small, but the average farm-forest area (49 acres) is less than half as great as the average area in nonindustrial forests (118 acres). All but 25 million acres of farm and nonindustrial private holdings are in the East, and almost half of these 296 million acres are in the South.

The characteristics of owners of farm forests and nonindustrial forests partly explain the haphazard way in which most of these lands are managed. The relationships are imperfectly understood, however, and it is not entirely clear how an owner's alternatives with respect to forest practices are affected by such factors as his age, income, education, residence, length of tenure, his purpose, the form of ownership, or the way he acquired the property.

As is true in many problems in land-ownership, we can hardly tell cause from effect. For example, small, run-down forest properties often are owned by low-income owners who cannot afford to invest in improvement measures. But is the owner's low income the cause of low productivity of the forest? Or is it simply that depleted holdings can be bought more cheaply than productive forests and hence are the only properties that persons with little income can afford to buy?

Small size of holding seems to be a major deterrent to intensive management. The smaller the holding, the lower its productivity is likely to be. The owner of a small forest may seldom be able to harvest the timber himself because he cannot supervise the work, hire the skilled labor, or justify the purchase of logging equipment. If he contracts the logging job to an independent logger or sells standing timber to the forest industries, he may lose control over the cutting. To attract buyers, he often must sell most of his standing timber at one time. If the tract is clear cut, the owner may never have another merchantable stand in his lifetime.

Since they seldom enter the timber market, few owners of small forests recognize timber values or are adept at operating timber stands and marketing them for maximum income.

In terms of number of holdings, about 85 percent of the 4.5 million farm and nonindustrial private forests are smaller than 100 acres, and about half of them cover fewer than 30 acres. Close to 50 percent of the commercial forest area on farms is in holdings of fewer than 100 acres. In the North, where there are many part-time and residential farms, 64 percent is in these very small holdings; in the South, 41 percent; and in the West, 14 percent. Of the commercial forest area in nonindustrial ownership, one-third is in holdings of fewer than 100 acres—46 percent in the North, 21 percent in the South, and 12 percent in the West.

There is a question whether much public effort should be directed toward improving the operation of the smallest properties. Those under 30 acres, for example, account for only 6 percent of the Nation's commercial forest land area. From the standpoint of timber production and watershed protection, it might be more efficient to direct public forestry assistance programs toward holdings larger than 30 acres, unless critical watershed problems are involved. Some timber would be produced by the smallest forests in any case. As in agriculture, the problem hinges on whether the primary goal of public assistance programs is to increase production or to reach as many owners as possible.

In view of the low and irregular income that small forests usually provide, it is often difficult to understand why so many people own forest land at all. When a woodlot comes with the purchase of a farm, the reason for ownership is clear enough. But in low-income farming areas, many farms contain much more forest than cropland. Frequently the farm buyer ex-

pects to log some of the timber and to obtain part-time off-farm employment on logging crews or at sawmills in the vicinity. Other owners buy forest property simply for the pleasure of owning land, without any specific objective in mind. City people often own forest land for recreational purposes. A study in the Tennessee Valley disclosed that timber production was the primary goal of only 3 percent of the owners.

Therefore it is not surprising that the small forests change hands rather often. A survey of owners of private forests in New England revealed that 23 percent of them had held their property less than 3 years and 41 percent less than 9 years.

Another important characteristic of farm and nonindustrial private forestry is the prevalence of absentee ownership. Farmers, of course, usually live on their farms, but many other forest owners reside in towns or cities distant from the land they own.

The time element is particularly important in forestry because of the long time it takes to grow trees. Many owners of small forests are older persons whose life expectancy is 20 years or less. Furthermore, the great majority of owners are individuals; incorporated ownerships are few. The time factor may deter many owners from investing in improvement, but it seems to have little weight in their decision to own forest land.

Perhaps as many as three-fourths of the farm and nonindustrial owners bought their forest land. The rest came into forest ownership chiefly through inheritance. If elderly people in the past have owned forest land for the sake of their children, the children apparently have failed to retain it.

Many—perhaps most!—owners do not know that their management practices are rated poor by foresters. When owners in Mississippi were asked why they practiced poor forest management, for example, more than half said they did not know they were using poor practices or said they did not know why.

The owner of a small forest may not be aware of the management and marketing alternatives he could use. Low income (or need for cash to meet emergency needs) only partly explains why some owners liquidate the growing stock in their forests.

Various institutional factors undoubtedly act as obstacles to owner investment in forest improvement and protection. Intermediate and long-term forest credit facilities are not available to most private owners of farm forests and nonindustrial forests. Considering the widespread lack of interest in forestry among them, there is some question whether many owners would use such facilities for forest investment purposes even if they were available. The establishment of credit channels is further hampered by the scarcity of forest fire insurance underwriting. Demand for such insurance has been relatively limited, and rates have been high.

Owners sometimes cite property taxes as a reason for clear cutting immature timber. It is true that forest assessment practices are often inequitable, but the effect of taxation on forestry often is overemphasized. Property taxes may be a major obstacle chiefly because yields are irregular and far below the income potential of the land and because owners are faced with long periods of waiting for returns; taxes during those periods may be a major expense. Yield and severance taxes have alleviated timber assessment difficulties in several States and may have helped to stimulate forest investment by reducing carrying charges.

Importance of small private forests in meeting future requirements for timber has long been recognized. Numerous public and private programs of education and assistance to forest owners are under way. Besides the forest industry programs I mentioned, various other assistance programs are sponsored by firms, trade associations, and private conservation organizations. Most of these private programs are educational, but in many of them professional foresters are employed to give direct technical assistance to forest owners. A few private cooperatives are organized to assist member owners with harvesting and marketing.

All these private assistance programs may reach 25 thousand owners of small forests annually.

Forest owners in every section can engage the services of private consulting foresters. For a fee or for a percentage of the sale, consulting foresters provide complete professional services in managing and marketing timber. These services are particularly attractive to owners of medium and large holdings, but many owners of smaller tracts, particularly absentee owners, find it possible and profitable to employ a consultant.

The public programs have been directed primarily toward owners of small private forests. Most of them are financed cooperatively by the Federal Government and the States. They involve activities such as protection, education, technical guidance, research, conservation payments, and distribution of young trees.

Many woodlot owners first become aware of forest values and possibilities when they come in contact with the public forester in their county, who is known as the farm or service forester. These public foresters help owners to mark their trees for cutting and provide technical guidance for tree planting and other silvicultural practices. There are so few service foresters in relation to the number of owners to be served, however, that only a small percentage of ownerships can be assisted in a year.

Private owners also benefit from the educational activities of extension foresters, from the use of cost-sharing measures under the Agricultural Conservation Program, from planting trees supplied at low cost by public nurseries, and from public research. Yet, outside of public forest protection programs, most of these assistance programs reach relatively few owners— possibly 300 thousand a year.

The care and use of national forests.

An assistant chief of the Forest Service reviews many details of managing our 149 national forests, which cover 181 million acres. Many changes have occurred in them. Multiple use and sustained yield are basic principles in management. The forests have growing importance as sources of water, and the watersheds they cover need protection and restoration as never before. By *Edward P. Cliff*.

AN ACT OF THE CONGRESS in 1891 gave President Harrison power to establish forest reserves from the public domain. The first, the Shoshone National Forest in Wyoming, was created on March 30, 1891. Before he left office, more than 13 million acres were set aside.

Presidents Cleveland, McKinley, and Theodore Roosevelt proclaimed many million acres of reserves.

The Congress in 1911 enacted the Weeks law, which authorized Federal purchase of forest lands for the protection of watersheds. The Clarke-McNary law in 1924 broadened the purchase program to include lands chiefly valuable for producing timber. More than 18 million acres of national-forest land were acquired under these laws in the Eastern States.

Now there are 149 national forests in 38 States, Alaska, and Puerto Rico. They embrace about 181 million acres of federally owned land.

Every American citizen owns a share in them. They are held in trust by the United States for the benefit of all. Under the direction of the Secretary of Agriculture, the Forest Service has been assigned the responsibility to manage, protect, and perpetuate their resources of timber, water, forage, recreation, and wildlife.

Fifty years ago the national forests were used chiefly by people who lived in them or next door to them—

prospectors, trappers, homesteaders, ranchers. The distant shareholders rarely visited them.

Yesterday's backcountry now is crisscrossed with highways, roads, and trails through the steepest mountain country. Dams, reservoirs, conduits, and powerlines are almost everywhere. New towns have sprung up. Transportation has improved. In 50 years our population has doubled. Each day there are more people, who have more time and more facilities and a greater desire to share and enjoy the resources of the national forests.

The changes have changed the forests, too. Railroad logging has given way largely to more flexible truck logging. Ranchers find it more economical to haul their sheep and cattle in trucks to summer range to avoid the long treks on foot over dusty trails. Large areas of rugged backcountry are within easy reach of the hunter, fisherman, camper, and tourist. The airplane and jeep have replaced the old prospector's burro, and in many places the bulldozer and the Geiger counter have replaced his pick and shovel and guess and hunch.

The shift in our industrial centers to take advantage of power, water, labor, and the mobility of our population has affected profoundly the use of the national forests: There is much more use—and more different uses.

The problems of managing the national forest grow in complexity with increasing population pressure and increasing demands for the products and services the forests provide.

TWO BASIC PRINCIPLES that govern the management of the national forests are multiple use and sustained yield, which in combination mean coordinated management for the maximum continuous yield of their products and services.

Multiple use does not necessarily mean that all important uses of the forest occur on the same acre. Nearly all national-forest lands have great watershed values, and the protection of watersheds ordinarily comes first, regardless of other uses that might be permitted. A few areas are closed to all forms of use in order to protect the watersheds on which cities depend for water. Harvesting of timber and grazing are not permitted on some watersheds where the erosion hazard is high. Timber production has priority over other uses on areas especially adapted to growing commercial timber. Here recreation, livestock grazing, and wildlife are integrated as fully as possible without undue interference with the dominant use.

In other areas, campgrounds and other improved recreation areas are dedicated exclusively to public recreation. Here again the rule is not hard and fast. The cutting of timber on a few recreational areas and roadside strips is necessary for safety and insect control. Limited grazing is permitted in some places in recreational areas after the recreation season is over. Some 14 million acres of national-forest land, mostly rugged, high-mountain backcountry, have been set aside as wilderness, wild, and primitive areas, in which timber harvesting and other commercial forms of use are prohibited, although grazing, fishing, hunting, and camping are permitted.

The practice of multiple use in national forests, where diverse interests and groups of users are competing for the use of the land, is a challenge: Every citizen shares in the ownership of the national forest and has a right to fair consideration of his needs and desires in his use of them.

THE VALUE of national-forest lands as sources of water was recognized when the first forest reserves were created. The Congress then specified that the forest reserves were to be managed "for the purpose of securing favorable conditions of water flows."

Legislation has continued to emphasize the important watershed values of the national forests. Maintaining a steady streamflow of satisfactory quality is an important function in the administration of the national forests.

Today the use of water for domestic uses, irrigation, power, industry, navigation, and recreation in the United States is about 145 gallons a person every day. By 1975 the estimated requirements will average about 284 gallons: Demands for water will double while the population is increasing about 21 percent.

National forests, including range, timber, brushlands, and the mountaintops above timberline, are among our most important water-yielding lands. They comprise 21 percent of the area of the 11 Western States, receive about 31 percent of the total precipitation, and furnish 53 percent of the annual streamflow. Average annual streamflow from the western national-forest area is estimated to be 14 inches. From all other lands in the 11 Western States, it is 3.3 inches. Some 1,800 communities in the West with irrigated agriculture and more than 600 hydroelectric developments depend to some degree on water from the national forests.

National forests in the East occupy only a small part of the land area. Many of them, however, are at the headwaters of major streams in hills and mountains, where the amount of precipitation is high. They therefore have particular importance as sources of rivers.

Two chief aims in managing watersheds are to obtain better water yields through improved control of streamflow and to produce water free of silt.

Good management of the national forests is based on proper attention to soil-vegetation-water relationships. To attain these aims, a constant effort is made to correlate the objectives of watershed management with other land-management activities in carrying on the day-to-day work in each national forest.

Much restoration work remains to be done on the watersheds. The need is greatest on the seriously eroded and denuded areas that cannot be treated in connection with other management programs. Many of these critically damaged areas predate the establishment of the national forests.

The needed work involves conservation measures to stabilize the soil and improve control of runoff—contouring, seeding and planting, gully plugs, check dams, water diversions, and spreaders and grade stabilizers.

Some pioneering work in watershed rehabilitation was accomplished in the 1930's by the Civilian Conservation Corps. These valuable demonstration areas show what can be accomplished. An active program to restore deteriorating watersheds has been undertaken since then. Work has been done on 66 projects in 53 forests.

I give examples of the results of such work.

Land-treatment measures completed in the Upper Meadow Creek watershed in the Fishlake National Forest in Utah are calculated to reduce the potential for flood damage to downstream property by 80 percent.

The hydrologic conditions on Trout Creek in the San Isabel National Forest in Colorado have been improved enough to allow restocking with fish in selected areas.

A start has been made on stabilization of coastal sand dunes in the Siuslaw National Forest in Oregon. The dunes have threatened roads, buildings, lakes, and recreational areas.

The downward trend of land and water depletion in a number of severely gullied areas in the Piedmont region of the Southeast is being checked, and favorable hydrologic conditions are being restored.

In the Jefferson National Forest, the quality of the water supply of Marion, Va., was changed from high turbidity following storms to one of clear flow. The stream ran clear and within its banks during a major flood on January 29–30, 1957. A similar stream nearby, which had not been rehabilitated, ran muddy and overflowed its banks.

Similar work was accomplished on some 45 rehabilitation programs in national forests in conjunction with flood prevention, watershed demonstration, and area projects under Public Law 566. Included were restorations of burned areas, which, untreated, would be potential threats to life and property following rapid runoff of water.

Protection of the quality of the water supply is the forest ranger's dominant concern and responsibility in managing municipal watersheds, although the principle of multiple use can be applied on them if it is safe to do so.

Maximum yield of water may be the chief objective of watershed management in some sections. Significant increases in yield may be achieved in certain circumstances by reducing the density of vegetation, which in turn reduces the use of water by the plants. The effects of manipulation of vegetation to increase water yield, however, must be balanced against the adverse effects that may result to other important forest resources and uses.

The question of obtaining more water from the land has become a land-management problem in the national forests in the semiarid West.

To find out if greater runoff can safely be obtained, a pilot project has been initiated on the Coconino National Forest in Arizona. Dense thickets of young pine trees are being thinned by cutting and by use of controlled fire and heavy machinery. Heavy stands of valueless juniper are being rooted out with tractors so grass can grow in their place. Experiments in controlling chaparral with chemicals have been undertaken. Timber stands at higher elevation on other Arizona forests will be cut patchwise to allow more snow and rain to get to the ground. The results of this work are measured in stream gages and sediment basins and in studies of soil and vegetation. They will give us information by which to evaluate the possibilities of watershed-management practices to get greater streamflow from national forests and improve the water supplies of other semiarid localities.

In the United States and coastal Alaska are 488,609,000 acres of commercial forest land—land suitable to growing continuous crops of timber of merchantable size and quality and not reserved for some other purpose. These lands now support some 2,000 billion board-feet of sawtimber. The national forests contain about 84.8 million acres of commercial forest land and 765 billion board-feet of sawtimber.

In the western national forests, which were reserved from the public domain, the timber is predominantly in old growth. The timber in the national forests east of the Mississippi River is predominantly second growth, because these areas were largely acquired by purchase of private lands and had been cut over before they were acquired.

The charter of the Forest Service directs the Secretary of Agriculture to manage the national forests for the continuous production of supplies of timber, to safeguard water yields, and to offer timber for sale at competitive bidding. The national forests are divided therefore into some 500 small units, or working circles.

A working circle is an area of timberland organized to produce a continuous supply of forest products. It may consist of a single large watershed, an entire national forest, or a ranger district. Each working circle is managed so it will produce a maximum of timber with full consideration for the other

resources. The timber crop may be saw logs, pulpwood, posts, and poles.

Timber is a long-term crop and takes many years to mature. The period—known as the rotation—varies with the type of tree species and productive capacity of the soil. For most national-forest working circles, the rotations are 80 to 150 years. That does not mean that cutting can only be done once during the rotation. On the contrary, good forest management requires repeated cutting at relatively short intervals.

Many methods of harvesting timber have been developed through experimentation and trial. All types of cutting can be assigned to two general classes—regeneration cuts and intermediate cuts.

A regeneration cut is the final harvest cut that occurs when the timber is mature; that is, at about rotation age. Individual trees or entire stands are removed, and the area is regenerated promptly. This may be accomplished by natural reproduction, or by planting of young nursery-grown trees, or by a combination of these methods.

Intermediate cuts are made at short intervals. Trees of poor form and quality, trees of less desirable species, and enough additional trees to leave room for remaining trees are removed. Such cuts are sometimes called thinning or improvement cutting.

Timber-stand improvement is another important activity in the management of the timber in the working circles. Undesirable trees and brush are removed, and the limbs from the lower part of the tree are pruned to produce clear lumber. Thinning also is necessary when the stands are too dense to make satisfactory growth. These measures help to produce a better crop of trees in less time.

The planting of nursery-grown trees often is necessary to keep the forest well stocked with productive trees. On 4.3 million acres in the national forests (mostly old burns), stocking is so poor or nonexistent that planting must be done in order to restore productivity.

Tree seeds are collected and planted, young trees are grown in nurseries, and the trees are planted on suitable areas according to methods we developed through research.

Trees are subject to many hazards. Many different bark beetles kill trees by tunneling under the bark. Several kinds of worms and caterpillars weaken or kill trees by eating the foliage. Wood-rotting fungi, various kinds of rusts, and some viruses attack trees.

A forest in a healthy growing condition is the best insurance against loss or damage from insects and diseases, and constant vigilance is necessary to detect unusual concentrations of them and to launch immediate attacks.

TIMBER from national forests is sold in predominantly small offerings. Nearly 30 thousand individual sales are made each year, of which about 90 percent are of less than 2 thousand dollars appraised value. Only one-fourth of the volume sold is in timber sales larger than 25 million board-feet. These sales are offered and sold at competitive bid.

About 7 billion board-feet of the timber is cut on sales annually with a total value of about 100 million dollars. By law, 25 percent of the receipts from the sale of national-forest timber is distributed to the States in which the forests are located. The distribution is made in each State on the basis of the area of national forests in each county. This money is available, in lieu of taxes, to the counties for expenditure for schools and roads.

The timber is managed so as to safeguard soil and other watershed values of the land. Roads are located away from streams and lakes. Culverts and bridges are designed to reduce erosion and silting of stream courses. Contracts for sales of timber specify that treetops and other logging debris be removed from stream courses or lakes.

Cutting in areas set apart for recreation is restricted to removal of unthrifty, insect-infested, and hazardous trees and thinning of the denser stands. Scenic roadside strips are left. Timber is cut along streams and lakes so as not to spoil recreation values.

Good silviculture helps wildlife in most forest types. Food—from low weeds and shrubs—for wildlife grows best in openings. Den trees are reserved from cutting if wild animals need them. Certain strips or patches are left when large areas are planted so as to provide suitable openings.

In the national forests in the West, where the grazing of domestic livestock is an important use, it is necessary sometimes to restrict grazing on cutover areas to permit the seedling trees to become established. Grazing is again permitted there when the danger of browsing or trampling by livestock has passed.

PEOPLE VISIT the national forests for many kinds of recreation—to camp or picnic, hunt, fish, hike, swim, climb mountains, take pictures, study nature, enjoy scenery, ski, play in the snow, find a cool place, and rest.

Life in the forest is informal, and recreation areas in national forests are kept simple. Basic improvements are provided to make camping and picnicking more pleasant and comfortable and to provide for sanitation and fire protection.

Campgrounds are developed to accommodate family groups. The camp areas or units are spaced widely enough to retain a degree of privacy and a natural forest atmosphere. A family camping unit consists of a rustic table, a fireplace, and a·level place for a tent. Toilet and garbage facilities are provided. In many areas water is piped to central locations.

Picnic areas have larger clearings and more group-play areas, and they are designed to provide for larger groups for shorter periods.

Most of the 4,900 improved public recreation areas in the national forests were constructed during the 1930's with emergency funds. Recreation use since the war has increased beyond any expectations.

Eighteen million persons visited the

national forests for recreation in 1946. Each year since then the number of visits has soared. By 1956 there were 52.5 million visits. We estimate that there will be 66 million annual visits for recreation by 1962.

To take care of them, the Forest Service developed a 5-year program. Its goal is to provide adequate sanitation and care at all national-forest public recreation areas; rehabilitate existing recreation facilities so that they will be safe and usable; and plan, develop, and install new areas to alleviate present overuse and accommodate future use as it develops. This program—Operation Outdoors—is planned for completion in 1962 at an estimated cost of 85 million dollars.

Under the program, only the basic improvements required for camping and picnicking are constructed. Resorts, hotels, motels, and ski lifts are not built by the Forest Service. Qualified individuals or companies are encouraged to install and operate them under special-use permits when there is a public need for them.

A special type of outdoor recreation need is provided by wilderness, wild, and primitive areas. Eighty-one such areas have been designated. They are managed so that the primitive environment will be protected and preserved. Roads and mechanized travel are prohibited in them. No commercial timber cutting and permanent occupancy, such as hotels, resorts, stores, or summer homes are allowed. A system of horse and foot trails and a minimum of fire lookout stations and other improvements essential to the protection of the forest are permitted.

Wilderness areas provide the last frontier where undisturbed Nature retains its primeval state in an area of more than 100 thousand acres. Wild areas are similar but smaller. Primitive areas are about the same as wilderness areas but were classified under a different regulation.

The maintenance and improvement of wildlife habitat are primary objectives in the management of national forests. Because wildlife is a product of the land—its soil, water, and vegetation—the Forest Service in its land-management activities sees to it that the needs of wildlife are protected and wherever possible improved.

One-fourth of the annual recreational visits to the national forests are mainly for hunting or fishing. Sportsmen's visits increased 186 percent from 1947 to 1956. This increase was more than three times the percentage rise in the nationwide sale of hunting and fishing licenses in those years.

Fish and game laws of the respective States apply on national-forest lands. The Forest Service and the States have formal agreements that clarify each agency's responsibility in wildlife management, integrate management objectives and practices, provide for joint surveys and investigations, and authorize cooperative construction of direct habitat-improvement projects.

There is a wide field for increasing national-forest wildlife productivity by direct habitat-improvement projects. Food and cover for wildlife often can be improved by making clearings, breaking up brush fields, planting desirable food and cover plants, and fencing stream bottoms. The habitat of fish can be improved by planting on streambanks, development of flow-maintenance dams, and creation of new fishing waters by impoundments.

Most States have carried out habitat-improvement work in national forests. Each project is planned so that the improvements are consistent with overall forest-use plans.

One-third of the Nation's big game animals spend at least part of the year in national forests. This includes 80 percent of the moose, elk, and grizzly bear and more than half of the mule deer, black bear, and bighorn sheep.

Big game animals had reached a low ebb in most parts of the country a half century ago as a result of uncontrolled hunting. Their numbers have increased greatly since then as a result of two general sets of factors.

The first was a series of protective measures. Restrictive game laws were enacted and enforced. Predators were intensively controlled. Numerous wildlife refuges were established.

The second factor was the change in vegetative composition that resulted from the lumbering, grazing, and burning of forests. The increased growth of browse and other food and cover plants was ideal for deer. As the herds increased, overpopulations developed. State game officials and forest officers alike now know that the number of game animals that can be raised for the hunter's bag depends on the amount of forage the range will produce. They recognize that it is easier to build back a game herd than a depleted range.

State game administrators and forest officers are working together to gain public support for management practices that will balance the numbers of big game with the available forage supply. Joint surveys are made to determine herd and forage conditions and to develop effective management plans.

The national forests provide one of the largest public fishing areas in the world—81 thousand miles of streams and 2.25 million acres of ponds and lakes. Visits by fishermen to these waters exceed 9 million each year. The maintenance, protection, and improvement of fishing waters is an integral part of national-forest management.

FORAGE in the national forests contributes materially to the Nation's production of meat, wool, and leather.

The 101 national forests in States west of the Great Plains comprise 138 million acres, of which 44 percent, about 61 million acres, is grazed by livestock. About 1.1 million cattle and 2.7 million sheep graze there under paid permit, usually during the summer. These livestock are owned by some 20 thousand holders of permits. A limited amount of grazing is permitted in the national forests of the East where conditions are suitable for this type of use.

In managing national-forest ranges, a plan of use is developed to restore forage production on deteriorated ranges and to sustain forage production on the rangeland that is already in satisfactory condition. The successful application of the range-management program depends on close cooperation between the stockmen who own and manage the livestock and the forest officers who manage the range to achieve the goals of soil stabilization, sustained yield of forage, stabilized livestock operations, and maximum yields of meat.

To assist in the planning of range management, the forest ranger collects information on the condition and trend of the soil and forage resource, relation of rangeland to other uses, and the best season and method of use. He uses the information to develop a practical plan that can be applied to the grazing allotment. Field inspections are made often to assure that the plan of use is being followed. The plan is revised when necessary to obtain better distribution of livestock and proper utilization.

Hundreds of local associations of holders of permits work with forest officers in the management of national-forest ranges. The Forest Service has encouraged the organization and operation of the local grazing associations and advisory boards for many years. Their advice is solicited and considered on all important questions. Local advisory grazing boards were given specific statutory recognition in an act passed by the Congress in 1950.

Approximately 6 million acres of national-forest range are in such unsatisfactory condition as to require special treatment to build up the forage crop. Range reseeding and control of noxious range plants offer possibilities for restoration of these depleted lands.

Methods of successfully reseeding certain types of western range have been developed. Range productivity is thereby increased many times. More than 750 thousand acres have been successfully revegetated and brought back into production. Stockmen in many areas help pay for the work. Successful reseeding requires the removal of worthless plants, proper seed-bed preparation, and protection from grazing during establishment of the new plants. Control of noxious plants is accomplished by controlled burning, spraying with such chemicals as 2,4-D and 2,4,5-T, and by mechanical means such as plowing with heavy tractor-drawn equipment and bulldozing out unwanted juniper trees or other weed trees and shrubs.

Control of livestock, proper season and distribution of use, and rest-rotation systems of grazing require fences, water developments, and stock trails. Work done by the Forest Service to date includes construction of 29 thousand miles of range fence, 19 thousand water developments, and 2.5 thousand miles of livestock driveways.

We estimate that 20 thousand miles of additional fence and 15 thousand new water developments are needed to provide adequate improvements for good range management, in addition to the reconstruction and betterment of 20 thousand miles of fence and 13.5 thousand water developments already in place. The Government has invested about 18.4 million dollars in range improvements. Stockmen have contributed substantially in private funds for the construction and maintenance of range improvements and range revegetation.

Grazing policies in the national forests are clearly defined. The local settler is given preference in grazing privileges over the itinerant stockman and speculator. Stability of livestock operations is promoted through long-term permits and renewal preferences to established permittees. Grazing fees are adjusted yearly in relation to livestock market prices. Where adjustments in permitted numbers of stock must be made, they are made gradually to avoid sudden or drastic upsets in the operations.

MINERALS in the national forests generally are of three categories, depending on the laws authorizing their disposal.

The United States mining laws apply to metalliferous minerals on national-forest lands withdrawn from the public domain. Citizens may locate and enter mining claims on the basis of a valid discovery of a valuable mineral and may develop or patent such mining claims in accordance with the provisions of the mining laws.

The act of July 23, 1955, known as the multiple-use mining law, amended the United States mining laws and provided that the United States retain the right to manage and dispose of the vegetative surface resources on new mining claims prior to patent. It also provided a way for the Government to regain control of the management of surface resources on the older unpatented mining claims. Under this law, mining claimants still retain their rights to prospect and develop their claims for mining purposes. The law gives the Secretary of Agriculture authority to dispose of common varieties of sand, stone, gravel, pumice, pumicite, and cinders on the national forests by permit or lease.

The Mineral Leasing Act of February 25, 1920, applies to oil, gas, oil shale, coal, sodium, potassium, phosphate, and sulfur in Louisiana and New Mexico on national-forest lands reserved from the public domain. The Secretary of the Interior has discretionary power to lease such national-forest lands for mineral development. The lessee pays rental and royalty as determined by appraisal of the minerals or by competitive bids. These payments are credited to the receipts of the Department of the Interior.

The Mineral Leasing Act for acquired lands applies to oil, gas, oil shale, coal, sodium, potassium, and phosphate on most national-forest land acquired by purchase. The President's Reorganization Plan No. 3 of 1946 applies to other minerals on most national-forest lands acquired by purchase.

The leasing and disposal procedure for such minerals on acquired lands is similar to the one provided under the

Mineral Leasing Act of 1920, except that the consent of the Secretary of Agriculture is required before a lease can be issued by the Secretary of the Interior, and rentals and royalties are credited to national-forest receipts. Mineral prospecting and development on national-forest land are extensive. In 1955, 7.4 thousand leases and permits covering more than 7 million acres were in force.

MANY SMALL TRACTS in the national forests are suitable for private uses, which are authorized by special-use permits if they can be justified and do not conflict with uses of greater public value. The permits specify the terms under which the use is authorized.

When land in national forests is used for a commercial purpose or by individuals only, a rental in keeping with the value of the use is charged. Public or semipublic uses usually are permitted without charge or for a small fee.

Approximately 55 thousand special-use permits in force in 1958 covered more than 3 million acres and a wide variety of activities, such as ditches, cultivation, summer homes, and rights-of-way for powerlines, pipelines, and roads.

Public-service uses—as for resorts, hotels, stores, organization sites, ski lifts, and boat docks—carry special stipulations as to the type of improvements to be constructed, the services to be offered, and public safety.

MORE THAN HALF of the nearly 10 thousand full-time employees of the Forest Service spend at least a part of their time on fire duties. Seven thousand additional men are employed seasonally for various jobs having to do with fire control. Many others are hired for short periods to fight large fires.

Machines have changed several aspects of the efforts to prevent and stop fires. "Smokechasers," who used to go to fires afoot or on horseback, now often use trucks, airplanes, and helicopters. When trucks cannot reach

them, the firefighters may get supplies by airplane or by trail tractors. Pack mules and horses are still used in rugged, remote areas.

Static-line parachutes and protective clothing make it possible to drop men near fires in mountainous areas. Men in the Forest Service make about 10 thousand airplane flights annually to detect fires and to transport airfreight, firefighters, and parachuted cargo for fire control. Ground lookout stations in many forests are supplemented by regularly scheduled air flights in order to discover fires more quickly.

Sometimes water and chemicals are dropped from airplanes directly on fires or just in front of them. The Stearman crop-dusting type of airplane has been used with marked success in this type of air attack. Several bombers that once belonged to the Navy have been adapted to this use. Helicopters also have been used for this purpose and to lay fire hose over rough terrain.

Much of the work to develop equipment has been carried out in cooperative projects with the armed services, industrial concerns, State forestry organizations, and others.

Mechanized equipment, such as tractors and plows, are building more of the firelines each year. This equipment can be effectively used on 15 to 20 percent of all fires and greatly reduces fire-control costs.

Smokejumpers—trained parachute-jumping firefighters—have been used in the national forests since 1939. They are used extensively on fires where fast initial attack is necessary. They have saved millions of dollars in firefighting costs and in resources.

Fire is still a hazard, however, and fighting fires is still a costly and dangerous job. As new areas of the forests are opened to use, more people come for work and play, and their activities increase the likelihood of fires. Operations connected with logging, saw-milling, mining, and transportation all cause some fires. Flammable cover in much of the forest area has changed and increases the fire problem. Tops and limbs of trees left after logging increase the danger. Annual growth of weeds and grasses, which are highly flammable in the dry stage, is greater after timber cutting and before young trees re-cover the ground.

There has been a steady general drop in number of man-caused fires since 1940 in most national forests—an indication of the success of increased prevention work and the response by visitors and woods workers to please be careful with fire in forests.

THE DEVELOPMENT and administration of the national forests require considerable engineering. Forest supervisors' staffs usually include one or more professional engineers. They oversee the construction and maintenance of roads, dwellings, trails, landing fields, warehouses, offices, water-supply installations, and similar facilities. They also examine plans and inspect roads built by permitholders, structures, and other installations and provide topographic and planimetric maps.

The transportation system in national forests in 1958 consisted of about 24,250 miles of designated highways, 124,000 miles of development roads, 116,000 miles of horse and foot trails, and 190 landing fields.

Some of these roads are public roads, maintained by States, counties, and other authorities. Forest-development roads are open to public travel but as a rule are not maintained for heavy traffic. Loggers and other users therefore have to maintain about 13 thousand miles of development roads to the extent required for their use. The Forest Service periodically reconditions its roads.

Thousands of additional miles of access roads must be built, and former truck trails must be rebuilt to move logs, lumber, pulpwood, and other forest products to market. Primary roads must be routed and constructed with special attention to roadbed stability. Thousands of miles of branch roads must supplement the primary system

445509°—58——27

in order to provide ready access for combating insect infestations and diseases and salvaging merchantable timber damaged by windthrow or lightning-caused fires. The Forest Service has the responsibility for routing and designing these roads.

More roads also are needed to truck livestock to and from the ranges. Improved wildlife management often depends on roads to encourage better distribution of hunting. More and better roads to make lakes and streams more accessible are needed in places.

A dollars-and-cents price tag cannot be placed on the great and varied resources of the national forests. They contribute much to the economy of the Nation and to the people. A look at one national forest will give an idea of the total picture.

THE TARGHEE NATIONAL FOREST in southeastern Idaho and western Wyoming is an example. It forms a timbered semicircle around the head of the Snake River. The 1,650,300 acres of public land provide water, wildlife, forage, timber, and recreation that help sustain communities in 10 counties. Farmers in the upper Snake River Valley use water from the forest to irrigate crops valued at 85 million dollars annually. Some 16 million board-feet of timber are harvested. People from all over the country fish in its 516 miles of streams and 14,465 acres of lakes and reservoirs. Hunters take more than 3,000 big game animals—elk, moose, deer, bear, and mountain sheep— from the Targhee National Forest each year. In the summer more than 14 thousand cattle and 118 thousand sheep graze the lands.

To keep the resources of the Targhee productive for public benefit is the job of eight district rangers and a forest supervisor. They integrate the uses and plan, manage, and protect the forest so that its abundance may serve the American people now as well as in the future. So it is in varying circumstances with all the 149 national forests.

Programs for forest management.

Through various programs, Federal and State agencies encourage and facilitate the protection and sound management of forest lands in private ownership. It is in the public interest that our forest lands be kept permanently productive. By *W. S. Swingler*, assistant chief, State and Private Forestry, Forest Service, and *Frank A. Connolly*, Division of Information and Education, Forest Service.

YOU MAY be one of the 4.5 million nonindustrial, small landholders who own 296 million acres of our remaining commercial forest area.

If you are, you are one of the largest block of owners of the land from which we must expect to get our future supply of wood products. The manner in which you manage your land can help or harm our future wood supply and our water, wildlife, recreation, and other resources.

The ownership pattern of our remaining commercial forest area is this: About one-fourth of our continental land area, some 484 million acres, can grow commercially useful wood products and is still available for that purpose. Some 126 million acres of this total are public forest lands, owned and administered by States, the Nation (principally in national forests), counties, and other units of local government. Only about 13 percent, some 62 million acres, are in industrial or other large ownerships. More than three-fifths of our available commercial forest area, some 296 million acres, is owned by small landholders.

There is responsibility and opportunity in this ownership. In a world that is growing closer together and has increasing populations, the ownership and management of land are becoming a matter of increasing public and private concern. The management of forest land is of particular concern

for it affects water supplies, drainage, other resources, and the supply of wood products, such as industrial timbers, boards and planks, cellulose for paper, particle boards, laminated beams and panels, and synthetic materials. It will take good management of our remaining commercial forest land to continue to produce them.

When the Forest Service was established in the Department of Agriculture in 1905, it was directed under its appropriation for that year ". . . to advise the owners of woodlands as to the proper care of the same. . . ."

Evidence that the public, the people, was as ready and anxious to receive advice and assistance as the public, the Government, was ready and prepared to provide it was given in the report of Gifford Pinchot, first chief of the Forest Service, for 1905.

He reported: "During the year 167 applications were received for advice and assistance in the management of private forest lands . . . . The most notable phase of the cooperative planting work during the year has been the increasing requests for assistance made by cities, water companies, railroads, and other large owners."

The assistance the Government could give at that time was more limited than today's landowner might suppose. The Government had established fire lookouts on the national forests. It encouraged private owners to post fire guards on cutover lands and encouraged the States to provide fire protection forces. It was able to give advice on land management, including plantings and cutting practices, to some landowners. Its public forest managers, the national forest rangers, were glad to have nearby landowners, singly or in groups, come to see how trees on Government lands were selected, marked, and sold.

Help in fire control was limited to advice on fire behavior and damage and encouragement to States and private owners to increase and extend protection. There was neither authorization nor funds to go further. Assistance with reforestation consisted largely in advice and in drawing plans for extensive planting programs on large ownerships. There were no funds for helping the States to grow planting stock so that the small landowner might reforest denuded areas at a cost within the reach of his purse, as he can do today. Not enough trained foresters were available to demonstrate, to more than a limited number of groups, how tree planting could be done efficiently.

The Weeks law of 1911 often is cited as the charter for the participation of the Federal Government in helping to meet the forestry problems of private landowners.

Its main purpose was to authorize the Federal acquisition and protection of forest lands on critical watersheds that affected the drainage to navigable streams. These lands, presumably to be selected largely in the East (as they generally have been), were to be managed and administered like the national forests, which had been reserved out of the public domain, principally in the West.

The law established the principle of a shared public responsibility where there was a shared public interest. It authorized, for example, a Federal-State cooperative program of fire prevention and control for the protection of non-Federal lands on the watersheds of navigable streams, because this protection was a matter of national interest for which the Government should share the cost.

As the Government's share of this program, Federal patrolmen were employed to work with State patrolmen in the States from 1911 to 1920, when Federal funds were allotted directly to the States to reimburse them for a part of their expenditures.

The Weeks law encouraged the cooperating States to strengthen and extend protection forces. It recognized the axiom that without adequate fire control the effort to get good forest management is a somewhat empty wish. But this legislation was not enough to meet full-on the ever-present danger of forest fire. Thirteen years after its passage, only 30 States had qualified for its cooperative program, and only 176 million acres were under protection.

The Clarke-McNary Act, passed in 1924, broadened Federal participation in the better management of forest lands and increased fire protection. One of its provisions extended the Federal fire-assistance program to lands necessary for the production of timber and to the watersheds of navigable streams.

It authorized the Secretary of Agriculture to cooperate with the States and through them with private and other agencies in protecting non-Federal lands classified as timberlands and watersheds yielding water for domestic use or irrigation. He may provide technical guidance and assistance and, within limitations, share the cost of such protection.

Forty-four States and Hawaii were cooperating in the nationwide forest fire control program in 1957. Some 390 million acres of forest land were under protection. Funds spent for forest fire protection amounted to 42.9 million dollars—including 32.9 million dollars of State and private funds and 10 million dollars in Federal contributions—in 1956.

The rate of burn had dropped to a small fraction of the former losses.

Such measures as State and local

patrols, law enforcement, educational campaigns, and modern fire-detection devices have helped to reduce the occurrence of fire and the spread of small fires into large ones.

State control forces, equipped with such helps as danger prediction instruments and data, rapid communication systems, and efficient fire-suppression equipment, and employees under continuous training to learn to do an effective job stand ready to suppress or control fires.

This protection service has now advanced to the point where several groups of States are matching equipment and conducting coordinated training courses so as to prepare themselves to come to one another's assistance when fires of major proportion threaten to get out of hand in neighboring States or communities.

IF YOU ARE ONE of the 4.5 million owners of small forests, you have other management problems that affect prospective income and the permanent well-being of your land.

It is easier to picture you statistically than to write a specific prescription for the proper productive management of your woodlands. That job should be done by a qualified technician who has inspected your land.

You own about 66 acres, the national average for your group. If you have cut it over, especially some years ago, the odds are against your having done a satisfactory logging job that left the land in the best condition for good reproduction. You might not have ruined it, but the chances are that you set back more than need be its potential for growing profitable new crops of good forest products.

There is reason to believe, as inquiry among some owners indicates, that if you did these things, it was not with such intent; you would have done better if you had better understood the needs of the woodlands. If you knew that you could have got technically qualified, unprejudiced advice, you would have sought it.

Such advice now is available in most localities as a free public service under one or another of the State or cooperative State-Federal programs.

Two important sources are the State forestry organization, which features technical assistance and general administration of overall State forestry programs, and the land-grant college, which features educational assistance, particularly advice to farmers on handling woodlands as a part of the farm operation.

The core of the forestry program in most States is based on a pattern of State legislation, enacted specially to meet landowners' requirements and administered by a recognized central forestry agency. This agency may be set up independently or it may be a part of the State department of conservation. It is customarily headed by a State forester. He administers the State forest programs and the cooperative State-Federal forest programs.

The State forester usually has a central staff of specialists and district foresters, who are his local agents or deputies.

Most States have a comprehensive program that embraces control of fire and pests, the production of planting stock, assistance in management, and marketing aids. When you need such assistance, you would normally turn to your State forester or to his district representative.

The extension forester conducts short courses for farmers at the State agricultural college, prepares bulletins on farm forestry, interprets research findings, instructs youth groups and students in forestry work, and shows how to derive advantages from self-employment in woods work. He provides demonstrations in the woods for farm groups in such matters as cutting and planting methods, fire prevention practices, and treatment and use of wood products.

The extension forester may help in the administration of the State program. He can be reached through the county agricultural agent or through the State extension service at the State agricultural college.

The State forester and the State extension forester work closely with soil conservation districts. After an individual farm plan is completed—usually a joint effort by the landowner and a technician from the Soil Conservation Service—the State forestry agencies are available to help the farm owner supplement and carry out the forestry phases of that plan.

The States have cooperated with the Federal Government in the programs in which State and national interests coincide—fire protection, pest control, watershed care and reforestation.

One such program provided technical help and guidance to woodland owners. It was begun nationwide under the Norris-Doxey Act of 1937—known as the Farm Forestry Act—which made it possible for the Federal Government to contribute increased technical help and financial support for State assistance to farmers regarding the establishment, protection, and management of farm forests.

The Cooperative Forest Management Act replaced the Farm Forestry Act in 1950. It extended the technical assistance program to other owners than farmers and included assistance to primary processors as a means of reducing loss and inefficiency in the processing of primary forest products.

The programs conducted under this legislation are administered in the State through the State forestry agencies. Federal contributions are made to the States, which employ foresters to provide the needed service and which direct the activities of the foresters in carrying out the provisions of the joint State-Federal forestry program.

In providing the service required when an owner asks for technical help, the forester usually goes on the land with the owner and he tries to learn the owner's plans and intentions—his present financial interests and needs and his plans for continued ownership and future operations.

The forester often can point out to the owner such opportunities as special markets for the type of trees growing in his woods and show him trees of more than average value.

The forester surveys the stand of trees in detail—its age, quality and species composition, its growth status and potential, and the physical conditions that may make proposed cutting operations easier or more costly.

With this information, the forester makes recommendations for carrying out the proposed operation.

The recommendations will be both general and specific as to numbers of trees by species, types, and sizes. The trees to be removed or left are marked to match the numbers, types, and sizes called for in the recommendation.

It is a management plan. Its purpose is to point out the trees available for a profitable sale and those that should be left for greater future values and to take into account other factors that contribute to a constructive operation rather than a destructive job.

The forester gives the owner lists of marketing outlets by products and species, sample outlines for asking bids, and sample sales and cutting contracts that should help make a secure and profitable deal. Included will be measures for avoiding damage to lands, roads, trees, and improvements from the depredations of cutting crews.

Since 1940, when State funds first became available, through 1956, the States expended 10,280,498 dollars on this program. The Federal contribution was 5,696,063 dollars. In that time the number of State service foresters grew from 9 to 285. They helped 291,300 landowners and made operating plans on 27,169,579 woodland acres. Sales they have guided involved 6.8 billion board-feet of forest products at a value of 128,440,659 dollars. The cost of this service was about 11 percent of total sales.

The public forester cannot give detailed management attention to the sale. In each State, in fact, there are limitations on the amount of time a forester can give to individual cases.

In most instances, however, and especially on tracts of moderate size, he is able to give the owner a usable plan.

If the sale is an extensive or complex job that requires detailed attention, the owner may be well advised to seek the services of a private consulting forester to carry it through.

SEVERAL State and Federal measures are designed to encourage owners to replant their forest lands.

The Congress in 1924 provided for Federal assistance to farmers in reforestation of private lands through the provisions of section 4 of the Clarke-McNary law. The results were encouraging. Three years later, 28 States were participating in the program.

The Congress amended the law in 1949 to remove the "farmers only" limitation. By 1954, Hawaii, Puerto Rico, and 43 States participated.

If you have land on which you should plant trees, you can buy seedlings from your State forester at a nominal cost. You should consult your nearest forester as to suitable stock available, costs, and proper planting time and methods, or you can send your check to the State forestry agency with a description of your land, its extent, and location. The stock will be shipped to you at the proper time.

The State will not undertake the planting, but you can receive technical help on what to plant and how to plant. Your nearby forester may be able to help you arrange for the hiring or loan of a planting machine or for the employment of planting crews.

The upsurge of interest in planting trees on private land has been notable. The States and Territories in 1954 distributed almost 500 million trees, enough to plant 500 thousand acres. In the fall of 1957, planting reached a level of 1 million acres a year. About 1 billion seedlings were produced during that year. It also reversed the dominance of public planting; 83 percent of forest planting was on private lands.

Despite the encouraging progress, however, we will not soon catch up with our planting needs—not even in the next half century. More than 50 million acres of poorly stocked and denuded land need restocking. Each year, through fire and other causes, additional denuded or understocked land is being added.

One of several new measures was included in the Agricultural Act of 1956, which established the Soil Bank, intended to encourage farmers to curtail, temporarily or on a term basis, their production of excess farm crops. A part of this program, the Conservation Reserve, was designed to encourage farmers to transfer some of their general cropland from unneeded crops to long-term conservation practices for 3, 5, or 10 years or longer. It would help the owner establish his chosen conservation practices and would pay up to 80 percent of the cost of establishing these practices. The owner would also receive an annual use payment in the nature of a rental for land taken out of crops and placed in the Conservation Reserve over the term that was agreed on.

The planting of trees on conservation-reserve land was one of the conservation practices authorized by the Congress. In carrying out the program, farmers have been specially encouraged to plant trees on their land that generally is poorly suited to crops.

In 1956–1957, the first year of the Conservation Reserve, 500 thousand acres were placed in the reserve for tree growing. The program is temporary, but it is expected to provide the stimulus for additional tree planting by farmers having land eligible for conservation-reserve practices. State nurseries were expanded in anticipation of the added requirements of the program.

The Conservation Reserve is another "farmers only" program, because only cropland is eligible. Farmers who want to participate make their arrangements with their local agricultural conservation and stabilization committee, usually at the county seat. The public forester is an adviser to the committee. Participants who choose to plant trees can arrange at the time their contract is approved to receive technical help in the procurement, planning, and planting of trees and their care.

The committee is also charged with carrying out local land-improvement practices under the national Agricultural Conservation Program. These are conservation measures or practices selected as locally desirable out of a group of measures authorized nationally by the Agricultural Conservation Program Service.

The Government encourages the landowner in undertaking needed conservation measures by sharing up to 50 percent of the cost of installing the conservation practice. There is no annual land-use payment, as in the Conservation Reserve. Trees may be bought from the State nurseries or through local conservation district group procurement sources.

The national Agricultural Conservation Program authorizes two forestry practices. Under the tree-planting practice, the Government shares with the farmer the cost of trees, planting, and fencing. Under the practice for improvement of a stand, cost sharing is authorized for thinning dense stands, pruning crop trees, removing or killing undesirable vegetation, preparing sites for natural reseeding, fencing, and using erosion-control measures on logging roads and trails. Technical assistance to farmers for these forestry practices usually is available from State forestry agencies through the local agricultural stabilization and conservation committees.

The Rural Development Program also furnishes opportunities in forestry on the farm. The Government, working with State forestry organizations, gives attention to areas in which farm incomes are unusually low. The Forest Service works with State and local organizations in surveying and reporting on timber products available from a specific area. Attention of wood-using industries thus is drawn to the availability of valuable timber in areas not usually recognized as profitable sources of wood supply. Residents of underdeveloped rural areas are finding that forests can provide employment and produce needed wood products. In addition to on-and-off the farm labor opportunities, home use of forest products saves out-of-pocket expenses. Marketing assistance by public and private foresters often helps the timber owner find markets.

Also of interest to farmers and ranchers is the Great Plains Conservation Program, authorized by Public Law 1021 of the 84th Congress. Tree planting is provided for.

Many States have programs for the improvement of wildlife habitat. Trees and shrubs are given to landowners for plantings on dedicated wildlife areas. One should apply to the wildlife service in the State conservation department if he wants to participate.

Title IV of the Agricultural Act of 1956 provides for a wood growing program and is directed toward meeting more fully our future needs for wood.

It authorizes the States to formulate programs that may embrace plantings on State or local public lands, private lands in cooperation with the owners, and Federal lands, where the responsible agency agrees to carry out or arrange for carrying out its part.

This program will be of special interest to individual landowners because under it share-cost planting arrangements may be made with private owners as well as with collateral or subordinate units of government within the States.

These State programs may be submitted to the Secretary of Agriculture for review. If he approves them as sound and practical, Federal assistance in the form of advice, technical assistance, or financial contribution will be authorized. The Federal financial contribution may not exceed the amount expended by the State in carrying out the approved plans.

FORESTS are subject to damage from a host of enemy insects and diseases. Many examples can be given.

The chestnut blight, brought in from Asia about 1900, has destroyed all but a few scattered trees of the highly valued American chestnut species.

The spruce budworm, which can destroy trees of all ages, is found over great forest areas in the Pacific Northwest, the Northeast, and Canada. An epidemic, uncontrolled from 1910 to 1920, hit the spruce-fir forests of northern New England, eastern Canada, and Minnesota. More than 25 years' supply of pulpwood was lost.

The white pine blister rust attacks the structurally useful and the highly valued five-needled pines, including the eastern white pine of the Eastern and Lake States, the western white pine of the Northern Rocky Mountain region, and the sugar pine of California and Oregon.

Among other diseases and infestations that require special alertness may be mentioned beetles that eat the seed crop of the western pines in the cone; white grubs, which eat off roots of young trees in the nursery and in the forest; white-pine weevils, which cause crooked growth; bark beetles, whose larvae feed under the bark next to the wood of overripe trees and can kill a tree in a single season; and oak wilt, which has spread rapidly in Midwestern States and has been found also in the East and Southeast. In the South, the brown spot needle blight retards the growth of the valuable longleaf pine seedlings, and the littleleaf disease kills the shortleaf pines.

THROUGH HIS good management, the landowner may keep the normal attacks of forest enemies under control.

In epidemic attacks, his individual efforts are often futile; even the State may be unable to provide adequate protection against attacks that extend beyond State lines.

Congress recognized this situation in 1940 and adopted the Lea Act to provide Federal help in the control of white pine blister rust. State, Federal, and private forces have cleared millions of acres of the ribes plants that

are the hosts of the rust fungus. The five-needled pines are now being jointly protected in 32 States.

The Congress in 1947 enacted the more general Forest Pest Control Act. Under it, the Federal Government provides the facilities for regionwide cooperation, including the protection measures on Federal lands, and participates through State agencies in the non-Federal control operations. Much of the research and coordination necessary to effective controls is being provided through Federal agencies, especially the Forest Service and other agencies in the Department.

THE CONGRESS authorized in 1953 the development of pilot watershed programs of a local character to be carried out in parts of one or more counties. The more comprehensive Public Law 566 was adopted in 1954. It required the participation of local sponsoring organizations and a sharing of costs. In these projects, technical forestry assistance in planting, management, and protection is provided on non-Federal lands under State-Federal agreements through the State forestry agencies.

The cooperative State-Federal-private arrangements have since been established on a practical working basis. A report for 1956 shows that under the various cooperative forestry and flood-prevention acts, assistance was extended to 1,300 landowners and operators in the management of 18 thousand acres of forests and woodlands included in authorized watershed-treatment areas. In addition, 47 million trees were planted on 37 thousand acres of critically eroded land. Additional fire control and prevention measures were provided on 540 thousand acres of forested watershed lands.

NONE OF THESE PROGRAMS is compulsory. If the full value of our forests is to be realized, therefore, the primary responsibility for proper care and management of privately owned land must rest with the individual owner.

Clearing land for different uses.

More than 3 million acres of commercial woodland were cleared as recently as 1952 and converted to other uses—cropland and pasture, homesites, highways, airfields, and industrial sites. Most of it was on existing farms and ranches. New farms have been made out of forest land ever since colonial times, but little of that is done now. By *James R. Anderson, Adon Poli,* and *Lawrence A. Reuss,* agricultural economists, Farm Economics Research Division.

FARMERS clear land for several reasons: They cannot buy or rent additional land to add to their tilled areas. They want to enlarge, consolidate, or reshape fields so as to make more efficient use of tractor-drawn equipment. They need to realine fields in order to carry out such conservation practices as contouring. They wish to obtain more land suited to production of crops like tobacco, rice, citrus fruits, and certain vegetables.

The clearing of forests in some areas may be related to improvement of pastures. Land clearing in the southern Piedmont is associated with changes in type of farming, in which greater emphasis is given to livestock production and less to crops, such as cotton, grown for sale. Ranchers in central Florida are clearing land to establish improved pastures that will complement the grazing of native grasses.

Clearing land for farms and homes has been continuous since colonial times. The original forests of the United States covered an estimated 820 million acres, not counting about 84 million acres of arid woodland. Only about 25 million acres were cleared before 1790. About 150 million acres of the eastern forest area had been cleared for farmland by 1880. Much good timber was burned and destroyed because there was no market for it and the trees stood in the way of cultivation.

An estimated 250 million acres in the originally forested areas east of the Great Plains have been cleared and were farmed in 1958. In the West, 6 million to 7 million acres had to be cleared before they could be irrigated. Unirrigated crops, pastures, and farmsteads in the West take up an additional 25 to 30 million acres of cleared land. Another 30 million acres or more of cleared land are used for cities, roads, and other built-up or developed areas.

Thus about 310 to 320 million acres of originally forested land are now in farming and other nonforest uses.

Probably as much as 75 million acres of formerly cleared land have reverted to forest and brush. An undetermined additional area of idle cleared land that is no longer a part of existing farms is located in the originally forested areas. Some of this idle land is held for urban development. Other idle lands are kept open for recreational and other purposes. Still other areas will revert to forest in time.

Until the early part of the present century, the forest area declined steadily. During the last 50 years in the country as a whole, however, land reverting to forest has exceeded the acreage of land that was being cleared.

The westward migration and the settlement of the prairies led to the abandonment of much farmland in the East. Often it reverted to forest. Substantial increases in production since 1920 have contributed to a relative stability of the area in crops, despite a rapid increase in population.

The boll weevil and economic problems encountered in growing cotton led to some reversion in the South. The westward migration of cotton production contributed particularly to the reversion of cropland to forest in parts of the Southeast.

Parts of the cutover counties in the Lake States proved to be uneconomic for agriculture, and much cropland has been abandoned during the past few decades.

THE PATTERN OF LANDOWNERSHIP tends to control the extent of land clearing and reversion. Extensive forest holdings indicate a growing appreciation of forestry values among owners. Corporations in the pulp, paper, and chemical industries have acquired large tracts and have raised the level of yield of forest products and of timber management. Among the economic factors in this ownership pattern is the desire to insure quantity and quality of the supply of raw materials and to obtain better bargaining power.

It is not probable, however, that a very large net reversion of farmland to forest will occur in the future. It is more likely that clearing of forest land will continue and that some further loss of forested area will occur, despite the economic and technological factors that continue to concentrate production of agricultural commodities on the better lands.

FOREST LAND SUITED to the growing of crops is still available.

The Soil Conservation Service estimated that woodlands and forests occupy 105 million acres that are suited to cultivation and are physically better suited to growing crops than are 90 million acres now used for them.

At least 40 million acres of the present cropland area should be returned to pasture and forestry uses.

The remaining 50 million acres are so subject to erosion that they should be cropped only with great care.

Thus, as far as physical conditions are concerned, opportunity exists for additional clearing of land to help in adjusting the use of land to its physical capabilities. Such shifts in use—particularly shifts to more intensive uses—however, are not necessarily recommended and may not be economically desirable under conditions in 1958.

Three-fourths of the forested area potentially suitable for cropland is in the Southern States. Some of this land was once used for tobacco, cotton, corn, and other cultivated crops. After reverting to forest, some of it was cleared a second or a third time for crops (like tobacco) of high cash value.

If we look more closely at this 105 million acres of forest land, we discover that about 42 million acres is good land that can be farmed with relatively little risk of erosion. It is level to gently rolling, has deep soils that are easy to work, holds water well, and is at least fairly fertile.

Some of this good land is in large forest holdings that are not used primarily for agriculture. A considerable acreage, however, is distributed in small wooded tracts on existing farms. It is this good land on farms that is most readily available for development if the need for farm products warrants its use and if farmers have adequate capital with which to do the clearing. Some of it may also require drainage or irrigation.

The remaining 63 million acres include land that should be cleared and cultivated only if such conservation measures as terracing and stripcropping on slopes and good water management on flat areas are installed.

Whether individual farmers will find it profitable to develop more of this kind of land on their farms will depend on several conditions. Among these are the acreage available for clearing, the cost of clearing, the use to which the land can be put in terms of the type of farming carried on, the prices of farm products, and the availability of capital.

ALTOGETHER, more than a million acres of land were cleared each year for agriculture from 1946 to 1955. Not included in that total are the acres of rangelands cleared of brush and the land cleared for nonagricultural uses.

A large part of the land cleared for agriculture is in the South. Two sections stand out—the lower Mississippi Valley and central Florida.

In the West, removing desert vegetation is a part of the cost of developing some new land for irrigation.

Brush control is important in the Southwest, particularly Texas, where undesirable woody plants, such as mesquite, scrub oak, and creosote, have invaded native rangelands. Mechanical and chemical controls of various kinds are used in attempts to eradicate them and to control their further spread.

THE MARKED INCREASE in land clearing since the war was stimulated by the favorable prices for farm products immediately after the war. A price-cost squeeze that came later fostered individual action to reduce costs and increase yields. Some farmers who were unable to adjust their farm organization and operations found off-farm employment and converted idle land to forests. Others intensified production on their cropland and pastureland. Still others reduced labor costs by clearing more land for pasture and shifting from crop or general farming to livestock production. Ranchers continued to use available equipment and manpower in slack periods to clear land for more forage.

A further encouragement for land clearing has come from development of new machinery and techniques for rapid, large-scale clearing operations. They make it possible to clear in a few weeks what formerly could be cleared in a year.

For example, at a land-clearing demonstration in Clay County, Fla., in 1952, it took less than 5 hours of machine and operator time for clearing and piling operations on an acre of heavy hammock land. For sparsely timbered flatwood plots from which the salable timber had been cut, it took only about 2 hours of machine and operator time for clearing and piling.

MODERN EQUIPMENT for land clearing has come into widespread use since 1945. Crosscut saws, axes, and crews of men largely have been replaced by heavy equipment and power tools—crawler-type tractors, dozer blades, tree cutters, stumpers, root rakes, brush rakes, bush-and-bog plows, brush choppers, undercutting plows, portable circular saws, and chain saws. Chemical brushkillers, flamethrowers, and mechanical shredders also are used.

The cost of clearing land depends on the density and size of trees and the type of timber stand; whether the timber is salable; the kind of equipment; and drainage, soils, and climate.

Higher wages have tended to make it cheaper to clear land by machine than by older methods. Machine clearing leaves land almost ready for use.

IN THE SOUTH, the major areas of extensive land clearing are in the Coastal Plain and Delta regions. Clearing of brushland for crops and the control of mesquite, oak, and other objectionable brush is done on the rangelands.

Clearing has been going on actively in eastern North Carolina, southwestern Georgia, southwestern Alabama, southeastern Mississippi, southern Louisiana, and the Mississippi River Delta of Arkansas, Louisiana, and Mississippi. In the ridge and flatwoods sections of Florida, much land has been cleared for agriculture, subdivisions, and urban uses.

Timber resources are affected by the location, extent, and type of land clearing and reversion to forest. The acreage of hardwood stands in the upland and Coastal Plain areas has increased faster than the acreage of pine, except in communities where pulp and turpentine are produced. That is partly because timber cutters and farmers prefer to cut pine trees. Also, hardwood trees are aggressive; they soon appear in the understory of pine stands. Clearing of bottom lands limits the hardwoods.

Surveys by the Forest Service indicated that an increase of 1.2 million acres, or 11 percent, in forest land occurred in the Piedmont and mountain counties of North Carolina between 1937 and 1956, mainly because of reversion of cropland and pastureland to forest.

The increase in forest land in the Georgia Piedmont in 1936–1954 exceeded that in the mountains. Much farmland has been abandoned since 1935 in the southern uplands of Alabama and the northern uplands of Mississippi.

The clearing of bottom lands along streams and reversion of slopes result in more intensive farming of a smaller acreage of more productive land in some upland areas.

Where only small parcels of land are available for clearing and farm labor has little opportunity for alternative productive employment, hand methods of clearing tend to persist. In the absence of uncleared productive lands, a little clearing may be done on relatively poor sites.

Crops with high gross value of product per acre tend to predominate on newly cleared cropland in the South. These include tobacco in North Carolina; truck crops in the eastern Coastal Plain, Atlantic flatwoods, and Florida peninsula; citrus groves on the ridgelands and in the Indian River area of Florida; and rice in Arkansas, Louisiana, and Texas.

Acreage restrictions on some crops, such as rice, however, have caused postponement of some land-clearing operations that had been planned. It is customary in central and southern Florida in most years to obtain new land for tomatoes and watermelons in order to minimize the effect of plant diseases. Much of the land cleared for these crops is converted to pasture in the third year.

Improved pastures also have been established on newly cleared land. A favorable level of beef prices after the war was an important factor. Farmers and ranchers selected sites with light stands of trees and favorable slopes. Bulldozers, heavy choppers, giant chains, chemicals, and other means of eradicating native vegetation were adopted for speed and economy, especially in Florida and the Southern Plains. A decline in the price of beef about 1952 slowed down the pace of clearing for pastures.

Despite lower prices for beef cattle and for many crops, substantial acreages were cleared for agriculture in 1953–1954. About 300 thousand acres were cleared in Florida, 245 thousand acres in Texas, 185 thousand acres in Arkansas, and 115 thousand acres in Kentucky. About 20 thousand acres were cleared in West Virginia.

Large commercial farmers and ranchers acquired their own bulldozers, draglines, and related equipment. Former servicemen and others have gone into the business of doing custom land-development work for farmers, ranchers, grove owners, developers of subdivisions, and others.

Farmers and ranchers who own their own equipment clear land in slack periods and so use available labor and machinery more efficiently. Custom operators work under contract by the job or hour.

No two land-clearing operations are the same. Methods and costs depend on topography, soil types, drainage, salvage of forest products, size and type of equipment, skill of the operators of the machines, and the type, size, and density of cover.

Crawler-type tractors, equipped with dozer or pusher blades, are widely used, although operators usually have available several sizes of tractors and attachments for different situations.

Cutover flatwoods in central Florida usually contain many stumps, scattered sapling pine, and thick palmetto. The operator there may remove stumps with a detachable stumper mounted on a crawler-type tractor. He then pushes and piles the pine trees, using the dozer blade. Finally, he uses an undercutting sweep plow and heavy disk to unearth and chop the palmetto plants. A medium or small crawler tractor with attached blade, stumper, or disk commanded a custom rate of 8 to 10 dollars an hour, with operators, in 1958. The undercutting plow mounted on a patrol cost 10 to 12 dollars an hour. The total cost of clearing was about 30 to 45 dollars an acre, depending on such items as the density of cover.

Sites covered with young trees and plants that can be eradicated by heavy-duty choppers, plows, and disks can be cleared cheaply. Scrub-oak tracts sometimes are chained or cabled at a cost of 5 to 25 dollars an acre—heavy chains or cables are dragged between two tractors through the brush. The preparation of marshlands for crops involves a low cost for land clearing but relatively high costs for ditching, diking, and draining.

Some operators in the sandy areas of the Coastal Plain and flatwoods believe that trees with big taproots are easier to pull or push than are trees with large root systems just below the surface, which are harder to rake, pick up, and burn.

Removing live oak and magnolia, which attain great size in hammocks, is costly and taxes the power of even the larger machines and the ingenuity and patience of the best operators. It costs 100 dollars or more to clear an acre in such places. In clearing for general crops or pasture, these trees are usually deadened and allowed to stand, but in clearing for construction, reservoir sites, and urban and industrial uses, trees of this kind are usually removed.

A clean job of clearing generally is required for crops, groves, and most nonagricultural uses of land. Trees may be cut at the surface of the ground, and the underground stumps are permitted to remain if the land is to be used for rice, pasture, or other crops that are to be disked, harrowed, rolled, or mowed, rather than put under deep cultivation.

The cost of clearing wooded sites for agricultural purposes in many parts of the South ranges from about 25 to 80 dollars an acre.

The availability of water may grow in importance in the selection of sites to be cleared for new uses.

TO CLEAR LAND in the West, mechanical measures, controlled burning, chemical brushkillers, and desiccants commonly are used when vegetation has to be removed quickly and the use of browse animals would take too long.

The native grasses are permitted to cover the area or are reestablished when the woody vegetation has been removed or is under control. This is the usual procedure when the native species are of the desired type.

When only remnants of the native grasses remain, when they are not of the desired type, or when natural factors are not favorable for rapid natural succession, the cleared areas are seeded to improved, adapted grasses.

Artificial reseeding of grass with tractor-drawn drills or broadcasting by hand and airplane are common in the West. Various mixtures of annual and perennial grasses are used, depending on the kind of land to be reseeded and the owner's preference. The cost is 1 to 8 dollars an acre.

CLEARING OF CUTOVER timberland for grazing is done in places in which commercial forest land and natural grassland are intermingled, as in northwestern California and the Pacific Northwest, when the grazing land is limited.

One way in which a rancher can get enough grazing land and maintain economic balance at the same time is to clear places next to the existing pasture or rangelands.

Clearing cutover timberland calls for

several operations. The first is to cut the trees and brush that remain standing. The tract then is readied for burning. The residue is piled. Fire lines are built. Burning follows.

The rancher gets a permit to burn. Then he selects, within the limitations of the permit, days when wind and moisture allow reasonably clean burns with small danger that the fires will get beyond control. The burning in some States is with State supervision.

Slashing the trees and preparing the land for burning costs 6 to 18 dollars an acre, depending on the density and size of the trees, steepness of terrain, the type of equipment, and the experience of the operator.

The first burn after logging costs the rancher 30 cents to 2 dollars an acre, according to the size of area burned, the kind and amount of slash on the ground, weather, and topography.

The burned tract may be seeded to grass. Seed ordinarily is broadcast by plane or hand. Grasses seeded on cleared timberland mostly are perennial and annual ryegrasses, orchardgrass, and subterranean clover. Mixtures may also contain smaller amounts of seeds of many other grasses and clovers. Costs of seeds and seeding are about 2 to 8 dollars an acre, depending mainly on the kinds of seed used.

Proper management after burning and seeding is important. The number and kind of animals grazed greatly affect the kind of vegetation that will develop and survive.

After a cleared area of timberland has been grazed by sheep or by sheep and cattle for 3 or 4 years, it is reburned to control the woody vegetation that has resprouted. A reburn costs the rancher 60 cents to 3.75 dollars an acre, depending on the success of the first burning, the species of vegetation, and other factors. Reseeding after a reburn is not always necessary. Ordinarily, 2 to 4 reburns, combined with browsing by sheep, are necessary to complete the clearing job.

Total costs of a successful conversion job, including three reburns, may be 10 to 40 dollars an acre. The average total cost of converting an acre of timberland to grassland in northwestern California was 26 dollars in 1958.

BRUSHLAND is cleared in the Western States in places that are covered by brush or woody species but have good enough soil and rain to support good stands of grass.

The sagebrush lands of the Intermountain region, the chaparral lands of California, and the juniper-mesquite lands in Arizona and New Mexico, for example, have large acreages that can be improved. Clearing brush is sometimes necessary to maintain the quality of forage on pasture and grazing land.

The improvement job is done by ranchers, associations of ranchers, Indian tribes, and State and Federal agencies.

Steep slopes, rocky soil, or rock outcroppings make mechanical removal nearly impossible. Then the brush is burned or sprayed with a chemical, such as 2,4-D or 2,4,5-T. Costs of applying chemicals have been 3 to 8.50 dollars an acre, depending on the method and the amount of chemical used. Chemicals also are effective as a followup after burning or mechanical clearing.

Level or gently rolling land usually is cleared by plowing, disking, or burning according to the nature of the vegetation, the type of seedbed that is wanted, and costs.

When the land has been cleared, the native grasses may be permitted to revegetate the area, or it may be seeded to grass. The type of native grasses, the adaptability of grasses that can be introduced, and the extent to which the vegetation has been removed determine the species. Crested wheatgrass, smooth brome, intermediate wheatgrass, orchardgrass, pubescent wheatgrass, tall wheatgrass, and tall fescue have been used.

Studies by J. R. Bentley and others of the California Forest and Range Experiment Station indicated that it costs 10 to 20 dollars an acre to uproot and windrow light and medium brush and 20 to 50 dollars an acre of heavy brush. Smashing the brush to the ground for controlled burning costs about half as much as piling it in windrows before burning. Heavy-duty offset disks or disk plows have been used to remove brush cover that is neither too large nor too dense.

Plowing or disking helps make a good seedbed. The seed can be drilled rather than broadcast. Better results ordinarily are had when the seed is covered. Better than average results have been got when the seed has been broadcast after a burning in which the amount of brush was enough to provide an adequate residue of ash.

Controlled burning to clear brushland has been popular in the West. The brush is burned standing in place without prior treatment or after smashing with a bulldozer. It is also burned after it has been piled and windrowed after removal by mechanical process. The procedure for burning brush is similar to the one we described for clearing cutover land. Controlled burning of brush without prior treatment has cost about 40 cents to 3.65 dollars an acre. Burning, including the use of a bulldozer to smash the brush, costs about 2.50 to 15 dollars an acre. Burning is more successful when the brush is knocked down and allowed to dry.

Mesquite and juniper are removed in several ways—hand grubbing, application of kerosene, aerial spraying with chemicals, chaining, and other mechanical processes. Costs are 2.50 to 32 dollars an acre.

Large acreages of sagebrush and other nonforest desert shrub lands in the semiarid regions have been improved for grazing through removal of the sagebrush. That is done by disking, railing (dragging heavy rails over the ground), controlled burning, or chemical sprays. The cost of removing sagebrush has been 1 to 8 dollars an acre.

LAND CLEARING in the North is done mainly to develop land for housing, highways, airfields, and industrial sites and to develop and improve pastureland. Maintaining the existing acreage of permanent pasture may require removal of encroaching trees and brush from time to time. Not much land is cleared for cropland, except that done to enlarge and realine fields.

Clearing small tracts for rural homesites is common in the Northeast. Clearing farm woodland for pasture and for cropland has been scattered throughout the Northern States. In no State, except New York, did the acreage cleared in conservation districts exceed 10 thousand acres in any year between 1952 and 1958. Pennsylvania and Maryland were the only other Northeastern States in which the clearing carried out in the conservation districts amounted to more than 2 thousand acres a year since 1952. Some land is cleared each year in the Corn Belt and Lake States, but only in Minnesota has the acreage cleared exceeded 3 thousand acres a year.

In general, the area of farmland that has reverted to forest in recent years has greatly exceeded the area cleared for pasture and crops in the Northern States. The need for a larger acreage of improved pasture on dairy farms has been a major incentive for the land clearing on farms in the North.

Most farmers contract with custom land developers on an hourly basis to clear their land, as ordinarily they do not have the necessary heavy equipment with which to do a satisfactory job. Most of the clearing is done with crawler-type tractors equipped with dozer blades and rakes.

The forest cover cleared generally varies with the intended land use. Land cleared for agricultural uses usually is cutover land or secondgrowth hardwood or brush. When land is cleared for residential, industrial, and other related uses, good stands of trees are cleared occasionally.

Approximate costs of clearing forest lands are 40 to 150 dollars an acre. Some costs run much higher for heavy forest stands.

The potential demand for timber.

From the standpoint of owners of forest land, the outlook suggests better market opportunities for timber and a greater stimulus for forestry than in the past. From the standpoint of forest industry and the public, the outlook emphasizes the need for strengthening forestry efforts. By *David B. King*, assistant director, and *I. Irving Holland*, economist, Division of Forest Economics Research, Forest Service.

THE NATION's need for timber products will be strikingly greater in the future than it is today or was at any time in the past.

This is one major conclusion reached in the 1958 publication of the Forest Service, Department of Agriculture, Timber Resources for America's Future, upon which the following is based.

Wood has physical characteristics that make it better than other raw materials in many uses. Lumber and plywood are relatively light, strong for their weight, and workable. They are preferred for some types of shipping containers, especially for heavy objects and for shipments overseas. No substitute has been found for wood for railroad ties. Wood is preeminent for flooring, piling, posts, utility poles, and household furniture and fixtures. Wood is the only low-cost raw material available in sufficient volume to meet the needs for fiber of the expanding pulp and paper industry.

Raw materials are of three general groups—foods, energy materials, and physical-structure materials.

Energy materials (including fuelwood) are used for heat, light, and power.

Physical-structure materials provide the substance of things we make and use. They include all timber products other than fuelwood.

Fuelwood comprised about 40 per-

cent of the energy materials—about 100 million cords—in 1900. Since that time the use of wood for heat, light, and power has declined steadily in favor of electricity, oil, and gas. By 1952 fuelwood represented about 3 percent of all energy materials; annual use was about 59 million cords.

Industrial wood—that is, all timber products except fuelwood—accounted for almost one-third of all physical-structure materials used in 1900. It declined steadily to about one-sixth of the total in 1940. The trend was reversed during the Second World War, and industrial wood made up about one-fifth of the total by 1952.

The use of timber products of all kinds in 1952 amounted to 12.3 billion cubic feet. That represented enough logs and bolts to make a solid block 1 thousand miles long, 48 feet wide, and 48 feet thick. Industrial wood comprised about 84 percent of the total volume and fuelwood the rest.

The proportions of all industrial wood represented by different timber products have changed considerably.

Sawlogs for lumber declined from 73 percent of all industrial wood in 1900 to 62 percent in 1952; pulpwood increased from about 2 to 27 percent; veneer logs and bolts increased from less than 1 to 4 percent; and other products, such as poles, piling, and posts, dropped from 25 to 7 percent of the total.

Three separate projections of potential demand for timber have been developed and are designated as medium, upper, and lower projections. They are based upon a series of projections of population, economic activity and other indicators and reflect the general assumptions of peace but a continued strong military position, high levels of employment, a continued rise in productivity and living standards, and continued importance of forest products.

The medium and lower projections assumed that the population of the United States will increase from 165 million in 1955 to 215 million in 1975 and 275 million by the year 2000. They also assumed that the gross national product—the total value of the Nation's output of all goods and services—will increase from the 1955 level of 385 billion (in terms of 1953 dollars) to 630 billion by 1975 and 1,200 billion by the year 2000.

The upper projection assumed a population of 228 million in 1975 and 360 million by 2000 with corresponding gross national product estimated at 645 billion and 1,450 billion dollars, respectively. Because the upper projection of potential demand for timber would not be appreciably higher than the medium projection in 1975, the upper projection has been made only for the year 2000 where the differences due to population are large enough to merit consideration.

All projections also involved assumptions regarding future prices and trends in the use of substitutes for wood. The lower projection assumed that prices of timber products would increase substantially faster than prices of competing materials and result in extensive price-induced substitution of nonwood materials for timber. The medium and upper projections assumed that prices of timber products would rise no faster than prices of competing materials and that timber would continue to hold its position in the mix of physical-structure materials.

With this explanation of assump-
445509°—58——28

tions upon which projections of future demand are based, attention now turns to past consumption and potential demand for individual timber products. The medium projection is considered the basic projection of demand in this chapter.

The use of lumber in the United States reached a peak of about 45 billion board-feet in 1906. Since then it has fluctuated considerably, especially during the 1930's, and totaled 41.5 billion board-feet in 1952.

Construction and repair of residences took an estimated 40 percent of the total. Nonresidential construction used about 35 percent. About 15 percent of all lumber was used in shipping. The remaining 10 percent went into furniture and other fabricated products.

The demand for lumber for residential construction is expected to go up sharply after 1965 because of the recent increase in population. A slump in formation of new households was expected between 1955 and 1960 because the birthrate in the 1930's was low, but an upsurge thereafter would reflect the high birthrate that came later. The average annual net increase in numbers of households may drop from a 1952 level of 1 million units to about 500 thousand to 600 thousand a year between 1955–1960 and then rise to a level of about 1.2 million by 1975 and to 1 million or 1.4 million by 2000—depending on whether the population by that time is 275 million or 360 million.

Projections of housing in the future must take into account several other factors. A margin for unoccupied houses—8 percent of the number occupied—must be included to account for seasonal dwellings and units awaiting sale or rental.

Another factor is the replacement of the housing units lost by fire, flood, and windstorm—an estimated average of about 40 thousand a year in 1952.

It is hard to estimate the rate of replacement of old and wornout housing, houses demolished in shifts in land use, and houses abandoned in shifts of population. Such annual replacements, however, may increase from about 568 thousand units in 1952 to about 1,250 thousand units by 2000.

The total annual requirements for new housing thus may increase from about 1.3 million units in 1952 to an annual average of 2 million units by 1975 and 2.5 million units by 2000.

Changes in type and size of dwelling also affect the demand for lumber. About one-third of all privately owned nonfarm dwellings built 50 years ago were two-family or multifamily structures, compared to fewer than one-tenth of the total built in 1955. This shift tends to move housing out of the field of heavy construction, in which concrete and steel have competitive advantages, toward light construction, in which lumber and other wood products can compete better.

The average floorspace in dwellings declined from an estimated 1,310 square feet in 1920 to 980 square feet in 1950. This trend changed after 1950, and the average size of dwelling units may increase further if families get bigger.

Brick, asbestos shingles, and other materials have displaced wood siding somewhat in exterior covering of wood-frame structures. About 60 percent of all single-family, wood-frame houses started in early 1954 were faced with material other than wood. Brick, masonry, and concrete-block construction is used to some extent in place of wood-frame structures.

Concrete slabs were used instead of wall or pillar foundations in about 16 percent of the single-family houses started in early 1955, and they had no wood girders, main-floor joists, heavy sills, flooring, and subflooring.

Some of the drop in the use of lumber, however, has resulted from the substitution of some wood products for others. Plywood and various fiberboards are used extensively in place of lumber for subflooring, wall and roof sheathing, and interior wall paneling.

The use of lumber in dwellings in 1952 amounted to an estimated average of 10 thousand board-feet per unit. The use of lumber per unit may decline further. Nevertheless, in view of the large demand for new and replacement housing, potential use of lumber in new residential construction is expected to increase from the 13 billion board-feet in 1952 to 18 billion board-feet by 1975 and 22 billion feet by 2000.

Much lumber is used for maintenance, repair, alterations, and additions to dwellings. The amounts have tended roughly to parallel the increase in number of households. Those requirements are expected to increase from about 3.9 billion board-feet in 1952 to 5 billion in 1975 and to 7.2 billion feet in 2000.

DEMANDS FOR LUMBER for nonresidential construction also are expected to increase with the expansion of population and gross national product.

Nonresidential construction includes many types of buildings, public utilities, and projects for conserving and developing natural resources.

Lumber is used chiefly in a facilitating role in most types of nonresidential construction. For concrete forms, for example, plywood, hardboard, and other sheet materials have displaced much lumber as facing materials, although the studs and bracing are still primarily lumber. Brick, masonry, concrete, and steel have largely displaced lumber in buildings of heavy construction, but a modern trend is to build schools, warehouses, suburban stores, garages, and churches as single-story structures, which make greater use of lumber. Glued, laminated arches have been used in place of steel girders in building churches and gymnasiums.

Despite the fluctuations in 1919–1955, largely as a result of depression and war, there is little doubt that nonresidential construction will increase with an expansion of the national economy. A larger population will require more factories, transportation, churches, schools, and theaters.

Potential demands for lumber for new nonresidential construction and maintenance and repair, including mining uses and farm construction as well as industrial and commercial uses, are projected from a level of 12.5 billion board-feet in 1952 to 15.9 billion board-feet by 1975 and to 26.9 billion feet by 2000.

Railroad construction accounted for about 5 percent—2 billion board-feet—of all lumber used in the United States in 1952. About 56 percent of it was used as ties; 24 percent went into freight cars; and 20 percent was used for buildings, bridges, crossings, fences, and other facilities.

The mileage of railroad track operated was 420 thousand miles in 1930 and 371 thousand miles in 1955. Continuing abandonment of unprofitable lines and relocation of main lines on straighter and more favorable grades may continue to reduce the total mileage of operated track in some areas. Further double tracking and other new construction may be required in an expanding economy.

The number of ties per mile of track averaged about 3,020 in 1955. If trends toward heavier tracks continue, increased numbers of ties under the tracks will be needed. The average size of ties also has increased from about 32 board-feet in 1916, for example, to 39 board-feet in 1955. Considering the trend toward heavier track, further increase in size of crossties may be expected. The average service life of ties is about 33 years.

Potential demands for railroad ties are projected from 1.1 billion board-feet in 1952 to 1.6 billion board-feet by 1975 and to 2 billion feet by 2000.

About half as much lumber—about 473 million board-feet—was used in 1952 for building and repairing freight cars as in 1920. The drop was due partly to a reduction in number of freight cars in service and partly to the substitution of steel for wood in framing and exterior covering and the increased use of plywood for interiors.

Because wood has several advantages

for freight cars, wood may hold its competitive position. Cargo can be fastened more easily to wood floors than to steel. Wood lining prevents condensation and serves as part of the insulation required in refrigerator cars. Wood floors absorb vibration better than metal, do not rust, and are easier and cheaper to repair.

Considering the number of cars probably needed in future years, the number requiring maintenance, and the volume of wood required per car of various types, we estimate the potential demand for wood for car construction will be 528 million feet by 1975 and 604 million board-feet by 2000, compared to an estimated 473 million board-feet in 1952.

Lumber used for railroad buildings, bridges, trestles, crossings, elevators, warehouses, and other facilities built by the railroads totaled about 400 million board-feet in 1952. Some decrease is expected in the use of lumber for these purposes because of the use of more treated lumber and the substitution of other materials. The demand is estimated at 250 million board-feet by 1975 and 300 million by 2000.

Potential demands for lumber by railroads thus is projected from a consumption level of 2 billion board-feet in 1952 to 2.4 billion board-feet by 1975 and to 2.9 billion feet by 2000.

SHIPPING used about 6.1 billion board-feet in 1952. About 15 to 20 percent of the lumber used in the United States goes into boxes, crates, and cases for transporting and storing industrial and agricultural products, for making and repairing wooden pallets, and for dunnage for blocking and bracing cargoes in ships and railroad cars.

About 4 to 6 billion board-feet of lumber went for shipping purposes each year before 1930. The huge overseas shipments of military supplies during the war required a large volume of shipping lumber. About 14.5 billion board-feet were used in shipping in 1944. Annual consumption since has averaged about 6 billion board-feet.

There has been considerable substitution of paperboard and wirebound veneer boxes and crates (which cost and weigh less) for containers made of lumber. Nailed and wirebound wooden boxes and crates nevertheless are used a great deal for fresh fruits and vegetables, mainly because they protect the contents better and are not weakened by moisture in refrigerator cars. Nailed lumber boxes and crates may continue to be used for shipment of manufactured goods that require protection; in overseas shipments, where containers are stacked on each other; and in the transport of heavy or odd-shaped products.

It is estimated that potential demands for container lumber will increase from 4.3 billion board-feet in 1952 to 5.8 billion board-feet in 1975 and 7 billion board-feet in 2000.

The use of wooden pallets for handling goods has expanded rapidly. Industry used about 23 million pallets in 1950 and an estimated 43 million in 1955. Annual production may reach about 70 million by 1975 and 150 million by 2000 requiring 1.7 billion and 3.5 billion board-feet of lumber. As the lumber required for pallets comes chiefly from plentiful, low-quality hardwoods, the substitution of other materials for lumber is unlikely.

The use of lumber for dunnage is set at about 1 billion board-feet a year. Because of the increase in shipments of merchandise by truck, loose rail shipment, and the development of steel strapping methods and of substitutes, such as inflated rubber packing, the use of dunnage lumber may drop.

For all shipping lumber, potential demands are projected to 8.7 billion board-feet by 1975 and 12 billion feet by 2000.

THE DEMAND FOR LUMBER for manufactured products is increasing. Approximately 10 percent of all lumber used annually in the United States is for manufactured products like furniture, fixtures, caskets and burial boxes,

truck bodies, television sets, boats, pencils, and innumerable other products. About 3.7 billion board-feet of lumber were used in manufactured products in 1928 and 3.9 billion board-feet in 1948.

Roughly half of the lumber used for manufactured products in 1948 went into furniture, primarily household furniture, which faces competition from plywood, hardboard, and particle board. Metal has been substituted for wood in some items of lawn and kitchen furniture, but not in living-room and bedroom furniture, two of the most important types. In view of the number of new dwellings to be furnished and the rate of replacement of wornout furniture, the demand for lumber for household furniture is expected to rise substantially.

Trends in the use of wood in non-household furniture have varied. Metal furniture has been popular in offices, but there now appears to be a swing back to wood. Thus in terms of value, wood furniture represented 27 percent of total shipments in 1947, 17 percent in 1952, and 21 percent in 1954. The only products almost completely taken over by metal are filing cabinets.

Demands for wood for such items as sports equipment, toys, musical instruments, and television sets seem likely to increase at about the same rate as disposable personal income. The demand for agricultural equipment containing wood can be expected to parallel trends in farm output.

Consumption of lumber for all uses in 1952 and the medium projections of potential lumber demand in 1975 and 2000 are summarized as follows (in billions of board-feet):

	1952	1975	2000
Dwellings	16.9	23.0	29.2
Nonresidential	12.5	15.9	26.9
Railroads	2.0	2.4	2.9
Shipping	6.1	8.7	12.0
Manufacturing	4.0	5.5	8.0
Total	41.5	55.5	79.0

The alternative lower projection points to somewhat lower levels of future demand, which is estimated at about 48 billion board-feet of lumber by 1975 and 55 billion board-feet by 2000. The corresponding upper projection of potential lumber demand in 2000 is 90 billion board-feet.

THE DEMAND FOR PULPWOOD has increased much faster than has demand for any other purpose—from about 2 million cords in 1900 to 41.9 million in 1955.

Potential demands for pulpwood depend largely on demands for paper, paperboard, and wood-derived products, such as cellophane and rayon, on expected changes in pulping processes, and on anticipated net imports of pulp, paper, paperboard, and pulpwood.

The consumption of paper, including newsprint, groundwood papers, such as those used for wallpaper and pulp magazines, book and fine paper, coarse and industrial papers, tissue and sanitary papers, such as toilet and cleansing tissues, and building paper, increased from 5.4 million tons in 1920 to 19.2 million tons in 1955, or 257 percent. The use of paperboard, which includes container board, bending and nonbending board, building board, and other paperboards, went up from 2.3 million tons in 1920 to 15.3 million tons in 1955—578 percent.

Consumption of dissolving grades of woodpulp for use in manufacture of products like rayon, cellophane, nitrocellulose, acetate plastics, photographic film, and smokeless powder has also required a considerable volume of high-grade pulp—about 45 thousand tons in 1930 and 547 thousand tons in 1955.

It is estimated that potential demands for pulp, paper, paperboard, and for nonpaper products may total 49 million tons by 1975 and 75 million tons by 2000.

Pulpwood requirements to meet these increases in potential demand are estimated at 72 million cords by 1975 and 100 million cords by 2000. It is further estimated that part of the total, amounting to approximately 14 million cords in 1975 and 15 million in 2000, might be imported in the form of pulpwood, pulp, paper, and paperboard. The alternative lower projection indicates an annual demand for pulpwood of 65 million cords in 1975 and 90 million in 2000. The corresponding upper projection in 2000 is 125 million cords.

DEMANDS FOR VENEER and plywood have increased greatly. The consumption of veneer logs and bolts rose to 3.4 billion board-feet in 1955, a tenfold increase in 50 years. Softwoods accounted for about 70 percent of the total veneer logs used in 1955, and hardwoods, 30 percent. Nearly all of the softwood veneer produced is used in softwood plywood. A small amount is utilized for containers. Roughly half of the hardwood veneer is utilized for plywood.

Softwood plywood has been substituted extensively for lumber in sheathing, subflooring, inside wall covering, and exterior siding, especially in prefabricated housing. Plywood can be installed with simple tools by relatively unskilled labor.

The use of plywood for concrete forms also has greatly expanded with development of synthetic resin glues used in moistureproof plywood. Plywood is used in increasing quantities in farm buildings, as lining and sheathing in railroad freight cars, in truck and truck-trailer bodies, and in home repair and construction. About 5.4 billion square feet three-eighths-inch basis of softwood plywood was consumed in 1955, of which an estimated 4.1 billion square feet was used in construction, and 1.3 billion square feet for containers and fabricated products.

Hardwood veneer production in 1953 amounted to 10.1 billion square feet, surface measure. About 1.9 billion square feet was high-quality material used mainly for its decorative effect in furniture and as facing in wall panels and flush doors. Some 4.7 billion square feet was used in plywood for containers and for core and backing stock in high-grade plywoods. About 3.1 billion square feet went into wirebound boxes and crates, baskets, hampers, and other containers in which no gluing is needed. The rest was used for specialty items, woodenware and novelties.

Demands for veneer logs are projected from 3.4 billion board-feet in 1955 to 5.7 billion feet in 1975 and 9 billion feet in 2000.

DEMANDS FOR MINOR industrial wood products have shown variable trends. Included in this group are cooperage logs and bolts, piling, poles, fence posts, turnery bolts, charcoal wood, shingle bolts, excelsior bolts, and farm poles. Into their production in 1952 went about 758 million cubic feet of logs and bolts.

Potential demand for all minor products is projected to about 913 million cubic feet in 1975 and to 1,450 million cubic feet by 2000.

To SUM UP, estimates of demand for timber products can be converted into terms of potential demand for timber cut from the Nation's forests by deducting that part of the volume of each product obtained from plant residues and sources other than forest-growing stock, adding the volume of logging residues, and allowing for improvements in future timber utilization practices and net imports.

In terms of growing stock—that is, trees above 5 inches in diameter—projections indicate that potential demands by the year 2000 might require the cutting of from 46 to 117 percent more than the stock cut in 1952.

In terms of live sawtimber—that is, eastern softwood trees above 9 inches in diameter and hardwoods and western softwoods above 11 inches in diameter—the potential cut by the year 2000 might be from 41 to 127 percent higher than the cut of sawtimber in 1952. Most of the potential demands for timber, as in the case of the actual cut in 1952, presumably will consist of softwoods.

Consumption of timber cut from the Nation's forests in 1952 for all products and projections of potential demand from all forest growing stock and from live sawtimber trees are summarized below:

	Growing stock (billion cu. ft.)	Live sawtimber (billion bd. ft.)
Consumption in 1952...	10. 8	48. 8
Projections to 1975:		
Lower...........	12. 4	56. 0
Medium..........	14. 0	65. 4
Projections to 2000:		
Lower...........	15. 7	69. 0
Medium..........	19. 7	95. 1
Upper...........	23. 4	111. 0

These projections of potential demands thus all indicate substantial increases over 1952 in the amounts of timber which may be required from the Nation's forests in future years. Most of the potential demands will have to be met from trees of sawtimber size, which take many decades to grow to maturity.

THE ABILITY of the United States to meet increased demands for timber will depend largely on action taken to improve forest management and timber supplies during the next few decades. If progress in forest management will continue as indicated by recent trends— and that means substantial progress— timber supplies would be sufficient to meet demands under the lower projection in the years immediately ahead. Within a few decades, however, projected growth would not be enough to meet all timber demands, particularly for the preferred softwood species, such as southern pine and Douglas-fir, and for high-quality timber. The higher projections of potential demand could not be supplied for long without dipping heavily into forest capital.

Projections of potential timber demands and prospective growth thus point to future timber supply problems and increased timber values. Many wood-using plants already face problems of raw material supply and pressure for such adjustments as greater use of hardwoods in place of softwoods.

These also are
our country—Seward's folly can be a great land—
Hawaii's problems and many assets—Puerto Rico: Change and
progress

Seward's folly can be a great land.

"Alaska" in native dialect means "the great land." We still do not know how great it is. Its remote expanses, which cover millions of acres, are practically unvisited. Its buried resources of minerals and hydrocarbon fuel are relatively unknown. Its waterpower potential is almost unused. Its forests and soils are only beginning to be utilized for permanent industry and agriculture. By *Hugh A. Johnson,* economist, Farm Economics Research Division; formerly head, Department of Agricultural Economics, Alaska Agricultural Experiment Station.

WHEN WE bought Alaska from Imperial Russia in 1867, the acquisition was praised by western expansionist interests and opposed by the eastern conservative bloc. Severe criticism was heaped upon Secretary of State Seward for his "folly" in buying "Seward's Icebox," "Icebergia," or "Walrussia."

Actually, the conflict between Great Britain and Russia in the Crimea provided the opportunity for the United States to buy out Russia's interest in North America for a few cents an acre and by the same stroke to limit further British activity in the area and capture a prolific source of furs, fish, and trade. Opposition in the Congress was strong, however, and no legislation for administration of the new possession was enacted until 1884.

Former Governor Ernest Gruening, a longtime student of Alaskan history, said of this admittedly stopgap legislation: "The act was . . . specific in its limitations and prohibitions, indefinite and equivocal in its grants. No legislature, no delegate, no general land laws. . . ." It extended the current Oregon Code to Alaska "as it applied" and as it was "not in conflict with this act or the laws of the United States."

A measure of self-government and

Territorial status came only with passage of the Second Organic Act of 1912. Since that date many Alaskans have been working for statehood in order to obtain greater control in the management of their own affairs.

The Organic Act of 1912 grants to the Territory specific powers comparable to those of the State legislatures, although the Congress has reserved to itself certain functions, such as responsibility for fish and game. It has prohibited Alaska from establishing a judicial system and has also prohibited the creation of counties without congressional consent.

The Department of the Interior administers most of the laws passed by the Congress for the management and development of Alaska's publicly owned resources outside the national forests.

Alaska's location is a handicap to development. It is far removed from established trade routes and is separated from the United States by the Canadian wilderness and the rough waters of the North Pacific. These and other factors, combined with the abundance of resources nearer populated areas, have kept Alaska in the hinterland of national development.

The presence of extensive natural resources has created durable myths as

424

to their worth in the minds of some Alaskans. Advocates of local development often fail to realize that some resources cannot be developed profitably under present economic and technological conditions. That hope for the use of at least a part of these resources need not be deferred much longer, however, is demonstrated by the modern pulp plant at Ketchikan, the interest in several large ore deposits, the oil and gas explorations, and the recurring industrial interests in potential hydropower sites.

Vilhjalmur Stefansson wrote in *Climate and Man*, the 1941 Yearbook of Agriculture: "If you are willing to be an old-fashioned pioneer—a Lincoln of Illinois, a Nordic of a Swedish inland valley, or a Mongol of Central Finland—you can make their type of living in the Alaska of today. But there are few places where it is more difficult than in Alaska to be a successful 'economic man.' The Finns and the Swedes colonized their northern lands when they were subsistence hunters, subsistence fishers, and subsistence farmers. . . . Alaska is a northern land which is at least open for development under our present culture—if a district can be called open that is fenced off by so many economic, sociological, and psychological barbed-wire fences."

The years and events that have occurred since Stefansson's observation have widened the economic gap. The old-fashioned pioneer is rarely found. Bulldozers and chain saws have replaced horses and axes. Airplanes have superseded dogsleds. Scintillometers explore terrain faster and more accurately than wandering prospectors.

FORTUITOUS PARTICIPATION in the Klondike and later gold rushes of men who were vocal and their bombardment of Congressmen with facts about Alaska and pleas for better government brought about the first serious appraisal of Alaska's resources by the Federal Government. Preliminary explorations were authorized to study the geology of the country, to determine its potentialities, and to discover whether agriculture was feasible.

Three Federal agricultural experiment stations—Sitka, Kodiak, and Kenai—were authorized by the Congress in 1898. Later reservations were made for experiment stations at Rampart (1900), Copper Center (1903), Fairbanks (1906), and Matanuska (1915). A fur experimental station was established at Petersburg in 1938. Only the Fairbanks, Matanuska, and Petersburg stations remained in 1958.

An opening wedge for agricultural settlement was forged in the Homestead Act of 1898. It limited land grants to 80 acres and required homesteaders to pay the expenses of surveying. No baselines for surveys existed, and no provision was made for surveys. No settler to my knowledge acquired title under this act. The law was amended in 1903 to permit entry on 320 acres of surveyed or unsurveyed land. Several good farms were developed from tracts entered under this law. The maximum size of a homestead was reduced to 160 acres in 1916 and has remained so.

Leasing for fur farming was first authorized in 1926. Grazing leases were authorized in 1927. Other widely separated acts over the years have regulated entry and use of land for mining, industrial and commercial purposes, homesite and headquarter sites, small tracts for recreational and residential uses, leases for oil and gas exploration, and for other special purposes. Tongass and Chugach National Forests, Glacier and Katmai National Monuments, and McKinley National Park were established by Presidential proclamation in the early era of conservation.

The depression-born Matanuska Valley Colonization Project established in 1935 generated interest in agriculture as 30 years of homesteading had not done. Wartime and postwar defense programs drew attention to Alaska as a place to live and work.

Alaska covers 586,400 square miles and more than 365 million acres of actual land area. Its great size and its

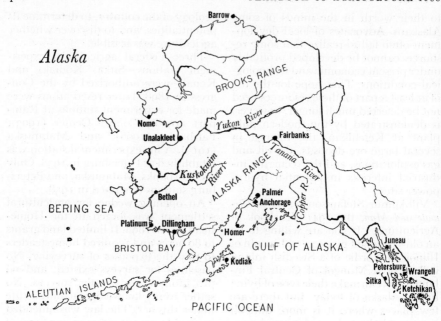

Alaska

variable climate create problems of land utilization. Each region has unique resources and problems. From east to west, Alaska extends through four time zones and about 38 degrees of longitude. In a north-south direction, it extends over more than 15 degrees of latitude. The distance from Barrow to Ketchikan is comparable with that from Boston to Baton Rouge or from Washington, D. C., to Denver.

Nearest the United States lies a long, narrow strip of mainland and islands, called Southeastern Alaska. It has a marine climate similar to that of the Olympic Peninsula in Washington. Rainfall is heavy, and there is much cloudy weather. Primeval forests cover the lower island and mainland slopes and reach up the mountainsides to about 3 thousand feet. Small areas of fairly fertile soils occur in narrow glacial valleys and on some estuaries. Sporadic interest in homesteading has kept a few of these tracts in the public eye, but history shows that farming is submarginal on all except the tracts that are most favorably situated. Agriculture in this region is limited to a few

intensive poultry, dairy, and vegetable farms. Only three fur farms remained in 1957. Southeastern Alaska is better adapted to commercial forestry, fishing, mining, and recreation enterprises.

Nearly all of the area outside townsite eliminations, the national monuments, and the public-domain area around Haines lies within the 16-million-acre Tongass National Forest. Preliminary Forest Service estimates show 84 billion feet of timber on about 6 million acres of merchantable forest. Three-fourths of the commercial timber grows within 2.5 miles of tidewater. Although the region has considerable potential for sawtimber, the immediate interest and need lie in pulp operations.

By early 1957, four large, long-term sales had been made by the Forest Service to private corporations that agreed to harvest forest growth on a sustained-yield basis. Included in these sales were the Ketchikan unit of 8.25 billion board-feet, the Wrangell of 3 billion, the Juneau of 7.5 billion, and the Sitka of 5.25 billion—a total of 24 billion board-feet.

A large, modern pulpmill at Ketchikan and small sawmills at Wrangell, Juneau, and Ketchikan were operating in 1957. A plyboard plant at Juneau had suspended operations temporarily after several years of operation. A large pulp plant was under construction at Sitka. Additional plants and expanded operations are to be introduced for the remaining forested areas when more investment capital has been mobilized and more is known about the economics of plant operations.

Northward lies south-central Alaska, which reaches from the Gulf of Alaska to the Alaska Range and extends westward to the base of the Alaska Peninsula. It includes the 5-million-acre Chugach National Forest, the 2-million-acre (both public and nonpublic lands) Kenai Moose Reserve, the 2.7-million-acre Katmai National Monument, the Anchorage metropolitan area, several large military reservations, and the Matanuska Valley and Kenai Peninsula agricultural areas. The climate and vegetation of this region are affected by its position between the North Pacific marine influences from the south and the shelter of the Alaska Range on the north and west. Spruce, birch, and aspen grow to sawtimber size in commercial quantities. Native grasses and other forage grow luxuriantly on suitable sites. Dairy farmers of the Matanuska Valley have grazing leases for 39 thousand acres of the Matanuska-Susitna area. Areas of fertile soils are sufficient to support several hundred farm families in production of food for local civilian and military markets. Irrigation of crops in spring and early summer is increasingly important to commercial vegetable growers and dairymen.

Central Alaska lies between the Alaska Range on the south and the Brooks Range on the north and includes the 1.9-million-acre Mount McKinley National Park. It includes the drainages of the Upper Yukon, the Tanana, the Koyukuk, and the Upper Kuskokwim. It has a continental climate with long, cold winters and short,

mild summers. Summer temperatures of 100° or more have been recorded, but such days are rare. Precipitation ranges from 8 to 16 inches.

Commercial agriculture is practiced near Fairbanks, and family gardens grow well on suitable sites throughout the region. Irrigation of crops often pays in spring and early summer. Although the Fairbanks area in the Tanana Valley is currently desirable for settlement because it lies near a market, unclaimed potential agricultural soils in other areas are fairly abundant. Climate and soils are suitable for agricultural production in several valleys of the Yukon and Kuskokwim. With limited demand for farm products in these areas, however, there is no pressure for agricultural development.

Both the south-central and the central regions contain forested tracts, although much of the forest is not of a commercial size or concentration. Spruce, birch, and aspen occur on the well-drained ridges and benches. The Bureau of Land Management estimated that there were 40 million acres of commercial forest containing 180 billion board-feet and producing 1.5 billion board-feet annually in these regions in 1956. Another 85 million acres classed as woodland (unsuited to sawmill operations) contain about 170 billion board-feet. Only a little of the commercial-class forest is harvested. Small sawmills process low-grade rough lumber as the needs warrant.

Southwestern Alaska includes Kodiak and nearby islands, the Alaska Peninsula, and the Aleutian Islands. Climate is generally moderated by its marine position. Rainy, foggy weather encourages growth of plant species suitable for grazing. Most of the region is treeless, although some trees grow in protected spots. Several bird and wildlife sanctuaries are on the islands, and Katmai National Monument is at the base of the peninsula.

Its rolling and mountainous grasslands and its relatively mild winters encourage some people to consider possibilities of range cattle and sheep production. As of June 30, 1956, the Department of the Interior had in effect 26 grazing leases on 767 thousand acres in southwestern Alaska. Seven ranches on Kodiak Island had 990 head of cattle in 1956. Beeves are butchered and sold locally as 3-year-olds. In the early 1950's, the lessee on Chirikof Island began to butcher bulls descended from the original American stock. He shipped the meat to Anchorage by air. This herd included about 300 head in 1957. About 300 sheep had been added to the operation. The largest and oldest managed spreads are on Umnak and Unalaska Islands. These operators had about 50 cattle, 8,500 sheep, and small herds of horses in 1956. Livestock were butchered for local use, but the major sales were of wool shipped to Seattle by air. The limited supplies of winter feed and distance from market are obstacles to expansion of livestock enterprises.

The climate of western Alaska—or, more precisely, of Bristol Bay and the lower parts of the Kuskokwim and Yukon drainages—is moderated by the Bering Sea. Except where hills or other topographic features provide a good drainage, this is a vast, flat area of tundra interspersed with thousands of small lakes and meandering streams. I have seen good family gardens growing on sites protected from cold sea winds at Unalakleet, Akiak, Bethel, Platinum, Aleknagik, Dillingham, and Naknek. Physical opportunities for farming communities exist in a few localities of this region, but markets currently are small and strictly local.

The Seward Peninsula and the Arctic Slope generally have summers too short and cool for crops and for livestock production other than reindeer. Except for isolated stands of protected spruce and cottonwoods along the southern fringes, the region is a tundra wilderness.

A. E. Porsild, speaking before the Second Alaska Science Conference in September 1951, stated of this region: "Plant life, everywhere in the Arctic, is too sparse, dwarfed, and poorly developed to make any considerable contribution to the food supply of man. Only a few Arctic plants produce edible and nourishing roots or stems, and only near the southern fringe of the barren grounds are there some that in favorable seasons produce appreciable quantities of small edible fruits. . . . The most promising and economically practical approach to the problem of utilization of the vast Arctic and subarctic tundra and taiga appears to be the wise and careful administration of the remaining wildlife resources."

Explorations for oil and gas, coal, and minerals may discover exploitable physical resources to form a basis for further settlement. But present knowledge and experience in Alaska and other northern areas of America, Europe, and Asia indicate that extensive food production is not economically feasible in these areas.

SOIL CHARACTERISTICS and cool climate are restrictive factors in present and potential crop production. Soils in Alaska are relatively young geologically.

Charles E. Kellogg and I. J. Nygard made a reconnaissance of Alaskan soils for the Department of Agriculture during the summer of 1946 as part of a task-force assignment to study agricultural problems of Alaska. A. H. Mick, of the Alaska Agricultural Experiment Station, later summarized their observations and his own knowledge of Alaskan soils in an article he and I prepared for the Arctic Institute of North America. These men stated that Alaska's mature soils include only the Podzol and Tundra great soil groups.

Tundra is Alaska's most widely distributed zonal great soil group. Vegetal cover subsists at very low levels of activity, and decomposition of organic materials by micro-organisms is still slower. The resultant carpet of tough, fibrous, peaty material increases in thickness year by year, unless it is disturbed by fire, drainage, or some other mechanical change. The high insulating properties of this layer prevent summer warmth from penetrating mineral substrata, which remain frozen for long periods. Most Tundra soils are underlain to varying depths by permanently frozen ground. The frozen subsurface, plus the spongy organic surface materials, usually results in a waterlogged surface condition during the summer.

Intrazonal Alpine Meadow, Mountain Tundra, and Mountain-Half Bog soils occur at higher altitudes. These soils have little potential agricultural value, except for extensive reindeer grazing or possibly as summer pasture to supplement other sites capable of producing winter feed for livestock.

Podzols usually are found in well-drained sandy sites. Where very fine sands and silts were deposited, podzolization is feeble and is transitional to the intrazonal subarctic Brown Forest soils.

Most crop production occurs on the well-drained phases of these subarctic Brown Forest soils. These soils are high in potash but deficient in organic matter, nitrogen, and usually in available phosphates. The surface layers are usually acid. Subsoils are well supplied with calcium and magnesium, although free carbonates generally are absent.

New settlers often are disturbed by the extreme acidity of newly cleared soils. Some buy limestone to neutralize this condition. Specialists at the Alaska Agricultural Experiment Station caution that many fields gradually become neutral or slightly alkaline under cultivation. This process is associated with the breakdown of organic matter and a narrowing of carbon-nitrogen ratios. It occurs on any reasonably well-drained soil in Alaska wherever tillage is carried on. The alkaline reaction of older fields is of concern to farmers in the Matanuska and Tanana Valleys who find their potato crops increasingly afflicted with scab.

I saw an extreme example of this change in pH in a small garden at Bethel on the lower Kuskokwim. The garden was on a small hillock in the Tundra where formerly moss, dwarf shrubs, and berries flourished. The strongly acid virgin soil had become almost neutral after only 3 years of cultivation.

Permafrost is of concern in central Alaska north of the Alaska Range. It takes two forms. The most widespread is a poorly drained situation, caused by insulating materials on the soil surface, which prevents thawing and internal drainage. Removal of trees, brush, and moss permits thawing to a depth sufficient for cultivation. Several settlers in the Tanana Valley have developed excellent cropland from these mechanically wet soils. Local frost pockets, however, sometimes limit the crops that can be grown. Vast areas now classed as muskeg probably can be dried out and made physically suitable for crop production, but microclimatic conditions still would be unfavorable on many sites. Extensive drainage of these wet lands eventually might affect ground-water supplies adversely and create serious erosion problems on associated light podzolic soils.

The second condition in permafrost is the occurrence of large blocks, or lenses, of solid ice under the soil surface. Disturbing the insulating materials permits heat to penetrate; the ice melts, leaving holes of various sizes. Sometimes the thermal action causes no particular loss, but it can be so extreme that the fields become untillable. Parts of older fields at the Fairbanks Agricultural Experiment Station are now too rough to be used even as pasture, and a few new fields on homesteads have become too rough for tillage.

The United States Geological Survey conducts studies designed to aid in locating areas where these conditions occur. Their investigations in 1948 helped to show that the Dunbar area, which was under consideration for a group settlement area, was submarginal because of frequent occurrence of these ice lenses.

Frozen ground is of concern also as it affects availability of potable water and

Regions of Alaska

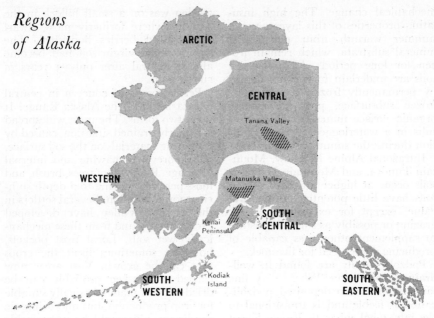

sewage disposal. Farmers in the Tanana Valley sometimes cannot develop livestock farms because of the high cost of developing adequate water supplies.

MORE THAN 99.9 percent of Alaska's land is owned by the Government.

Vacant, unreserved public lands estimated at 270 million acres, reserved lands at 28 million acres, and 185 thousand acres of unperfected homestead entries are controlled by the Bureau of Land Management. The Bureau and the Navy jointly manage 23 million acres of oil and gas reserve. Another 18 million acres are under the control and management of the National Park Service, the Fish and Wildlife Service, the Bureau of Indian Affairs, and the Bureau of Reclamation. The Forest Service has nearly 21 million acres in two national forests, and the Department of Defense has nearly 4 million acres in military reservations. Land withdrawals of all kinds amounted to 92.3 million acres in 1956.

The Department of the Interior is responsible for 93 percent of the Federal lands, the Department of Agricul-

ture for 5 percent, the Department of Defense for about 1.5 percent, and other agencies for a small percentage.

About 450 thousand acres had been patented by June 30, 1956. Homesteads account for a major part of this acreage, but trade and manufacturing sites, homesites, and similar nonagricultural uses account for about 25 thousand acres of privately owned lands. Alaska has no real-estate taxes, except in school districts and municipalities, and there is no convenient way of ascertaining the proportion of patented lands that are currently used. We do know that absentee ownership and land abandonment are serious problems in the major settlement areas. The revised land registration act of 1957 may help to make absentee-owned lands available to farmers.

Before June 1954, veterans of the Second World War who had had 19 months or more of military service could acquire 160-acre homesteads after 7 months of residence and construction of habitable dwellings. They were not required to cultivate any land. Hundreds of veterans entered tracts under these regulations, but many of them abandoned their entries before patent, and nearly as many more abandoned their holdings after patent was acquired.

The obvious need for nonfarm holdings and for enabling legislation other than the homestead laws have been recognized by the Congress and the administrative departments. Townsites, small tracts, industrial and commercial tracts, and recreation and public-purpose sites are authorized under special legislation, and their development is promoted within the Department of the Interior.

In 1954, I studied 110 predominantly veteran homestead entries made in the Matanuska Valley between 1945 and 1950. Eleven entrymen were full-time farmers, 20 were part-time farmers who combined farming with off-farm work, 22 were in businesses other than farming, and 57 had left the valley. Most of those who had left had applied for entry at the Land Office but had not established residence on their tracts.

The Alaska Agricultural Experiment Station, cooperating with the Bureau of Land Management, in 1955 made a detailed study of agricultural settlement on the Kenai Peninsula. Homesteading had been going on in the Homer area for 40 years. Yet we found that 59 percent of all entered or patented land on the Peninsula was unoccupied and abandoned in July 1955. Another 31 percent was used solely for rural residences by persons who had no intention of farming. This left only 10 percent of the homesteaded land occupied by persons who were farming or planning to farm. Only 1.3 percent of the occupied land was cropland—and nearly half of this had been cleared since 1950, when we made a study here. Only 14 percent of all income reported by homesteaders in 1955 came from sales of farm products.

Detailed study of the Homer community showed that 60 percent of all homestead entries from 1915 to 1945 had been canceled, relinquished, or closed by decision. Abandonment, in the sense that the entryman failed to carry through to patent status, increased from 44 percent of all entries before 1930 to 72 percent for the entries made in the 5 years ending in 1945. Activity picked up between 1946 and 1950, when 172 entries were made, 84 patents were granted, and 95 homestead entries were relinquished.

An additional 237 entries were made between 1950 and 1955. Three-fourths of these were relinquished, canceled, or terminated otherwise than by granting patent before June 1956. Several tracts had a long record of entry and abandonment—one had been entered and abandoned 9 times before it was patented to an institution that still had not occupied it by 1956.

The Kenai Peninsula story is repeated with variations in the Matanuska and Tanana Valleys. The question logically follows, "What happens to change homesteaders' minds?"

Unsatisfactory subsistence from the land and lagging development of markets provided a low level of living in the 1930's. Wartime and postwar defense activities drained active potential farmers from their undeveloped homesteads in the early 1940's.

Publicity about new opportunities to be found after the war brought hundreds of veterans and nonveterans alike to Alaska. Many combat veterans seemed to have had a psychological need to get away from the pressures of modern urban society. Many were deeply interested in farming. Some were lured by stories of possible new Government-aided settlement programs akin to the Matanuska Colonization Project. Many of those who came—veterans and nonveterans alike—lacked fundamental knowledge of modern agricultural methods, and most had overlooked the difficulties of clearing land and getting into production. Very few were financially equipped for the task, and costs proved to be prohibitive. Too many learned from hard experience that productive land is not free, that the raw homestead is not the finished farm. Between the two lies a heavy investment in labor, money, management, and time.

Speculation was another strong influence. With no tax on real estate, hunger for landownership and a rural way of life, publicity about development programs, activity in oil and gas explorations, no land-clearing requirement, and only a 7-month residence requirement, it looked as though relatively unsettled veterans had much to gain and little to lose. Some thought they could live off the land by hunting and fishing.

Both the Department of the Interior and the Department of Agriculture spent considerable effort, thought, and money to help veterans choose the best available lands after the war. Areas known to contain the best soils were surveyed and mapped by technicians of the Soil Conservation Service. The Department of the Interior built roads into settlement areas and attempted by available means under existing limited authority to guide homesteading activity to tracts known to contain areas of tillable soils and away from noncultivable lands.

EARLY SCIENTISTS in Alaska estimated its agricultural potential at 200 million to 300 million acres based on what could be observed from boats or trails and gleaned from hearsay. Their reports were too optimistic. We now say that probably 2 million to 3 million acres are physically suitable for cropping. Another 3 million to 5 million acres would be usable for summer pasture in conjunction with cropland; 2 million or 3 million acres more of grassy islands are suitable for year-round use as rangeland, although preservation of forage as silage for winter use and some feeding of concentrates would be desirable on most of them.

Employees of the Departments of Interior and Agriculture work together closely on problems of land settlement and utilization. Absence of legal authority to classify lands according to indicated best use is a handicap in administration of public land-development programs. The Bureau of Land Management through reconnaissance delimits areas that are obviously unsuitable for settlement and locates others that appear to have possibilities.

Specialists in the Department of Agriculture make detailed studies of soils, cover, terrain, and other features. Priorities for work are established, and tasks often are integrated. Delineations of potential agricultural land by the Bureau of Land Management tend to be high, as they are usually of a preliminary reconnaissance nature. The more detailed surveys made by the Soil Conservation Service show the physical limitations of soils. Their estimates of potential agricultural land might be interpreted as low, if productive soils were in short supply. We know that lands considered to be unsuited to agriculture under present conditions might be made to produce under different economic circumstances.

Surveys to date cover the known best lands in or near present settlement areas. They have helped to guide potential farmers away from such marginal areas as the Dunbar area near Fairbanks and the Fritz Creek withdrawal area on the Kenai Peninsula. Their efforts, however, did not prevent entry for nonfarm purposes in the Fritz Creek area under veterans' rights provisions of the homestead laws. The Soil Conservation Service has mapped other withdrawn areas where enough tillable lands exist to support farm enterprises. The Bureau of Land Management used these reports as guides when developing areas for settlement. The Alaska Road Commission used the combined recommendations in planning its expanded road system.

Of more than 2 million acres mapped by field parties, roughly 35 percent is in class II or III and about 10 percent is class IV land. Slightly less than half of the area mapped thus is physically suited to some type of cultivation. No judgment is passed on the economics of the situation in this type of analytical study. Some of this land lies in small blocks that cannot be developed economically. More can be utilized only in carefully balanced conjunction with other resources on areas much greater than the present 160-acre homestead.

THE FIRST FARMS were developed by disenchanted miners during the gold-rush era. They found growing grain and hay for freighters' horses and food for roadhouse tables easier and more profitable than searching for gold. Much of the acreage developed during this heyday later was abandoned and reverted to brush. Its extent was not to be duplicated in Alaska until after the Second World War.

During his visit to Alaska in 1914, H. H. Bennett estimated that a minimum of 1 thousand acres had been cleared for cultivation in the Matanuska Valley. M. D. Snodgrass, a former superintendent of the Matanuska Agricultural Experiment Station, reported about the same acreage (though on other farms) about 1934. Acreages in the Tanana Valley reached a peak of around 1,760 acres on 107 farms in the early 1920's and then declined steadily until after the war. Surveys in 1948 and 1950 found only about 30 full-time and part-time farmers remaining. Farming in the Homer area was largely fur, livestock, and subsistence. Little cropland had been developed. Stagnation in mining, railroad construction, and general activity caused stagnation in agriculture. Small farming areas that had been developed in the Chilkat Valley, at Gustavus, at Point Agassiz near Petersburg, in the McCarthy area, and elsewhere, disappeared from the scene. Fur farming has almost disappeared from the islands and the mainland.

The only significant land clearing from 1935 to 1941 was done in the Matanuska Valley Colonization Project. About 4,300 acres were cleared, although part of the land was used for nonfarm purposes. Only 3,926 acres within the colony were tillable in March 1940. Much of this was idle because many men were working on

defense projects. A strong effort was made to fulfill commitments to the remaining colonists after the end of the war, and by 1948 an estimated 8,500 acres had been cleared. More than 12 thousand acres in the valley had been cleared by 1957.

Land clearing and breaking cost 150 to 200 dollars an acre—and much hard work. Money was scarce, and individuals could not afford to expand their farms. Efforts were made therefore to find sources of public funds for farm development.

Legal limitations and administrative policies never intended for homestead development have prevented the Farmers Home Administration and the Farm Credit Administration from meeting Alaskans' needs for credit. These lending agencies will not advance funds because most applicants do not have title to their land and do not get more than half of their income from agriculture. Until recently, banks as a rule loaned available funds for nonfarm activities only.

Payments for land clearing became authorized practices under the Agricultural Conservation Program, beginning in 1945. An average of 587 acres a year was cleared under this arrangement between 1945 and 1954. Allotments were divided roughly in proportion to the agriculture in each area. Inadequate controls during the early years of this program permitted some diversion of cleared land immediately into nonfarm uses.

The Alaska Legislature in 1953 passed an agricultural loan bill with a million dollars authorized and 200 thousand dollars appropriated. In 1955 and 1957, respectively, 150 thousand dollars and 125 thousand dollars were appropriated. These funds are administered by the Commissioner of Agriculture and a five-man board for both development and production loans. The Board of the Alaska Rural Rehabilitation Corporation authorized 50 thousand dollars for land-clearing loans in early 1955. All were allocated by May 1955.

Favorable repayment experience on farm loans held by these agencies encouraged liberalized local bank policies on short-term agricultural loans, and a slight easing of funds resulted. More and more settlers were able to clear enough land for efficient farm units. Progress was particularly notable in the Tanana Valley during the mid-1950's. In the Matanuska Valley, new farms entered commercial production and older units were expanded. Activities in the Kenai Peninsula still lagged.

THE 1940 CENSUS OF AGRICULTURE showed 7,305 acres harvested in Alaska during 1939. The 1950 census showed only 6,450 acres harvested, 3,586 acres idle or without a crop, and 2,449 acres of cropland pastured in 1949. Nearly half of the statistical decline in harvested cropland between enumerations was accounted for by a decrease in the reported acreage of wild hay. It occurred despite the 2,637 acres cleared in 1945–1949.

Statistics on agricultural production have been compiled cooperatively by the experiment station and the Territorial department of agriculture since 1953. This annual series shows 8,123 acres harvested in 1953 and 15,743 acres in 1957. Land-clearing activity under the Agricultural Conservation Program was at about the same average tempo, but other funds were used also. Less than half of the clearing in 1955 was supported by the Agricultural Conservation Program. More than 1 thousand acres a year were cleared in 1953 and 1954; 1,710 acres were cleared in 1955 and 2,292 acres in 1957. Estimates of the total acreage of cropland have increased from an optimistic 12,385 acres (because of a questionable figure of 2,449 acres listed as "cropland pasture") in 1949 to 14,764 in 1955 and 20,000 in 1957.

Idle cropland and acres on which crops failed have continued at about 2 thousand acres a year, much of it in raw cleared status and on nonfarm tracts. This figure has declined in significance from 28 percent of cropland reported by the 1949 census to 14 percent of that reported in 1955 and 10 percent in 1956.

ABOUT 350 COMMERCIAL farmers were concentrating on dairy, potato, poultry, and vegetable types of farming in 1957. A few beef and sheep enterprises were on the islands.

Another 500 to 700 part-time and "nominal" operators (of underdeveloped homesteads) were in varying stages of farm development. This net estimate recognizes that roughly half of the present homestead entrymen will not acquire patent and that others will become absentee owners of undeveloped land. It compares favorably with the breakdown of 525 farms into 217 commercial, 14 grazing or fur, 58 part-time, 52 residential, 5 abnormal, and 179 nominal farms from the 1949 census tabulations in "Agricultural Land Use in Alaska," by Robert J. Coffman and Hugh A. Johnson.

The rapid increase in numbers of commercial farms during this 5-year period reflects the vigor instilled into the agricultural scene by a new generation of farmers, a new program of basic agricultural research and extension, a modern marketing program, liberalized credit, and a strong market.

The gross value of farm products sold increased from 1.6 million dollars in 1949 to 2.7 million dollars in 1955 and 3.3 million dollars in 1957. Production of milk accounted for 49 percent of farm sales in 1957, followed by potatoes, 25 percent; eggs and poultry, 11 percent; other livestock products, 8 percent; and vegetables, 7 percent. The Matanuska Valley-Anchorage area supplied 67 percent of this production; the Tanana Valley, 16 percent; Southeastern Alaska, 9 percent; the Kenai Peninsula, 4 percent; and Kodiak and the Aleutians, the remaining 4 percent.

TYPES OF FARMING IN ALASKA vary by regions and within regions according to degree of farm development. We must first rule out an undetermined number of entrymen whose tenure is too new to show what they will do finally—367 homestead entries, for example, were made at Anchorage and Fairbanks Land Offices in fiscal 1956.

The Tanana Valley probably will develop into a region that is largely self-sufficient in milk, eggs, feed grains, forage, and acclimated truck crops. It may sell feed grains to the Matanuska Valley and Kenai Peninsula. In the 1950's, however, its roughly 100 established homesteaders and farmers were far from this goal. About 30 families depended on potatoes for farm income. About a dozen grew potatoes and small patches of vegetables, a half dozen were full-time general truck-crop farmers, 3 were dairymen, and 2 or 3 specialized in poultry. The rest were part-time farmers, who depended on nonfarm income while they cleared land and grew small acreages of potatoes or other truck crops.

The pattern in the Matanuska Valley appears to be fairly well established. Dairying predominates and is probably the climax type of farming. It is followed in importance by potato, poultry, vegetable, and mixed or general small farms. Farm ownership and occupancy were changing rapidly in the mid-1950's as families adjusted to the Alaskan situation. New farmers, rather than those with long experience, are the rule. Only a few farms were retained by the second generation of a single family. These rapid changes hinder overall, long-range planning on farms and detract from the group decisions so necessary in an agricultural economy.

Richard A. Andrews, of the Alaska Agricultural Experiment Station, determined from a study of farm-management records in the Matanuska Valley that it took an average full-time dairyman in the valley 13 years to develop a dairy farm of adequate size from wilderness. Methods of financing and stocking varied. Most had started with small acreages of vegetables, shifted to potatoes as they cleared more land, and finally dropped the potato enterprise as their acreages and livestock numbers became sufficient to support their families. Shifts to dairying from other enterprises were made in 4 to 7 years. Increases in cropland cleared or rented generally paralleled livestock increases at a rate of 5 acres per animal unit.

An efficient, family-sized dairy farm, therefore, requires about 150 acres of cropland and a tract of 300 acres or more if the soils are distributed in average proportions. Potato, vegetable, or poultry farms require smaller acreages, although the better producers find that grains and grasses must be included in the rotation to insure proper tilth.

Agricultural development on the Kenai Peninsula is in its early formative stage, although parts of this area were occupied almost as early as were the Matanuska and Tanana Valleys. Half of its full-time farms in 1955, nearly all of which were in the Homer sector, were primarily livestock operations. None of the beef or dairy farms was sufficiently developed to provide a satisfactory family living. The largest number had beef enterprises, followed in order by poultry and dairy. Greenhouse, potato, and truck farms were found, particularly among the part-time group.

Climate, soils, and competition probably will encourage farmers in the Homer area to specialize in dairy, beef, poultry, possibly wool, and a few vegetable and greenhouse enterprises. Farther up the coast in the Kenai-Kasilof sector, potatoes, vegetables, dairy, poultry, and some general farming may develop. The climate and marketing conditions will encourage development of grassland farming in the Homer area and probably of truck farms in the Kenai area. They will prevent extensive culture of small grains on the Kenai Peninsula.

Beef and sheep enterprises based on use of native forages are practically exclusive on Kodiak and the islands to the westward. This situation probably will continue. A few dairy and poultry farms may develop from time to time to fill local needs. Limited local markets and expensive transportation to other markets are major limiting factors in this region.

Types of farming in Southeastern Alaska historically have involved dairy, fur, poultry, beef, potatoes, and mixed truck crops. Markets are local, and the success of enterprises apparently depends on the operators' resourcefulness and energy. Relatively little land exists for extensive use as cropland.

TENURE in a frontier area differs from the tenure pattern of established communities. Most farms are operated by their owners, and most owners have debts. Raw land is available. Few families are willing to rent. Few farms are large enough to warrant paid managers. Various arrangements for renting fields are common in the Matanuska Valley and to a lesser extent in the Tanana Valley. This tends to affect "part-owner" status by the census definitions.

The census of 1950 showed 85 percent of farm operators were full owners; 10 percent, part owners; and the rest, managers or tenants. No later tabulation has been made. I estimate that the proportion of tenants has increased in relation to that of managers and that the proportions of part owners and full owners have remained about the same from 1949 to 1957.

The average mortgage of 3,655 dollars per farm on 22 percent of all farms shown in the census of 1950 provides no guide to the present debt load. Most of the mortgages were on colony farms in the Matanuska Valley and possibly on some of the large island operations. The proportion of mortgaged farms may have declined, but the proportion of farmers having developmental debts of other kinds has increased because of the kind of loan funds available and because many loans are made on a man's character and reputation rather than on the tangible assets in his balance sheet.

The capital value of land and build-

ings, equipment, and livestock in Alaska increased after the war, particularly after 1953. No total estimates are available. Farm management studies begun by the Department of Agriculture in 1948 and continued by economists at the experiment station disclosed that farms are in all stages of development. The average investment in buildings and equipment on 27 potato farms in the Tanana Valley in 1953 was 8,400 dollars. Their average of 37 acres of cropland and 194 acres of other land was worth another 8 thousand dollars to 9 thousand dollars. Few of these farms would support a family as yet.

Thirty-six dairy farmers in the Matanuska Valley had an average investment of 13,500 dollars in buildings and equipment and another 7,900 dollars in livestock. They had about 20 thousand dollars in an average of 288 acres, of which 104 acres were cropland. Most of these farms still were not fully developed but largely supported their operators.

Sample farm budgets prepared by the experiment station and the Bureau of Land Management agree that the equivalent of 40 thousand to 60 thousand dollars must be invested before a family has an efficient 20-cow dairy farm. Almost as much is needed for a commercial potato or truck farm. A beef or sheep ranch that can support a family usually requires a greater investment.

EMERGING PROBLEMS of landownership and control in an area so huge and with problems so diverse mean that the limited capital resources must be husbanded and efforts must be concentrated.

No useful purpose can be served by unwarranted hopes that the great balance of unreserved public lands in Alaska will enter private ownership within the foreseeable future. Most of this land has no known economic use in private hands. The best allocation attainable will occur under intelligent, prompt, and equitable administration when economically feasible enterprises appear—as true under statehood as under Federal control.

Alaska's population is clustered in widely separated areas and communities. Any frontier or sparsely settled area has basic requirements for an economic-social "infrastructure"—a minimum set of facilities required for living and for production.

Harold Jorgensen, of the Bureau of Land Management, summarized the situation thus: "Experience has shown that it is only when effective land and mineral laws, efficient public land administration, and a basic economic-social infrastructure are provided that orderly, economical, and permanent settlement and development occur on America's northern public lands in which private initiative plays its full part, and then only if all are carefully knit into a suitable pattern of area development."

The social costs of isolated settlement have received too little attention.

Alaska has the soils and the climate to permit production of large quantities of grains, forage, cool-weather vegetables, and certain fruits. Under the present economics of trade and transportation, however, products from its farms and interior forests must be consumed locally. Its market, therefore, is limited by the numbers of civilians, military dependents, and military personnel within its trade areas. Only certain crops and livestock products can be produced in competition with goods shipped to Alaska from the United States and other countries. The varied diet of our modern society requires importation of many foods from other producing areas just as in any State. Alaskans can hope to meet about half the total amount of food required by a modern population from the products they can produce.

Analysis of the production and consumption potential in 1949 by Wendell Calhoun and me showed that between 3 thousand and 4 thousand acres of cropland would supply all local farm products needed for each 10 thousand effective consumers at current yields. These estimates were generally verified by independent studies by the Bureau of Land Management. This relationship has not changed basically. Thus, a future consuming population of 200 thousand persons would utilize the products from 60 thousand to 80 thousand acres. Alaska now has between 15 thousand and 19 thousand acres prepared for production and a large unfilled market for certain items. It has several hundred underdeveloped farms and homesteads in private resident or nonresident ownership. Sudden development to full-time farm status on half of these farms and homesteads would create serious surpluses of farm products.

Emphasis on technical, financial, and marketing assistance is needed for the farm families that are already partly in production. No economic need appears to exist for new or additional homesteading lands in the next few years. It would seem wiser to consolidate present gains before additional areas are opened to settlement.

An almost untapped market exists both in Alaska and in the States for specialty products such as low-bush cranberries (similar to European lingenberries), blueberries, smoked and dried salmon, sheefish, ling cod, shellfish, reindeer meat, artifacts, and other local products.

One enterprising firm at Homer has processed local berries successfully and developed a national luxury market for its products. A homesteader on Iliamna Lake hired Indian women to gather cranberries to be shipped by air to Anchorage and Seattle. Similar enterprises offer hope of cash income in currently distressed areas.

Problems inherent in this type of enterprise are almost insurmountable for persons without capital and contacts. Assistance from public and private agencies in establishing necessary production standards, perfecting transportation schedules, and developing market outlets and loans for development would open the way for a possible multimillion-dollar industry based on harvesting and processing the products of natural resources.

Stateside experience in the West under the homestead acts demonstrated that individuals, unless prevented by law, will settle and try to farm land unsuited to agriculture. The western provinces of Canada had this problem, which was aggravated by the scattered population. The foresighted Canadians closed to settlement their public domain that was not in well-defined blocks. Public services thus could be concentrated within prescribed areas.

The experience with homesteading in Alaska demonstrates anew the need for guided and controlled settlement. New legislation is needed to permit classification of land for efficient and economical administration of future settlement and development. Only through this process will it be possible to keep costs of governmental services within bounds.

A tax on real property would aid development of concentrated areas. Nonresident owners currently can hold good undeveloped land, and there is no way to make them bear a share in community expenses. This problem is particularly critical on the Kenai Peninsula, although it exists wherever title has passed to absentee owners. Scattered families have great difficulty in developing stable communities. The intervening vacant and idle tracts often contain land that is better than average and should be developed and used before the margins of settlement are extended. The new land registration law may help to alleviate this problem.

Despite the impression in some quarters that policies of the Bureau of Land Management and past slowness in some of its operations have retarded use of resources, the facts show that the Bureau has been generous in its administration of public lands. The principle behind the Homestead Act was to encourage the development of productive farms from the public domain. Pressure to open more lands to entry is constantly brought to bear. Data show that farms develop from about 10 percent of the tracts homesteaded. Of 49 grazing leases in effect on June 30, 1956, covering almost a million acres, most were stocked below the lease requirements. Many were stocked at less than 50 percent of the number scheduled in the leases, and several had no livestock, although the leases had been in effect for at least a year.

THE MAJOR PROBLEM is not to get more land under private control but rather to get into development and use the lands already appropriated or patented. Too many people are trying to develop farms and ranches without adequate financing or knowledge of farming.

Problems of financing have been made less acute in recent years through the half-million dollars of Territorial and Alaska Rural Rehabilitation Corporation revolving funds made available for production, expansion, and development loans. Some local banks are venturing into short-term agricultural loans. Federal lending agencies still lag in their Alaskan programs. Some additional funds are needed to speed worthy operators of underdeveloped farms toward full-time, efficient farming status.

Alaskan consumers are cosmopolitan in their tastes and sophisticated in their requirements. They demand and will pay for high-quality products only. Market development and improved marketing techniques must occur simultaneously with increasing production.

Through the agricultural research program, which was revitalized in 1948, outstanding gains have been made in solving problems of physical production in adapted crops and in dairying. The marketing and consumer-preference problems have been described. Future emphasis focused on storage conditions, packaging, and processing probably would be desirable. The extension program needs strengthening in its technical aids to farmers and expansion of its information service to retailers and house-wives. The marketing, grading, and information programs of the Territorial department of agriculture have been expanded in recent years. However, the department has a key role in the future of agriculture and needs further expansion and strengthening in conjunction with a vital extension program.

Relations between the public and its officials in charge of land settlement and development programs may be strained at times, because neither fully understands the problems faced by the other. Greater use of advisory committees and consultation on economic development programs would be mutually advantageous.

IN CONCLUSION: Resident Alaskans want action. They want the opportunity to develop agriculture, trade, and industry. They live among potential resources that they believe could form the foundation for growing and prosperous communities. They want to make Alaska a settled, integral part of the United States. They become impatient at restrictions that appear to them to limit the growth of population and, therefore, of trade and business opportunities.

The frontier attitude toward land and resources still thrives in Alaska, where soils await farmers while food-stuffs are shipped in from other places. The forests, the minerals, the water-power of Alaska are potentials still to be developed. To Alaskans, any prospect of eventual economic overproduction seems far in the future. They believe that resources should be developed now to meet present needs and in anticipation of continued growth.

It should be evident from the record briefly developed here that no simple solution exists for land problems in Alaska. The Federal Government has seemed to move slowly and not always in the direction desired by many Alaskans. But real progress has been made in many fields. Extension of the mining and homestead laws and specific legislation enabling entry and use of land for homesites, recreation, commercial and industrial development, oil and gas exploration, and other purposes has made land resources available for use.

I have tried to demonstrate or illustrate the hard economic facts with which land users in Alaska have been faced. More than laws are required to convert wilderness into prosperous farms. Local markets for farm products are necessary to economically successful farm development.

A majority of the homesteaders who have failed did so because they lacked the necessary capital to develop farms from raw land, the requisite technical knowledge of agriculture, and the tenacity and singleness of purpose required to overcome hardships common on any frontier. Getting additional land into private ownership does not guarantee that food production will follow.

Farm families who have overcome their problems and developed commercial farms within transportation distance of urban areas have a market for nearly anything they can produce. More recent settlers are finding loan funds a little less tight, much more information available about technical production problems, a much larger market, and a market more favorably inclined toward local products.

The potential market for farm products is not unlimited. The problem is to encourage farm development to the point within the available market at which the greatest number of farm families are making satisfactory incomes from their efficient methods.

In this light, one can better understand the current conflicts of interest in landownership and use. Alaska can be a great land. Common understanding, mutual good will, responsible planning based on careful research, and recognition of economic facts are necessary for sound development of its land resources in the best interests of all the people.

Hawaii's problems and many assets.

The primitive, self-sufficient economy that Captain Cook found in 1778 has undergone many changes. Hawaii now exports about 280 million dollars' worth of sugar, pineapples, coffee, tropical flowers, canned fish, and other products. The population has grown apace. So has pressure on the land. The people and the Territorial Legislature have taken steps to assure the best possible use of their land heritage. By *Perry F. Philipp*, agricultural economist, University of Hawaii.

THE USE and ownership of land in Hawaii and in the continental United States differ from each other in many ways because of differences in location, climate, and history.

The eight major islands of Hawaii lie entirely in the Tropics. Honolulu, the largest city, is 2,100 nautical miles from San Francisco, the nearest Mainland harbor. The people of Hawaii refer to the continental United States as the Mainland.

The Islands are of volcanic origin. Large parts of the interior of all of them consist of rugged, mountainous terrain. The two highest peaks are close to 14 thousand feet above sea level. Plateaus, coastal plains, and the lower mountain slopes, although they comprise a small part of the total area, are the most important lands.

The climate is mild. Temperatures change little between summer and winter in most of the inhabited parts. The average annual rainfall in agricultural areas varies from 200 inches to less than 20 inches within a few miles, mostly because of topographic influences. The range from the tropical to the desert and from sea level to high altitudes permits the production of a great variety of agricultural products.

The land area of the Hawaiian Islands is 4.1 million acres, or 0.2 percent of the land area of the Mainland. Less than 8 percent of the total land area is used for crops, about 25 percent is grazed, and 29 percent is forest or woodland. (All figures I give are for 1956, unless otherwise stated.)

The remaining land, more than a third of the total land area, is used for purposes other than agriculture and forests. It includes special-use areas such as cities and towns, roads, parks, and military areas and wasteland, such as bare lava flows and gulches.

When Captain James Cook discovered the Hawaiian Islands in 1778, he found a primitive, self-sufficient economy based mainly on fishing and small farms held under feudal tenure. Hawaii today has a highly developed trading economy, heavily dependent on the Mainland. Its agricultural exports amount to more than a quarter of a billion dollars.

The oldest and largest agricultural industry in the Islands is growing and processing sugarcane. Sugarcane was indigenous to Hawaii at the time of its discovery, but production had reached only 2 tons a year in 1837. The value of 1,100,000 tons of raw sugar, together with molasses and other byproducts, amounted to 148 million dollars in 1956. About 221 thousand acres were in cane.

Most of the land in sugarcane consists of what used to be forested areas, semiarid pasturelands, or useless arid areas. The sugarcane acreage is in lowland tracts. Attempts to grow cane at levels above 2,500 feet are seldom made. Some land has been planted to cane almost continuously for more than a century, yet with heavy fertilization and good soil management, these lands are at least as fertile today as when sugar culture began.

It takes about a ton of water to produce a pound of sugar. Slightly more than half of the cane area is irrigated; it produces a little less than two-thirds of the total sugar. The rest of the sugarcane is grown on the wet windward sides of the Islands and depends on rainfall.

The unit of organization in the sugar industry is the plantation, which grows the cane and manufactures it into raw sugar. A steady decline in the number of plantations has been offset by a corresponding increase in their size.

Twenty-seven plantations were in operation in 1957; the average area planted to sugarcane per plantation was 8,200 acres. The largest plantation had 27,700 acres in cane. The smallest had 600 acres. Plantation operations were geared to year-round employment for the 17 thousand employees in the industry.

A plantation consists of the land controlled by the company, the sugar mill, shops and central offices, a road system, and the plantation town and housing areas for plantation employees. About 70 percent of the plantation employees and their families lived in plantation-owned homes in 1957. The plantation town often is a self-contained community. It usually has a business district with stores, a school, churches, a theater, a recreation field and gymnasium, a hospital, and public services and utilities.

Besides the land used for growing sugarcane, many sugar companies hold considerable acreages of nonarable land, which is used mainly for water conservation or grazing.

Approximately 1,300 small growers, raise sugarcane on about 9 percent of the total sugarcane acreage. A majority of these operate independently and sell their sugarcane under government-approved contracts to the plantations.

PINEAPPLE PRODUCTION, primarily for canned fruit and juice, is the Islands' second major agricultural industry. The annual output of processed products is valued at 117 million dollars. The acreage in pineapples increased from 5 thousand acres in 1909 to 77 thousand in 1956. The fruit is grown at altitudes ranging from near sea level to about 2 thousand feet.

The most productive pineapple lands have a rainfall of 25 to 60 inches of rain a year. Areas with less rain are usually too arid unless irrigation water is applied. More rain may adversely affect yield and quality. Pineapple production makes it possible to use many areas too dry for most other crops.

The pineapple industry, like the sugar industry, has developed in the direction of large-scale, integrated plantations. Nine pineapple companies operate 13 plantations and 9 canneries. A minor part of the crop is raised on about 120 small, nonplantation farms, most of which have contracts with canneries. The pineapple industry provides employment for about 22 thousand persons during the peak summer canning season and year-round employment for more than 9 thousand.

CROPS OTHER THAN SUGAR and pineapple, called diversified crops in Hawaii, occupy 16 thousand acres—5 percent of the total cropland in the Islands. Their wholesale value, however, is high—about 13 million dollars.

Coffee, the largest of the diversified crops, is grown on nearly 6 thousand acres. About 1 thousand small farmers operate groves, which usually are 5 to 10 acres in size. They are mainly in the Kona district of the Island of Hawaii. The coffee is grown at elevations of 800 to 2,200 feet on steep, rocky, and stony slopes. The soil is productive. The climate is excellent for coffee. The yield is high. Kona coffee is highly regarded and is shipped chiefly to the Mainland.

The area planted to macadamia nuts, which are confectionery nuts of excellent quality, has almost tripled since the war. It amounted to about 2,800 acres in 1956. The nuts are planted mostly in tracts previously used for grazing or forest. Hawaii is apparently the only place where macadamia nuts are grown commercially on a sizable scale.

For Island consumption, Hawaiian farmers grow many western vegetables, such as cabbage, tomatoes, and cucumbers, and such Oriental vegetables as burdock, daikon, and watercress. The limited size of the Hawaiian market means that most production is on small fields. This, together with many insects and diseases and high requirements of fertilizer and irrigation, make production costs high.

Papayas, bananas, and passion fruit are the most important of the commercially grown fruits. The rest are mainly avocados, citrus fruits, mangos, guavas, and lychee. Most vegetable and fruit farms are family operated. Only a few are larger than family size. The area in commercially grown fruits and vegetables is about 6 thousand acres.

Taro is the plant from which poi, the Hawaiians' staff of life, is made. The area in taro is about 600 acres, only a fraction of the taro acreage at the time Hawaii was discovered. A decline in the number of Hawaiians and the competition of cheaper starchy foods caused this drop.

Rice, once second in importance and area only to sugar, occupies 200 acres or less. Development of the large-scale mechanized rice industry in California doomed the Hawaiian industry, the mechanization of which is limited by the small size of the paddies.

The growth of air transportation in the postwar period helped Island growers to develop a million-dollar export of floral products, primarily tropical foliage, orchids, and anthuriums. They also produce commercially many other floral products, mainly for the flower-loving Islands. Farmers use an estimated 600 acres for flowers.

Many other crops—cotton, wheat, tobacco, rubber, silk, and sisal—have been tried commercially in Hawaii but have proved economically unsound.

LIVESTOCK PRODUCTS are valued at 27 million dollars annually. Most of Hawaii's grasslands are used for cattle and a few sheep.

At least three-fourths of all beef cattle, numbering about 160 thousand head, are raised on large ranches, many of which extend from dry lowland to wet upland zones. The best pastures in the zones of moderate rainfall are set aside for grass fattening. The less productive areas and the wetter rangelands are used mainly for breeding animals and young stock. Most of the small ranches are in areas of moderate rainfall in which there is year-round grazing.

Keeping plant pests from overrunning pastures is a major job of the ranchers. To control brush and weeds, they use some of the largest bulldozers known, which pull big anchor chains or disks. Herbicides also are used.

Locally produced milk amounts to 47 million quarts annually, compared to 2 million quarts in 1900. It is mainly consumed as fluid milk. Most cows on the 89 dairies of the Islands are in large herds. Twenty-seven dairymen keep more than 150 cows each and eight keep more than 300 cows. Corporations own several large dairies.

Most of the dairymen operate on the Island of Oahu (on which Honolulu lies) to supply the city market. They usually keep their cows in feedlots and use their limited arable lands for growing soilage crops. They prefer Napiergrass for this purpose, because it yields 100 to 150 tons of green feed an acre. Some dairymen on the Islands other than Oahu pasture their milking cows, but few on Oahu can afford to use their small holdings so extensively. Except for molasses and pineapple bran and pulp, almost all concentrate feeds have to be brought from the Mainland.

Swine producers sell 70 thousand

hogs a year for slaughter. They raise their animals in concrete or wooden pens. They feed them garbage, imported grain, and rations compounded of local feedstuffs.

Poultry farmers raise about 1 million chickens mainly on feed imported from the Mainland and usually keep them in wire-floored houses off the ground. Typical Hawaiian poultry and swine farms are small in land area and operated by the farm family.

Hawaiian farmers expect to expand their output only slowly from now on. Sugar exports to the Mainland—Hawaii's main export market—are limited by Federal law. Sugar planters expect no substantial increases in the near future. The production and export of pineapples will depend on the competition of other domestic fruits and juices and of foreign and Puerto Rican pineapple producers.

Exports of other agricultural products are small, although exports of tropical fruit and nut products have a large growth potential. Farmers have increased their production for Island use in the postwar period at the average rate of about 1.5 million dollars a year. They may increase production further if Hawaii's population continues to grow and if they can compete with the prices and quality of Mainland food imports.

LARGE-SCALE FARMS are more important in Hawaii than on the Mainland. According to the 1950 United States Census, farms with annual sales of 25 thousand dollars or more each made 91 percent of all farm sales in Hawaii but only 26 percent of all farm sales on the Mainland.

Many large farms in Hawaii are highly mechanized and efficient. Labor shortages during the Second World War and unionization of workers in the processing plants and in the fields brought much higher wages and shorter hours. Average daily earnings for nonsupervisory sugarworkers on plantations increased from 1.70 dollars in 1935 to 11.20 dollars in 1957.

These are cash wages; the 1935 figure does not include substantial perquisites, such as free housing, medical care, fuel, light, and water.

Operators of plantations and other large farms have been trying to offset higher labor costs by more mechanization, laborsaving practices, and higher yields per acre. In the sugar industry, for example, the labor force was cut more than two-thirds, but output per worker more than tripled since 1932. The sugar tonnage per acre increased 50 percent at the same time.

Farmers selling from 2,500 to 25 thousand dollars' worth of agricultural products a year made only 7 percent of all farm sales in Hawaii, compared to 62 percent on the Mainland. These farmers nevertheless are important in Hawaii; they are the backbone of most of the diversified agricultural industries. Their productivity has increased greatly since the war.

Two-thirds of all Hawaiian farmers, 3,750 in number, sold only 2 percent of all agricultural products. Some of them are marginal full-time farmers; their number has been declining. Most farmers in this group are part-time or residential farmers, who derive most of their income from occupations other than farming. Their number increased several times between 1940 and 1950.

In view of the shortening workweek and the increasing urbanization in Hawaii, this trend toward part-time and residential farms probably is a healthy one. It can help to reduce the tendency toward overcrowding into thickly populated areas and offers the family a healthy outdoor life and some economic return.

MANAGERS are the most important type of farm operator in Hawaii. They run the plantations and many large ranches and other large agricultural enterprises. According to the 1950 census, there were only 109 managers, or fewer than 2 percent of all farm operators, but they controlled 78 percent of Hawaii's agricultural land and an even larger share of all the cropland.

Full and part owners amounted to 40 percent of all operators. They used 20 percent of the agricultural land. About 58 percent of the operators were tenants, but they used less than 2 percent of the agricultural land.

Farmers in Hawaii are highly specialized, and many produce only one type of product, such as sugarcane or milk or pork. They become so efficient in producing their specialties that it often does not even pay them to raise their own food for home use.

The numerical importance and status in agriculture of the several races represented in Hawaii vary greatly—depending largely on the time of their arrival in the Islands, their experience, and their traditions in their countries of origin.

The Filipinos were the latest racial group to come to Hawaii. They constitute the largest part of the hired labor force in agriculture and are beginning to establish themselves as tenant farmers, especially as coffee farmers.

The Japanese, second to the last to arrive, are the second largest racial group among plantation workers. Most of the small farmers are of Japanese ancestry.

The Chinese were the earliest immigrants of Oriental origin. They once constituted a large group of plantation workers and farmers, particularly rice growers, but most of them have left agriculture.

Caucasians own or manage many of the large agricultural enterprises. Hawaiians and part-Hawaiians operate some ranches or work on them. They also produce some crops, and a few come close to subsistence farming.

Island farmers, like Mainland farmers, operate within an extensive system of laws and regulations. Regulating authorities include Federal, Territorial, and county agencies.

Public and private agricultural experiment stations do extensive research. The University of Hawaii and the public schools offer courses and training in agriculture.

Commercial banks furnish credit for large-scale agricultural enterprises and small sugarcane producers. Other small farmers, however, obtain most of their capital from the Farmers Home Administration or from their families and friends. Dealers also sometimes carry their accounts for feed, fertilizer, and other supplies.

Farmers owning land, like all other private landowners, pay a Territorial tax on real property. The tax is based on the assessed value of the land and its improvements. A part of the assessed value of an owned home is tax exempt to encourage homeownership. Agricultural land bears the same tax rate as urban property.

IRRIGATION has long been important in Hawaiian agriculture. The old Hawaiians used efficient methods of irrigation. They brought water through ditches to their taro fields from streams that often were far away. Sugar planters built large-scale irrigation systems. The East Maui ditch system, for example, has a capacity of more than 500 cubic feet a second. Subterranean water resources have been developed by large-scale pumping.

Development of irrigation water in Hawaii has been made almost entirely with private capital. In 1953 the Territorial Legislature created an agency now called the Hawaii Water Authority and provided it with public funds for the further development of the water resources of the Islands.

In 1950, 117 thousand acres were irrigated according to the United States Census. By far the largest part of it was in sugarcane. Most of the rest was in diversified crops. An increasing acreage of pineapple fields and pastures is irrigated in the drier sections.

SOIL EROSION is a serious problem in Hawaii because of steep slopes and heavy rainfall on some of the farmlands. Conservation of water is vital in many areas.

Farmers and ranchers, assisted by Federal and local agencies, have given soil and water conservation increasing attention. The Territorial Legislature adopted an enabling act in 1947 for the creation of soil conservation districts. Such districts had been established in many areas by 1958.

Territorial forest and water reserve zones cover about 30 percent of the total area of the Islands, or 1.2 million acres. More than two-thirds of the reserve zones are public land. The rest is privately owned. Their primary purpose is to provide plant cover that will prevent rapid runoff and erosion.

A growing trend is to put forest and water reserve zones to such multiple uses as game management, public hunting, hiking, and other recreational purposes. Large areas are used for military training.

Many species of commercial timber can be grown successfully in Hawaii, but the timber industry is still in its infancy. The value of all forest products sold in 1949 was less than 50 thousand dollars. Both the Government and private landowners are interested in the better utilization of forest timber resources, and timber research has been initiated.

About 250 thousand acres have been set aside for recreational use. The Hawaii National Park contains 231 thousand acres. Its larger section, on the Island of Hawaii, includes the active volcanoes Mauna Loa and Kilauea and surrounding areas. Its smaller section, on the Island of Maui, covers mainly the vast crater of Haleakala, an extinct volcano. All major islands have a number of Territorial and city and county parks and playgrounds. Beaches, which are public to the high watermark, are another important recreational asset of Hawaii.

THE ONLY MINERAL RESOURCES used commercially at present are rock, limestone, and sand. The possibility of economical development of other mineral deposits, primarily bauxite, is being investigated.

Surveys and classifications of land resources of the Territory have been made for various purposes. A detailed soil survey of the Territory was published in 1955. The Soil Conservation Service has classified the capabilities of land for agricultural uses in many areas. A comprehensive economic classification and study program of Hawaii's lands at the University of Hawaii was initiated by the Territorial Legislature in 1957.

THE PATTERN OF LAND tenure in Hawaii is largely the result of the land division in the 1840's and 1850's (called the Great Mahele), the development of large-scale agricultural enterprises, and the largely unsuccessful policy of homesteading a part of the public domain. In Old Hawaii, all land belonged to the king, who distributed it to his principal chiefs on a feudal basis. They in turn allotted the land to lesser chiefs, who subdivided it among the common people.

The landholding system changed during the Great Mahele. The king divided the land among the chiefs, the Government, and common people, and kept some for himself. The king's own property, or crown land, amounted to somewhat less than 1 million acres; the Government land, about 1.5 million acres; the chiefs', a little more than 1.5 million acres; and the people's, a little less than 30 thousand acres. The farms given to the common people, however, consisted primarily of irrigated taro lands, which were regarded as the most valuable lands at that time.

Much of the land soon passed into the hands of non-Hawaiians (particularly sugar planters and cattle ranchers) by sale, lease, or marriage. Fifty-seven percent of the taxable land belonged to them by 1896. Title to all Government and crown land was conveyed to the United States by the act of annexation in 1898. Agencies of the Territorial Government have continued to manage most of the public lands, however.

Public land amounted to about 42 percent and private land to 58 percent of all land in the Islands in 1956. Of the Government-owned land, 1,250 thousand acres were Territorial; 10 thousand acres were county lands; 170 thousand acres belonged to the Hawaiian Homes Commission; and 320 thousand acres were Federal land.

The Territorial Department of the Tax Commissioner set the market value of all lands in the Territory at 1.4 billion dollars in 1956. Private landholders owned 70 percent of it, and public land accounted for 30 percent.

The most valuable part of the public land was held by the Armed Forces. Much of the Territorial public land is poor. More than 800 thousand acres are in forest and water reserve zones. Most of the rest is leased out for agricultural purposes, mainly for grazing.

The Hawaiian Homes Commission land was set aside by an act of the Congress in 1920. The act provides for granting land to persons of not less than half Hawaiian blood for homesteads, farms, or pastures under 99-year leases at the nominal rent of 1 dollar a year. Hawaiian Homes Commission land includes areas in or near the major cities, some valuable agricultural land, and some poor land. Most of the residents of Hawaiian Homes Commission settlements are city oriented, rather than the men of the soil apparently contemplated by the framers of the act.

A few trusts, corporations, and individuals hold most of the private lands. The 11 largest landowners in 1956 owned 50 percent of all private lands in the Islands, and the 60 largest owned 80 percent.

About half of the agricultural land is owned by the farmers and plantations who use it, and one-half is leased by them. The ratio between owned and leased land, however, varies from industry to industry. For example, sugar plantations own about 60 percent of the cane land, ranchers about half of the pastures, and coffee growers about a fourth of the orchards, which they operate.

In view of the large amount of leased land, good leasing practices are essen-

tial. Farmland usually is rented for cash. Only about 10 percent of all rental agreements are on a share basis.

Public leases are for up to 15 years for cropland and up to 21 years for pastureland that cannot be irrigated. Private grazing, sugar, and pineapple leases for large areas often run for 20 years—some for more than 40 years. Small farmers in diversified agriculture often have to be content with shorter leases and sometimes with only oral leases of a year or less.

Lessees of both private and public agricultural lands ordinarily do not get any credit for improvements they make on the leased property. Removal of these improvements, while not allowed in most old rental agreements, may be permitted in new ones at the expiration of the lease.

THE LAWS GOVERNING WATER rights in Hawaii with respect to surface waters appear to be unique in the United States. In general, the owner of land has the right to the surface water that originates on his land, subject to rights that may be vested in others by ancient usage or deed.

The law is vague on ground water except for artesian waters—that is, subterranean waters confined under pressure. According to one court decision, all owners of land over an artesian basin have a common right to the reasonable use of the artesian water.

Title to surface water is held by both private owners and by the Government. Like land, the control of water resources is highly concentrated. On the larger Islands, except for a few public departments, irrigation water is controlled largely by sugar and pineapple plantations or private water companies closely connected with the sugar-growing interests.

TWO METHODS OF LAND REGISTRATION exist in Hawaii, the regular system and the land court system.

Under the regular system, the owner has a merchantable, fee-simple, recorded title.

A land court title is considered better than a regular title, because the titleholder is insured with the Territory against losses resulting from a faulty title. About 40 percent of all lands on Oahu and about 8 percent of all lands on other Islands have such titles.

The metes and bounds system is the principal means of measuring land in Hawaii. A land court title to any subdivided piece of land is always conveyed by block and lot number.

The population of the Islands, including military personnel, has grown from 368 thousand in 1930 to more than 600 thousand in 1958.

The importance of agriculture as a source of employment has declined greatly. About one in three gainfully employed persons worked on farms in 1939; in 1955, only about one in nine. Most people not employed in agriculture moved to the cities, mainly Honolulu, to work for the Armed Forces, or in the tourist industry, nonagricultural industries, trades and services.

The population of the "city" of Honolulu—the urbanized area on the leeward side of Oahu—rose from some 20 thousand in 1890 to 138 thousand in 1930 and 302 thousand in January 1958. Express highways were built to bring all parts of Oahu within commuting distance of the center of Honolulu. The population of Oahu outside the "city" of Honolulu increased by 32 percent between January 1955 and January 1958.

Oahu, with 9 percent of the total land area, had 76 percent of the civilian population of the Territory in January 1958. With 735 persons to the square mile, its population density exceeded that of Japan.

A major military base is maintained because of the Islands' strategic location. Almost all of the defense installations are on Oahu.

The military area amounts to almost 15 percent of the land area of Oahu.

THE MAJOR PROBLEM of land use on Oahu is to develop additional residential and industrial areas but to retain enough land for agricultural production and for military and recreational purposes.

About 43 percent of Oahu in 1956 was forest and water reserve zones or was unimproved; 31 percent was agricultural land; and 10 percent was in urban use. At the 1957 rate of population growth, additional urban development would require about 1.7 square miles more land each year. At that rate, by 1980, the urban area would amount to 17 percent of the land area of the Island.

Most of the urban expansion can be expected to take place on the rather flat lands, which have been used for crops. Accordingly, nearly half of Oahu's lands with slopes of less than 10 percent may be urban by 1980.

In the development of additional residential and industrial areas, the scenic beauty of the Island should not be sacrificed. Tourism is Hawaii's fastest growing industry, and Oahu is its center. More than 160 thousand visitors came to the Islands in 1957. Oahu's appeal to tourists may decline greatly unless foresight is used in land development.

Land available for fee-simple purchase in the Islands is scarce—particularly fee-simple land on Oahu that is suitable for urban use. Major reasons for this short supply are the policy of many large landholders not to sell their holdings and the unwillingness of agricultural users to release land for urban use. High land prices have been the result. In suburban areas up to 12 miles from the center of Honolulu, fee-simple homesites sold from 75 cents to 1.25 dollars a square foot in 1957. Many homes, commercial buildings, and industrial installations therefore have been built on leased land.

Urban leasing practices have been improving. Leases for homesites, which formerly ran mostly for 30 years, now are often made for 50 years or more and permit the removal of improvements at the expiration of the lease.

In contrast to the expanding population on Oahu, the number of people living on the other Islands was smaller in 1958 than in 1930. The decline was caused primarily by the mechanization of plantation operations, which forced some residents to seek employment elsewhere.

Land on these other Islands is used mainly for agriculture and forest and water reserves. Cities are generally small, and urban development has been slow compared to Oahu. Hilo, the largest city on the outside Islands, had about 25 thousand inhabitants in 1958.

The location of more industry on Islands other than Oahu might well be encouraged. Such a policy would retard the rate of urban development on Oahu and at the same time strengthen the economy of the outlying Islands. On Oahu, it would tend to reduce the upward pressure on land prices, permit the retention of more valuable agriculture, and allow the use of more land for recreational purposes and scenic reserves. Relocation of some military establishments from Oahu to the other Islands would have similar effects.

LAND-USE PLANS existed for several areas in the Islands in 1957. Some private landowners had prepared such plans for both the agricultural and urban development of their lands.

The City Planning Commission of Honolulu had adopted a master plan for future land use, including the location of proposed schools, parks, and other community facilities and major thoroughfares. Plans for several other urban areas, on Oahu and the other Islands, had been made or were under study.

The Armed Forces and the National Park Service had prepared plans for the areas under their jurisdiction, but no comprehensive plan had been made for the best use of public land administered by the Territorial Government.

There existed no basic land policy or land utilization guide for the Territory as a whole in 1957, although modern communication and transportation had brought the several Islands closer

together. Practically all interisland travel and transportation of some commodities is by air. An air trip between Honolulu and the most distant airport on the outlying Islands now takes little more than an hour.

THE TERRITORIAL LEGISLATURE in 1957 created the Territorial Planning Office, headed by a director of territorial planning. He was given the task of preparing a long-range, comprehensive plan to serve as a guide for the future physical and economic development of the Territory. The plan is to include a statement of development objectives dealing with land use and such topics as population density, transportation, and public facilities.

The director was instructed by law to consider the following projects: The reclamation of submerged reefs by creating offshore islands; the return of certain military lands to civilian use; the need for and location of industrial sites and public buildings; the economic feasibility of establishing water sources and systems for underdeveloped or arid areas; and the economics of a further development of land, air, and water transportation between and across the various islands of the Territory. The director was instructed also—in cooperation with Government agencies on all levels—to plan a comprehensive system of parks and recreational facilities throughout Hawaii.

The director is to guide and integrate the planning work of Territorial agencies and may assist in similar work of local bodies. The Governor of Hawaii is primarily responsible for coordinating the activities of the several agencies of the Territory within the framework of the general plan.

The director is required to prepare the general plan of the Territory in sections, one for each county. A county plan (or amendments to it) is to become effective only when enacted by a county ordinance. The director does not have the power to zone or control subdivision development. Those responsibilities belong to the counties.

Puerto Rico: Change and progress.

One can appreciate the meaning of the pressure of population on land in Puerto Rico if he tries to visualize what would happen to the land if the entire population of the world moved within the boundaries of the United States. By *Julio O. Morales*, president, Inter-American Investment Management Corporation, Puerto Rico; *Bartolomé M. Morell*, director, Bureau of Production and Marketing, Department of Agriculture and Commerce, Puerto Rico; *Efrain Diaz-Cruz*, chief, Division of Agricultural Statistics, Bureau of Production and Marketing; *Ismael Ramirez-Murphy*, agricultural economist, Bureau of Production and Marketing.

PUERTO RICO is the smallest of the four major islands of the West Indian chain. It is a little more than 100 miles long and 35 miles wide, and 2,264,000 persons live in this small area.

Natural resources are limited. There are no mineral resources suitable for the development of heavy industry. Water is impounded in reservoirs for the production of electric power, but steam plants generate more than two-thirds of the electricity.

Land is the principal resource. Its use for agriculture is a predominant factor in the welfare of Puerto Ricans. Sugar, rum, molasses, cigars, coffee, and other agricultural products contribute to the economic structure.

An east-west range of mountains, reaching almost 4,400 feet above sea level, is the main topographic feature.

The relief south of the mountains is more craggy, and the coastal plain is narrower than to the north. The northern slope is less rough, and the grades change gradually to the coast. Most of the rivers begin high in the mountains and flow northward into the Atlantic. The rivers that flow down the southern slope are smaller and usually are dry a part of the year. The rivers are not navigable.

Trade winds that blow from the northeast make a mild climate throughout the year. The mean monthly temperature for the island is 73° F. in January and 79° in July. The highest recorded temperature is 103° in the lowlands; the lowest is 39° in the mountains.

Marked fluctuations in rainfall result mainly from the wide diversity of topography. The annual average is 60 inches in the north, 35 inches in the south, and almost 200 inches in the Luquillo Mountains. The mountains that divide the country cool the winds from the northeast and cause a higher precipitation on the northern side of the island. The dry periods usually extend from February to May in the north and from December to May in the south. The heaviest rains usually are in September to November.

A total of 115 soil series and 352 soil types and soil phases has been recorded. Such a large number of soil types result from the variations in climate, relief, vegetation, age, and parent material.

Physical factors restrict the use of

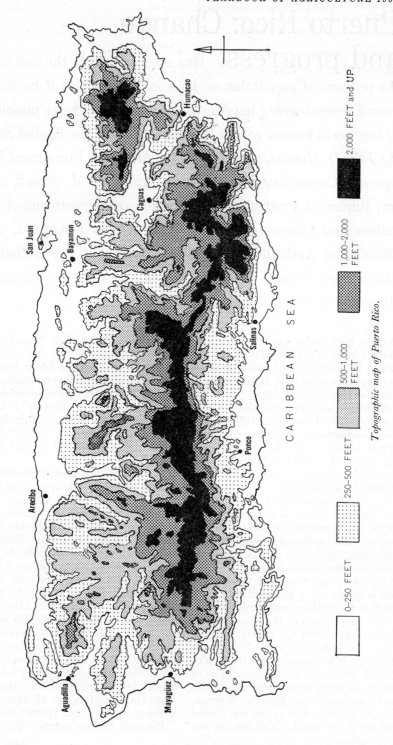

Topographic map of Puerto Rico.

land for crops more than they do for pastures. Climate, topography, soil differences, and personal choice—as influenced by economic, social, and related forces—determine the pattern of land use.

The few Indians who originally inhabited the Territory lived from farming, hunting, and fishing. They cultivated small plots of cassava, cotton, tobacco, and a few other plants.

When the Spanish colonists first settled in Puerto Rico, much of its land was fertile and forested. Their original interest was gold, and they paid little attention at first to agriculture. Toward the end of the 16th century, when the gold deposits had become exhausted, they turned to farming. They initially cultivated plantains, bananas, coconuts, ginger, and a few other tropical plants, and raised cattle, hogs, and some other animals. This start led to the gradual accumulation of knowledge of what agricultural uses are more adapted to the resources of the island.

The land resources of Puerto Rico have been grouped into 14 regions according to their agricultural adaptability. They epitomize centuries of experience with the interplay of physical, social, and economic factors.

Topography and temperature are dominant factors in the classification of land in the lowlands, foothills, and mountains. Within the broad categories of foothills and lowlands, rainfall is taken into account by dividing each into the northern and southern sections.

The mountain and northern foothills and lowlands categories are each subdivided into two sections, reflecting variations in rainfall and soils. The social and economic factors interacting with these physical limitations gave rise to present patterns of use and ownership of land.

THE PHYSICAL ENVIRONMENT has been brought through the centuries into productive use by farmers, operating as a basic part of society. Many of the adjustments and changes they have made through time in the use and ownership of land are essentially reactions to changes in relationships within society.

Drastic changes occurred when Puerto Rico became a Territory of the United States in 1898. Spanish relations with Puerto Rico had favored the cultivation of coffee; relations with the United States favored an expansion of the sugar industry.

The efforts of the United States to apply modern techniques of health, education, and public administration in the new Territory led to a rapid growth in population, and the island became one of the most densely populated areas of the world. A tremendous pressure of population on the land has had deep influences on the patterns of land use and ownership in Puerto Rico.

The early decades of this century brought a fast expansion of agriculture. Export crops, primarily sugarcane and tobacco, accounted for a major share of the expansion. Coffee dropped rapidly from the position of principal export crop to a level that barely covered local requirements.

The process of economic development since 1945 has been characterized by an expansion in the industrial, construction, and service sectors of the economy, and agriculture has remained almost the same.

The earlier period of agricultural expansion brought a pronounced displacement of population from the highlands, where coffee is grown, to the lowlands, where sugarcane is produced. It brought also the corporation as an important instrument of ownership and use of land.

The period of industrial and service expansion, which is still unfolding, has resulted in a fast growth of urban populations, particularly in the San Juan, Caguas, and Ponce metropolitan areas. Investors have been much less interested in land for agricultural uses than in sites for industrial and urban housing developments.

Agricultural enterprises are under

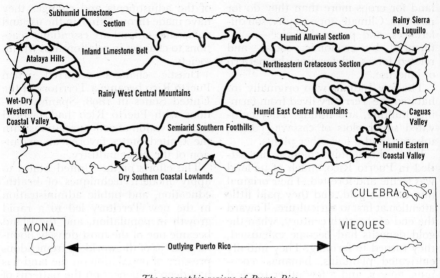

The geographic regions of Puerto Rico.

heavy pressure to improve the efficiency of their operations in order to hold their labor and other resources in competition with the other sectors of the economy. The patterns of the use and ownership of land that are evolving or may evolve will be largely the result of the relative success achieved by operating units in meeting this competition.

The pressure of population on the land and the establishment of corporate control of large tracts brought the issue of landownership and control to the foreground of the political campaign of 1940. A broad program involving legislative and administrative measures designed to spread ownership and control of land among a larger number of people and to increase the shares of farm laborers in the value of agricultural production was put into effect. The measures had great impact.

Technological improvements also have influenced land use. The sugarcane, pineapple, and dairy enterprises have applied on a broad basis a larger number of significant technological improvements than have the tobacco, coffee, and food crops enterprises.

Easy and free trade with the mainland United States market has led to the development of a land-use pattern that stresses the importation of many food items and the exportation of a few cash crops. That trend has continued through the period of industrial expansion, after a slowdown during the war years, when emphasis was placed on local production of food to compensate for limited imports.

Another factor, essentially a part of the trade relations with the Mainland, is the production-control measures for sugarcane and tobacco, that were established as a part of a national program. The control program for tobacco is a responsibility of the Commonwealth Government. The production allotments and policies of administering the programs have tended to influence the trends in the use and ownership of land since the war.

These factors—density of population, the process of development, technology, political movements and trade, and the physical aspects—form the background and the future of Puerto Rico's land use and ownership.

THE TOTAL AREA of the island and

the adjacent islands of Vieques, Culebra, and Mona is 2,254 thousand cuerdas. (A cuerda is 0.9712 acre, and for most purposes the measures can be regarded as equal.) Only 13 percent of the total area is in nonagricultural uses. The 300 thousand cuerdas of nonagricultural land are taken up by urban areas, military reservations, highways, parks, cemeteries, airports, and miscellaneous uses.

The number of farm units has fluctuated from 41,078 farms in 1920, 55,519 in 1940, and 53,515 in 1950. Changes in the definition of a farm from census to census account for part of this variation in the number of farms.

A total of 1,841 thousand cuerdas was in farms in 1950.

The area in farms has declined 9 percent since 1930, reflecting the change from cropland and pasture to urban uses, particularly in the metropolitan area of San Juan, and the impact of activities pertaining to road building, military installations, hydroelectric power, and other public developments. The 1950 census recorded 53 thousand cuerdas in rural holdings too small to be classified as farms.

Of the 1,980 thousand cuerdas in farms in 1955, 910 thousand cuerdas were in cropland, 727 thousand were in pasture, and 204 thousand were in forest and brush. Other uses accounted for the balance of 139 thousand cuerdas. Besides the land in farms, 112,800 cuerdas were in forest reservations, of which 77,800 belonged to the Commonwealth of Puerto Rico and 35 thousand to the Federal Government.

Shifts among the major agricultural uses of land since 1920 have been negligible. But as population has continued to increase and the total of land in farms has dropped, the amount of land per capita in the various uses has declined. Thus a greater demand for food could be met only by more imports or higher production per acre, or both.

Greater production may involve higher yields from the same crops or shifts toward more intensive crops. A higher level of imports, however, seems to have been a major factor in closing the gap between increased consumption requirements and local production.

As plants grow the year round and land is so scarce in Puerto Rico, intercropping and double cropping are used extensively in many types of farming. Complex systems of intercropping and double-cropping arrangements are used for coffee, tobacco, and minor crops.

Often the systems are difficult to unscramble, even by men experienced in farm management and land use. Smaller farms, which depend to a large extent on human labor for raising crops, tend to use these practices more than larger, more highly mechanized farms. Intercropping and double cropping may increase cropland used relative to net land in crops by as much as 75 percent in some special situations.

The six geographic regions that include the lowlands and valleys account for one-third of the total area. These regions have a somewhat higher proportion of the area in cropland and a lower proportion in pasture and forest.

Other uses take up a relatively high proportion of the acreage because urban uses, roads, military installations, and swamps tend to be concentrated in these areas.

A high proportion of the southern foothills is in pasture. Pasture and cropland are balanced in the northern foothills. In the east-central mountains, pasture covers a larger area than crops. The opposite is true in the west-central mountains. Forests tend to be concentrated in the foothills and mountains.

The three main crops—sugarcane, coffee, and tobacco—are grown on almost two-thirds of the cropland. The other third is devoted to forage, starchy vegetables, fruits, cereals, and other food crops. A part of the cropland is in fallow, but much of it probably is used regularly to pasture animals.

The land devoted to sugarcane, the main cash crop, has almost tripled since 1917. It occupies about two-fifths of the cultivated land. It was grown initially in the coastal plains, but it has tended to displace coffee, pasture, and food crops in some sections of the foothills and mountain regions. The harvested area of sugarcane has increased by almost 150 thousand cuerdas since 1940.

Coffee occupies 22 percent of the cropland. It is grown mainly in the deep, reddish upland soils of the west-central mountains. The acreage in coffee has been reduced gradually since 1920 from 194 thousand cuerdas to 176 thousand in 1956. Oranges, bananas, and other food crops are grown as part of the coffee plantings, and the coffee area is a major source of them.

Tobacco uses about 4 percent of the cropland and is planted mainly in the east-central mountain region and a section of the west-central mountains. It is a cigar-filler type. A limited acreage of chewing tobacco is produced in the western coastal lowlands. The area planted to tobacco has shown an irregularly declining trend since 1930. Production, however, has shown less reduction because the yields have increased.

Starchy vegetables, fruits, cereals, and legumes are grown on about one-fifth of the cropland, mostly on small tracts in the foothills and mountain regions. Bananas, plantains, and oranges are intercropped with coffee. Some of these crops are planted as double crops in the tobacco area. The small farms and the plots around rural nonfarm dwellings produce sizable amounts of them.

Nearly one-third of the total area in farms is in pastures. Among the improved pasture grasses are guineagrass in the south, molassesgrass in the northern foothills and mountains, and pangola and paragrasses in humid lowlands. Merker is the number one cut grass and tropical kudzu is used for forage.

About 40,500 cuerdas have been improved under the pasture improvement program of the Commonwealth Department of Agriculture and Com-

Total Area = 2,254,000 Cuerdas

Other Uses 13.3%

Forest 14.0%

Pasture 32.3%

Cropland 40.4%

Major uses of land in Puerto Rico, 1955.

merce. An extensive area has been improved as a part of the Federal soil conservation program and by independent farmers. The major portion of the pasture acreage, however, is still unimproved, particularly in the foothills and mountain regions. Farmers in the milksheds of San Juan, Ponce, and Mayagüez have been the leaders in improvement of pastures.

The land with rougher topography, particularly in places where food crops and tobacco are grown, are tilled more frequently and intensively than the lowland areas.

The type of farming that has been practiced presents a conflict in this respect with recommended practices for soil conservation and improvement.

NEARLY THREE-FOURTHS of the land area is hilly. The Soil Conservation Service has estimated that 48 percent of the total area showed severe erosion and 23 percent showed moderate erosion. The extent of this deterioration is partly confirmed by the rapid rate of silting of water reservoirs.

If one adds together this situation, the tremendous pressure of population on the land, the rapid growth of population, the limited possibilities of land reclamation and development, and the apparent lack of widespread soil-building practices, he can see the seriousness of the problem. Shifts of people to nonagricultural employment may ease the pressure on the land, but more direct measures are also required.

Efforts to reclaim and develop land have centered mostly on irrigation. The Spanish Crown made several concessions before 1898 to permit the use of water for irrigation. Most of the grants facilitated irrigation of the level lands in the southern watershed. Today there are 18 public reservoirs in Puerto Rico. Five supply water for irrigation. Eight are used both for hydroelectric power and irrigation. Together they supply three irrigation systems—the south coast irrigation district, Isabela irrigation service, and the southwestern irrigation project. There are several privately controlled systems. The three public irrigation systems, when fully developed, will irrigate 64 thousand cuerdas. The land under both private and public irrigation is close to 100 thousand cuerdas, or about one-tenth of the cropland.

PUERTO RICO is divided into 17 soil conservation districts. Considerable progress has been made since 1940 in the adoption of more effective practices of soil conservation, but the problems of soil erosion and maintaining soil fertility were acute in 1958.

About 220 thousand tons of fertilizer are applied each year—about one-fourth ton per acre of cropland. Most of it is applied to the acreage in sugarcane. Tobacco, pineapples, and food crops take most of the rest. The use of fertilizer for pasture and coffee, although increasing, is still limited. Not much lime and other soil amendments are used. Manuring, crop rotation, and other practices designed to maintain or improve land resources have been applied to a limited extent.

The sugarcane, coffee, and livestock farms, when properly managed, have achieved a relatively good balance in maintenance of fertility. Tobacco, minor crops, and some pasturelands seem to be still in need of an adequate

land-management system. The overall situation would probably show a net loss, even after reclamation, irrigation, and other land improvements are considered.

THE FRAMEWORK of landownership and control was set during the Spanish rule. The system of "encomiendas"—grants of large tracts to a few chosen people—was applied here, as in most of the other Spanish colonies of the New World. By the time Puerto Rico became a part of the United States, the island presented a pattern of landownership that combined plantation, subsistence, and commercial family-size farms.

During the first 30 years as a Territory, the major change in the ownership and control of land was the development of the corporation as an instrument of landownership. The enactment of a joint resolution of the Congress in May 1900 to restrict the ownership and control of land by one corporation to 500 acres was not enforced until 1941.

Fifty-nine operating units, or fewer than 1 percent of the sugarcane farms, controlled 58 percent of the area planted and produced 67 percent of the tons of sugarcane by 1935. The 1940 census reported that farms of 260 cuerdas or more represented 2 percent of all farms and covered 42 percent of the land in farms.

THE LEGISLATURE in April 1941 approved the Land Law of Puerto Rico, which was designed to promote a broader distribution of land and of the economic proceeds of its cultivation among those who tilled it. The law created an administrative body, the Land Authority of Puerto Rico, to develop the new policy directive. This organization acquired 100 thousand cuerdas of land by purchase or expropriation. Two-thirds of this land was placed in proportional-profit farms, and most of the balance was parceled in small lots for resettling farm laborers. The proportional-profit farms are operated on a rental basis, and the manager and the workers share in the profits.

The law also provided for assistance in the settlement of family-type farms and for the establishment of rural communities with certain public services. A total of 28 thousand cuerdas have been distributed by the Social Program Administration for the resettlement of laborer and sharecropper families in rural communities. This area has been divided among 41,600 families in 246 communities. In addition, 12,702 cuerdas have been distributed in 778 family-size farms. Similar efforts, conducted under the Homestead Act, from 1920–1940 had led to the establishment of 2,400 farms covering 26 thousand cuerdas. The Puerto Rico Reconstruction Administration distributed land in small lots to 10,350 families during the period 1935–1943. The Farm Security Administration, which later became the Farmers Home Administration, has helped in the establishment of family-size farms since 1938.

Sharecroppers were included in the census figures as tenants before 1940 but not in 1950.

The percentage of owner-operated farms has varied from 80 to 94 percent since 1910. The proportion of the land in owner-operated farms has varied from 52 to 75 percent. These figures have shown considerable variation from census to census, particularly in the owner- and manager-operator groups. Manager-operated farms covered 17 percent of the area in farms in 1920, 37 percent in 1935, and 18 percent in 1950.

The number of tenant-operated farms represented 20 percent of all farms in 1940, but was down to 5 percent in 1950. The area covered by tenant-operated farms was 11 percent in 1910, 7 percent in 1930, 13 percent in 1940, and 7 percent in 1950. Changes in the definition of a farm and in other census enumeration procedures, particularly in the latest census, accounted for some of the differences.

Land takes on the average about 70 percent of the total farm investment, and buildings 10 to 15 percent, depending on the size and type of farm. Livestock, supplies on hand, and miscellaneous assets account for the balance. These figures reflect the importance of land relative to buildings, machinery, and other farm resources. They also reflect the pressure of population on land resources.

OF THE TOTAL COST of producing coffee, tobacco, and sugarcane, labor absorbs 40 to 60 percent and the use of the land takes about 12 percent, except for tobacco. Use of the land accounts for only 3 percent of the cost of producing tobacco which is in the ground only a few months.

The net income of all industries of the island was 232 million dollars in 1939–1940 and 1,004 million in 1955–1956.

Agriculture contributed 70 million dollars to the 1939–1940 figure and 162 million to the 1955–1956 net income. Agricultural raw materials accounted for about half of the value added by manufacture and processing—including sugar mills and refineries, distilling and bottling of spiritous liquors, miscellaneous food products, and tobacco products. Agricultural activity also provided an important share of the volume of business of finance, trade, and other service industries.

LAND VALUES are high relative to those on the Mainland and in other less densely populated countries. Land values near the three principal metropolitan centers have gone up about 1,000 percent since 1940, but the price of farmland that has not been affected by demand for other uses has increased 300 to 500 percent.

Credit is concentrated in short-term production credit and store credit. The equity of farmers generally is high. The net worth of 347 sugarcane farmers in 1939–1940 represented 80 percent of the assets; mortgages accounted for 10 percent and short-term credit for an additional 10 percent. As 70 percent of their assets were in real estate, one can realize the proportion that mortgage credit represented of their total investment in real estate.

A similar situation, although not so pronounced, prevailed among tobacco farmers. The credit available annually for agriculture was estimated in 1956 to total 95 million dollars; that included 8 million dollars for intermediate and long-term credit. Federal agencies, mostly the land bank, provided the major part of the long-term loans. Commercial banks and other private agencies were the principal sources of short-term credit.

The nature of the market for farmland and the system of transferring land from generation to generation influence (and in turn are influenced by) the long-term credit situation. The agricultural land market in Puerto Rico apparently is considerably less active than in most agricultural areas of the Mainland.

The system of taxation of agricultural land is similar to the system on the Mainland, but collection and allocation of tax proceeds is centralized in the Commonwealth Government. The proceeds from real-estate taxes represent a small percentage of the total government income.

IF THE TREND of development of the Puerto Rican economy toward more industry and services continues, the fast rate of change toward urban living and employment will undoubtedly continue to ease the pressure of population on agricultural land.

Part-time farming, which has become a significant aspect, may develop to be an important farming procedure. It may be found, as in Switzerland, that some industrial activities can become an integral part of farming and rural living.

This shift in emphasis toward industrial and service activities presents an opportunity to promote necessary adjustments in the use, ownership, and control of land. In regions where tobacco and minor crops are grown, a basis has not been built for adequate use and development of land. This basic maladjustment may force an intensified search for solutions within the next decade. Probably livestock, orchards, and some forest uses, with a reduction in the clean-cultivated acreage, may bring about the necessary balance.

FARMERS WILL FACE keen competition for labor, management, and capital from other sectors of the economy. A wider use of technological improvements will be necessary to meet such competition.

These changes may lead to more intensive uses for areas of better soils, with higher capital inputs for equipment, supplies, better livestock, and so on, and to less intensive uses for the poorer soils. A lower premium will be attached to land; alert management and capital will be in high demand. A more dynamic type of farming, ready to adopt scientific advances, will be necessary. Farms having an active, direct management will have the best chance.

Government policies and programs designed to promote a well-informed, active management and improve the credit and marketing channels for agriculture should foster this necessary change. Research, extension, and vocational education would emphasize the development of new farm management practices and leadership among farmers. More effective systems of farming, rather than the improvement of isolated practices, would be the desired end result.

As the technical evolution of agriculture tends to increase sharply its demand for capital, more diversified and ample credit will have to be secured. Special efforts should also be made to assure that improved efficiency on farms is matched by a parallel improvement in grading and processing and other phases of marketing farm products.

Farm Production Regions

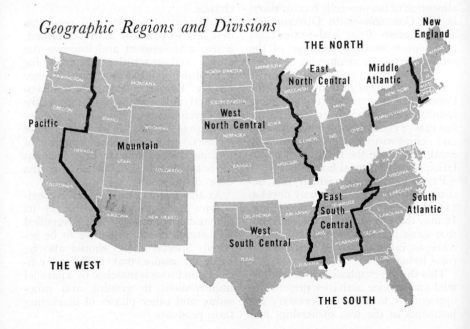

Geographic Regions and Divisions

Our growing
needs and problems—How our production

has expanded—Prospective needs for food and fiber—Our future
needs for nonfarm lands—Land and advances in technology—
Cities, transportation, and technology—Urban expansion: Will
it ever stop?

How our production has expanded.

A fivefold increase in farm output between 1870 and 1958 was due mainly to an expansion in cropland, a shift from animal power to machines, and technological developments. Now the greatest need is for adjustments in production—to gear output to total market needs at home and abroad. By *Glen T. Barton*, Farm Economics Research Division.

FARM OUTPUT in the United States in 1958 was five times the production in 1870. This expansion accompanied threefold increases in population and in exports of our farm products.

The sources of our large increases in farm production during the past century have been many and varied: An expansion of the cropland base; a shift from use of animal to mechanical power on farms; and a greater production per acre and per animal.

The expansion of our cropland base was the major factor in growth of output during the half century between the Civil War and the First World War. The total cropland used, the volume of farm output, and the number of horses and mules on farms were each about three times larger in 1920 than in 1870.

The steady increase in acreage of cropland, as agriculture pushed westward, provided the chief basis for the steady growth in production of food, fiber, oil, and tobacco for sale in markets at home and abroad and for use in farm households. The opening up of new fertile lands enabled farmers to produce the additional grain and hay required to feed the increasing number of horses and mules, which then were the major source of power needed for the expanding agriculture.

Land development added to the productivity of our cropland base. The area of improved land in organized drainage enterprises was increased by more than 40 million acres from 1890 to 1920. Much of it was fertile land in the Corn Belt.

The number of roughage-consuming animal units (cattle, sheep, horses, and mules) on farms in 1920 was twice as great as in 1870. The total volume of farm power—including horses, mules, machinery, and equipment—was five times larger in 1920 than in 1870. That was a much greater increase than occurred in either acreage of cropland or farm output. It was a key factor in the expansion and westward growth of agriculture during the 50 years.

Farm output continued upward during the period between the World Wars. The average annual rate of increase in output, 1.2 percent, was much smaller than the 2.1 percent during the previous half century.

The chief difference between the two periods, however, was the abrupt change in the major sources of increase. Especially noteworthy was the changing role of land. Our total area of cropland no longer expanded. Instead, existing cropland was used more intensively, and a greater part of the land base was used for producing crops and livestock for human consumption.

Our total acreage of cropland reached a plateau about 1920 and has changed little since. Improvement of land, however, contributed to the rise in farm production during the interwar period. Millions of acres were drained. Substantial additions were made to the acreage under irrigation. Shifts from less productive land to more productive land also helped to increase average yields of crops.

The relative stability of the total acreage of cropland for the United States as a whole during the interwar period was the net result of markedly different but compensating trends in acreage of the cropland in the various regions.

Most of the geographic regions east of the Mississippi River recorded substantial reductions in acreage of cropland from 1920 to 1940. Those to the west ranged from no change to substantial increases.

A decline of more than 20 percent occurred in New England and Middle Atlantic States. The acreages of cropland in the mountain and west south-central regions expanded by 20 and 10 percent, respectively.

Mechanization of farming operations was the dominant factor in the step-up in output during the period between the World Wars. About half of the increase came from land released from feed production for the declining numbers of horses and mules. At about the same time that our acreage of cropland arrived at its plateau, the number of horses and mules on farms reached a peak. Since the end of the First World War, the number of horses and mules has declined steadily with the growing importance of tractors, motortrucks, and automobiles as sources of farm power.

About 80 million acres of cropland were used just after the First World War to grow grain and hay to feed horses and mules on farms. That was more than one-fifth of the total acreage of crops harvested at that time. By 1940, only about 40 million acres, or slightly more than 10 percent of the total acreage harvested, were used to produce feed for horses and mules. Millions of acres of pastureland and large amounts of labor and other production resources also were shifted to the production of food and fiber for people.

Scientific progress affected farm output in still other ways from 1920 to 1940. An increase of 10 percent in average crop production per acre occurred.

Greater use of chemical fertilizers added to crop yields. Hybrid corn began to boost yields of the major feed grain. Improved varieties, better methods of pest control, and additions to our irrigated acreage all helped to raise yields.

Government programs also affected yields during the drought and depression period of the 1930's. Fewer acres of major crops were planted, but they were on land of above-average productivity. Conservation programs of the period also helped to increase production per acre.

Important forward strides were made in livestock feeding and breeding practices from 1920 to 1940. Average livestock production per breeding unit— milk per cow, eggs per hen, and so on—rose by more than a third. Improved breeds, heavier feeding of balanced rations, better sanitation, and advances in management generally were among the more important factors behind this step-up in output per animal.

The effects of another important factor in crop production—weather— were demonstrated during the interwar period. Widespread droughts in 1934 and 1936 sharply reduced yields. Average crop production per acre dropped by 17 percent in 1933–1934 and nearly 15 percent in 1935–1936. Economic depression during the mid-1930's also served as a damper on the upward trend in crop yields. Lack of economic incentive slowed the rate of adoption by farmers of improved practices. Depression and drought also interrupted the upward trend in livestock production per breeding unit.

THE REVOLUTION in farming methods continued at an increased tempo in the 15 years after 1940. Farm output increased at an average annual rate of 2 percent from 1940 to 1955, a substantial rise over the rate of 1.2 percent recorded in the interwar period. Farm output rose by more than a third, de-

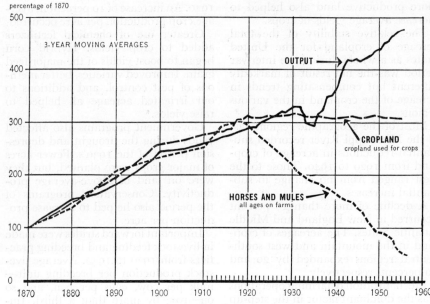

percentage of 1870

3-YEAR MOVING AVERAGES

OUTPUT →

CROPLAND
cropland used for crops

HORSES AND MULES →
all ages on farms

1870   1880   1890   1900   1910   1920   1930   1940   1950   1960

Farm output, cropland, horses and mules.

spite a 30-percent reduction in man-hours of labor used on farms and little change in the total area of land used for crop production. Substantial increases occurred in the use on farms of modern machinery and equipment, fertilizer, and many other goods and services purchased from the nonfarm economy.

Unprecedented demand for farm products during the Second World War and afterwards created economic conditions that were favorable to rapid adoption by farmers of improved techniques of production. This and a backlog of research results from previous decades put production into high gear.

Average crop production per acre rose by nearly 20 percent in the 15 years. About half of the increase in total farm output in 1940–1955 came from this source.

The yields per harvested acre of some crops in 1939–1941 and 1954–1956 and the percentage of change between the two periods were: Corn, 30 and 42 bushels (40 percent); oats, 32 and 36 bushels (12 percent); hay, 1.29 and

1.48 tons (15 percent); soybeans, 18 and 21 bushels (17 percent); peanuts, 758 and 928 pounds (22 percent); wheat, 15 and 19 bushels (27 percent); rice (rough), 2,174 and 2,869 pounds (32 percent): potatoes, 77 and 164 hundredweight (113 percent); tobacco, 981 and 1,461 pounds (49 percent); and cotton, 241 and 409 pounds (70 percent).

Progress in technology was the dominant influence in the larger average outturn per acre. The greater use of commercial fertilizer, for example, was the largest single factor farmers applied. The total of 6 million tons of plant nutrients used in 1955 was nearly 3.5 times the amount applied in 1940. A favorable relationship between costs and prices was a reason.

Outstanding among the improved varieties was hybrid corn, which ordinarily raises yields per acre about 20 percent over yields from open-pollinated varieties. Hybrid varieties were planted on 73 million acres in 1955, or on nearly 90 percent of the total acreage planted to corn in that year. Hybrid seed was used on only 30 percent of the planted acreage in 1940.

Seventy percent of the acreage of cropland in 1954 was planted to varieties that were unknown 20 years earlier. The varieties of seed used in planting cotton, oil crops, and sugar crops changed almost completely.

The smallest change in varieties occurred in hay crops. Only 1 in 5 acres of hay in 1954 was of a variety not used in 1935.

Much of the change in varieties was an important part of the fight against plant diseases, especially among small grains. More than 75 percent of the acreage of small grains in 1954 was planted to varieties that were unknown two decades earlier. The development and use of disease-resistant varieties did much to increase yields.

Great advances were made in controlling insects, diseases, and weeds. New kinds of poisons and chemicals for weed control were discovered.

Increased use of supplemental irrigation in the Eastern States during the 1950's helped to raise yields. Practices such as terracing and contour farming that conserve moisture were important forces in raising yields in many sections.

Weather also influenced the change in crop production. On the average, growing conditions were more favorable for crop production at the end of this period than at the beginning. Although better weather helped to increase crop production per acre, its relative influence was dwarfed by the upward push given to yields by greater use of fertilizer and by other technological developments.

Variations in growing conditions from one year to the next can affect crop production greatly. The droughts in 1934 and 1936 markedly reduced the total crop yields. Years of very favorable weather over most of the country, such as those of 1942 and 1948, saw a sharp rise in output. These years of widespread drought or excellent growing conditions are the exception. In most of the years of the mid-1950's, crop production was adversely affected by severe droughts in important producing areas, but above-average growing conditions prevailed in many other areas. Because crops are grown all over the United States, the effects of variations in weather on total crop production usually tend to balance out for the country as a whole.

Production per breeding unit rose by more than a fifth in 1940–1955. Nearly 1,200 pounds were added to average milk production per cow, an increase of one-fourth. The average layer produced almost 5 dozen—more than 40 percent—more eggs at the end of the period than at the beginning.

The number of breeding units of livestock went up 12 percent from 1940 to 1955. That rise and the substantial rise in production per unit brought livestock output to record levels in the mid-1950's. A greatly expanded supply of feed crops formed the chief basis for the large increase.

As in the interwar period, several factors contributed to the increase in livestock production per breeding unit. Heavier feeding of improved rations and better management practices in general were encouraged by the economic conditions that prevailed during most of the period.

An outstanding development from 1940 to 1955 was the phenomenal growth of the broiler industry. About 3.3 billion pounds, live weight, of broilers were produced in 1955—eight times the outturn in 1940.

Improvements in technology from 1935 to 1954 made possible a reduction of 30 percent in the number of pounds of feed required to produce 100 pounds of meat. During approximately the same period, production of broilers per man-hour of farm labor rose by more than 60 percent.

Mechanization continued to be an important source of increase in farm output from 1940 to 1955. Land, labor, and other production resources released by the shift from animal to mechanical power made possible about a fourth of the increase in farm output during the period. In addition, the

Farm Production

percentage of 1947-49

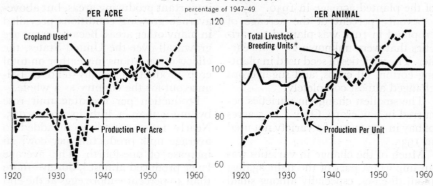

PER ACRE

Cropland Used*

Production Per Acre

PER ANIMAL

Total Livestock Breeding Units*

Production Per Unit

*Estimated acreage from which one or more crops were harvested plus acreage of crop failure and summer fallow

*Includes all breeding livestock except horses, and all livestock production except farm-produced power of horses and mules

accumulation of a large inventory of modern machines and mechanical power added to the timeliness of farming operations.

Although advancing mechanization contributed importantly to the upsurge in output from 1940 to 1955, this direct source of increase in output was largely exhausted by 1955. The shift from animal to mechanical power was relatively complete by the mid-1950's.

Application of improved technology in crop production and land use was the dominant factor in the increase of farm output from 1940 to 1955. The total acreage of cropland used for crops in the United States as a whole increased by only 4 percent. Substantial changes in acreages of cropland occurred in the major geographic divisions, however. During 15 years, the acreage used for crops decreased by a fourth in New England. A drop of more than 20 percent occurred in the southeastern part of the central region. Decreases of 10 to 15 percent were recorded in the Middle Atlantic, South Atlantic, and west south-central regions. The acreage of cropland used increased by more than 40 percent in the mountain region, and additions of 10 to 15 percent were registered in the Pacific and north-central regions.

Additions to irrigated acreage in the subhumid regions and improvement of

land through drainage raised the average productivity of our cropland base. Contributing to the same end were shifts from less fertile to more fertile acres. The increased use of tractors and associated modern machinery has been an important influence in the shifts to the level, fertile lands, to similar wet areas subject to drainage, and to dry areas on which irrigation is feasible.

THE COMPOSITION of total farm production has changed substantially since the end of the First World War. The shifts in relative importance of the various crop and livestock enterprises resulted from a combination of factors, including shifts in demand and differences among enterprises in technological progress, cost reduction, and relative profitability to farmers.

In response to shifts in demand, livestock production increased much more than crop production after the war. Output of poultry and eggs rose about twice as much as production of meat animals and dairy products. Most of the increase in production of poultry and eggs occurred after 1940 when technological developments were most rapid.

The step-up in outturn of feed grains, hay, and forage was considerably less than the large increase in output of meat animals, dairy products, and

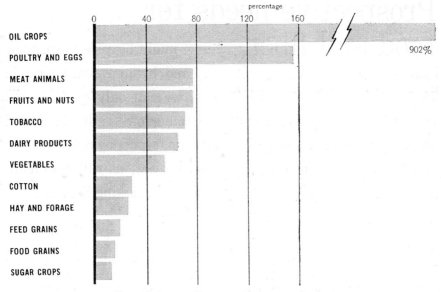

Change in farm production, 1919-1921 to 1954-1956.

poultry and eggs. Much of the increase in feed supplies needed for the large expansion in livestock production during the 35 years resulted from the release of feed resources because of the decline in number of horses and mules.

A rise of 50 to 75 percent in production of fruits, vegetables, and tobacco from 1920 to 1955 reflected the growth of the population and the expansion in consumer demand for those products. The much more modest increase in production of food grains, cotton, and sugar crops was a reaction to a number of forces, including shifts in consumer demand, changes in export markets, and Government programs of production control.

An outstanding development was the phenomenal expansion in production of oil crops. The combined output of soybeans, peanuts, and flaxseed in the mid-1950's was 10 times the production 35 years earlier. Although the production of flaxseed increased fourfold and output of peanuts doubled, the great expansion in production of soybeans dominated the growth in oil crops. Soybeans changed from a minor to a major crop; they are now the chief

source of protein feed for our livestock. In 1924, the first year of record, only 5 million bushels of soybeans were produced. In 1957, the production was 480 million bushels.

Farm output in 1957 was the greatest recorded to that year. The total in 1957 was about equal to that projected as needed to meet market demands in 1963. Accumulated surplus stocks and efforts of Government programs to reduce farm production in the mid-1950's underline the fact that the productive capacity of agriculture exceeds immediate prospects for demand.

The greatest need in the latter part of the 1950 decade, and perhaps in the longer run, is for adjustments in production. We need to gear total output to total market needs at home and abroad.

Continued growth of the population of the United States eventually will mean market requirements for farm products greater than the volume of farm output attained in the mid-1950's. But there is little reason to doubt that the productive capacity of agriculture will be adequate to meet market demands by the end of another decade.

Prospective needs for food and fiber.

Things might be easier if we knew exactly how much meat, potatoes, and bread we will need in 1965. Lacking that foreknowledge, we can only estimate the land and production we shall need tomorrow—estimates based on past and present trends in population, economic relationships, and habits of people. Estimates and projections will help us in planning. By *Rex F. Daly*, Agricultural Marketing Service.

WE CAN EXPECT more people, higher incomes, and generally improved living standards to expand total requirements for farm products about 20 percent in the next decade and possibly as much as 50 percent in the next two decades.

The projections that follow are based on trends in population and economic growth, economic relationships, and a framework of reasonable assumptions. Such a look at the future—albeit through a glass, darkly—will help us in planning policy and developing research programs.

Growth and prosperity in agriculture are interrelated with growth and prosperity in the general economy. A few major assumptions with respect to general economic growth therefore are necessary as a basis for projecting requirements for farm products.

Population, a major factor in the demand for farm products, has grown fast during the 1950's. Estimates for recent years exceed the highest projections made a few years ago. The number of persons reaching 18 years of age will rise rapidly in 1960–1965. They will join the labor force and probably marry and found new families. A substantial increase in the number of women 20 to 34 years old—the most prolific age group—will begin about 1965. With prospects for fairly rapid population growth, the population assumed for 1965 (193.5 million) is up 15 percent

from 1956; for 1975, the assumed level of 230 million is 37 percent above 1956.

The economy will continue to grow in the next two or three decades, possibly even faster than in the past. We were producing about twice as much goods and services in 1951–1955 as in 1925–1929. Population was up more than a third, and consumer buying power, after adjustment for higher prices, increased 55 percent between these periods.

The size of the economy by 1975 could easily double the 1951–1955 average, if past trends continue. With rising output per man and rapid population growth, real consumer incomes per person in 1975 may be about 40 percent above 1956. Consumer incomes projected for 1965 are about 16 percent higher than 1956. Such expansion of the economy assumes peace and a high level of employment.

Requirements will also depend on relative prices of farm products, particularly nonfood commodities and products for export. Two levels of relative prices were assumed: The first assumes prices around 1956–1957 average levels. A lower level was also assumed for major export crops, feed grains, and livestock products, in order to illustrate probable effects of a substantially lower price on domestic use and exports. The lower level reflects approximately world prices for major export crops.

Most formal theories of economic growth are oversimplified. A complete economic framework for the economy or any major segment of it would require consideration of a host of economic, social, and political factors and relationships. Qualitative judgments must be made; we cannot specify the usual limits of statistical probability.

In this analysis, I base most empirical measurements on a series of simple single-equation functions of demand. They express consumption as a function of changes in relative prices received by farmers and consumer buying power. For some commodities, I considered prices of competing products as a factor affecting consumption.

Trends in consumption also reflect many other influences, including developments in nutrition, fads in food and clothing, medical findings, new products, and new uses for old products. Consumption trends also must be considered in light of technological developments in supply, such as those that influenced citrus fruits, broilers, and fibers in the past quarter century.

CHANGES IN DEMAND for farm products depend primarily on the domestic consumer and the foreign market. We are interested in this analysis in demand for products of the farm. But consumers do not buy farm products—they buy food and clothing at grocery stores, department stores, and restaurants. The farm product is an incidental raw material of many consumer goods. Some foods are highly processed. Most are packaged. All must be assembled, shipped, and made available at distribution outlets.

Retail purchases of farm products thus include many services of processing and distribution. In 1956 and 1957, for example, the farmer received only about 40 cents out of the consumer's retail food dollar. In most years he probably receives only about a third of the dollar the consumer spends for food, clothing, tobacco, and other products that contain farm commodities.

The relatively small share of the value of the final product that goes to the farmer complicates the problem of appraising changes in demand at the farm level.

Expenditures for food at retail stores and restaurants tend to increase by about the same proportion as consumer income. A 10-percent increase in income leads to about 10-percent larger outlays for food.

Consumption at retail, however, includes the farm product as well as the marketing and processing services necessary to move the product into consumption. Consumption of the farm product itself changes relatively little in response to changes in prices and income of consumers. Thus, at the farm level, a 10-percent increase in real incomes of consumers may increase consumption of farm products per person by only 1.5 to 2 percent. Likewise, a 10-percent drop in relative prices may increase per capita use by only 1.5 to 2 percent.

RISING INCOMES, price changes, and other factors that affect preferences of consumers have a relatively small influence on per capita use of farm products as a whole.

Pounds of food and numbers of calories consumed per person have changed little in the past quarter century—but there have been changes in the pattern of consumption. Big declines in the use of grains and potatoes have been offset by increases in consumption of some other vegetables, fruits, and meats. This shift to higher cost foods results in an upgrading of the diet and some increase in resources needed to produce the diet. The shift to higher cost foods resulted in a rise of 8 percent in the index of per capita consumption from 1925–1929 to the 1951–1955 average.

Many of the trends in our eating habits will continue, although the downtrend in the use of cereals and potatoes may moderate somewhat.

Under the conditions of income and the relative prices that I assume for

Growth of the United States Population

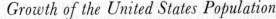

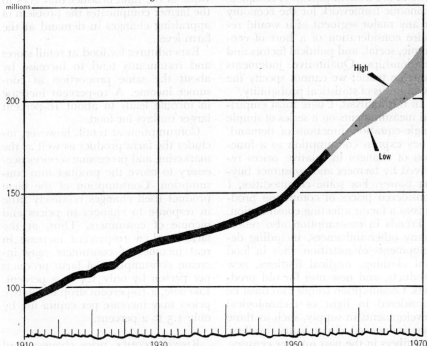

1975, projected per capita use of farm products will increase about 8 to 12 percent above 1956. Per capita use of food would be about 7 to 11 percent higher and of nonfoods 13 to 21 percent higher. That range reflects the relatively small differences in consumption associated with assumed variation in relative prices.

Domestic requirements for farm products in 1975 are projected at levels 48 to 53 percent above 1956. A further rise in per capita use and a projected increase of 37 percent in population account for the gain, but no such gain is in prospect for exports of farm products.

If there are no special disposal programs, projected exports (if we assume the higher prices) probably would total no more than 50 to 60 percent of exports in 1956. Should we assume the lower price, however, exports may be well maintained, possibly close to the

near-record exports in 1956. Projected requirements for both domestic use and export in 1975 thus would increase about 37 to 46 percent above 1956.

Domestic requirements also include imports of coffee, tea, cocoa, bananas, sugar, wool, and some other products. These imports averaged about a tenth of domestic use in 1951–1955. If we deduct imports from utilization and take account of the stock buildup in 1956, an increase in farm output of around 34 to 44 percent would supply projected increases in requirements. This calculation of total output needed makes no allowance for the large previously accumulated stocks of cotton, wheat, and feed grains. Any substantial liquidation of these stocks in the next few years will require an adjustment in the pattern of production.

THE CONSUMPTION of livestock prod-

Trends in Our Eating Habits

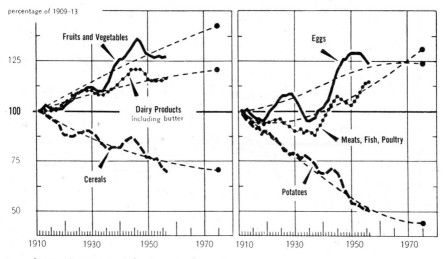

5-year moving average centered
Per capita civilian consumption, U. S. (using 1947-49 retail price as weights)

ucts generally is more responsive to changes in income and relative prices than the consumption of most other farm products. Food uses of livestock products accounted on the average for about 70 percent of total food use during 1951–1955. Nonfood animal products (such as wool, tallow, greases, and some products for feed) are largely byproducts of livestock production. Both exports and imports comprise a relatively small part of total utilization.

Consumption of meat animals was at a high level in 1956, partly because of the cyclical high in supplies of beef and a rising consumption of poultry. Projected increases of 8 to 14 percent per person from 1956 look conservative. But assumed prices for meat animals under the assumption of high prices are about a fourth above the relatively low prices in 1956. Even the 8-percent increase over the record 166 pounds of red meat (beef, pork, and lamb) in 1956 would result in a high level of meat consumption, however. Probably more and more people will prefer beef to pork, especially if we do not develop a leaner hog.

Per capita consumption of red meats in 1951–1955 averaged 12 percent above 1925–1929, but relative prices for meat animals increased a fourth during the period. Per capita consumption of poultry increased more than two-thirds during the same period. Rapid technological developments in feeding and producing broilers and turkeys brought a decline of more than a third in relative prices for poultry, which contributed to the big increase in consumption. Further sizable increases in the use of poultry are in prospect, but the gains are expected to be much smaller than those of recent decades.

The pattern of milk utilization has shifted substantially in the past two or three decades. Per capita use of butter in ° 1925–1929 averaged 17 to 18 pounds, but consumption in recent years has been about half as large. More whole milk, skimmed milk, and fluid milk products with a low fat content are consumed. Use of all milk solids combined (fat and nonfat) has increased moderately in the past quarter century and probably will rise

Utilization of Farm Products

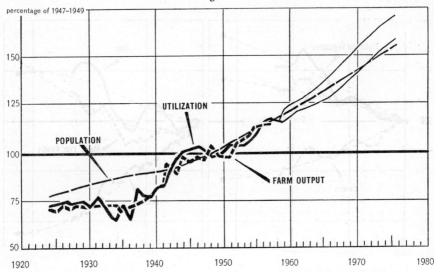

further in the next two decades. The demand for milk fat is expected to continue to be less promising than for other milk solids because of the tendency of processors as well as consumers to substitute lower cost fats.

The long-run trend in egg consumption has been upward, although in recent years consumers have materially reduced their consumption of eggs. Apparently a tendency to eat lighter breakfasts led people to eat fewer eggs, although the recommendations of some nutritionists as to the value of adequate breakfasts that include protein foods may reverse the trend.

Consumption in 1950–1952 averaged about 390 eggs a person. It was down to 369 eggs in 1956 and 360 in 1957. Experience of the last decade gives no basis for expecting a rise in consumption of eggs.

The combined use of livestock products per person for 1975, as projected above, increases 7 to 11 percent from the high level in 1956. Nonfood use per person may continue to decline. These uses, which include feed, hatching eggs, wool, and tallow and greases, accounted in 1951–1955 for a little more than a tenth of livestock production. The

downtrend in livestock products used for feed, mainly dairy products, is expected to continue but at a slower rate. We will need a substantial increase in eggs for hatching. Domestic production of wool is not likely to change materially.

The growth in population and the projected rise in per capita use indicate domestic requirements for livestock products in 1975 some 45 to 50 percent above 1956. Both exports and imports are relatively small—approximately 3 percent of production in 1951–1955. An increase in production of about 40 to 46 percent from 1956 would be needed therefore to match projected requirements for 1975.

DEMAND FOR CROPS derives in large part directly from requirements for livestock products. Consumer purchases of food, tobacco, and clothing and utilization in paints, soaps, and other industrial products also provide major domestic markets for crops, however. In 1951–1955, the use of crops for feed and seed represented about half of total domestic use. (In order to avoid double counting, feed and seed are deducted from crop utilization and supply be-

Carryover of Major Farm Commodities

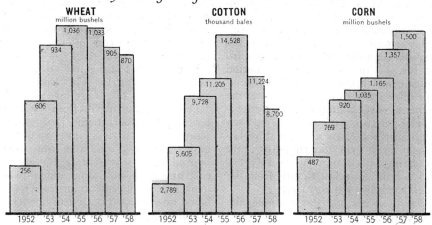

WHEAT million bushels
COTTON thousand bales
CORN million bushels

CROP YEARS BEGINNING: WHEAT, JULY 1; COTTON, AUG. 1; CORN, OCT. 1.
Heights of bars are proportional to value. 1958 bars based on prospects for production and disappearance as of September 1958

fore combining with livestock to get a total for all products. Because of increased efficiency, use for feed rises less than use for food and other nonfood uses. The increase for all farm products combined consequently usually is greater than for crops as a whole or livestock products.)

Food accounted for about 36 percent, and the other nonfood crops—mainly cotton, tobacco, and some oils and grains—made up the remaining 14 percent of total domestic use of crops.

Our per capita consumption of all crops combined has varied little during the past quarter century. The consumption of individual crops, however, has responded to changes in relative prices, incomes, and habits.

The average person today consumes much less of such foods as cereals, potatoes, and dry beans than did the average person 25 years ago. He ate 144 pounds of potatoes in 1925–1929 and averaged 104 pounds each year in 1951–1955. Wheat consumption dropped from 254 pounds to 181 pounds and is still declining. The use of potato chips and french-fried potatoes, despite nutritional considerations, apparently have bolstered consumption of potatoes in recent years.

The consumption of these heavier foods apparently is influenced little by price changes, and people tend to eat less flour, cereals, and potatoes as their incomes rise. Lighter work and concern about overweight also have contributed to reduced consumption of the heavier foods. The smaller consumption of these foods has been largely offset by increases in use of fruits and vegetables. Rising incomes probably will further reduce our consumption of grains and potatoes, but the declines may moderate if arguments advanced by some nutritionists convince consumers that they should eat less fat, particularly some types of animal fats and solid-type vegetable fats.

The consumption of fruits (especially citrus fruits) and such vegetables as tomatoes and the leafy, green, and yellow vegetables has tended to rise with rising incomes and relatively lower prices. A better knowledge of nutrition also has encouraged people to eat more of these foods. The projected increase in consumption of fruits and vegetables from the 1951–1955 average is relatively small because of offsetting trends. This group contains such commodities as apples, cabbage, and dry onions, and the consumption of them apparently is not sensitive to changes in prices and incomes.

Use of food oils per person is expected to continue to rise but much less rapidly than the gain of nearly a third in the past quarter century—a period during which consumption of vegetable oils expanded rapidly partly at the expense of such animal fats as butter.

The per capita use of coffee and tea combined increased nearly a third between 1925–1929 and 1951–1955 and probably will continue upward if retail prices hold or decline slightly from the high levels in 1956 and 1957.

For domestic crops as a whole, the trends in consumption point to a small rise in per capita use. Projected levels for 1975 are only slightly above the 1951–1955 average.

Nonfood crops, besides feeds and seeds, include cotton, tobacco, oils, and some grains.

Cotton and some of the oils that compete with synthetic products probably are fairly responsive to changes in price and income. An appraisal of prospective requirements for cotton is complicated by competition with synthetic fibers and likely price policy. In this appraisal, cotton prices were assumed at two levels: The higher is close to the average for 1956; the lower approximates world prices. This range was assumed in order to indicate possible variations in domestic use and export. Some increase in the per capita use of cotton is expected in the economic framework assumed for 1975, and the increase could be sizable under the lower price assumption. The higher projection for cotton under the lower price assumption suggests that cotton would regain some of the market for fibers.

Some further rise in the per capita use of leaf tobacco is expected, although the gain may be slow for several years as manufacturers make substantially more products from a pound of leaf. Extensive use of filter-tip cigarettes and the development of a "processed sheet" tobacco has permitted greater use of stems and thus the use of less tobacco leaf per cigarette. Medical findings may continue to influence consumption, but the extent and direction of the influence is uncertain.

Nonfood uses of oils and grains are also expected to rise. They could rise substantially if prices are low.

Feed comes primarily from hay and pasture, the four major feed grains (corn, oats, barley, and sorghum grains), other grains, and from such byproducts as the mill feeds, oilseed cake and meal, and some animal proteins. Feed requirements for crops were based on projected output of livestock products. It was assumed that feeding efficiency would improve by at least one-tenth in the next two decades. This would result in an increase in total feed use by 1975 of about 31 to 37 percent. Projected requirement for feed increased by considerably more than during the past quarter century, when a big decline in the number of horses and mules released feed for other livestock. This decline is almost completed, however.

Domestic requirements for crops projected for 1975 range 41 to 46 percent above 1956. These gains reflect a small rise in use per capita and the assumed increase of 37 percent in population. The increase in food uses would be about 50 percent from 1956, with virtually no variation in consumption associated with lower relative prices. Nonfood uses are projected to rise 57 to 68 percent with the larger increase under the lower price assumption. But crops used for feed and seed (about half of all crops) increase less rapidly than other uses; that fact accounts for the gain of around 41 to 46 percent from 1956 in domestic requirements for crops. Domestic requirements for crops rose 27 percent on the average from the 1925–1929 period to 1951–1955. But requirements for feed and seed rose only 20 percent during this period as declining numbers of horses and mules released feed for other animals.

THE FOREIGN MARKET for our farm products depends on a complex of forces, many of which are noneconomic and hard to appraise. World demand for food and fiber will increase. World markets probably will continue to take relatively large quantities of our cotton, grains, tobacco, and fats and oils. World population by 1975 may be 40 to 45 percent larger than in 1950. Such growth alone does not assure an expanding demand, but incomes of consumers and the general level of living are expected to rise. The demand for food therefore should increase more rapidly than growth in population.

With existing technology and readily accessible new lands, foreign agricultural production probably could be increased rapidly enough to meet a large part of projected needs in most areas of the world. Furthermore, the trend toward self-sufficiency in the production of food and fiber probably will continue in most foreign countries for reasons of politics and security.

Under the higher price level, exports might fall off as much as 50 percent in the next few years without export programs. Projected exports for 1975 were assumed under these conditions at around 50 to 60 percent of the relatively large exports in 1956. At the lower price assumption, however, exports probably would be well maintained and may exceed the volume exported in 1956. Such exports probably would include substantial quantities of cotton, wheat, tobacco, and oils.

That level of exports plus domestic requirements would mean an increase in total requirements for crops of about 30 to 40 percent from 1956 to 1975. A part of the domestic requirements is supplied by imports of such crops as coffee, tea, cocoa, sugar, and bananas. These imports may increase 45 to 50 percent by 1975. Consequently, an increase in domestic crop output of about 25 to 35 percent from 1956 would match prospective needs for crops. Although these gains reflect the small increase in stocks in 1956, they make no

allowance for working down substantial carryover stocks of cotton, wheat, and feed grains.

Large supplies, low prices, and low incomes have characterized agriculture in the past few years. The domestic market has continued to expand, and exports have been large, except for a decline in 1952 and 1953. But the small gain in total utilization tells only part of the story: In recent years record exports were made possible by special Government export programs. If we assume that half of total exports in 1956 and 1957 moved under special Government programs (and the proportion is probably greater), excess output above normal outlets in these years would approximate 8 percent or more of total output. In addition to excess production, carryovers from previous years are large for cotton, grains, oils, and tobacco.

Although about 28 million acres of cropland were in the Soil Bank in 1957, crop output was near the record level of 1956 because of a sharp increase in production per acre. It is not easy to control farm production. Despite a number of special programs to stimulate domestic consumption and exports, agriculture in 1958 was faced with surpluses, particularly of the grains.

Let us assume that excess stocks can be worked down in 1958–1963 and that exports are maintained to help move the surpluses. Stock reduction and demand conditions in prospect for those years indicate that farm output may have to be reduced in the adjustment period, possibly as much as 5 to 7 percent below 1956 and 1957 unless the expansion in requirements greatly exceed those in prospect under the higher price assumption. Even by 1965, a balanced crop output may need to total little more than in 1957.

We would expect needs to be larger, especially for export and nonfood uses, under the lower price assumptions. Even with larger requirements, we probably would need to hold crop output near the 1957 rate until excess stocks are worked off.

Our future needs for nonfarm lands.

A thoughtful answer is given here to the question as to how much land will be needed for a growing list of the nonagricultural uses to which about 10 percent of our land is now devoted: "Our expanding requirements can have a relatively small impact on our total agricultural potential. But this assumes the orderly development of our land resource base." By *Raleigh Barlowe,* professor, Department of Agricultural Economics, Michigan State University.

APPROXIMATELY 10 percent of the surface land area of the United States is now used for nonagricultural purposes.

This total includes the 8.2 percent officially reported as nonagricultural land in 1954. It also includes an additional 1 to 2 percent that was counted as agricultural land but that actually was used for the unincorporated subdivisions, small villages, nonfarm rural residences, rural commercial and industrial sites, storage areas, reservoirs, gravel pits, quarries and mines, golf courses, cemeteries, and other nonagricultural uses.

How much land will we need for these uses in the future? No one can answer this question for sure. Too much depends on the rate of increase of population and the effect of technology and changing tastes of consumers on our demand for land for the various nonagricultural uses. Much also depends on the future pattern of competition between different land uses and the impact of changing prices and public policies on the possible reallocation of tracts among competing uses.

We can only guess at the effect of these variables. But if we start by making assumptions regarding them, we can get a fairly good idea of our prospective demand by projecting our present pattern into the future.

Let us think in terms of the acreages needed for populations of 225 million and 300 million—totals we could very well have by 1975 and 2000, respectively. Let us also assume the continuation of our 1954 patterns of per capita demand respecting these uses, no major adjustments resulting from technological changes, a continued tendency for our major nonagricultural uses to outbid agriculture for the use of land, and no public measures that restrict the shifting of agricultural land into nonagricultural uses.

We must differentiate also among the principal classes of nonagricultural lands—residential, commercial and industrial, transport, recreational, and military. We must give attention to the impact of the increasing demand for nonagricultural uses upon our resource base of farmland and to some of the measures we can use to facilitate an orderly shifting of lands from agricultural to nonagricultural uses.

We have only fragmentary data on the acreages used for nonfarm residential purposes. Hugh H. Wooten and James R. Anderson, of the Department of Agriculture, indicated that 18.6 million acres were occupied in 1954 by incorporated cities and villages with populations of 1 thousand or more. That is about half of our total urbanized land area. They estimated that another 10 million acres were used by villages of 1 hundred to 1 thousand people. It seems reasonable that upwards of 8.6 million additional acres were used for unincorporated subdivisions and for rural nonfarm residential, industrial, and commercial holdings.

Harland Bartholomew's studies of land use (summarized in his research monograph, *Land Uses in American Cities*, which was published by Harvard University Press in 1955), show that about 40 percent of the developed land area in 86 typical cities is used for residential purposes. A higher percentage—between one-half and two-thirds of the total area—applies with the urbanized lands in villages, unincorporated subdivisions, and rural nonfarm holdings.

If we assume that 40 percent of the land in cities and 60 percent of the urbanized areas outside cities are used for nonfarm residential purposes, it appears that around 18.6 million acres were used for this purpose in 1954. This area was used by some 41 million nonfarm households, which included a population of 140 million persons.

Very likely our total farm population will continue to decline; our anticipated increase in population then will accrue entirely to the nonfarm sector of the economy.

If we assume a future farm population of 20 million and no change in our average size of nonfarm household, a national population of 225 million will call for living quarters for 60 million nonfarm households. A national population of 300 million will call for quarters for 82 million households.

A projection of the per capita and per household areas used for nonfarm residential purposes in 1954 suggests that we may need more than 27 million acres for this purpose with a population of 225 million and more than 37 million acres with 300 million.

These two projections are high, but they can come about if we maintain our balance between in-city and out-of-city residential holdings. They may

go even higher if we permit the wanton and wasteful conversion of sizable rural areas into premature subdivisions and other only partly utilized residential holdings.

Several reasons may be given for lowering these estimates: The assumption that the average nonfarm household used 0.45 acre for residential purposes in 1954 is too high a standard for projection purposes. It gives too much weight to the large and often only partly used holdings of some suburban and rural nonfarm residents. It underemphasizes the fact that the 74 percent of our nonfarm population that lived in cities and towns in 1950 used an average of only 0.25 acre per household for residential purposes.

Suburbanization and the demand for wide-frontage lots undoubtedly will contribute to a substantial shift of rural land to residential holdings. We must take care, however, not to overemphasize the importance of these two factors. Only 57 percent of our nonfarm dwellings were single-family units in 1950. There are good reasons for assuming that multifamily developments with their relatively low land requirements per household will provide for a larger rather than smaller portion of our future residential needs.

About 80 percent of our increase in population during the 1940's came in standard metropolitan areas. A comparable trend may be expected in the future. Many of the people who make up this expected increase will locate in the outskirts of cities, which qualify as metropolitan centers. With the continued outward sprawl of these cities, however, people will become more and more conscious of time and distance. A place in the country still will have its appeal, but the desire to reduce the time and effort expended in going to and from work and a realization of the artificialities of exurbia will keep many from moving to the distant suburbs.

As our cities expand in area, an increasing proportion of our total nonfarm population will probably live in cities. They will want more and better housing within the cities, and their wants will lead to the redevelopment and more intensive residential use of many centrally located sites.

The operation of these factors suggests a need for separate projections of our prospective demand for residential lands inside and outside cities. In making these projections, let us assume that we will need approximately the same residential area per household within as well as outside cities in the future. Let us also assume that 77 percent of our nonfarm population will live in cities and villages when we have a population of 225 million and that this proportion will rise to a level of 80 percent with a population of 300 million. These assumptions lead to the estimate that we will need about 26.2 million acres for residential uses with a population of 225 million and 33.8 million acres with a population of 300 million persons.

These estimates are more conservative than those listed earlier. Even they could be high, if rigidities in the real-estate credit market or depressed business conditions should cause a doubling up of urban households, such as that experienced during the 1930's. All things considered, however, the estimate that we will need 7.6 million additional acres of residential land for a population of 225 million and 15.2 million additional acres for a population of 300 million appears realistic enough.

We can also assume comparable increases in our demand for other non-agricultural land.

Harland Bartholomew found that approximately a tenth of the developed area in his 86 cities was used for commercial and industrial purposes. His index suggests that 1.9 million acres were used for those purposes in cities in 1954 and that more than a million additional acres were so used in villages and various suburban and rural nonfarm developments. With the trend toward large retail shopping centers and single-floor industrial establishments, it is likely that we will need at least 4.5 million acres for these uses with a population of 225 million and 6 million acres with a population of 300 million.

Messrs. Wooten and Anderson indicate that 19.8 million acres were used in 1954 for rural highways and roads (not including farm roads and lanes), 3.4 million acres for rural railroad rights-of-way, and 1.3 million acres for airports outside city limits. Some 6.2 million acres of streets, alleys, parking areas, railroad holdings, and airfields—one-third of the developed area of our cities—were used for transportation purposes. More than 2 million acres were also used for transportation in small villages and unincorporated subdivisions.

Our demand for railroad lands probably will remain fairly constant. New areas will be developed for commercial and private airfields. But after allowances are made for the areas now in airports that may shift to other uses, our demand for airfields may require only 1.5 million acres with a population of 225 million and 1.8 million acres with 300 million.

Most of our need for additional land for transportation uses will come with the laying out of new subdivisions, the clearing of urban sites to create parking areas, the building of new roads, and the relocation and widening of the existing highways. If there are no changes in the proportions of our urbanized areas used for streets and parking, we probably will need about 4.2 million additional acres for these purposes when the population is 225 million and slightly more than 8.9 million additional acres when it is 300 million.

The 13-year expanded roadbuilding program projected after the passage of the Federal-Aid Highway Act of 1956 calls for the acquisition of some 2.5 million acres for building, widening, and relocating highways. This suggests that at least 3 million acres will be added to the areas used for rural highways and roads by the time our population reaches 225 million. Two million acres or more will likely be added to this total by the time our population reaches 300 million. Altogether, these projected increases call for about 40.4 million acres for transportation with a population of 225 million and 47.4 million acres with a population of 300 million, compared to 33 million acres in 1954.

Approximately 32 million acres were used primarily for recreational purposes in 1954. This total includes 18.7 million acres of State and national parks, 8.8 million acres of wildlife areas, and about a million acres of city parks and playgrounds. An estimated 3.5 million acres were used for local parks, golf courses, beaches, and private recreational developments.

More and more demand will rise for outdoor recreational opportunities as our population increases. This increasing demand will call for additions to our recreational landholdings, a more intensive use of the areas currently held for this purpose, and a more intensive use of our public waters, forests, and wilderness areas.

Most of the increasing demand for land for recreation will be in urban areas. The National Recreation Association recommends that 10 acres of recreational land be provided for every thousand residents in cities of 10 thousand or more and that a sliding scale calling for up to 1 acre for every 40 residents be used in smaller cities. It is also argued that an additional 10 acres per thousand persons should be provided around our larger cities for county and metropolitan parks and that still more facilities be made available within a 2-hour drive of our metropolitan centers.

Mr. Bartholomew's studies indicate that fewer than half of our cities have as much as 5 acres of land in parks and playgrounds for each thousand residents. Efforts are being made to improve this situation. Open spaces are being acquired and dedicated for recreational use in and around many cities. Residential and industrial areas also are being redeveloped for this use,

but the scope of this activity is definitely limited by the high costs associated with the acquisition and development of these sites. With the continued expansion of our cities and our growing demand for places for recreation, we will probably have upwards of 2 million acres of city parks and playgrounds with a population of 225 million and 3 million acres with a population of 300 million.

LITTLE CHANGE is expected in our need for wildlife areas. The growing demand for State parks and to some extent for national parks, however, will likely boost our need for these recreational areas to about 19.5 million acres with 225 million people and 21 million acres with 300 million people. Our need for county and other local parks, golf courses, and private recreational developments will probably go up to 5 and 7 million acres, respectively. Added together, these projections call for 35.3 million acres of recreational lands with a population of 225 million and 39.8 million acres with a population of 300 million.

Among the lands used for service areas and other miscellaneous nonagricultural purposes, Messrs. Wooten and Anderson report that we had 7 million acres in major reservoir areas in 1954, 3.9 million acres in floodcontrol areas, 2 million acres in atomic energy sites, and 1.2 million acres in State-owned institutional sites. About 2.1 million acres—slightly more than a tenth of the developed area in cities—were used for public and semipublic uses. It is estimated that close to 4 million additional acres were used for rural schools, churches, cemeteries, gravel pits, quarries, mining sites, and other miscellaneous rural, nonagricultural uses. Our demand for these miscellaneous uses will probably call for 22.5 million acres with a population of 225 million and 25 million acres with 300 million, as compared with 20 million acres in 1954.

As the summary of these projections given in the accompanying tabulation

Types of land use	Millions of acres used in 1954	Millions of acres needed for a national population of—	
		225 million	300 million
Residential lands	18. 6	26. 2	33. 8
Commercial and industrial	3. 0	4. 5	6. 0
Transportation areas	33. 0	40. 4	47. 4
Recreational lands	32. 0	35. 3	39. 8
Military and defense	21. 5	21. 5	21. 5
Service areas and other	20. 0	22. 5	25. 0
Areas in nonagricultural uses	128. 1	150. 4	173. 5
Wasteland areas not included in farms	55. 5	54. 5	53. 0
Total nonagricultural land	183. 6	204. 9	226. 5

indicates, we shall need about 150 million acres for nonagricultural uses with a population of 225 million and 174 million acres with a population of 300 million. This compares with the 128 million acres used for these purposes in 1954.

Most of the additional areas needed in the future will come from lands now used for farming, grazing, or forestry. Some of the needs, however, will be provided from the 55.5 million acres of marshland, bare-rock areas, deserts, sand dunes, and other relatively barren areas not included in farms in 1954.

NO PARTICULAR case is made for these projections. They may be several million acres high or several million acres low. But high or low, they show that the expected changes in our demand for nonagricultural land will have only a minor effect upon our overall land-use situation during the next half century. The demands expected of a population of 225 million call for the use of only 11 percent of our total land area for nonagricultural uses. The demands expected of a population of 300 million involve less than 12 percent of our total land area.

Except for our need for new highway sites, these prospective shifts will have a negligible effect upon land-use conditions in many productive farming areas. But they will have an extremely important impact in the already highly urbanized area that reaches from Portland, Maine, to Washington, D. C., and that sometime may extend to

Miami; in the industrial corridor that stretches from Buffalo and Pittsburgh to Chicago and Milwaukee; and in many smaller and more local urban and suburban sections.

Large areas of land in farms and forests will shift to residential and other nonagricultural uses in these urbanized areas. Lands now regarded as of prime value for farming will be bid off to non-farm uses.

Much of the land that shifts will be of little value for farming, however. A study of subdivision trends in southwestern Michigan, for example, showed that only half of the area subdivided in a six-county area between 1946 and 1956 was regarded as good or even fair cropland the year before it was subdivided, 36 percent was rated as idle or poor cropland, and 14 percent was land that had never been farmed.

As long as we rely on the market-price mechanism to allocate the ownership and use rights in land among competing operators and uses, we can expect some shifting of areas of high agricultural potential to nonagricultural uses. This process will occur because of the higher values ordinarily associated with these uses and their consequent ability to bid lands away from agriculture.

If our supply of farm and forest lands was definitely limited relative to our demand for their products, we would probably bid farmland values up to the level at which they would not shift to other uses. This situation is not imminent. Until it is, we must rely on other measures if we want to keep our better agricultural lands in their present use.

Several types of public measures can be used. Certain areas may be zoned for agriculture and forestry. Police powers may be used to prescribe minimum standards for subdivision and land development. Contractual arrangements that involve subsidies or the promise of favorable tax treatment may be used to induce farmers and other rural landowners to keep their properties in their present use. The powers of eminent domain, spending, and public ownership may be used to acquire ownership or long-term lease rights to lands that might then be sold to individuals with deed restrictions or be leased or subleased for agricultural and forestry uses.

These measures can be used to establish social priorities in land use—priorities that would take precedence over the rights owners ordinarily have to use their properties pretty much as they wish. It should be noted, however, that these social controls involve a protective or defensive approach.

Legal restrictions and the promise of subsidies or possible tax savings are used to preserve community values and very often to prevent individual owners from shifting their lands to uses which may offer them a higher return.

Other measures of a more positive nature are needed if we are to safeguard the prime agricultural lands near some of our cities. We must recognize that additional lands are needed for nonagricultural uses in these areas and that some lands are bound to shift to these uses. But we should also recognize that these needs can often be channeled to sites regarded as less desirable for agriculture.

Suburban developments often congregate in the better farming areas around our cities. They do so because the suburbanite wants a well-drained location. He frequently wants good soil for his garden, lawn, and flowerbeds. But most of all, he is buying accessibility. He wants access to all-weather roads, schools, water supplies, electric power, and other facilities. He picks the better farming areas because this is where he finds these facilities in greatest abundance. He usually prefers high and rolling sites to level bottom land. But he will not locate at these sites if they do not offer him the access to roads and the other facilities he demands.

If local governments want to keep good farming areas in their present use, they must plan for this end. They must go beyond their use of zoning and other restrictive land-use measures to develop programs that will channel their growing needs for nonagricultural uses to other sites. They must sponsor public works programs that will open up and develop alternative sites—often more desirable building and recreational sites—for urban and suburban uses.

It should be emphasized again that our expanding requirements for the nonagricultural uses of land can have a relatively small impact on our total agricultural potential. But this assumes the orderly development of our land resource base.

Without a certain amount of overall coordination, the suburbanization movement can very easily lead to wasteful and chaotic land-use conditions in many places. It can give birth to the slums of tomorrow and many other undesired developments.

A positive program for better land use calls for the joint use of measures to prevent undesired land-use practices and measures to direct nonagricultural uses to those areas which have the highest social utility for these uses. A program of this type will not just happen. It will come only as the result of careful planning. This process calls for more emphasis on metropolitan and regional area planning. It also requires broad recognition of the social responsibility our various local units of government have for giving guidance and direction to the use we make of our land.

Land and advances in technology.

Here is a terse, cogent survey of new progress in mechanization, fertilization, insecticides, the breeding of animals and plants, and other advances that have a bearing on land and farm production. Technology has two faces, however. By *Orlin J. Scoville*, head, Farming Efficiency Section, Farm Economics Research Division; *Lewis B. Nelson*, head, Eastern Soil and Water Management Section, Soil and Water Conservation Research Division; and *Elco L. Greenshields*, head, Water Utilization Unit, Farm Economics Research Division.

BETTER MACHINES, new chemicals, improved breeding of plants and livestock, and the extension of scientific knowledge can help us meet future needs for products of the land.

They can increase production per acre. They offer possibilities for adjustment among farm products to meet changing market needs and to assure us of abundant, low-cost production in the future.

We report on important innovations as examples of the potential effects of advances in technology. We give some indication as to their effects on production, although many of them are so new that we have only preliminary estimates.

Technology has two faces.

It may serve as a substitute for land. By increasing the amount of a commodity than can be produced on an acre, it may make the classes of land that are less well adapted to the new techniques submarginal for certain uses. Tractors, diskplows, and combines, for example, brought the Great Plains into wheat production and simultaneously caused the virtual abandonment of wheat growing in New England.

Technology also may remove the conditions that had made land submarginal for a certain use. Irrigation, for instance, has brought into crop production thousands of acres of arid lands formerly suited only to grazing.

Technology often is thought of in terms of machines, structures, fertilizers, or other things that require investment of capital. But other technological developments that represent new ideas—ridge-row tillage, for instance—require little additional capital except the modest amounts that went into the research from which the ideas came.

The amount of capital used in agriculture has increased greatly, but new technological developments are creating opportunities for use of even more capital. These developments will make more land available for human use by reducing production costs. They will make land more productive. They will lead to reduced waste in storage or transit.

The main effect of mechanization on output for human use in the past has been the reduction in the number of acres formerly used to grow feed for horses and mules. Because fewer than 3.5 million horses and mules remained on American farms in 1958, there is little further opportunity to increase output for human use by substituting

480

mechanical power for the animal power. The next most significant effect of mechanization has been to increase a worker's productivity. There are fewer workers on farms, but some of the labor saved by technology has been used to increase output. Laborsaving machines and equipment reduce costs. That in turn makes it profitable to till lands that once were submarginal for crops. Mechanization and other technological improvements have made labor more efficient, but the various enterprises have differed in degree of progress. There is room for much progress in the mechanization of tobacco, cotton, fruits and vegetables, forage crops, and most of the livestock enterprises.

Among the improvements in machines that will increase production in the next few years are precision planters for row crops. These tractor planters are designed for accurate placement of seed and fertilizer in one operation. They reduce labor requirements and permit more timely planting. Fertilizer is placed at the right distance from the seed so that crop growth is enhanced and there is less stimulation to weeds than with older methods and equipment.

The new combination "plow-plant" methods and equipment accomplish the preparation of land, seeding, fertilizing, and sometimes weed spraying in one operation. They will reduce costs, lessen soil compaction, and sometimes increase yields through more timely operation.

Equipment and management practices are being developed that will reduce the yield-depressing effect of mulch farming. We have long known that erosion and runoff on row-crop fields can be reduced by planting and tillage practices that keep crop residues on the soil surface. But mulch farming often reduces yields in humid regions. Stalks and stubble tie up plant food; there may be more weeds; soil aeration may be hindered. New improvements include better tillage implements, new fertilizer practices, and an improved

445509°—58——32

knowledge of soil management. Encouraging progress has been made, but much remains to be learned before mulching becomes a standard farm practice.

Harvesting equipment has undergone revolutionary changes, which have brought about increased efficiency and a great reduction in the cost of harvesting. Production has been increased because the acreage that can be profitably used for crops has been extended.

Grain was harvested by hand methods from antiquity to the invention of the McCormick reaper in 1831. The next 50 years brought the development of the binder, the thresher, and the combined thresher-reaper.

We now have the one-man combine. It is used everywhere, and the more expensive and laborious binding-shocking-threshing method is on its way out. The new machines have been adapted to the harvesting of grass and legume seeds, beans, and grain sorghums.

The invention and improvement of harvesting machinery have been major factors in reducing the number of man-hours required to produce a crop of grain. Wheat required about 58 man-hours per acre in 1830. Only 1.8 man-hours are required on the Great Plains today.

Similar advances are being made in machinery for harvesting hay and forage, corn, cotton, sugar beets, and specialized crops like castorbeans and celery. Many of these machines were invented long ago, but they needed evolutionary changes before they became widely accepted. The snapping-roll cornpicker was patented in 1874, but not until the 1930's was it used widely.

The introduction of the picker-sheller and accompanying developments in onfarm drying open a new stage in mechanization of the corn harvest. This new method reduces losses in harvesting and storage by permitting earlier harvest and better control of mold and insect damage in stored grain.

The first cottonpicker was patented in 1850, but even now only about a fourth of the American cotton crop is harvested with machines. Machine picking will continue to expand, and cotton production will continue to adjust itself toward higher yielding areas as a consequence.

Advances in the design of fertilizer spreaders are lowering costs and permitting more efficient use of fertilizers. Machines and fertilizer attachments are available for broadcasting dry fertilizers on the soil surface, placing dry fertilizers precisely at different depths and spacing for all major crops, injecting liquid and gaseous fertilizer into the soil, and mixing fertilizers with irrigation water. Many improvements have been made to give more uniform distribution of a wider range of amounts. One distributor has a range of 10 pounds to 8,500 pounds an acre and will meter accurately all of the common types of dry fertilizers. Machines are being designed to give more accurate placement of the fertilizer in relation to the seed or the plant.

The use of high-speed equipment, along with high-analysis fertilizers, has made obsolete much of the older equipment, which misplaces the fertilizer and causes injury to the crop.

Increases in the power of farm tractors and improved subsoiling equipment have increased the attention given to subsoiling. Mechanization also has contributed to the need for subsoiling in areas in which the use of machinery on moist soils has resulted in the formation of hardpans.

Subsoiling in some places and under certain specific soil conditions has strikingly increased crop production. In the Mississippi Delta, for example, the cost of subsoiling is 3 to 8 dollars an acre, and the yield of cotton has been increased an average of one-half bale an acre on hardpan soils.

Subsoiling has been most effective in places where compacted or hardpan layers occur fairly near the surface. The pans occur in the East and South, mainly in sections where intensive row-crop farming is practiced and where moist soil is subjected to machinery traffic.

Subsoiling is often misused. Sometimes it has no beneficial effects; it may even reduce yields. It is estimated that about 400 thousand acres in the Mississippi Delta are deep tilled each year and that at least half of this deep tilling is not needed. Results from subsoiling on the Great Plains have shown no consistent increases. Results in the West are favorable only sometimes.

NEW EQUIPMENT and techniques have brought about a large expansion of acreage under irrigation and have increased the effectiveness of the distribution and application of water. More efficient motors and pumps have made economically feasible the exploitation of vast underground supplies of water for irrigating field crops. Large increases in irrigation have taken place within the past decade through the use of ground water in central Nebraska, southern Arizona, northeastern Colorado, and rice-growing areas in the Gulf Coastal Plains. One of the significant facts revealed by the 1950 Census of Irrigation was the increased use of ground water in relation to surface-water supplies. Only about 10 percent of the water used for irrigation was from wells in 1940, but a third of the irrigated acreage was supplied with water from wells in 1950. The proportion of irrigation water obtained from ground-water storage has continued to rise since then.

The harnessing of the waters of the Nation's large rivers by multiple-purpose dams has made it possible to place large areas under irrigation. An example is the Columbia Basin project, the central feature of which is the Grand Coulee Dam, which will supply water to more than 500 thousand acres once mainly wheat or grazing land.

The development of lightweight, portable sprinkler-irrigation equipment has brought great changes in irrigation. Many farmers use irrigation pipe and sprinklers made of aluminum.

More than 80 percent of all irrigation in 28 Eastern States is done by portable sprinklers. Except for the furrow irrigation of cotton in the Mississippi Delta and the flooding of rice, most of the rest is done by gated pipe or fixed overhead sprinklers. In 17 Western States and Arkansas, Louisiana, and Florida, only 2.5 percent of irrigation in 1949 was done by sprinklers. Sales of equipment indicate that sprinklers are now used for about 10 percent of the irrigation there.

Sprinkler systems have advantages on new land developed for irrigation, on rolling or rough topography, on crops that require frequent, light irrigation, and in cases where seed germination is difficult.

There is opportunity for further expansion in irrigated acreage and for greater efficiency in the use of water. It has been estimated that with customary irrigation methods, about 125 pounds of seed cotton are produced on an acre for each inch of water actually used by the plant. More than 200 pounds of seed cotton can be produced by judicious use of water at critical growth stages and with good management practices. We are gaining a better understanding of the chemical, physical, and biological interrelationships between soil condition, soil moisture, and the physiology of plant growth. This knowledge will help to develop combinations of farming practices that will give 400 pounds of seed cotton for each acre-inch of water used.

FERTILIZERS AND LIME may have contributed more than any other technological advance to sustained production and efficient use of land. Without fertilizers and lime, intensive farming would no longer be profitable in many areas that are now intensively farmed.

The need for plant foods has been recognized for centuries, but chemical fertilizers have come into use only in the past 100 years. The American fertilizer industry produced a few hundred tons in the 1850's and 22 million tons in 1957.

About 20 percent of the increase in farm output in the United States since 1940 may be attributed to fertilizers. Crop responses from fertilizers generally are greatest in the Southeast, the Middle Atlantic States, the Northeast, and the irrigated areas of the West. Crop responses to fertilizer in the North and Central States tend to diminish from east to west. Only small responses are observed generally under dryland conditions in the Great Plains States.

The use of fertilizer will continue to increase. Only vegetable crops, tobacco, and a few other high-return crops receive anywhere like the most profitable rate of application per acre. Some important crops, such as hay and pasture, receive little fertilizer. Only 10 percent of the acreage of hay and cropland pasture in 1954 was fertilized, compared with 97 percent of the tobacco acreage, 60 percent of the corn acreage, and 68 percent of the acreage in fruit, vegetables, and potatoes.

The use of lime on acid soils is a necessary part of farming programs on most humid-region soils. Liming became a general practice in this country around 1900; 23 million tons were applied in 1957. An estimated 80 million tons of liming materials are needed annually to maintain soil fertility and permit maximum crop yields.

Lack of adequate liming affects crop production and efficient use of fertilizer to a marked extent. Of the soil samples tested by soil-testing laboratories in several Southern States, 54 to 74 percent showed a need for lime. This is particularly serious in that when soils become too acid, stands of legume forage fail, growth of other crops is inhibited, and fertilizer nutrients revert to insoluble forms that the plant cannot use. The increased use of nitrogen fertilizers is increasing soil acidity. It takes about 550 pounds of limestone to neutralize the acids that result from a 500-pound application of ammonium sulfate fertilizer.

Many changes in fertilizer technology have reduced the cost of commercial fertilizers—notably the shift from natural organic sources to synthetic sources of nitrogen.

Natural organic materials used to supply 90 percent of the commercial nitrogen. Now they supply less than 3 percent—a consequence of the discovery of methods of fixing nitrogen from the air through the electric arc and cyanamid processes and later through the union of hydrogen and nitrogen to form ammonia. Large-scale manufacture of ammonia opened the way for low-cost nitrogen materials, such as ammonium nitrate, urea, aqueous nitrogen solutions, and anhydrous ammonia. The only other large sources of commercial nitrogen are the ammonium sulfate produced as a byproduct of the coke and steel industries and the South American deposits of sodium nitrate.

The importance of technological advance in the manufacture of nitrogen is illustrated by the wide concern over the supply of nitrogen fertilizers that developed about 1900. It was estimated at the time that at the current rate of use the reserves of sodium nitrate would be exhausted in 20 to 30 years. Some persons thought that the world would be faced with starvation if that happened, unless economical methods for chemical fixation of atmospheric nitrogen were developed. They were developed within 10 years.

A great advance in the preparation of phosphate fertilizers occurred more than 100 years ago with the manufacture of superphosphate, which still is the most widely used commercial carrier of phosphorus. After scientists proved that mineral phosphates were suitable for making superphosphates, explorations disclosed widespread and almost inexhaustible phosphate deposits, some of the largest of which are in the United States.

Many other advances in the manufacture of phosphate fertilizers contribute to cheap sources of phosphorus. The process for producing triple superphosphate insured a permanent low-cost source of a concentrated superphosphate. Development of processes for the manufacture of fertilizer-grade ammonium phosphates have made possible extensive production of this important material.

Mineral reserves of potash have been discovered and exploited. Improvements have been made in the methods for mining and refining the crude salts of potash. Large salt deposits in the Southwestern States insure a continuing supply of low-cost potash for about 100 years. Processes for reclaiming potassium from sea water show promise.

Considerable progress has been made with mixed fertilizers that contain varying quantities of two or more plant nutrients. Until about 1920, mixed fertilizers involved only dry mixing of individual materials. Changes since then have reduced the cost of mixed fertilizers and have permitted much higher analyses. The costs of transportation, handling, and application have been reduced. The material also is easier to handle and cakes less.

The concentration of primary nutrients in mixed fertilizers before 1925 averaged about 14 percent. The average was more than 28 percent in 1957. An important recent change was the manufacture of fertilizers in granular form, which cakes less in storage and flows from a drill more uniformly than a powder.

ANOTHER IMPORTANT capital resource that can substitute so to speak for some land to meet production needs is the rapidly expanding group of chemical weedkillers and insecticides. Farmers in 1957 spent 231 million dollars for agricultural chemicals other than fertilizer.

Weeds cause losses on American farms that are estimated to run to 5 billion dollars annually. Weeds compete with crops for water, nutrients, and light. They increase the cost of labor and equipment and reduce the quality of farm products.

A ragweed plant is said to need three times more water than a corn plant. One plant of common mustard takes twice as much nitrogen and phosphorus and four times as much potassium and water as an oat plant. Weeds also add to costs of tillage and seed cleaning, give milk off-flavors, reduce the quality of grains, and make harvesting difficult.

Big steps in the development of the control of weeds by chemicals include the discovery of selective herbicides about 1900, the discovery in 1944 that 2,4-D kills some weeds but not grasses, the development of low-volume application techniques, and the development in 1947 of ways to apply weed-killers before the seedlings are above the surface.

More than 100 chemicals that kill weeds have been developed since 1940. Herbicides have been applied on more than 30 million acres of cultivated cropland. Around 12 percent of the planted acreage of the principal small-grain crops and 11 percent of the acreage of field corn were sprayed one or more times in 1952, and about 2 million acres of pastureland and 2.6 million acres of other cropland and noncropland received treatment.

New types of sprayers have been developed. Equipment to spray herbicides from airplanes was first used in 1947; by 1956 more than 6 million acres of cropland were so sprayed.

Herbicides are efficient and economical, but their use requires care and precision. We do not yet have a chemical for use on crops that will kill all weeds without injury to crops. Chemicals cannot fully replace other methods of control.

As the control of weeds with chemicals becomes even more effective and cheaper, new opportunities to increase acre yields and reduce costs will arise. If we could eliminate all cultivation by using chemicals, for example, closer spacings of plants might be feasible if plant nutrients and water supplies are adequate.

We still have several serious weed problems.

Witchweed, a parasitic weed on corn, sorghum, and sugarcane, is entrenched in North Carolina and South Carolina. If it becomes widespread, it will be a tremendous threat, as heavy infestations destroy the host crops.

Dodder, another parasitic weed, is becoming increasingly serious in alfalfa and lespedeza seed crops. It reduces yield, lowers the quality of the seed, and interferes with harvesting.

Although 2,4-D is effective in controlling weeds in small grains, it kills the legumes seeded in the small grains. Annual weedy grasses in rice are not now subject to control. Some of these troublesome weed problems may be solved as weedkillers are improved.

Infestations of nematodes affect crop production in many sections. The numbers of these tiny worms increase under systems of intensive cultivation. Farmers just a few years ago were nearly helpless when nematodes were in their fields. Improved crop rotations, maintenance of soil fertility, and soil fumigation have done much to control serious infestations.

Several chemicals have been produced to kill nematodes. Dichloropropane and ethylene dibromide have been used for a number of years, and more recently 1,2-dibromo-3-chloropropane has been introduced. These are effective and are used widely on high-valued crops such as tobacco, vegetables, and pineapples. They are too costly for many crops.

Outstanding advances have been made in insecticides and ways to apply them.

A generation since, grasshoppers could be controlled somewhat by applying 20 pounds of poison bait on an acre. Two men could cover perhaps 150 acres in a day. Now a thousand acres can be sprayed with chlorinated hydrocarbons in a few minutes from an airplane, and better protection is provided. Ground and aerial equipment for applying chemicals are being improved to give more thorough treatment with smaller amounts of insect killers.

The value of chemical insecticides

applied to cotton has been demonstrated by experiments at Tallulah, La., and Waco, Tex. The insecticides increased the yield of seed cotton at Tallulah by an average of 25 percent over a 34-year period. The average increase at Waco was almost 40 percent for 16 years. Inorganic chemicals, such as the arsenicals, were relied upon for insect control before 1945. Organic chemicals (particularly the chlorinated hydrocarbons, such as toxaphene and benzene hexachloride, and organic phosphates, such as parathion) became available after 1945. In the experiment at Waco, the average increase in yield from insecticides was 33 percent through 1945 but nearly 53 percent from 1946 to 1954—an indication of their increased effectiveness.

But it is not so simple as it might seem. As growers strive for greater and more efficient production of cotton, insect problems often become more acute. When cotton is grown under irrigation and large amounts of fertilizer are applied, the larger plants and the longer growing and fruiting periods that result favor a buildup of boll weevils and other pests. The wise use of insecticides throughout the growing period is essential to obtain the extra yield that such practices will provide.

Encouraging progress has been had in the discovery of natural enemies of insect pests, such as the corn borer parasite, Lydella; and diseases, such as the milky spore disease of Japanese beetles.

The development of wheats resistant to the hessian fly has prevented losses formerly caused by this pest. Corn varieties resistant to the European corn borer offer promise of reducing the losses it causes.

Efforts to achieve better control of insects are a continuous struggle to cope with newly introduced pests or strains of insects that have become resistant to standard chemicals. The arrival and establishment of the spotted alfalfa aphid, a new pest of alfalfa, cost alfalfa growers an estimated loss of 42 million dollars in 1956. The ap-

pearance in some areas of strains of the boll weevil that are resistant to the chlorinated hydrocarbons has made necessary an intensive search for suitable substitute insecticides.

The value of the crops lost to insects runs into billions of dollars each year. Even moderate improvements in ways to control pests would add a lot to agricultural production and income.

Chemicals have become more and more important in the control of the insects, mites, and ticks that attack domestic animals and that have reduced the total income from livestock products by at least 5 percent—about 800 million dollars—each year.

Control methods involving the use of chemical insecticides for cattle grubs, lice, screwworms, and mangemites have been developed to a point at which most animals can be kept free from attack. Otherwise it would be difficult to maintain profitable livestock enterprises in some sections.

The control of livestock pests reduces death loss, improves animal health, and increases the efficiency with which feed is converted into animal products. As a result, fewer acres are needed to produce feed needed for a given number of pounds of meat, milk, or wool.

Many technical improvements are being made in storage and processing facilities for use on and off the farm. About 119 million bushels of stored cereal were ruined by insects in this country in 1952. As much as 10 percent of the stored wheat in the Great Plains may be destroyed in a season. Insect damage to corn stored in the South under farm conditions may be 9 percent a month in bad seasons.

The number of farm crop driers has been going up rapidly, but relatively few farmers have adequate equipment for conditioning, drying, and storing grain and hay.

Proper equipment can reduce storage losses. Proper drying and cooling can cut the losses from spoilage brought about by heat and dampness and losses from molds and insect infestations.

It may be possible to use radiation

to reduce storage losses of agricultural products by exposure to the rays emitted by X-ray, by fissionable materials, or by accelerated electron streams. The shelf life of meat products can be increased by radiation. Radiation also inhibits the sprouting of potatoes and so prolongs the time they can be stored. Much research remains to be done with respect to the radiation of stored foods to find cheaper processes and to determine the effects on flavor and quality, but the process may eventually permit substantial reduction in spoilage.

Experimental work has been done on the use of antibiotics on stored food products to reduce spoilage, enhance quality, and extend shelf life. Promising results have been obtained with some of the tetracycline compounds and a few other antibiotics in experiments conducted with fish, meats, milk, and eggs.

Chemicals are used also to modify the growth and development of plants. Some of these compounds are plant hormones. They affect plants in many ways. Some stimulate the rooting of cuttings. Root-inducing chemicals are widely used by commercial plantsmen. Two products in common use are indolebutyric acid and naphthaleneacetamide.

Other hormones retard the dropping of fruit at harvest. Naphthaleneacetic acid was first used in 1939 and continues to be used by many apple growers. A newer compound is 2–4–TP.

Caustic chemicals, such as the dinitros, are used under close supervision in western apple orchards to reduce the set of fruit. Growth-regulator types of chemicals are preferred in the East.

Growth regulators can be used to increase the size of fruit and advance the date of flowering of tomatoes, blackberries, strawberries, peaches, apricots, and some other crops.

Japanese scientists discovered more than 20 years ago that a plant hormone, gibberellic acid, was responsible for producing abnormally tall rice plants. These plants lodged, and yields were reduced. The growth-stimulating hormone was produced by the fungus, gibberella. Gibberellic acid has been used in experiments to double or triple the height of many varieties of vegetables, flowers, shrubs, and trees.

Experiments have revealed several kinds of growth response to gibberellic acid, including an increased rate of growth and size of fruit, production of bushier plants through development of lateral vegetative buds, counteraction of genetic dwarfism, shortened rest periods or reduced cold requirements of the biennial and perennial plants, altered date of flowering, changed leaf area, increased length and size of petioles, improved seed germination, less root growth, and stimulation to offset the effects of a virus disease.

Many biochemists and plant scientists are studying gibberellic acid to see if these experimental results can be put to practical use and if the chemical can be produced more cheaply. It is now produced by fermentation methods.

It was discovered in 1950 that one group of the quaternary ammonium chemicals could be used to reduce plant size and in some instances extend the life of annual plants. The life of bean plants in experiments has been extended by 30 to 40 days by use of one of these chemicals, whose full name is (4-hydroxy-5-isopropyl-2-methylphenyl) tremethylammonium chloride, 1-piperidine carboxylate. This compound is known as AMO–1618.

IMPROVED VARIETIES of crops maintain or raise yields in some areas and may enhance quality. A new variety usually does not result in striking increases in yields, although at the time of its introduction it may be superior to the varieties it replaces. This is because new disease strains in epidemic proportions may attack a variety that has been grown for a number of years; the new variety may be disease resistant, but it may have only a slightly higher yield potential than the old variety when the disease is not present.

Improved varieties cost the farmer

little extra. The increased cost of seed is a minor part of the cost of production, and the difference in cost of production between improved and standard varieties is negligible.

Hybrid corn has become the usual example of varietal improvement. It began with theoretical research, which led to the first crossing of inbred lines by detasseling at the Connecticut Agricultural Experiment Station in 1916.

The first commercial hybrid seed was produced in 1923. One percent of the acreage of corn in the Corn Belt was planted to hybrid seed corn in 1933. More than 99 percent of the acreage of the Corn Belt and 92 percent of the Nation's corn acreage were planted with hybrid seed in 1957.

S. C. Salmon, O. R. Mathews, and R. W. Leukel, of the Department of Agriculture, in their review, "A Half Century of Wheat Improvement in the United States," reported that most wheat varieties grown before 1900 have disappeared. Between 1900 and 1950, 284 new varieties were developed and grown on farms. The newer varieties have resulted in substantial increases in yield. At the same time, quality has been improved, losses from shattering and lodging have been reduced, and production has been stabilized by reducing losses from winterkilling, diseases, and insect pests.

Plant breeders believe that future progress will equal or exceed the progress already achieved. Atomic energy is being used to speed up the production of mutations through irradiation. These mutants increase the chances of finding plants with desirable characteristics for crossing to produce new varieties.

Diseases threatened the Nation's oats crop three times in 1938–1958. New varieties have been developed that resist the diseases and are of higher quality and better yield.

Crown rust and smut attacked the susceptible Kherson and other varieties in 1941 and 1943, and new Victoria strains were introduced. Victoria blight struck, and the Victoria strains were

forced out of production by 1947. Plant breeders were ready by that time with the Bond strains, which were resistant to the blight and to many races of crown rust. Bond strains were attacked by race 7 of stem rust and by race 202 and other races of crown rust in 1957, and new disease-resistant strains of oats again were introduced.

Hybrid varieties of grain sorghums have been available since 1952, when a type of male sterility was discovered that made it feasible to breed hybrids. Up to that time, development of sorghum hybrids was not commercially practicable because on sorghum, unlike corn, stamens and pistils occur in the same flower. With corn, cross-fertilization to produce a hybrid can be forced by growing two varieties in the same field and detasseling one of them.

Individual plants of the Day variety of Milo sorghum in which the stamens were sterile because they lacked pollen were found in 1954. This type of sterility was bred into several sorghum varieties to provide female plants that could be cross-fertilized by other varieties to produce desirable hybrids. Hybrid sorghums may become as important to sorghum growers as hybrid corn has been to growers of corn.

Male-sterile plants have also been discovered in other species. They open the way for better varieties of sugar beets and onions, among others.

A promising start has been made on breeding resistance to diseases and pests into plants. An early achievement was the development of Pawnee wheat, which is resistant to loose smut and is widely grown in the winter-wheat areas of the Great Plains. The Indiana Agricultural Experiment Station has produced Dual, a soft-red winter wheat that has resistance to hessian flies and to leaf rust. The same station has also produced La Porte wheat, which is adapted to northern Indiana and is resistant to loose smut.

A few years ago, race 15 B of stem rust became a serious pest in Durum wheat areas of North Dakota and Minnesota. Since 1950, five moderately resistant or highly resistant wheats have been bred. They have virtually replaced all the former varieties in areas affected by this race of stem rust. These varieties are Langdon, Towner, Yuma, Ramsey, and Sentry. Research goes on, and new varieties with even more resistance are on the way.

SEVERAL IMPROVED management practices for crops and livestock could substantially increase production if they were fully adopted. Frequently these practices come in bundles, and the productivity of any one is influenced by the adoption of other complementary practices.

In the South, for example, sod seeding is a pasture-building practice that helps to control soil erosion and provides offseason grazing crops on permanent sod. Cereal grains also can be drilled into sod. Wheat and oats drilled into a Bermudagrass-Dallisgrass pasture sod in Mississippi in late November have yielded 35 and 55 bushels, respectively. The sod was in good condition for grazing after the cereals were harvested.

Other pasture-management practices that may increase yields per acre include rotation grazing, the cutting and feeding of pasture forage (sometimes called soilage or zero pasturing), improvements in pasture mixtures, and the use of fertilizer and lime. With ordinary management, pastures produce less than half the feed that is usually obtained from the same acreage in feed grains. But with equally good management, pasture production often is almost as large per acre as is obtainable from grains.

Soil-testing programs in various States have contributed materially toward more efficient use of fertilizer and lime. Improvements are being made that permit rapid and fairly accurate diagnosis of deficiencies of plant nutrients in soils, as well as the determination of the approximate amounts of fertilizers and lime required to correct the deficiencies.

There are more than 600 publicly supported soil-testing laboratories in the United States, and more than a million samples are analyzed each year.

One technique may make improvements in other practices possible. Along with improved methods of irrigation has come the adoption of a number of practices—the use of fertilizer, plant spacing, chemical weed control, and use of improved varieties and hybrids, among others.

Much can be done to improve the efficiency of use of irrigation water on crops through better understanding of timing and rates of application.

Irrigation gives best results when it is integrated with other cultural practices. An example comes from tests on corn in Georgia. Three rates of nitrogen application and three different plant spacings were used on irrigated and unirrigated plots. On the nonirrigated plots, closer spacing and the use of more nitrogen increased the yield of corn 27 bushels an acre. With irrigation, the yields were increased 58 bushels an acre. Irrigation showed the greatest response in yield increases with the closest spacing and highest rate of nitrogen application.

Irrigation tests were carried out with and without nematode treatment on cotton, corn, flue-cured tobacco, and sweetpotatoes in South Carolina. On the nonirrigated plots, nematode treatment showed significant results for all four crops. On the irrigated plots, nematode treatment improved yields only slightly for corn and sweetpotatoes but quite substantially for cotton and tobacco. The yield of irrigated cotton with nematode treatment was 318 pounds of seed cotton an acre higher than without such treatment. The yield of irrigated flue-cured tobacco with nematode treatment exceeded the yield without treatment by 735 pounds an acre.

A study in Montana showed that a vigorously growing crop greatly increased the effectiveness of 2,4-D in controlling Canada thistle. Thistles were almost eliminated in 3 years by the use of 2,4-D in spring wheat that had received nitrogen fertilizer. Crop income increased from 61 to 172 dollars an acre when compared with wheat grown each year without weed-control treatments.

CONSERVATION STRUCTURES and devices have become an important means of stretching our supply of land. With most of them it is very important that a suitable bundle of practices be used and that they be applied in the proper sequence. The soil conservation district has been an effective means of advancing conservation.

There were more than 2,700 soil conservation districts in the United States and Territories in 1958. They covered more than 1.5 billion acres—about 87 percent of our farmland and 91 percent of our farms and ranches. About 1.75 million farmers and ranchers were district cooperators, and 125 thousand more become cooperators each year. More than 1 million of them had basic conservation plans to cover their land.

Each of these plans outlines a program of soil treatment and land management that will promote sustained production and highest long-run income. In addition to its direct value to the farmer, each plan is a reference for extension workers, bankers, and others whom the farmer may ask for assistance. It is a guide to the Agricultural Conservation Program with respect to the needs of that particular farm.

We foresee a continued acceleration in conservation activities. Two million cooperators are expected to have 1.5 million basic conservation plans in operation by 1960. Very likely they will have applied to their lands two-thirds of the practices they have planned.

Conservation practices are improving steadily. Parallel terracing systems have been introduced to eliminate bothersome point rows. Terrace spacings are being widened to reduce cost and permit easier use of modern farm machinery. Leveling of land is proving advantageous on many fields for facilitating surface drainage and irrigation,

permitting use of parallel terraces on sloping fields, and removing depressions and rough spots that interfere with the use of farm machinery.

IMPROVEMENTS in breeding, feeding, and managing livestock have increased the efficiency of feed utilization. Further improvement is possible. A saving in feed releases land for other uses.

The average feed consumption per pound of broiler produced has dropped from 4.25 pounds in 1940 to less than 3 pounds today. In experiments, broilers have been produced on less than 2 pounds of feed per pound of broiler, live weight. This gain has resulted from improvements in breeding, feeding, sanitation, and management.

Experiments show that the use of stilbestrol, a hormone, in rations for fattening beef cattle will reduce the feed required per pound of gain by 10 to 15 percent. The addition of antibiotics to the rations of young pigs may increase the growth rate from 10 to 20 percent, and increase feed conversion efficiency as much as 5 percent. Antibiotics are also of value in the rations of young dairy calves.

Urea, a synthetic nitrogenous compound, can be used to supplement feeds produced from the land. Added to the rations of ruminants, it becomes a source of food for the micro-organisms in the rumen. The bodies of the micro-organisms in turn provide protein for the animal. One pound of urea plus 6 pounds of grain will replace about 7 pounds of oil meal in the rations of cows, sheep, or goats. Urea can also be used to improve the feeding value of low-quality roughages. Urea is toxic in large quantities. Not more than a third of the total nitrogen in the diet should be supplied by urea. The quantity fed must be controlled carefully and mixed thoroughly with the ration. Most of it is fed in ready-mixed formula feeds. In 1957, 87 thousand tons of urea were fed, permitting the replacement of almost 610 thousand tons of oil meal as a source of protein.

It is evident that most of the technological improvements that we have discussed will increase the acre yields of crops and the yields of meat, eggs, and milk.

For such improvements as fertilizer, irrigation, pest control, and improved animal nutrition, the effects are immediate. Others have a long-run effect and may even reduce production for a year or so.

Benefits to crop production from soil and water conservation practices usually are more long-time than immediate in nature. Yield increases from terraces may be small or lacking at first and gradually increase over time, or their principal benefit may be to prevent the continued decline in yields because of erosion. The conservation practices that may benefit yields immediately include the use of cover crops, practices that increase infiltration of water into the soil or remove excess water, and development of on-the-farm supplies of water for irrigation.

How MUCH MORE can we expect technology to increase yields? There must be some physical limit to production from an acre of land. In a study by the Department of Agriculture, estimates of economic maximum yields that might be reached by 1975 have been prepared. These estimates assume the full, efficient utilization of all presently known technological advances under conditions of cost and income that would encourage higher agricultural production. It is assumed that there are no limitations of management, materials, equipment, or capital.

We give the economic maximum yields for the United States and the reported yields for 1956 on a harvested-acre basis: Grain sorghum, 28 and 22 bushels; wheat, 24 and 20 bushels; soybeans for beans, 30 and 22 bushels; corn, 67 and 45 bushels; potatoes, 460 and 292 bushels; cotton lint, 616 and 408 pounds; hay, 2 and 1.5 tons.

These economic maximum yields are far below the maximum yields that are physically possible. Some outstanding yield records that have been reported include 63.6 bushels of soybeans an acre in 1954 from a 5-acre field entered in the Indiana soybean yield contest; a corn yield of 304 bushels on a measured acre in 1955 near Baldwin, Miss.; 1,156 bushels of potatoes from an acre near Stockton, Calif., in 1933; and 117 bushels of wheat an acre from an 18-acre field in Island County, Wash., in 1895.

Reductions in harvesting and storage losses and improvements in livestock feed-conversion efficiency have the same effect on total output for human use as an increase in yield. There are many opportunities for improvement here.

Some improved technologies do not increase production and may actually reduce it, but they may be worth adopting because they reduce costs. Summer fallow is an example in areas where it does not at least double yields per seeded acre. In other words, the yield per acre used for wheat and fallow is reduced. But to be economically feasible, fallow must give a sufficient increase to result in a lower cost per bushel. In these areas, where summer fallow will pay even though it does not double the yield per seeded acre, it is the reverse of what we have talked of earlier. It can be thought of as a practice that substitutes land for capital.

It may be possible in some instances to reduce the cost of field operations with row crops by altering the width of rows and the spacing of plants in the row. This would reduce the amount of machine time and travel per acre. It would be economical to the extent that the value of production per acre was not reduced by as much as this saving in cost. More research needs to be done on optimum plant spacings with particular reference to effect on yields and costs of production.

The most important possibility for reducing production per acre in a short period lies in a major shift in land use from crop farming to grass or trees. In a typical Corn Belt area, it is estimated that an acre in corn produces about twice as much feed as the same acre would produce in pasture as usually managed. A shift from corn to grass would encourage production of more beef and less pork, giving a further reduction in output per acre because it takes more feed to produce a pound of beef than a pound of pork. An acre of cropland in pasture under average management would produce about one-fifth as many pounds of beef as could be produced in pork and lard from an acre of corn fed to hogs. But technological improvements have encouraged farmers to keep less land in hay and pasture and more in cultivated crops. Mechanization has reduced labor requirements for many cultivated crops relative to production and feeding of hay and forage. And the production of abundant, low-cost inorganic nitrogen has reduced farmers' dependence on green manures.

IMPROVEMENT in methods and equipment for growing and handling pastures and hay would improve the competitive position of these crops. In themselves, however, they would not greatly alter the pattern of land use. Wider adoption of improved varieties of grasses and forage crops and better management practices also would be needed. These improvements could substantially increase feed production per acre in hay and pasture. The feed production from the land shifted from feed grains to grass might still be reduced on the average, but as the productivity of existing grasslands would be increased also, the net effect probably would be an increase in output over a period of years.

Taking into account the accompanying shift from grain-consuming to forage-consuming classes of livestock, however, the net effect on food production could well be downward, at least in the short run. A shift toward grassland farming would have long-run effects of conserving soils and increasing long-run potential production.

The extent that conversion of cropland to production of forest products would affect production of food and fiber crops would depend upon the quality of the land reforested. Most of the cropland that has gone into forest production up to now has been of low productivity for crops.

Shifts in land use can be encouraged by finding out ways to lower the cost of grassland or of tree farming and by having the kinds of cost-sharing and price-support programs that will make land-use adjustments profitable to farmers.

There are only moderate possibilities of using improved practices to reduce short-run production, but these practices will facilitate the adjustments that are needed in agriculture and will help substantially to increase our long-run production potential.

These practices include terracing where it is needed, retirement from cropping of areas subject to gullying or severe sheet erosion, resting land to leach out alkalies, fallowing for noxious weed control, and a few others.

Technological progress has increased output on balance. We need some new techniques that will greatly increase the profitability of farming land more extensively. Practices that would make pasture or woods more profitable than crops on some of the land now in cultivation would tend to reduce production, at least in the short run. Most technological improvements have had the opposite effect. Only a few encourage more extensive farming, but these should be utilized in production-adjustment programs, and other "extensifying" techniques should be sought.

As LONG AS WE continue to promote technological progress through research, we can look forward with reasonable expectation to meeting future needs for agricultural products. It may be that in order to be always sure of enough, we cannot avoid intermittent periods of short-run surplus. This is not too great a price to pay for assurance that we will not go hungry, but we should use research to achieve production that is both abundant and adjusted to our needs.

Cities, transportation, and technology.

Expressways, a new development in transportation—which is a basis of cities and technology—have meant new urban growth. There has not been an equal expansion of the horizons of social and political organization to plan systematically for the new conditions. By *Harold M. Mayer*, professor, Department of Geography, the University of Chicago.

TWO DEVELOPMENTS of human culture have been outstanding during the past century: The rapid advance of technology and the growth and spread of cities. Neither would have been possible without the other. Together they have made a revolution in the organization and pattern of land use. Transportation is a basis of both.

About 4 percent of the United States population was urban in 1790. Now about 70 percent of the population lives in metropolitan areas and other urban places, and the proportion is increasing rapidly. There also has been a substantial growth of rural nonfarm population, which depends on urban areas for employment or on the passing highway traffic from the cities.

The growth of cities has accounted for most of the increase in the population during the 20th century, while the farm population has declined.

Agricultural areas, because of improvements in farming, have furnished a substantial portion of the inmigrant population, which, added to the high net reproduction rate in cities, has been responsible for much of the increase in urban population.

The largest metropolitan areas have been growing, in general, at a faster rate than smaller cities.

The location of the areas of most rapid population growth has shifted significantly since about 1920 with respect to their situations within the metropolitan areas. Until about four decades ago the cities were being subjected to increasing populations at ever higher densities, but since the end of the First World War the maximum rates of growth generally have been outside of the central cities of metropolitan areas. Suburban communities and unincorporated areas have grown much faster than the central municipalities in recent years. Metropolitan areas in many instances have had substantial increases in population but actually have shown declines in the populations of their principal or central cities.

Part of the reason is that municipal boundaries rarely coincide with the limits of the built-up urban areas.

Cities once could rather easily annex nearby areas that became urbanized. Extensive areas could be annexed in advance of the spread of urban development. The formation of many small incorporated municipalities next to the central cities more recently has made annexation difficult or impossible. These small cities, towns, and villages have developed local governments and vested interests in their perpetuation. Many people move to the suburbs with the expectation of being able to have a more personal and intimate relation to their local affairs, and subsequent merger with the big city is therefore almost invariably resisted.

The average population density of most cities has dropped sharply in recent years. This reflects a demand for land that is increasing at a much

493

faster rate than even the spectacular rate of increase of urban and metropolitan population. Ranchhouses or ramblers have become popular and 60- and 80-foot lots are replacing 30- and 40-foot lots. Single-story industrial plants, with extensive areas for parking and with substantial setbacks from the highways and access streets, are replacing the multiple-story industrial and loft buildings of the congested central parts of cities. The modern planned outlying shopping center includes at least three or four times as much area for automobile parking as it does floor area of selling space.

THE INCREASING demand for land for urban uses has been met by an accelerating expansion of cities into the rural areas.

It has recently been estimated that urban areas in the United States occupy slightly more than 18 million acres—a little less than 5 percent as much as the total land area occupied by railroads and highways. The urban land area is about 1 percent of the total land area of the United States.

The outlook is for a faster rate of conversion of agricultural land into nonfarming use, particularly for urban expansion. Many of the metropolitan areas may be expected to double the amount of area they will occupy within the next two or three decades.

Much of the land they will occupy is cropland that is used for intensive production of specialty crops and has a higher value per acre than the average value of all agricultural land. These croplands, being devoted to intensive cultivation of specialized crops, are characterized by small farms. Thus they have a population much denser than the average for all agricultural areas.

Certain important areas of specialty crops, such as the truck-farming areas of New Jersey, the citrus areas of southern California, and perhaps the fruit belt of southwestern Michigan, may be expected to be invaded by the urbanization from nearby large cities.

While the total loss of cropland may not represent an actual net loss of agricultural production nationally, the loss of specialty crops, involving conversion to nonagricultural use of some of the best land for such crops, could well become significant.

MOST CITIES exist primarily to satisfy economic needs. Growth of population occurs in response to economic opportunities. People live where they can earn a living. Since economic opportunities are greatest in number and variety in the larger metropolitan areas, it is those areas which have been experiencing the fastest growth. Great concentrations of economic opportunity depend on concentrations of labor force, which in turn produces additional incentive for population growth. Thus the metropolis expands.

Urban and metropolitan concentrations could not exist were it not for transportation facilities. Many of the outstanding technological advances have been in transportation, which affects the size, functions, structure, and growth of cities and metropolitan areas.

Functional specialization of areas—the differentiation of one land use from another—is made possible by the availability of facilities for the movement of goods and people between those areas.

Cities produce manufactured goods and perform certain services which are "exported" to other areas, in return for the goods and payments that are brought into the urban areas from other urban areas and from the countrysides.

The interconnections between cities and between individual cities and their respective service areas or hinterlands—as well as the interconnections among the various functionally specialized parts of city and metropolitan area—depend on efficient systems of transportation.

Streets alone in most cities account for 25 to 35 percent of the total built-up urban area. The building and maintenance of facilities for internal circulation, including streets, constitute a sizable part of the budgets of all cities.

Most urban street patterns have been inherited from the past and are inadequate for the needs of modern traffic. The obsolete patterns have been extended to newly developed areas on the outskirts of cities.

While street traffic faces delays because of insufficient numbers and capacities of arterial routes, an excessive proportion of the areas of most cities paradoxically is devoted to local access streets.

The largest parcels of land devoted to a single urban use and under single control in most cities are the airports, which may cover several square miles and influence land uses far beyond their own boundaries.

The construction, maintenance, and operation of transportation facilities and equipment directly contribute substantially to the employment base of urban areas. More than 20 million Americans are employed in public and private transportation. Automobiles and trucks account for a large proportion of this employment—nearly one-third of the total employment in the Nation.

A study by the Port of New York Authority indicated that about one in every four jobs in Greater New York is attributable directly or indirectly to the port function, which represents only a part of the multiplicity of basic transportation functions performed by the New York metropolitan area.

The effects of the transportation industries are felt through the entire economy, because transportation uses vast amounts of materials and equipment, the manufacturing and supplying of which create other millions of jobs.

The automobile industry used 22 percent and the railroads 11 percent of the steel produced in the United States in 1957, a typical year. Large tonnages of steel also were used in building highways and ships. Most of the oil and rubber and a major share of the coal used in this country are used in transportation.

THE RAPID CHANGES in transportation are reflected in the changes in the growth and structure of cities: Each major innovation in intercity and local transportation has been followed by significant changes in urban areas.

The uses of urban land are related closely to their "circulatory" systems. The relationship is reciprocal. Land uses—other than such uses as agriculture, forestry, and mining, which depend on primary production on the site—are where they are largely because of differences in the availability of transportation from place to place. On the other hand, land uses (individually and in combination) generate varying amounts of movement of goods and people that in turn make it necessary to provide varying amounts and kinds of transportation.

Each type of nonagricultural use of land has a different set of requirements as to location. For some—as, for example, the bulk-receiving industries that use raw materials in shipload amounts and therefore need locations along navigable waterways—the choice of location is narrow and rather inflexible. A much greater variety of locations is suitable for other uses, such as one-family homes.

TRANSPORTATION in one sense is a substitute for nearness. Other things being equal, the best locations for interrelated activities are close together in order to reduce the amount, and hence the cost, of the transportation of goods and people.

Transportation costs—whether measured in money, time, or distance—are incurred because it is physically impossible and sometimes undesirable to place the activities and uses of land in the best locations for each because other activities and uses that require similar sites bring competitive pressures.

The increasing size and complexity of cities widens even more the separation of the urban functions and increases the amount of transportation that is needed. Separation of places of work from places of residence gives rise to the daily journeys to work, which are responsible for half of the total number of trips made in metropolitan areas.

The competition among all urban functions and land uses that could operate most effectively near each other engenders a high demand for centrally located sites. The demand drives up the values of such sites. Not all urban land uses or functions can afford central sites. Indeed, some functions can better be carried on at some distance from the urban centers if adequate transportation is available. Thus, in the normal operation of the real-estate market, urban land uses are sorted out in accordance with their relative ability to pay high costs for sites that are most desirable because of proximity to other uses or because of the accessibility provided by the convergence of local transportation in the central parts of cities.

For any given type of use, a balance exists between the costs of competitive sites and the costs of overcoming the friction of distance. The uses that depend on maximum accessibility can afford the high costs of central locations. The others select locations at varying distances from the points of maximum accessibility in accordance with their ability to pay site costs. Transportation in most instances is the factor that makes possible the concentrations of land values, because it converges and produces maximum accessibility at the urban core.

The forces that affect the patterns of land uses in urban areas may be described as centrifugal, or outward, and centripetal, or inward. The resultant of these forces is reflected in the degree of decentralization or deconcentration of any individual land use or groups of land uses in urban areas.

When the centripetal forces are stronger, the city develops with heavier concentrations at higher densities.

When centrifugal forces are stronger, the average densities are lower. The relative importance of the forces varies for each type of urban land use and for each establishment, whether industrial, commercial, residential, or institutional.

The development of improved transportation generally has strengthened the centrifugal forces by making greater and more extensive areas around cities accessible for urban expansion. On the other hand, however, transportation has increased the numbers and the strength of "linkages" among establishments and so has created a demand for increasing concentrations of business activity in the larger cities, especially in the central parts, where face-to-face contacts are maximized.

The central business district is still the major core of most American cities. While certain functions—for example, retailing, which has in part expanded into outlying shopping centers—have been moving out, such functions as administrative offices and specialized professional and entertainment services have continued to concentrate in the cores of the large cities.

Manhattan has had a spectacular boom in office buildings since the war, and many large office buildings have been constructed in the downtown districts of other cities. At the same time, retail trade has suffered a relative decline in most downtown areas. Manufacturing, which was a major activity on the fringes of most central business districts, generally tends now to locate farther out, because the relative freedom from congestion and the availability of large parcels of land very largely outweigh the advantages of central location with respect to the metropolitan area.

THE INVENTION of the steel frame building, which make skyscrapers feasible, the development of the electric elevator and escalator, the improvement of power generation and transmission, and the development of electric communication, including the telegraph, telephone, and facsimile reproduction—besides developments in transportation—have made these concentrations possible.

Also significant among the technological advances are those in the field of public health, which have made it possible for huge concentrations of population to exist without unduly endangering health. Medical facilities, including the greatest variety of specialists and specialized services, are for the most part concentrated in the largest cities. Great medical centers in New York, Chicago, Baltimore, and other cities are famous. Very few small cities—Rochester, Minn., is a notable exception—can offer extensive specialized medical services.

Vast and elaborate systems of water supply and of sewerage collection, treatment, and disposal have been developed to assure healthful urban living conditions. Sanitary and safe water can be assured in large cities, where the controls over quality are rigid and constant.

Advances in the transportation, processing, and storage of foods have made it possible to sustain large urban concentrations, just as advances in farming methods have released large numbers of workers from food-producing activities and made them available for activities performed in cities.

Large-scale processing and packaging of food products, as well as mechanical refrigeration, freezing, and cold storage, are indispensable to the modern city. These operations employ a large labor force and are major elements in the economic base of many cities.

Large grocery distribution warehouses are characteristic of many large cities. On the other hand, many food-processing activities, such as canning and freezing, are characteristically located in smaller communities, nearer to the producing areas.

THE CONCENTRATION of people in cities, the rapidly increasing number
445509°—58——33

and complexity of urban functions, and the resulting competition for space have brought about an ever-increasing separation between places of employment and places of residence.

In the medieval city, manufacturing, commerce, and residence were usually on the same parcel of land or in the same structure. The craftsman produced and sold his goods and lived with his family in one building. With the Industrial Revolution, these functions had to separate because of the development of the factories, which formed nodes or nuclei in the urban pattern, and of markets, which later became the central business districts.

Thus the modern city has many nuclei: The central business district, which generally has the heaviest concentration of employment, industrial areas, and outlying commercial developments, which have other concentrations of basic economic activities.

The increasing complexity of the land use and functional patterns of cities has attracted the attention of many economists and sociologists, who have tried to make generalized descriptions that would fit most cities.

Ernest W. Burgess developed the concentric zonal hypothesis, based upon the work of J. H. von Thünen, a German economist, in the early 19th century.

Burgess described the city as consisting roughly of concentric zones. The central business district is the nucleus. The land uses in each successive zone outward from the core are sorted out in order of their relative ability to benefit from (and pay the costs of) proximity to the center. As a city grows, land uses and people successively "invade" each zone outward from the center. This creates a succession of land uses in each zone, and each succeeding group of uses is developed at higher density as a result of increasing competition for centrally located land.

Homer Hoyt, then of the Federal Housing Administration, later propounded the wedge, or sector, theory.

It describes the process of urban growth and expansion in terms of differentiation of land uses and functions along wedges radiating out from the central core. The general character of the uses along each radial or wedge is similar in nature from the core to periphery.

Chauncy D. Harris, of the University of Chicago, and Edward L. Ullman, of the University of Washington, described the city as a series of nuclei—generally concentrations of employment. The various urban land uses are located with relation to relative proximity to each of the multiple nuclei.

None of these generalized descriptions fits all cities. All are based upon the concept of the balance of proximity to the core and other urban nuclei and the availability of transportation to overcome the lack of proximity resulting from the impossibility of locating all land uses with maximum mutual proximity.

Whatever the specific patterns of urban land uses and internal functional organization of cities may be, the specialization of areas and their separation from one another are made possible by the availability of transportation.

Each successive form of urban transportation has had significant effects in accelerating both the expansion of cities, on the one hand, and concentrating industrial and commercial activities in the nodal portions of cities, on the other.

Before urban transportation was mechanized, the extent of a city was limited by horse-drawn transportation, at an average speed of 3 to 4 miles an hour. Cities had to be small and compact so that all parts could be reached in a reasonable time. Factories were relatively small, and little need existed for wide separations of places of work and of residence.

The horse-drawn street railway car was the dominant form of urban transportation from the period immediately before the Civil War until nearly the end of the 19th century. Although placing the vehicles on rails reduced friction in comparison with the free-wheeled vehicle, speeds were limited, and cities, though expanding, remained crowded and compact.

The steam railway, with commuter schedules, offered opportunities for urban expansion during the latter part of the 19th century in the vicinities of some of the larger cities. Beyond the main urban mass, with its radius of 3 or 4 miles from the commercial core, the steam railroad, with its higher speeds, made possible the development of nodes of suburban growth.

The result was a moderately densely developed series of outlying settlements, clustered about each suburban railroad station, the railroad forming an axis. The pattern that developed resembled beads on a string, with nonurban land lying along the railroads between the stations.

Since the railroads radiated from the urban core, the resulting pattern consisted of radial strings of suburbs, each radial separated from the next by open country, and each suburb along a rail line separated from its neighbors by open country between the railroad stations. Beyond each railroad station, urbanization was limited by the range of horse-drawn transportation. Since the practicable commuting time in each direction to and from the core of the city was about 1 hour, the distance from each outlying station at which urbanization took place was limited by the combined time of rail trip and connecting trip by horse-drawn vehicle, or, in a few instances, by local electric car.

The development of electrified railway transportation in the early years of the 20th century expanded the areas available for urban development. The electric street railway lines were extended beyond the limits that were possible for the horse-drawn streetcar, because of the higher speed. The speed was still limited by urban congestion, however. Along the street railway lines, land values (and hence density of development) were concentrated.

The street railway made it possible for the main urban mass to expand along the routes that were in operation. The resulting pattern of the expanded urban development was roughly in the shape of a star, whose points developed along streetcar lines. Within the urban mass, the densest development was also along streetcar lines.

The main lines in most cities were radial, focusing on the central business district, where most of the employment was located. In some of the larger cities, circumferential or crosstown routes were in operation to provide service to factories and offices not directly associated with the commercial core. At the intersections of the radial and circumferential routes, major outlying shopping centers tended to develop at the transfer corners. Some of them became almost small-scale reproductions of the central business districts and created problems of traffic congestion and competition of commercial land uses to get nearest to the major intersection.

The application of electric power to suburban transportation beyond the main urban mass took two forms. One was extension of the street railway into suburban areas. The first two decades of the present century marked the heyday of the interurban electric railway. Because a car or train could stop at any place along the line, suburban development was freed from dependence on proximity to outlying railroad stations.

The electric suburban or interurban railway represented a considerable advance in opening up new areas for urban expansion. Rapid acceleration and deceleration permitted more frequent stops. The operation of several cars in a train related its power and speed to the fluctuations of traffic from day to day and hour by hour more readily than could the steam railway train. The result was that on the fringes of many cities electric railways were built parallel to the earlier steam railways in order to secure initial traffic from preexisting suburbs. These lines permitted a filling in of the areas between the steam railroad stations. The radial tentacles of suburban development filled in and became more or less continuous. Farmland was subdivided and converted into suburban residential land more rapidly than in the previous period.

The second form of application of electric power to suburban and urban passenger transportation was by the electrification of steam railroads near some of the larger cities. The advantages of the railroad as a heavy mass carrier of passengers on high-density routes was combined with the advantages of multiple-unit operation.

The electrified steam railroad, however, did not approach the flexibility of the interurban electric railway, which usually represented less investment and could be extended more easily into newly developing suburban areas.

Five large cities—New York, Chicago, Philadelphia, Boston, and Cleveland—developed rapid transit elevated and subway railways for internal transportation when the concentrations of traffic exceeded the capacities of the streets.

The rapid transit line, unlike other forms of urban transportation, is separated from all other traffic. It is on a reserved right-of-way and has no conflicts with street traffic. Most rapid transit lines are operated with multiple-unit trains at relatively high speeds and with distances of one-third mile to several miles between stops. A busline operating on a right-of-way or lane reserved for its own use would also be a rapid transit line. The capacity of a rapid transit line exceeds that of any other form of local transportation in terms of the number of passengers that could be moved in a certain period.

Electric surface transportation has almost gone full cycle. The electric interurban railway has nearly disappeared in the United States, being largely replaced by the automobile. The local street railway survives in only a few places, having been replaced by the motor bus. Only in the rapid transit line and the electrified suburban steam railway does the application of the electric power survive in rail passenger transport of daily home-to-work movements.

THE DEVELOPMENT of the automobile and motortruck has produced the most rapid and far-reaching changes of any technological innovation in transportation in the rate, direction, and scale of urban expansion. No longer need urban development be tied to the limited number of routes feasible for rail transportation. The flexibility of the individual privately owned vehicle opens up vast areas beyond the former limits of cities and suburbs for urban development.

Our cities have been building up around the automobile. Many newly developed areas depend entirely on automobile transportation, for they are beyond the range of public carriers. The areas between the older radial prongs of suburban growth are filling in, because the automobile can go anywhere where passable roads exist.

The areas of countryside available for urbanization are several times as extensive as the areas that could be developed when people had to depend on public carriers for the journey to work. Many industries no longer need to locate near the convergence of public transportation in order to assemble workers, who increasingly come by automobile.

The truck makes possible the assembly of raw materials and semifinished products from many sources and the delivery of manufactured goods—for which sometimes railroads now are not used at all. Many industries do not need railroad sidings, for they can truck their shipments to the nearest rail freight station. Piggyback—the transportation of motortruck trailers on railroad flatcars—combines flexibility of motortruck transportation and the economy of the railroad as a large-scale hauler.

Factories more and more are tending therefore to locate away from congested industrial districts, which were built when railroads provided the only intercity freight transportation.

Highways and motor vehicles also are opening up opportunities for lower urban densities. Thus residential areas can develop free from some of the disadvantages and limitations imposed by the need to be near mass transportation.

The effect of the new flexibility is generally to reduce the emphasis on relatively few focal or nodal areas and to spread the demand for land over larger areas.

Lower densities—if there is proper planning—provide opportunities for more open space and for many amenities that are lacking in the older sections of many cities. Parks, playgrounds, ample backyards, and larger sites for schools can be provided.

The amount of service provided by the mass carriers is less in most urban areas than ever before. Local transit systems face prospects of further cutbacks in service as their costs rise and patronage declines.

Some form of public transportation is essential in most cities, however. Central business districts still are the major foci of employment and shopping in nearly all cities, where parking has become the biggest problem of all. The larger the city, the more dependent is it on mass transportation, even though the relative dependence is declining.

The result is that mass transportation, instead of being the basic general intracity and suburban form of transportation as in the past, is increasingly specialized in function. It is best adapted to the transportation of heavy volumes of passenger traffic along high-density routes and during the peak hours of the day. Since the highest densities exist in the older sections of cities and the peak volumes are to and from the central business districts, mass transportation is most used for the journey to work in the central business districts of residents in the older and more densely developed sections of cities.

In outlying areas of sparser population, combining the flexibility of the automobile and the economy of the mass carrier sometimes is feasible by providing outlying parking facilities along the transit lines and at suburban railroad stations.

THE EXPRESSWAY is a new element of increasing significance in the evolution of future urban land use.

An expressway—or freeway or thruway—a specialized traffic artery for the high-speed movement of vehicles, is free of the delays and hazards of conflicting cross traffic. It is separated from other traffic routes. The ordinary arterial street combines through movement, local movement, parking, and loading and unloading of vehicles. The expressway has only one function—to speed up through movement.

Several hundred miles of expressways have been completed in cities and metropolitan areas. A number of cross-country expressways, some of them turnpikes, connect major cities. The program of Federal interregional highways, authorized by the Congress in 1956, provides for 41 thousand miles of modern highways. A substantial part of their mileage will be in metropolitan areas.

The effects of the expressways will be tremendous. The new routes will be basic elements in the entire structure of urban and metropolitan uses of land. Because the rights-of-way are 250 to 300 feet wide, each expressway in an urban area removes from other uses of a strip at least a city block wide for the entire length of the route. At the interchanges between expressways and between expressways and other arteries, vast areas of land must be taken and hence made unavailable for other development.

In the areas that must be taken for the rights-of-way are thousands of business establishments and hundreds of thousands of residences, which must be relocated. The selection of the relocation sites will strongly influence the future patterns of the cities. Relating the major transportation routes to comprehensive city and regional plans becomes more important than ever.

The expressways are being located primarily with reference to their ability to move vehicular traffic. That is their function. But too little thought is given to the relationships of the routes to the present and future patterns of commercial, industrial, and residential areas they serve.

Several vital questions need answers.

Will the new traffic facilities cause additional concentration and congestion in already congested areas?

What additional parking facilities will be needed to accommodate the vehicles after they arrive in the congested areas?

What effects will their routes have on the residential communities through which they will pass?

Will they increase neighborhood and community cohesion by forming barriers at the boundaries of the neighborhood and community areas—or will they disrupt existing communities by causing the removal of substantial populations and by creating barriers between the residences and such community foci as the schools, churches, parks, and shopping centers?

Time will provide answers of sorts to some of the questions. Right now we need to study objectively and thoroughly the existing physical and social patterns of cities that the expressways will affect.

We can foresee some of the effects of the expressways. By providing high-speed transportation for both the private automobile and the motor-truck, they will increase further the difficulty of providing mass transportation facilities for peak loads to and from the central business districts. At the same time they themselves will not provide complete solutions to the problems of transportation to and from such districts.

Integration of planning of expressways and mass transportation—in other words, thinking about the movement of people and goods rather than just the movement of vehicles, and thinking about cities rather than about transportation alone—is essential.

A word about advances in the generation and transmission of power, which also have affected the use of urban land. The concentrated markets for power in cities have meant the installation of generating and transmission facilities to meet the demands for industrial expansion. Since electric power can be transmitted economically for several hundred miles, the major industrial areas have not had to restrict their patterns of development because of power demands.

Atomic energy will improve further the availability of power. Probably atomic energy will not have any important localizing effects on industrialization or urbanization but may actually encourage a further decentralization within metropolitan areas.

After the Second World War, the Federal Government encouraged new industrial establishments to locate at least 4 miles from concentrations that were regarded as particularly vulnerable to attack. Later the limit was raised to 10 miles. The hydrogen bomb brought the realization that no metropolitan area is large enough to avoid being crippled by an attack anywhere near it. It is now questionable whether any security can be derived against attack by any degree of deconcentration. In fact, the question may well be raised whether deconcentration may not actually increase vulnerability by exposing more mileage of highways and railroads to possible crippling attack and thereby making the maintenance of industrial production more difficult.

THUS THE NEW FORMS of urban growth, like the new technological inventions, produce new problems and accentuate the urgency of solving old problems.

They also produce new challenges. Among the most urgent challenges is the one represented by the lag of our social and political institutions behind the increasingly urgent problems which they are being called upon to solve. Our metropolitan areas, for example, are fragmented into dozens or hundreds of small political units—cities, towns, villages, school districts, park districts—each concerned with its own functions or its own limited area of jurisdiction.

Cities expand—but without equal expansion of the horizons of social and political organization. Some groups of the population, attracted to cities by the greater employment opportunities, meet resistance in some cities. Schools in most newly developed suburban areas are not planned and built sufficiently in advance of the population growth, and their problems are complicated by the small size and financial inability of many of the political jurisdictions.

Few metropolitan areas have adequate machinery to plan for the new conditions systematically and comprehensively.

Technological advances therefore must be paralleled by social, political, and economic advances if their full potentialities for the benefit of man are to be realized.

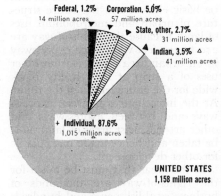

Ownership of farmland in the United States, 1954.

Federal, 1.2%
14 million acres

Corporation, 5.0%
57 million acres

State, other, 2.7%
31 million acres

Indian, 3.5% △
41 million acres

+ Individual, 87.6%
1,015 million acres

UNITED STATES
1,158 million acres

+ includes partnerships, estates
△ principally under Federal jurisdiction

Urban expansion—will it ever stop?

This essay raises thought-provoking questions, contains many challenging details, and steps on some toes. It will arouse disagreement and maybe controversy. Everyone will do well to attend closely to the compelling problems it discusses of harnessing urban land—a resource that "holds economic forces of titanic power for welfare or destruction." By *M. Mason Gaffney,* associate professor of agricultural economics, the University of Missouri.

WHEN YOU walk down Main Street in any large city, each step takes you past several thousand dollars' worth of frontage. Frontage is a common measure of city land, and it goes by the foot, like a precious commodity. A front foot is a foot along the sidewalk with a strip behind it 100–150 feet to the rear of the lot. A foot on the right street is worth whole farms.

Among the dearest is State Street in Chicago, where some frontage goes for 30 thousand dollars a foot. At that rate an acre would bring 13 million dollars. Market Street in San Francisco runs up to 10 thousand dollars a foot. A foot on Fayetteville Street in Raleigh, N. C., is worth about 4 thousand dollars.

Why do these strips of otherwise common dirt command such prices? The answer lies in the forces of urban centralization.

Urban land, which serves a region much as the farmstead serves a farm, is a central storage base for collecting and distributing outputs and inputs and for sorting, processing, and reassembling them.

It is a center that affords easy, reliable access to enough volume and variety of resources to supply complex, specialized, continuous, and large-scale operations, and enough markets to absorb their outputs and byproducts.

It is a reservoir of goods and labor whose abundance gives the slack to allow flexibility of operations, meet emergency needs, and afford the innovator endless possible combinations of skills and resources to experiment with.

The city is a convenient gathering place where buyers can rely on finding sellers, and sellers buyers—a place to inspect, compare, and exchange goods and render and receive services. Its large local market attracts a variety of specialized goods and services. Its compactness permits cheap distribution, which in turn facilitates savings from large-scale central operations.

It is a central store of information and ideas—a place to confer and arbitrate face to face, to plan and administer, to do research and educate. It is a place where many minds can associate freely to stimulate, evaluate, and diffuse new techniques and ideas: In all, the brain, control, and power center of society.

Urban land commands a premium, too, as a place to reside. For living, as for business, its advantage is access to a wide selection of opportunities and associations.

Although it need not be fertile, or flat, or even dry, good urban land is scarce. The value of land for urban functions depends on its location relative to transportation, resources, and markets. Large-scale producers attach a special premium to the best lands, as they require access to the widest markets for economical operations. Being large, they also require large areas, so that competition for the best land is extremely keen.

The entire network of location factors defies simple analysis. But the greatest cities develop at strategic central locations, where they assemble and process many resources for many markets. Junctions and hubs of transportation have obvious merits, as do heads of navigation and other load-breaking points.

Good location is not enough to fit land for urban functions. Access, the basic urban resource, is partly manmade. The city enhances its natural advantages by pushing out routes to tap wider territories, but that is only a start. To realize its full potential, the city develops a network of local transportation—a system of general access through which its lifeblood moves.

So vital is transportation that most cities devote more than half their developed land to it. In 53 central cities—"central" meaning the major downtown city of a metropolitan region, excluding suburbs and satellites—which were studied by Harland Bartholomew for his book, *Land Uses in American Cities*, streets and alleys alone occupied 28 percent of the developed area.

Autos are voracious off-street land consumers, too. One parking space, with access lanes and a little to spare to allow for human weakness, preempts more than 300 square feet. The driveway and garage on a residential lot occupy about as much surface as the house. Many factories occupy less space than their own parking lots and loading and delivery aprons. The modern, auto-oriented shopping center allows 4 or 5 square feet of parking for each square foot of floor area. Filling stations are almost entirely open space.

Other forms of transportation are less demanding, but still they take a good deal of land. Railroads took 5 percent of the cities studied by Mr. Bartholomew, including much very costly land near downtown. Considerable space is devoted also to docks, bus terminals, airports, and easements for pipes and wires to transport water, gas, and electricity. Halls, elevators, and stairs take space inside buildings.

Most of this spacious network of public and semipublic lands dedicated to free movement yields little direct income, but the city can ill afford not to devote generous spaces to these corridors, which allow full release of the enormous productive forces inherent in specialization and exchange and give the private lands their value.

The final essential for productive urban land is the improvement of adjoining land. One lonely storehouse no more makes a city than one smoldering stick makes a fire. Assembled buildings compete for customers, suppliers, and use of public spaces, but generally they also complement each other so as to enhance enormously their overall productive value.

For the essence of urban value is access, and every resource the city adds increases the volume and variety of resources accessible to all. Each new seller is a magnet for more buyers.

Each buyer is a magnet for sellers, pulling trade from farther away, attracting more transportation routes and scheduled runs, and helping establish the city as the place to rely on finding what you want, selling your wares and services, and, in a dynamic, competitive world, keeping touch with the latest products, information, techniques, and ideas.

Each addition to the local market helps also to spread the overhead of more specialized and larger operations. Each new taxpayer shares the burden of large public works and improves the city's credit. Each new producer helps diversify the city's economic base and insure its stability. Each new seller tends either to bring in outside money or reduce leakages of money to outside sellers, and thus he creates new demand for local services.

A growing city therefore may enjoy a long stage of increasing returns, when growth begets more growth. Thus the one best location in a region has a decisive advantage over the second best, and the earliest development has a commanding lead over later comers. The largest urban nucleus tends to snowball, while others shrivel.

The European scholar Georges Widmer has provided an interesting demonstration of increasing returns in urban growth. Widmer worked with Swiss census data, and published his results in the Revue Economique for March 1953. He found a direct relationship between size of city and several measures of per capita economic activity, such as wages and tax revenues.

A limit to increasing returns is the cost of transportation. The larger the city grows, the farther it has to range for markets and materials. And many cities are stopped short of this limit by the city fathers' fears of spoiling their markets, lowering rents, risking money on public works, raising wages and taxes, admitting outsiders, spoiling the fishing, or losing control of city hall.

But a number of metropolitan titans have burst these bonds to accumulate a large share of the population, capital, and the land value of the country. New York City (excluding suburbs and satellites) in 1955 had about 7.8 million people (4.8 percent of our population), and its annual real-estate taxes were 746 million dollars, 7 percent of the national levy.

THE GRAVITATIONAL pull of a city does not stop at its fringes. The center of gravity, the downtown district of maximum access, draws the whole city in upon itself, story on story. In this focusing of demand, the city finds further increasing returns from large-scale building.

The most economical layout to interconnect given space users is in three dimensions, in which central heating and other utilities can be distributed over shorter conduits than in two dimensions and each room has quicker access to most of the others. One roof and one foundation serve many stories.

Inner partitions need not be weatherproof; the outer surface of a cube increases in less proportion than the space it encloses. So a large, multistory building provides given space, services, and access more cheaply than several small buildings.

There are limits to the economical height of buildings and to the amount of crowding people will endure, of course, and everyone knows that a conspicuous centrifugal surge started some years ago. But nevertheless a city keeps its basic cohesive tendencies, which are its reason for being.

JUST HOW LARGE an area cities occupy no one knows, for no one can say where a city ends. The United States Census defines "urbanized areas" roughly as those in and around cities of at least 50 thousand inhabitants. That was about 8 million acres in 1950, evenly divided between the central cities and their urbanized fringes. Eight million acres equals the area of Maryland and Delaware, 0.42 percent of the continental United States, and a little less than the 9 million acres in farmsteads. It seems a modest space requirement for its 70 million residents, particularly the 50 million in central cities.

The census has been conservative in its definition, for the area enclosed inside farflung urban outposts would be much greater. Eight million acres is the area of a circle with a 63-mile radius, or two circles with 45-mile radii, and stray bits from any one of our metropolitan giants may be found that far from its center.

But even the census' limited area is urbanized only in a loose sense. Despite the advantages of compact land use, central cities themselves are surprisingly patchy. In Mr. Bartholomew's 53 central cities, the undeveloped portion was about 29 percent. Although his surveys are not all up to date, many local planning surveys show comparable figures after 1955.

His developed urban land was about 0.06 acre per capita, or 5 yards on a football gridiron. At that density, the 50 million inhabitants of central cities of more than 50 thousand use nearer 3 million acres than 4 million.

Even some of that 3 million acres they "use" only in a poetic sense. It is mostly open space. The area actually covered by buildings is probably less than 400 thousand acres, less than some western ranches and less than 15 percent of the developed area of the central cities.

No one expects that every building should occupy 100 percent of its site, but just how big a yard and grounds should be so as to be designated as developed by a building somewhere on it is a puzzle. Some urban buildings do occupy their entire sites, and by contrast such other sites as the 75 acres around Ford's new administration building in Dearborn seem nearer akin to undeveloped lands. No one can say exactly how we are to designate such lands, but some sort of allowance would certainly reduce the central cities' land "use" appreciably below 3 million acres.

If the central city is a little patchy, its outskirts are in shreds. Here, to be sure, are big users of land like golf courses, dumps, drive-ins, and airports, serving the central city. But it would be hard to define any segment of this nebulous territory that was not largely in weeds. Probably less than half the 4 million acres of urban fringe cited in the census deserves to be called "developed."

For cities under 50 thousand, our data are progressively less detailed. Hugh H. Wooten and James R. Anderson, of the Department of Agriculture, estimated that all cities of more than a thousand inhabitants in 1954 occupied 18.6 million acres— about the area of South Carolina and 1 percent of the continental United States. Smaller communities may occupy another 10 million acres. But all these figures include empty spaces, which make up larger portions of the smaller cities.

As to urban values, they are pro-

digious. It is easy to underestimate them because of the comparatively modest space requirements of cities. There is nothing modest about the prices of urban land, however.

Residential lots in respectable established neighborhoods sell for 50 dollars to 250 dollars a foot and for more than 500 dollars a foot along a few gold coasts. Apartment sites average higher, going above 1 thousand dollars along Lake Shore Drive in Chicago. Slum sites are often held at fancy prices because of an expectation of future industrial, commerical, or public demand. Some subsidiary shopping districts sell for 1 thousand dollars a foot. The best industrial sites in large central cities command well over 100 thousand dollars an acre.

Prices of land out from the center are much lower, but still impressive, especially after the multifold increases since 1950. Undeveloped residential or industrial land along new superhighways was bringing several thousand dollars an acre in 1957, and more around New York City. Industrial acreage near Eastshore Freeway, Oakland, averaged 10,500 dollars as early as 1953. Potential sites of shopping centers brought 10 thousand to 50 thousand dollars an acre, as did motel sites near the better interchanges of the new turnpikes and thruways.

Airspace above the golden ground of the city also carries high price tags. An option on air over the Pennsylvania Railroad tracks in New York specified more than 3 million dollars an acre in 1955. A Times Square billboard brings 15 thousand a year.

At such prices, it does not take many cities to outvalue all the farms in whole States, and in most States one or a few of the largest cities do. New York City real estate in 1955 was worth some unknown but large amount over its assessed valuation of 20 billion dollars, which was the current market value of all the farm real estate in New York State and 19 other Eastern States. For the whole country, urban values exceed farm values several times over.

It may even be that urban values exceed farm values per capita. One cannot be certain. Land prices swing violently and rapidly, yet the only general source of data on urban values is from moss-covered tax assessments. Urban assessments are more obsolete than rural assessments—if that is possible.

But we do know how much taxes property pays. It may surprise some farmers to learn that farm property taxes are less per capita than nonfarm property taxes—roughly 54 dollars, compared to 72 dollars in 1956. Of some 11.7 billion dollars levied that year, farm property bore only 1.2 billion dollars.

The higher urban levies might reflect higher urban tax rates, rather than per capita values. The average rate on farm real estate, as reported in 1957 by the Agricultural Finance Review, was about 1 percent of market value. There is a general impression that urban real rates average higher—and some evidence to back it up. David Rowlands, of the University of Pennsylvania, in a report on the Property Tax in Atlanta and Other Large Cities, estimated effective tax rates in 20 large cities for 1956. Only 2 of them fall under 1 percent, and a few exceed 2 percent.

On the other hand, a study published in the Review of Economics and Statistics for February 1957 found otherwise. Scott Maynes and James Morgan, analyzing voluminous questionnaire data from the University of Michigan Survey of Consumer Finances and the United States Census Residential Financing Survey, found the real rate of property taxation on owner-occupied urban residences in 1953 to be nearly 1 percent.

They did not check the possibility that respondents may have tended to understate their taxes. Nor did they discover to what extent the low tax rates on owner-occupied residences resulted from homestead exemption, which would not apply to other classes of real estate. Still, it is other classes of real estate, especially rented slum and vacant land, that are most frequently found to be underassessed.

One might reason that city tax rates must be higher because city property pays city taxes on top of county taxes—although, of course, the most urbanized counties might have lower overall rates than predominantly rural counties. City people get more local governmental services, it is true, but they get them cheaper because they live closer together. They also have more non-property-tax sources of revenue.

Then, too, a census study under Allen Manvel found farm real estate overassessed—hence overtaxed by the counties—relative to urban real estate in 101 counties of downstate Illinois in 1946. Arthur Walrath found the same in several counties around Milwaukee in 1955. Remember, too, that an appreciable share of urban real estate is tax-exempt institutional ground.

None of these studies provides a solid basis for estimating urban real-estate values. The United States Census of Governments planned to release in 1958 what should be a definitive study of tax assessment ratios. Even that omits tax-exempt real estate from consideration, and also it omits suburban acreage, but still it may provide the first firm estimate of urban real-estate values in the United States.

Meanwhile, we have reasonable grounds for putting the real rate of urban property taxation between 1 and 2 percent, which means the aggregate value of urban real estate is of the order of seven or eight times greater than farm real estate. It is entirely possible that a 100-percent comprehensive reckoning, including tax-exempt holdings and suburban acreage, would reach as high as 10 times farm values, or 1 trillion dollars.

Other indirect evidences of real-estate values are the mortgages they carry. As of September 1957, the farm mortgage debt was 10 billion dollars, compared to 143 billion dollars on nonfarm residential and commercial real estate. Nonfarm real estate in 1957 probably carried a higher ratio of debt to value—it is impossible to say for certain because most real estate is unmortgaged. On the other hand, however, nonfarm mortgage figures do not include the debt on industrial, rail, or utility holdings, or on institutional and public real estate.

Several studies also indicate that urban families occupy dwellings valued at two to three times their annual incomes. This suggests that urban residences alone are worth more than 500 billion dollars.

These last two lines of reasoning yield no definite numerical estimates of urban values, but they do confirm the belief that they dwarf the value of farm real estate.

Real estate is more than land, of course, and conceivably urban real-estate values inhere largely in the buildings—we hear a good deal about the declining importance of land in an urban society. That may be a misconception, however.

Builders putting new single-family homes on cheap outlying land reckon the site at one-sixth or one-fifth of the total cost. But not many urbanites live in new homes on cheap outlying land. Even in 1957, after 12 years of record-smashing construction, 75 percent of all urban dwelling units were built before 1945 and most of them before 1929. There are almost no new residences in older central cities. A study by the Real Estate Board of New York in 1953 found that 80 percent of Manhattan's apartments were more than 50 years old.

In fringe areas, where new buildings do outvalue their own sites, a large share of the sites have no buildings. Around Cleveland, for example, 57 percent of the Cuyahoga County Planning Commission's "suburban ring" and 84 percent of the "rural ring" were vacant in 1954. In commercial districts, with their majestic frontage prices, it takes a new and substantial structure to match the site value.

All in all, from the limited information available, there is no reason to dismiss land value as a minor part of urban real-estate value, especially if we include vacant lands at their current market prices. It may even be the larger share. And, interestingly enough, the ratio of land to building values tends to be highest in the centers of large, densely populated, and built-up cities, where economic life is supposed to have lost touch with the land most completely.

A STRIKING ASPECT of today's cities is their rapid outward thrust. Urban values being what they are, cities gobble up farmland at will. There is no accurate survey of the wide and ragged urban frontier, but various estimates suggest it has been advancing recently about 400 thousand acres a year into the heart of America's farmlands.

Is this in the farmers' interest? Many thoughtful observers are raising voices in alarm for the future. The most vocal of them seem to think the city should be contained. There is another side to the question, though.

The city serves the farmer and buys his products. It is the farmer's interest that cities have ample land to serve him well. He would only suffer if he were to confine the city into a bottleneck between the barn and the table.

In fact, the city is all too likely to become a bottleneck, anyway, with no help from the farmer—but much to his detriment.

Because of increasing returns in urban growth, many cities in strategic spots have a measure of monopoly power over parts of their trade territories. Without the spur of competition, they are easily tempted to settle back comfortably and take their customers' money without the costs and bother of offering very adequate or modern service. Their strong position lets them do this simply by vegetating quietly without necessarily having any active monopoly motive. Because downtown sites are favorite investments for absentees and heiresses, too, a high proportion of them fall into ownerships that tend to resist progressive management and risky improvements.

There is competition within each city, of course, but the city fathers who are so inclined can minimize it by restrictive policies. They may lay out streets so as to limit the business frontage; maintain obsolete traffic patterns to protect vested investments; discourage new buildings by overassessing them relative to old—a practice that has become especially common since the war—and assessing undeveloped land at next to nothing; zoning out new developments; limiting the height of buildings; winking at tax-delinquent land speculators and selling off foreclosed properties only slowly; fostering obstructive building codes; endowing tax-free institutions with grounds vastly beyond their needs; neglecting essential public works and services; and refusing to act decisively against obsolescence and blight.

Whether by design, apathy, or sincere devotion to an obsolete tradition, probably most cities contrive to remain inadequately developed to serve fully the demands on them.

To protect themselves, the farmers' best assurance of adequate, modern, and competitive urban services may be to release lands for new development around stagnant central cities. With all its faults, such expansion does introduce new competition for farm trade.

The urban expansion bears critical watching, however.

Are efficient cities evolving—cities that distribute goods with minimum time, motion, and cost?

Are cities swallowing much more farmland than they need?

Above all, does the present pattern of urban expansion contain the same elements of instability that have brought most previous land booms to collapse?

To answer these questions, it is necessary to analyze the process of urban expansion more closely.

Like the eager suitor who leaped onto his horse and dashed madly off in all directions, the city moves out hither and yon with little apparent consistency or reason. Here is Washington, D. C., growing out from the back door of the Capitol, in defiance of its planner's best-laid schemes. There is the shopping district gravitating toward a high-income residential area, but radiating influences that create slums in its van and erode away the attracting force. Here are sewers without houses, while out beyond arise new houses without sewers. There is hardly any predicting where the construction crews will turn up next.

What are the builders seeking?

More space? There is considerable unused space in the central city itself.

Lower taxes? Fringe residents, scattered broadcast with more schoolchildren per capita and without the downtown commerce and industry to share tax burdens, in general must pay more taxes to finance given municipal services.

Surveys in 1955 by Amos H. Hawley and Basil G. Zimmer, of the University of Michigan, found fringe residents around Flint, Mich., actually more willing than residents of the central city to assume higher taxes. And it is evident that many people flee central cities in search of better schools and other costly public services that the city fathers are too parsimonious to finance.

Freedom from traffic? The farther one lives from jobs and markets the more traffic he must buck in between.

Freedom from restrictive policies? Often so—yet many suburban enclaves become more restrictive than the central city.

Of the many, many things that urban refugees are seeking, most are to be found in the central city. The refugees want municipal services, access to social and economic opportunities, and other urban advantages—but not at any price. To oversimplify a complex politico-socio-economic phenomenon, urban outmigrants, like the westward pioneers before them, are seeking cheap land. The very advantages of the city prove its major liability when they promote asking prices so high as to drive builders out of town.

The quest for cheap land leads the

city not just to expand, but to disintegrate. The quest turns very much on the individual seller. Asking prices for comparable lands vary widely with the seller's finances, tax position, information, sentiments, or just plain cussedness. Jack Lessinger, of the University of California's Real Estate Research Program, has found tentatively that in the Santa Clara Valley, around San Jose, it is the smaller farmers who succumb earliest to the city, and larger landholders who hold out longest. The French geographers, M. Phlipponneau, J. Tricart, and C. Precheur, describe the same tendency around Nancy and Paris. Buyers find a bargain here, another yonder, and build accordingly, so that development proceeds in patches and freckles.

State highway builders can stretch funds much further where the right-of-way is cheap. Besides, holders of cheap land are less likely to band into militant "Property Owners' Protective Leagues" and the like to block new thruways; and railroads are just as happy to see highway funds diverted to routes not paralleling their own. New highways, like railroads before them, often tend to bypass congested areas and develop earliest and most fully in less settled territory. They open wide new areas to hunt-and-peck development and establish new urban nuclei where they converge.

These outlying nuclei are bases from which even farther flung developments are launched. Especially along trunk routes, they coalesce into gangling, diffuse urban complexes that some writers, fancy running free, are describing as "polynucleated urbs," "conurbations," "cities as long as highways," "atomic megalopolises," and "scrambled eggs" and hailing, with enthusiasm or resignation, as forerunners of a new era.

Our first question was, "Are they efficient cities?" By any ideal standard they are not.

Transportation and utility lines to join the scattered pieces cost billions. The result at best is a poorly coordi-nated tangle. Commerce bypasses old bottlenecks but meets an obstacle course that consumes untold time and motion and can hardly avoid reflecting itself, among other ways, in a wider farm-market spread.

Such coherent patterns as do emerge are geometrically imperfect. Some variation on a linear theme, strung out miles along a railway, waterway, or highway, is commonest. But why go 20 miles west when there is open land 5 miles north? It takes three-dimensional development to afford maximum access at minimum cost among given users of space. Linear developments do not even use two dimensions, but force all traffic along one long, congested line. That, often as not, was built originally for through traffic.

One can probably understand how linear patterns develop: Cities fail to provide adequate two-dimensional street networks; and interurban trunk lines, financed by the State or National Government, offer ready-built, open-ended avenues of escape to cheap, accessible land. Landholders along existing routes can subdivide without dedicating 25 percent of their land for streets and without submitting to central controls over subdivision plans. But to explain is not to justify.

Our second question was: "Do cities need to swallow so much good farmland?"

We should probably concede the city first choice over the best land, even the most fertile, just as farmers concede corn first choice of the best wheatland. It may not make much sense to farm steep slopes in the Ozarks, but it would make less sense to put St. Louis there, to put Minneapolis in the north woods, and so on. But this hardly settles the question.

Cities, even central cities, are not using nearly the land they already contain. These undigested pieces are of negative value to the city itself. Cities exist to bring people together. Vacant and underdeveloped lands keep them apart and thus destroy part of the city's basic resources: Cheap distribution and easy access. Even if land had no alternative use in farming, it would pay many a city to draw itself together.

Dispersion also forces heavier reliance on those hungry land gobblers, automobiles and trucks. Their demands for highway, turning, and parking space displace tens of thousands of dwelling units a year, scatter the city out farther, and consume more farmland. Dispersion requires that each plant, far from the storehouses and services of the central city, be more self-sufficient, which of course increases its space requirements.

It is especially out from the center, though, that cities preempt vast lands they do not use and may never use. Little urban fragments, prospering busily among fields and orchards, excite speculative hopes for land sales around and between them until urban price influence extends millions of acres beyond the city limits.

Urban prices have a baleful influence on farming. The dirt farmer has struggle enough financing title to lands priced by their anticipated income from agriculture alone. Urban prices push him out of the market completely. Landholders near cities must be speculators as well as farmers.

Often they are not farmers at all. High-priced lands in areas with urban possibilities tend to gravitate to those who have the financial power to wait. Urban financial power is something few working farmers can match.

Federal income-tax laws tend to aggravate the dirt farmer's disadvantage, for they make speculative gains especially attractive to those in higher tax brackets. To begin, any interest and local taxes are fully deductible. Then the speculator may qualify for "capital gains" treatment—that is, for excluding 50 percent of any realized increment from taxable income, with a maximum tax rate of 25 percent on the increment. That is of great value to the man in an 80-percent tax bracket and tends to make him a high bidder in the market for appreciating suburban lands.

To qualify for capital gains treatment, the speculator must establish that he is not "in the real-estate business," but is a passive "investor," neither improving land for sale nor soliciting buyers. Or he may establish that he is "using the land in his trade or business" (other than real estate).

Should he lose on one sale he can offset the loss against other capital gains. Better yet, if he establishes that he is using the land in his trade or business, he can offset losses against ordinary income, even though any gains would not be taxed as such.

Still better, if it is his residence that he sells, and he puts the proceeds into a new residence within the year, the entire gain is tax free—and with a little effort a commuter may learn to "reside" over a considerable investment.

Best of all, one who buys land years ahead of his own needs never pays a tax on the rise of value so long as he does not sell—something many large corporations, with huge reserves "for expansion," have little expectation of doing. Wilbur Steger, writing in the National Tax Journal for September 1957, estimates that 90 percent of all capital gains were thus left tax free from 1901 to 1949.

The result of all this is a virtual scorched-earth policy for many lands around cities. Why risk any improvement or overt sales effort that might land you "in the real-estate business" and thus disqualify your increments from "capital gains" treatment? Why not hoard up vast industrial estates for "future expansion"? Should your alleged need actually eventuate and if the value of the land has gone up in the meantime, you will have achieved a kind of tax-free income. Should you sell, you can probably get capital-gains treatment for increments and ordinary offset for any losses.

For lands that do remain farmed, the influence of urban prices often means a wasting away of farm fertility and capital.

Dr. Lessinger has documented this phenomenon in his dissertation, *The*

Determination of Land Use in Rural Urban Transition Areas (Berkeley, Calif., 1956). Around expanding San Jose, Calif., prune and apricot orchards are deteriorating as the city infiltrates the Santa Clara Valley. He analyzes the age distribution and bearing condition of orchards in different zones around the city and finds deterioration of orchards closely related to anticipations of urban demand, as reflected in land prices.

Thus the city takes land from the farm long before actually putting it to urban use. To a degree this is economical: Farm improvements are wasted on lands marked for immediate urbanization. But Dr. Lessinger's studies indicate that urban prices, with their blighting influence on agriculture, already extend over an area of the Santa Clara Valley well beyond any likely urban demand. Is this a general condition throughout the United States?

Suppose we allow the entire nonfarm population of the United States the luxury space standards of Winnetka, a Chicago suburb. With a golf course, spacious parklands, playfields, beaches, wide, tree-lined streets, two railroad rights-of-way, large lots and yards, private driveways and two-car garages, estate districts, and almost no apartments, Winnetka has 0.16 acre of developed land per resident—far more than the 0.06 acre in the 53 central cities that Mr. Bartholomew surveyed.

At the Winnetka standard, an urban population of 150 million would require 24 million acres—about the area of Indiana—which we can safely take as beyond any foreseeable demand.

The "regional cities" that enthusiasts are envisioning and promoters are touting along the Atlantic, Pacific, and gulf coasts, the Great Lakes, dozens of State freeways and turnpikes, resurgent inland waterways, and anticipated Federal-program superhighways (along with a more conventional accretion around established cities) by the simplest count exceed that 24 million acres by a wide margin.

Twenty-four million acres would be contained in 6 circles with 45-mile radii; or 24 circles with 22-mile radii; or 120 circles with 10-mile radii. As small a city as Eugene, Oreg., extends its price influence more than 10 miles from the center (not around a full circle), but there are 340 cities in the country larger than Eugene and the price influence of some of them radiates more than 50 miles. If that were not enough, there are thousands of smaller towns. A careful survey would probably show at least 100 million acres—the area of California—under the influence of urban prices.

The answer to our second question, then, is that cities are taking and leaving undeveloped more farmland than they need.

This raises the third question: "Can urban expansion continue?" Or have the onrushing urban armies overextended their lines and lost themselves in agriculture's defense in depth?

Many writers since 1955 have been projecting trends of the past 10 years forward another 20 years or so and viewing with alarm the startling inroads on farmland. History warrants few things less than it does projecting land booms far into the future. Cities typically have expanded in waves.

May we expect the present wave to break and recede?

This also is a prospect to view with alarm. The enormous financial impact of urban expansion is a vital element of our prosperity. New construction, excluding farm and military construction, has been running around some 40 billion dollars annually. That is nearly 12 percent of the national income. It consists mainly of residential, commercial, industrial, highway, and public-utility building. Most of it is tied closely to urban expansion.

The role of construction in sustaining the flow of spending is greater than its volume alone would suggest. A good deal of purchasing power in most years leaks out of the circular flow of spending into savings and allowances for depreciation. The leakages must be offset each year by new investment to avoid a multiple decline in national income.

A decline of annual investment under most conditions will produce a multiple decline in national income because consumption spending, which declines when income declines, is also a creator of money income. Lower investment means lower income. Lower income means lower consumption. That in turn means still lower income—and so on through several stages.

Autonomous declines in consumption would have similar multiple effects, but consumption usually is a relatively passive factor, which economists are inclined to treat as primarily a function of income itself. Investment is more independent and temperamental a variable, and probably most economists would agree that maintaining national income is in large part a problem of maintaining investment spending.

Of the investment on which so much hinges, 40 billion dollars of construction spending is a large share. It is also the most independent share. Other private investment is mostly in less durable goods—machinery, equipment, and inventories. Replacement and turnover of these are passive functions of time and income to some extent. Other public spending is mostly relatively rigidly committed.

THE IMPORTANCE OF THE third critical question is equaled by the difficulty of answering it.

On one hand, cities have rarely expanded rapidly without tragedy—neither, for that matter, has agriculture. We have experienced land development booms along wagon roads, canals, steamboat channels, plank roads, steam railways, horse railways, cable carlines, trolleys, subways, elevated railroads, and motor highways, with townsites and subdivisions proliferating on every hand. Most of the booms busted.

The disasters of 1819, 1836, 1857, 1873, 1893, and 1929 greet the tourist through history like bones bleaching by the trailside. Will future historians shake their heads sadly over the "second automobile bubble," as today they do over the first, and over the "canal fever," "plank-road delirium," and "railroad mania" of the past?

Perhaps—but, on the other hand, history is under no iron necessity to repeat itself. Optimists who seem to believe that collapse is unlikely today cite several reasons: Increasing population; strengthened monetary and banking regulation and insurance; Federal willingness and ability to spend; longer term, fully amortizable mortgages; more prudent subdividing practices; large private holdings of liquid assets; and other reassuring phenomena.

These are not completely tranquilizing, however, in light of the cocksure optimism that has preceded and even accompanied—yes, even followed—great crashes of the past. It is worthwhile questioning more closely the stability of forces that lead cities to preempt lands beyond their needs.

THE DYNAMIC PROCESS of overexpansion seems to be a complex urban variation on a familiar problem of agricultural land settlement.

The process in simplest outline is this: New demand raises land prices; supply responds slowly but massively; high prices over the long period of response ultimately stimulate more new supply than the demand can absorb.

Supply responds very slowly to demand because the process of converting land to urban use involves many steps by several slowly moving, poorly coordinated, frequently reluctant and sometimes downright obstructive public and private agents and because it usually takes land speculators a long time to release or develop most of the sites for actual service.

Say a new State-financed freeway begins the process of bringing farmland into an urban market. Besides transportation, the land needs water, storm and sanitary sewers, telephone, gas, electric power, schools, fire and police protection, and sidewalks, to name some elementary items.

Not only are many services needed. Several steps must be taken to extend most of them from trunklines out through forks and branches to the ultimate distributive tracery that finally brings service to each parcel of land. Governments and utilities must decide to extend their lines and networks to individual parcels. Landholders must decide it is time to receive them—that usually means subdividing, dedicating lands for streets and easements for utilities, often paying for part of the utility extensions and street improvements, and perhaps being annexed and saddled with municipal taxes.

It would be nice for each party involved if all the others would commit themselves to development before he did—or at least when he does. Then he need only pluck the ripe fruit from the tree, instead of undergoing years of risk, interest, depreciation, and obsolescence while he waits for complementary investments to help his own pay out. The situation lends itself to a long impasse of "after-you-my-dear-Alphonse." At every stage, there is inertia, nostalgia, fear, and long bargaining and jockeying.

The final step—actual building on prepared lots—may be as slow as the others, for there are still the lot speculators to wait out. Even when all utilities are in, there is a further rise to speculate on as homes, stores, churches, and so on make a community.

We are also witnessing a sort of municipal land speculation on a grand scale. Many metropolitan suburbs have incorporated undeveloped land, which they proceed to overzone out of reach of the middle-class market. That is done in hopes that its exclusive tone will one day attract upper crust residents who will pay high taxes, handsomely support local merchants, and send their few children away to school. Many communities are ready to wait a long time for such profitable fellow citizens, even when chances of success are slim.

Ralph Barnes and George Raymond, New York planning consultants, warn in the Journal of the American Institute of Planners for spring 1955, that such municipal policies have become more restrictive than even the communities' parochial self-interests would dictate. New Canaan and Greenwich, Conn., New York suburbs, have actually increased the minimum size of building lot to 4 acres in some sections, in the most congested metropolitan area in the United States. Mountain Lakes, N. J., has gone so far as to buy up a large share of its land to forestall building.

Now scarcity breeds substitution, and while supply is thus developing so dilatorily in areas most logically destined for urban growth, the impatient demand probes outward. It finds a warm welcome in many outlying communities that have urban aspirations. Some of them even offer subsidies, tax favors, and sites to woo industries.

Moreover, a large share of building is outside any incorporated area. The Sacramento housing market is an extreme instance. An unpublished report of the Federal Housing Administration, dated April 1957, states that 80 percent of all private dwelling units authorized there from 1954 through 1956 were outside incorporated areas.

These latter-day pioneers demand utilities, which often are willing to come if the customers are there first, especially if rival sellers are within striking distance and if regulatory commissions let them balance any losses with higher rates charged to all their customers. The newcomers also demand public services, which usually come where there are votes and a tax base.

Thus the scattering of urban settlement leads the basic urbanizing distributive networks and services to proliferate over wider territories than the ultimate demand can absorb.

Just how wide and how empty these territories are is startling to discover. The New York engineering firm of Parsons, Brinckerhoff, Hall & Mac-

Donald surveyed land uses and potentialities in connection with its 1953–1955 report to the San Francisco Bay Area Rapid Transit Council. It found ample suitable acreage in the Bay area for the entire projected 1990 population of the whole State of California: 22 million to 31 million people—7 to 10 times the Bay area's population of 3 million in 1953–1955. This is allowing ample areas for recreation and industry.

The California State Water Resources Board surveyed the area independently in 1955, using aerial photographs, and published the findings in its Bulletin No. 2. For the 10-county Bay area metropolitan region, only 15 percent of the suitable urban land, or 10 percent of the gross land area, was actually developed for urban use in 1955.

In the crowded city of San Francisco itself, the Water Resources Board survey showed 23 percent of the usable land was undeveloped in 1955. Along the Bay side of San Mateo County (the "Peninsula"), which is often hastily described as having become "a solid mass of suburbs," 75 percent was undeveloped. On the Bay side of Alameda County, which includes Oakland and Berkeley, the survey reported 62 percent was undeveloped.

In the Santa Clara Valley (around San Jose), whose "total urbanization" is often forecast as imminent, 86 percent of the suitable land was undeveloped for urban use in 1955. The total suitable urban land in this valley, 155 thousand acres net of streets, exceeds the area used in 1955 in the entire Bay area (129 thousand acres, also net of streets). The developed portions, however, are scattered over the valley floor. By one estimate, 7 square miles of postwar subdivisions in 1954 were scattered over 200 square miles of Santa Clara County, with at least one subdivision in each square mile. Transportation and utility networks are or must someday be extended to most of these urban islets, and thereby to the lands among them.

The California Water Resources Board bulletin said that 65 percent of the suitable land was undeveloped for urban use in the Los Angeles hydrographic unit—that is, in the city of Los Angeles, the immediately surrounding cities, and the more or less urbanized unincorporated lands.

Another 1955 survey, Bulletin 87 of the Regional Planning Association of New Jersey, New York, and Connecticut, reported the following percentages of suitable land undeveloped in some of the counties of metropolitan New York: Bronx, 9 percent; Kings (Brooklyn), 44 percent; Richmond, 32 percent; Hudson, 21 percent; Bergen, 54 percent; Westchester, 63 percent; Fairfield, 81 percent. (They counted estates of 2 acres and more as "undeveloped.") For the entire 22-county, tristate metropolitan region, dotted from end to end with fragments of New York City and laced with transportation and utility lines, only 21 percent of the suitable land, or 16 percent of the gross land area, was developed for urban use.

To occupy these vast territories calls not only for transportation and utility networks, but also for enormous private investments in autos, trucks, service stations, and the whole complex of individualized transportation equipment. This mobilizes consumers to bring their demand to every nook and cranny of undeveloped territory. Scattered stores, schools, factories, churches, and other basic creators of urban land value also shed their influence on the included undeveloped lands.

The unfilled demand pushes upward, too. The high price of land stimulates more intensive vertical building (and generally closer economy of land) on a few sites than demand can begin to absorb over the entire area subject to urban influence.

HERE ARE THE MAKINGS of a cycle of overexpansion that should come to light when speculators holding the better lands try to find markets. But a great deal remains unclear.

Perhaps some land developers do plunge ahead under the sole stimulus of current prices, but it seems doubtful whether most investors would commit themselves for long terms without an eye to the future.

How shall we explain the tenacity of the speculators who confidently hold for a rise and the dauntless optimism of developers, builders, home buyers, utilities, municipalities, and still more speculators who invest in growing areas in contempt of mounting hoards of half-urbanized land within the market sphere?

ONE REASON for surplus development is that rival districts and cities race for position. Racing differs from economic competition, as usually conceived, in that races end. Where new population and transportation are opening and promising to open new urban potentialities, the fixed layout of routes becomes temporarily fluid. During the developmental period of uncertainty, several contestants vie enthusiastically for prized positions in the new pattern before it freezes.

Because of increasing returns in urban development, these positions, once established, are quite secure and should appreciate in value as outsiders flock to them. So it makes sense for each contestant to risk great resources in a race which most of them must lose.

Cities and districts race by improving themselves to attract trade, routes, and investments. They push out their own routes to capture undeveloped trade territory from rivals, just as some cities push out aqueducts to stake out scarce waters well ahead of need. Because the motive is to secure territory and position quickly before it is too late, extension of trunklines may proceed when the fever is high without much thought for immediately foreseeable demands.

Trade racing also helps explain the behavior of land speculators. Should a district win its race, it is primarily the land that would appreciate, buildings being duplicable. But should it lose, any buildings, being immobile and fairly specialized, would stand a good chance of finding themselves obsolete. The rational gambler therefore may often prefer to bet on the race from the sidelines by holding unimproved land, postponing building until the uncertainties of racing have been resolved.

He thus lessens his district's chances of victory by retarding its development, of course, but one individual is not likely to think his influence is great.

The irrational gambler also is a factor—a major one—to consider. With several contestants running for the same prize, the average chances of success obviously are not good. Yet land prices in each contending district often seem to run higher than the statistical probability of success would warrant, and the sum of the prices over entire developing areas seem to exceed considerably what would reasonably be justified by income from the land.

Just why this should happen is a mystery social scientists are only beginning to probe. Milton Friedman, of the University of Chicago, and G. L. S. Shackle, of Cambridge, England, have developed some interesting hypotheses about it. The fact that it does happen is well established, however. Economists of several generations have observed, with Alfred Marshall, a renowned Victorian economist, that ". . . if an occupation offers a few extremely high prizes, its attractiveness is increased out of all proportion to their aggregate value." Certainly the urban land market is of that description—frontage prices in some areas increase 100 times within a few blocks.

Just as gamblers who love gambling for its own sake will bet against a wheel they know is fixed, land gamblers bid up land prices higher and over more area than the possibilities of urban income can justify.

Perhaps the most powerful stimulant to demand for land is the emergence of a Malthusian climate of opinion. Opinion is a powerful agent in the land market because land prices are based on opinions of the future and because there is so little factual information to go on.

Try to find a simple statistic, like the number of lots subdivided annually in the United States or, indeed, in any region. Few jurisdictions compile even this information, and few of those include entire metropolitan areas.

Urban outskirts especially are beyond the ken of established centers of information—and it is in these far reaches that the greatest excesses have occurred in the past. There might be enough land prepared and preparing for urban use to swamp a metropolitan market for 20 years, and it is doubtful if more than a few real-estate men, who are not given to broadcasting such gloom, would be aware. Not until June 1957 has there been any semblance of an inventory for the Nation. That, compiled as part of the study of urban tax assessments by the Census of Governments, does not purport to tell anything about the lots other than that they are "of record."

We have no systematic data at all on more difficult but equally important questions, such as the trend of land prices, the number of unrecorded and illegally subdivided urban sites, the areas in various stages of partial urbanization, plans for impending redevelopment, and so on.

Land developers must grope to decisions primarily by the present feel of the market, without factual basis for the longer sighted analysis that is so essential to an activity whose product is as nearly permanent as anything produced by man.

And so, lacking information, the market relies on opinions, which always are in long supply. Some of these are based on careful inference. Others are sheer folklore or glib platitudes circulated by professionally optimistic salesfolk.

MANY STUDENTS of past booms have commented on the propensity of contemporary opinion, unsoundly based, to underestimate the emerging supply of urbanized land and overestimate the demand for it. It is possible to trace out several primrose paths by which opinion falls into these errors.

One is the plausible presumption that construction tends to exhaust the supply of urban land. The sight of childhood haunts covered with fresh masonry seems especially to stir deep Malthusian anxieties that find their way into poignant articles, indignant editorials, goading investment counsel, and finally urgent land hoarding that transcends prosaic computations of supply and demand.

Yet construction urbanizes as much land as it consumes, or more. Even if a city grew in a compact circle, the ring around its widening circumference would grow ever larger, roughly with the square of its radius. And because cities scatter out all over the landscape, building (especially of roads and utility networks) brings wide supplies of new land into the urban market.

Another primrose path is the equally plausible presumption that skyrocketing land prices reflect an acute scarcity of urban land. But this is to reckon without the vast supplies held in cold storage by speculators and holdouts of one kind and another. The economist's nightmare of inflation without full employment of resources has characterized land markets toward the close of every boom period.

There also seems to be a tendency to underestimate the regenerative power and absorptive capacity of downtown.

There is no denying that autos and trucks, unbound by central terminals and fixed routes, have made it more feasible to bypass downtown and thus have drastically weakened its central position. The big swing has been toward expansive, cheap-land, single-story development. But many persons in their enthusiasm tend to write off downtown land as though it had become as obsolete as the buildings on it, without due account of human factors like inertia, monopolistic thinking, absentee ownership, speculative land pricing, and restrictive policies.

Others seem to have accepted too uncritically part of the thesis of the late

Harvard economist, Joseph A. Schumpeter, and others, that capitalists require security from competition before they will risk funds in large investments like buildings.

But the sleeping giant downtown once aroused by the sting of effective competition and running scared is still no mean competitor itself. Decentralization has tended to deflate speculative anticipations that buoy up downtown land prices and thus has made the most expensive land in the world a bargain relative to outlying sites whose asking prices have multiplied since 1950. Downtown can rebuild and finally has begun to do so.

When downtown rebuilds, it still has the primary advantage of location that made it downtown in the first place—why run around end when you can step through center? And a few skyscraping hotels, office buildings, department stores, and apartments—as only downtown has the focused demand to support—can do the work of square miles of sprawl outside the city limits. 3-D development can work wonders with very little surface. In Philadelphia, for example, just one building, No. 3 Penn Center, increased by 4 percent the city's rental office space when it opened in 1955.

There has been a widespread idea that downtown building space is saturated. Yet the editors of Architectural Forum noted in March 1957 that the architect, Victor Gruen, retained to replan downtown Fort Worth, found that "the underused or derelict reservoir was large enough to provide space for a belt highway, parking garages for 60 thousand cars, greenbelts, a 300 percent increase in office space, 80 percent in hotel space, and new civic, cultural, and convention centers. . . . Fort Worth is not a special case. . . ."

The urban economic geographers, R. E. Murphy, J. E. Vance, and B. J. Epstein, discovered from a close study of eight central business districts that six of them were so decayed at the core that building heights in the zone of peak land values averaged much less

than in the central business district as a whole. Large parts of the districts were taken up with what they considered "noncentral business district" uses, especially in the older eastern cities. Central business districts occupied well under 1 percent of the areas of their cities and thus had ample room to expand. The authors published their work in Economic Geography, January 1955.

In the downtown of downtowns, Manhattan's accelerating office boom accounts for much more than half of the postwar office space in the country. The postwar increase alone exceeds the total space in any other city in the United States. It is augmenting Manhattan's office space by 40 percent over 1946, yet—far from exhausting the land supply of that tiny island—it is contained in a mere 84 new buildings. And these are focused on two narrow districts, the financial and commercial centers, which are already most congested.

Homer Hoyt, an urban planning consultant, in his monumental *100 Years of Land Values in Chicago*, has shown how the percentage of Chicago land values contained in the Loop has risen and fallen many times in the short span of Chicago's lifetime from 1833 to 1933. Decentralization has not been a continuing process. In the development of American cities, both centralizing and decentralizing forces have worked. Now one dominates; tomorrow it may be the other.

Opinion often seems to stray, too, in interpreting the effect of a few skyscrapers and other intensive developments on future land values. Their advent convinces many landholders that high land prices can be met.

But multistory buildings are substitutes—enormously effective ones—for land. A few of them can pay high land prices, but to do it they drain demand from blocks around. To be sure, they are also magnets pulling trade to the city from miles away. But when cities all over the country are racing to the sky, outside competition tends to offset this benefit.

High buildings are symptoms of high land prices. But to let a symptom be a cause is to run a danger of circular reasoning.

If land prices are prematurely high to begin—higher than long-run supply-demand balance warrants—intensive vertical development must ultimately deflate the price balloon. The longer this deflation is delayed, the more the error compounds, and the more violent must be the reaction.

The same general lines of reasoning apply to horizontal urban expansion. This is land substitution, too, destined ultimately to cheapen urban land. Yet the psychological impact may be to create a feeling of central position that leads to higher asking prices, more horizontal extension, and a rude awakening some day.

ALONG WITH THOSE UNDERESTIMATES of supply there are overestimates of demand.

A prominent cause is exaggerated reliance on population forecasts. These have been notoriously unreliable in the past. Techniques have improved, but there is little warrant for the utter confidence with which forecasts are often repeated. But this is not the main point.

Population forecasts, if accurate, tell us something about the volume of "need," but not so much about effective demand, which is another animal, and the one whose power makes the economic world go round.

Some half of the postwar building boom has been to produce more space per person—that is, greater spending per capita has been as much a factor as greater population. Undoubling of families, which was one element in this trend, has now virtually halted—the average number of persons per household has leveled off at about 3.3 since 1954. The recent and immediately forecast swelling of population is in the relatively unproductive age groups under 18 and over 65. But neither babies nor aged dependents increase one's income or borrowing power.

Supporting them does tend to reduce breadwinners' savings. Many analysts translate this into increased effective demand. It may increase demand for toys and TV, but no factor that increases the urgency of present over future needs is likely to increase the investment demand for a long-term, deferred-income asset like title to land, especially undeveloped land. Reduced saving, higher interest rates, and lower land prices follow in logical sequence. More schoolchildren also mean higher real-estate taxes, which tend to reduce the investment demand for land.

Then there are two sources of demand that almost by necessity are only temporary but that operators on the field of action may be unable to distinguish from more permanent sources of demand.

One is demand premised on anticipations of rising land prices. High prices themselves, once realized, tend to depress demand, of course, but expectations of rising prices have the opposite effect. They increase demand not only from avowed speculators but to some extent from all land buyers, including builders and owner-occupants, who are as glad as anyone to board the price elevator on the ground floor.

This demand is inherently very unstable. On the way up, it helps fulfill its own expectations, in the familiar pattern of speculative markets wherein expectations of rising prices make prices rise. Eventually, however, even if higher prices fail to dampen expectations of further rises, they certainly increase carrying costs and dampen the basic demands of ultimate consumers.

Once prices stop rising, this unreliable element of demand is likely to collapse. If it is a large share of the total demand, its desertion will then let prices sink. Stability is next to impossible in such a market. Prices either continue up or turn down.

A second unstable element of demand is that generated by investment in construction.

Construction is largely a migratory industry, which creates temporary demands on local facilities in areas of growth. This poses no difficult forecasting question around fly-by-night construction camps. But elsewhere it is all too easy to confuse temporary demand from construction spending with demand from more permanent sources. They are hard to distinguish in a complex, interdependent, growing urban economy.

A small confusion of this sort may be multiplied into a large error because of the leverage effect of outside money on the development of a region.

Because growth areas are capital-hungry as a rule, construction usually is financed largely from outside. Outside money flowing into an area serves as part of its economic "base"—that is, it sets up demand for local services and sustains it by offsetting the inevitable cash outflows.

Because local services account for roughly half of the incomes of most cities, each dollar of income financed from outside serves as "base" for another dollar or so of income from services sold locally. Then there are many market-oriented or camp-following industries, which move to an area largely because consumers are there ahead of them. When we consider them, a dollar of outside money may exert several dollars' leverage on local income, depending on the locale.

Because these local sellers also require buildings and urbanized land with utilities for working and living, they set up demands for more construction, which means more outside money—and so on. Such a sequence, once started wrong, can send development veering off course like a sliced golf ball. We have seen this happen in the midst of our postwar prosperity around the atomic boomtowns of Portsmouth, Ohio, Paducah, Ky., and Aiken, S. C. With full foreknowledge that construction payrolls were temporary, these three communities contrived to overbuild anyway, and each suffered its depression-in-a-teapot when the crews left town.

Expansion of local banking often adds to the possibility of error. Outside money flowing in increases the reserves of local banks and encourages them to lend. Under our banking system, they can expand their loans by more than the increase of reserves. This expansion would generally lead to drains on reserves that would stop it short. But it need not happen immediately, especially in a booming district, where much of the banking system's new loans come back to it in new deposits. The expanding loans of local banks meanwhile, serve like outside money, as part of the economic "base."

The situation may be complicated once more where outside money flows in, not simply to finance construction or buy land, but to speculate in the extreme sense of the word—to buy and sell and buy again. It is well known that New York banks have large deposits held to speculate in Wall Street. When a city or district catches the imagination of the more colorful part of the investment community, funds pour into its banks for similar purposes. Homer Vanderblue, then of Harvard University, found that bank deposits tripled in 14 months of 1924 and 1925 in the Florida land boom, only to flow out rapidly with the crash.

The wisdom of investors, or at least their conservatism, might seem proof against this sort of folly. But investors in boom times have been notoriously susceptible to fads and stampedes.

Homer Hoyt laid down as a general rule: "In each successive land boom there is a speculative exaggeration of the trend of the period. . . ."

And as long as outsiders are ready to finance it, there is nothing to stop a new district or town from prospering while the residents, exporting little but mortgages, deposit slips, and land titles, simply build the place and take in each other's washing.

Outside investors are not going to do this knowingly. Jacob Stockfisch, economist at the University of Wisconsin, maintains that individuals can foresee tolerably well the complex interactions of their investments with those of others and trim their sails so as to achieve an orderly integrated economic development. But history leaves little doubt that this ideal behavior presupposes a foresight and exchange of information which fallible, suspicious man seldom achieves.

We return to our third critical question: Can urban expansion be a stable process?

A pattern of expansion that stimulates vast oversupplies of urbanized land to meet a demand that is partly collapsible obviously presents some danger of instability. The United States Census of Governments, in its Advance Release No. 3 for 1957, reported the number of vacant lots of record in the United States at nearly 13 million (not counting parking lots). That is 21 percent of all city lots, and about 13 times the annual consumption in new construction.

The census figure does not purport to be more than an aggregation of local records, and some of the "lots" recorded are no doubt that in name only. On the other hand, some actual lots never find their way into local records. And the figure is especially striking in light of the universal observation that subdividing land for sale of lots to avowed speculators has been at a minimum during the postwar building boom, with its emphasis on mass-produced suburban developments from which lots are sold only underneath houses.

The larger part of the land hanging over urban markets is acreage not yet subdivided into lots, but with ready access to farflung urban transportation and utility networks.

A study of Greensboro, N. C., in 1956 by George Esser, Jr., of the Institute of Government of the University of North Carolina, found 125 thousand persons scattered over a quasi-urbanized area big enough for all the needs of 600 thousand. We have no reason to believe that that is anything but typical of American cities.

Will private and public developers add indefinitely to so swollen an inventory?

Will speculators and holdouts want to continue meeting the rising carrying costs on just the present supply?

Will lenders continue to extend credit on such hazardous collateral? With 143 billion dollars in nonfarm residential and commercial mortgages (in September 1957), could the credit system stand a real-estate collapse?

No one knows for certain. History puts the burden of proof on the affirmative. Cities have rarely expanded other than in crashing waves, and today one sees several portents reminiscent of previous crests.

Some of these portents are:

The rapid, manyfold rise of land prices around growing cities since 1950;

the sharp rise of construction costs;

the wildfire spread of municipal zoning and regulations very hostile to mass-market building;

the decline of residential construction since early 1955, coupled with an increase of land-substitutive construction in extensions of roads and utilities, and multistory buildings;

the disproportionate increase of transportation costs and utility rates since 1950;

the disproportionate increase and high level of residential and commercial debt. (Its average annual increase has been 9.5 billion dollars from 1945–1956, and its annual percentage growth rate 14.4 percent over the 1946 base. That compares to 2.2 billions, and 9.4 percent, for the period 1920–1930. In September 1957, it reached 143 billions, 48 percent of disposable personal income. That compares to 37 billions, and 45 percent, in 1929.);

the general deterioration in the quality of credit, as noted by Geoffrey Moore, of the National Bureau of Economic Research, and others, and as exemplified by the growth of second-mortgage financing;

the high level of interest rates;

the almost universal confidence that growing population and living standards are pressing on the land supply and insure a continual rise of land prices.

The result of these combined causes will depend largely on human response, private and public, which few would be so bold as to forecast.

Past mistakes, if that is what they are, have not trapped us in any dilemma beyond the power of informed, intelligent action to resolve.

It is heartening to see so much concern quickening today over problems of urban expansion. There is hope that today's more literate and prudent American public can avert the disasters that beset the past.

But whatever the immediate outcome, the public and its representatives, including farm-dominated State legislatures, would probably serve themselves well to attend closely to the compelling problems of harnessing urban land. This resource holds economic forces of titanic power for welfare or destruction. Harnessed, these forces could serve the public commensurately with their unrivaled market values. Untamed, unpredictable, and irresponsible, they could figure in a national calamity.

Indeed, they have already done so in a measure. The disintegration of our cities could be described conservatively as a national calamity of some proportions, whose mischievous consequences only wait to be recognized. To forestall more of the same, the reasoning of this chapter suggests that policymakers might do well to take steps to lower the prices asked for urban lands.

The thesis of this chapter is that urban land prices are uneconomically high—that the "scarcity" of urban land is an artificial one, maintained by the holdout of vastly underestimated supplies in anticipation of vastly overestimated future demands. I think this uneconomical price level imposes a correspondingly uneconomical growth pattern on expanding cities. High land prices discourage building on vacant lands best situated for new development and divert

resources to building highways, utility networks, and whole new complexes of urban amenities so as to provide and serve substitute urban lands further out—substitutes for something that is already in long supply. Not only is this pattern wasteful of time, steel, cement, gasoline, and good farmland; it founds national prosperity on the film of a land bubble.

And so it would seem wise for policymakers to set about lowering asking prices for urban land. But here they meet a dilemma. What stimulates building is not falling prices, but the end result of the fall—low prices. Falling prices themselves tend to depress building. Few there are who want to invest their money on the foundation of a sinking land market.

Policymakers are tempted to put off the day of reckoning, to tolerate and, in fact, actively support high land prices. But the irony of such policies is that they stimulate development of still more substitute urban lands, and set the stage for more drastic ultimate collapse.

There seems one obvious escape from this dilemma. As it must be done, do it quickly. Bring land prices down fast, and get it over with.

If this is a desirable policy, however, history offers little comfort that it will be enacted without painful changes in established attitudes. Squeezing the water from speculative land prices has usually been a slow process of attrition, with public agencies often bending their efforts toward delaying the inevitable as long as possible, while building stagnated.

But whatever policies are desirable, I believe there certainly is urgent need for public-minded citizens to agree on what those are now, before an emergency strikes. For the suburban land boom shows many evidences of evolving along the same lines as its notorious predecessors, which have confronted us with several of the most trying crises in American history. We can ill afford to meet one today as indecisively and ineffectively as in the past.

Planning for
a better use—Planning and zoning for the future—
Planning for stability in a great area—Safe, efficient, and attractive highways—Public development of resources—Arrangements for our public lands—Tenure and the use of farm resources—Planning for the new land frontier—Balanced development of resources

Planning and zoning for the future.

Most people plan for the future—for the education of their children, for their own progress and security, for their old age. Communities, too, have learned—sometimes too late—the wisdom of making blueprints for future growth. A tool is the zoning ordinance. By *Erling D. Solberg, agricultural economist, Farm Economics Research Division.*

LONG BEFORE the United States was formed, the tiny settlements along the Atlantic coast were adopting measures to restrain people from using their land in ways that would cause injury to others or to the community.

The earliest measures grew out of unhappy experiences with explosions and fires and were simple regulations to keep gunpowder mills and storehouses outside a settlement.

Market towns, like Boston, were authorized to assign locations for slaughterhouses, stillhouses, and buildings in which tallow was tried and leather was tanned.

The early laws were passed in the interest of people's health, comfort, and safety. No more restraint was placed on the use of private property than was deemed necessary to protect the rights of others.

As the country grew, cities and problems grew. The way people used their land sometimes hurt others. Areas with mixtures of homes, stores, and factories sometimes ended as slums. Slums sometimes became hazards to health, safety, morals, and the general welfare.

As was the case many years before, vexing land-use problems resulted in the shaping of corrective measures. Separate zoning districts were created for homes, for business, and for industry. Conflicting land uses were thus set apart. Other zoning regulations were shaped to prevent overcrowding. This was done by limiting the height and size of buildings. The same objective was attained by regulating the size of building tracts and yards. Larger lots with ample yards allow for fewer houses and fewer persons on an acre.

A bursting of city boundaries in the booming 1920's brought unguided growth to the fringes of cities, but it was gentle compared to what was to come later.

Urban expansion became an explosion after the Second World War. All over the country new forces transformed rural communities. Good roads and automobiles permitted city people to spread over the countryside. Farm people in great numbers found employment and new homes in and near urban centers.

Trade areas and daily commuting distances came to be measured in terms of travel time rather than in miles. Millions of people began to make hour-long morning and evening trips between home and work. Expressways and higher permissible speeds brought outlying areas within commuting zones. New suburbs burgeoned beyond suburbs, and beyond were scattered subdivisions.

New communities took shape in forms that could not be foreseen, as pups of unknown ancestry may become dogs of unexpected size and shape. Urban expansion meant the building of many well-planned business and industrial districts and attractive residential suburbs, but it also brought ugly areas of haphazard growth and mixed uses—ribbon districts of roadside blight, dreary miles of honkytonks, billboards, gas stations, junkyards, shops, and homes. Yesterday's good residential areas came to look like untended orphan tracts.

In places there was a helter-skelter peppering of nonfarm dwellings on small rural tracts, premature subdivisions that were not sold, and scattered housing strung out along country roads.

Mushrooming communities developed fiscal ailments. Many improvements—roads, streets, schools, libraries, water and sewage facilities, and so on—were needed at once. Many citizens encountered an unexpected increase in assessments and taxes to pay for the necessary public services. Crowded highways and road hazards presented dangers.

Some farmers faced new problems as subdivisions engulfed their farms. A few moved away with windfall profits from the sale of their land at high prices. Those who remained had higher taxes for public improvements and services that they did not need or want. Their farm plants were damaged, and their operating costs increased.

As in colonial days, the problems stem from unwise relationships in the uses of neighboring tracts of land. In colonial days, however, the problems were obvious, and the corrective restraints were simple. Today's problems are a complex mixture of fiscal matters, public services, the use and changing values of land, health, safety, and attitudes.

Measures adopted in efforts to solve such problems should be preventive, rather than curative: They should prevent problems from arising. They require a community plan, a general blueprint that will suggest how present and future public and private improvements and land uses should be related to each other.

Has urban expansion swept through your community and left a host of problems? Is it only beginning or still ahead—and have preparations been made for the expected guest? Must room be found for urban growth—new homes, stores, factories, schools?

A community can choose the pattern of its growth. It can sit idly by and allow the development of a haphazard mixture of conflicting land uses, or it can guide growth in such a way as to prevent uses that will be harmful to other landowners and to the community.

It can forestall a mixture of factories, stores, junkyards, and homes. It can allow the development of desirable residential districts and protect them with zoning regulations. It can regulate the size of lots to assure a safe separation of wells and septic tanks. It can enclose productive agricultural areas on the urban fringe in districts from which unwanted business and industry are excluded. All these it can do for its safety, comfort, and its prosperity by planning and zoning.

EVERYONE PLANS. You hear it every day: "I plan to build a new barn." "We plan to save our money for a vacation." "We plan to build a new school." Each time, the speaker has examined what he possesses and has considered ways for obtaining what he or the group wants. Each plan embraces problems, needs, and goals.

A community plan is only a large-scale version of a family or group plan.

The basic steps in preparing a community plan are the same as in preparing one for a family.

First, the community makes a careful study of what it has now.

Second, it gives thought to its current and future problems and needs and to its potential. It decides what it wants in the future. This step involves the preparation of a master plan.

The final step is for the community to develop practical ways to put the master plan into effect.

WHAT DOES THE COMMUNITY have now? It has land, improvements, an economic base, local government, and people. Essential information about each of these may be presented on maps or in reports.

Maps will be useful that show topography, mineral resources, soil types and land-use capabilities, streams and other sources of water, and present land uses. Areas used for industry, business, homes, farms, forests, and recreation are indicated.

Other maps will be needed to show the location of transportation facilities, public utilities, services, schools, parks, and other public buildings and improvements.

It will be well to have data on the economic base of present industries, trade and market areas, employment, wages and income, and the contribution to the community's economic base from agriculture and related processing industries and supply firms.

Information should be available about public activities in the community—the location of publicly owned lands; copies of plans of local, State, and Federal agencies to develop those lands; data on taxation and bonded debt; current public construction; and the cost of providing public services in various parts of the community.

Copies will be needed of subdivision and zoning ordinances, if any exist.

Highly important will be information about the people in the community; trends in the growth of population; the age distribution; educational levels and technical and trade skills; private and public housing and the rate of construction; and provisions and future requirements as to public welfare, health, and cultural life.

Such matters will determine the amount and location of facilities that make a community worth living in—schools, churches, health clinics, theaters, libraries, community centers, ballparks, swimming pools, townhalls, and many more.

ASSEMBLING INFORMATION about what the community has is like taking inventory. It permits the community to base its plans on facts rather than guesswork. This second step in the planning process involves preparation of a master plan to guide growth.

Planning for a community, like planning for a family, is using foresight about its own needs and objectives. Growth brings changes, for better or worse, and problems that become harder to solve as time goes by.

Each master plan therefore should have maps that show a desirable scheme of land use, including areas for new industry, business, homes, and agriculture, if it is a rural community. More people will need more jobs, safe and convenient places to shop, attractive homes, land for farming and gardening, and areas for rest and play. Determining the areas in a community that are most suitable for each of these land uses requires study.

A GROWING COMMUNITY also needs new roads and streets, schools, public buildings, water mains, sewers, and other public facilities. Estimates of how many of these improvements a community will need and when are based on population trends and on realistic, careful studies of expected industrial, business, and residential growth: An overinvestment in public improvements may become burdensome.

Where should the proposed public improvements be located? Locations might be selected with a view to making the fullest use of present and proposed facilities.

The location of public buildings, roads, and other facilities will influence the use made of land. Because their absence tends to discourage most kinds of nonfarm development, the community's control over the location of facilities can foster its orderly growth.

Most plans suggest ways for obtaining new development but try not to sacrifice what is valuable in the old. They reserve productive areas for agriculture, but look far enough ahead to a time when it may be necessary to let them be turned to nonfarm uses.

Thought should be given to guiding growth, where practical and feasible, toward the less productive land so that the better lands are reserved for farming.

A realistic safeguarding of the community's agricultural base will benefit many persons besides those already on the land—those who own, operate, or work in plants that process farm products and dealers, truckers, banks, merchants, and others who provide the goods and services that farmers buy.

Planners should be aware of possible conflicts between urban and agricultural interests. Townspeople may object to smoke from smudge pots, dust from farming operations, noises and smells from farm animals, noise of tractors at unusual hours, and the spraying and dusting of crops. Water tables may drop because of pumping for subdivisions in some farming areas. Pollution of streams may affect water for irrigation. Drinking water from wells may be contaminated with septic tank effluents. Farmlands may be flooded because of runoff from roofs and streets of subdivisions. Trespass increases, particularly at harvesttime.

THE THIRD STEP is to put the master plan into effect.

That is done by the government of the county or community and by private persons and concerns. The master plan is their guide in making public improvements—roads, schools, water mains, sewers—and the private homes, stores, factories.

The success of the plan depends a great deal on the cooperation of private builders and developers—as well as on the interest, understanding, and support of the citizens.

A way to gain that support is to let people know the purposes of the plan and to give them ample opportunity to express their views. Public hearings on the proposals give them this opportunity; besides, they are necessary in a democracy.

A good plan may be expected to receive support from all groups, but a community will need to provide direction and guidance through subdivision regulations, a sanitary code, a building code, and a sound zoning ordinance.

The adoption of a plan or ordinance is in itself not the whole goal. It must be administered; that means it must be properly drawn up and subject to revision to keep step with developments and the wishes and needs of the community.

A GOOD ZONING ORDINANCE is a useful tool for assuring development according to the master plan.

The ordinance sets forth the zoning districts in the community or county and specifies the uses permitted in each. Many agricultural counties and townships have three to five kinds of districts. Most county ordinances establish agricultural, residential, business, and industrial zones. Counties in the midst of rapid urban expansion may need two or more districts of each major type, as, for example, a zone for light industry and another for heavy industry.

Zoning districts and their related regulations are legal instruments for doing certain tasks for the community.

Many factors need to be kept in mind in selecting suitable areas to zone for residences, business, industry, and farming.

Places that are especially well suited to certain kinds of uses ordinarily should not be diverted to other uses that might conveniently be located elsewhere: If the best locations for factories are zoned for houses, industry may go elsewhere. If the better soils are to be devoted to factories or homes, agriculture may be forced out, and a valuable agricultural base may be lost unnecessarily.

The principles of zoning are based on commonsense and experience. Land zoned for residential areas should be well drained. To be avoided are lowlands that flood; low, wet areas; and places where soil is tight, unless sewers are provided. Such tracts might well be reserved for other uses, such as for recreation. Residential areas should have open spaces. They should be attractive and free of soot and grime. They should be convenient to parks, playgrounds, schools, churches, shopping centers, and places of work. Owners of homes on them should have assurance that conflicting land uses will never be permitted to encroach and lower property values. Roads and streets and water and sewer mains and other service facilities must be considered. Often many tax dollars can be saved by guiding residential development to areas in which public services can be provided most efficiently.

Proper zoning of residential areas will enhance the prosperity and well-being of any community. Most persons who move to the country prefer to live in one-family dwellings. Zoning should protect them by preventing invasion of conflicting land uses, overcrowding, and the depreciation of property values and the tax base.

Regulations for residential districts ordinarily permit harmonious uses of land and buildings and exclude all others. In one-family residential districts, for example, these uses usually are permitted: One-family dwellings; accessory buildings, activities, and uses not conducted as businesses; occupations customarily conducted in the home by doctors and other professional people; buildings and facilities such as schools, playgrounds, parks, churches, libraries, and museums; and customary farming operations. Other uses may be permitted, depending on the wishes of the community.

Uses ordinarily excluded from one-family residential zones include factories, taverns, junkyards, billboards, roominghouses, trailers, stores, filling stations, and theaters. Industries may produce noise, smoke, fumes, and traffic. Stores may cause an increase in noise, litter, fire hazard, and traffic congestion. Areas of mixed uses—to repeat—require more costly roads and streets, water and sanitary facilities, and public services than do areas set aside for homes only.

During the time it takes to change from a farming to a residential district, questions may arise about the keeping of animals. Some zoning ordinances contain no regulations. Others prohibit the keeping of some kinds of farm animals and farming operations; limit the numbers of animals that may be kept on small tracts; relate permissible numbers to tract sizes; or regulate the condition and location on the tract of animal shelters and roaming yards.

It seems fair to exclude such enterprises as commercial hog ranches, goat farms, and mink farms from areas that are zoned for residential use.

No public purpose is fulfilled by applying regulations concerning the keeping of animals on farms, which have ample room.

SEVERAL POINTS should be considered in prescribing the minimum permitted sizes of building lots in residential areas. If public water and sewer mains are available, building tracts may be small, although overcrowding should be avoided. If wells and septic tanks are used, lots must be larger to assure safe water supplies and sanitary fields for the septic tanks. Still larger tracts are required if farm animals are kept.

The shape and the size of yards need to be specified. Wide, rather than long and narrow, tracts allow for adequate open spaces around the houses. Dwellings set far enough back from roads get less dust, noise, and fumes from traffic. Uniform front yards or setbacks add to the appearance of a district. Adequate backyards reduce the fire hazard from houses to the rear, afford a measure of privacy, allow more light and air, are a place for rest and recreation, and provide a safe place for play.

Zoning ordinances often limit the height of residential buildings. One-family dwellings usually are limited to two and one-half stories, not more than 35 feet in height. Church spires, barns, silos, poles, and so on may be higher. Restricting the height of buildings assures a fair sharing of view, light, and air; prevents the pocketing of dwellings, with gloomy, airless siderooms, between taller buildings; keeps one owner from taking advantage of the open spaces provided by others; and controls the density of population. Tall buildings house more people and attract more traffic. Fires are more readily suppressed when houses are low. Homeowners may move away and values may decline when attractive residential areas are invaded by buildings that do not harmonize.

WHERE ARE THE BEST AREAS in a community for expected business growth and for new industry? Recent trends suggest some answers.

Neighborhood shopping centers with ample off-the-road parking space for customers are springing up over the country. These centers, which consist of about a dozen stores, cater to the shopper's everyday needs. Even larger are the community shopping centers and regional shopping centers, which, like the neighborhood centers, are located near traffic arteries. Off-street parking space and proper access lanes are necessary for all of them. The stores should not be close to the roadside.

Industries have special needs. Modern factory buildings of one or two stories are spread over a large acreage. Landscaping and off-street parking areas are provided. Land for industry should be fairly level, well drained, free from floods, and near transportation and utilities. Land fronting on navigable waters, areas near freeways (particularly near important crossings), sites near major airports, and areas up to 2 thousand feet wide between a main highway and railroad tracks are favored.

A community that contains areas with these physical and locational qualities should not permit their use for residences. It will zone enough of this land for industry to take care of present and foreseeable needs. Until they are needed for industry, the reserved areas can be held in large tracts and used for farming.

In many changing rural communities, industry may well become an important base of a new economic life. If suitable industrial sites are not available, industry will look elsewhere.

445509°—58——35

IS THERE ROOM in your county for both urban growth and farming?—or must farming eventually go to make room for residential development and for new business and industry?

In either instance, is the expected transition likely to be orderly and to make the best use of all land resources? Or, is the community's fertile soil likely to be sacrificed?

Among factors other than fertility to be considered in zoning land for farming are location, topography, and weather, including air drainage. Important also are soil type and water, and the presence of irrigation, drainage, and soil-conservation improvements.

Fertile soils are not irreplaceable in the sense that their crop yields cannot be replaced by farming elsewhere, but the fertile soil in a community is irreplaceable. Once converted to nonfarm uses and covered with streets and houses, it is not likely to be reconverted to farm use.

Farmers should realize that zoning in their community protects them. Without zoning, their neighborhoods can easily become a dumping ground for activities that are excluded elsewhere.

Farm-zoned districts may be grouped into three main classes. Those of the first class enclose agricultural areas that are closed to objectionable business and industrial uses. In the second group, nonfarm homes are also discouraged, but not barred. In districts of the third class, the zoning ordinances forbid the construction of nonfarm homes in agricultural areas.

In districts zoned for farming, as in other kinds of districts, certain land uses are permitted and other uses are excluded. The specifications vary with localities.

Regulations for general-farming districts in the first group usually permit all kinds of agricultural land uses, buildings, and activities, except farms for disposal of garbage and offal. Also permitted are residences, both farm and nonfarm, plus home occupations, schools, churches, and the many other uses and facilities that are allowed in residential districts. Other uses that sometimes are permitted are roadside stands that are owned and operated by farmers, plants for processing and storing agricultural products, mining, quarrying, and earth-extraction industries. Additional uses often allowed are noncommercial recreation, public utility buildings and facilities, and airports.

Other uses and activities are excluded from these farming districts and invited to other zones. Among them are most kinds of business and industry, except agricultural industries. Business activities that sometimes are expressly prohibited in farming districts are wrecking yards, taverns, public dancehalls, auto courts, and trailer camps.

IN THE FIRST GROUP of districts, nonfarm residences are permitted on building lots of suitable size. Usually subdivisions are made for nonfarm homes. They usually require more public services, including new schools, and so bring an increase in local assessments and taxes. In an effort to avoid these consequences and to retard premature parceling, another zoning tool—the large minimum building lot or tract regulation—has been used in the second group of districts. Sizable minimums that range up to 5 acres have been required at times. (In a district near an airport in Colorado, a minimum of 20 acres was set.) Large building tracts discourage residential development in agricultural districts.

A more direct approach is used in a third group of zoned farming districts. Only agriculture, a few related activities that further the use of land for farming, and certain public and semipublic uses are permitted. All other uses, including nonfarm residences, are excluded. To be doubly sure, large minimum tracts ranging by districts up to 10 acres also are required. The designation of such districts is new in agricultural zoning, but—almost since the beginning of zoning—suitable areas have been set aside for homes and related uses only. In Wisconsin and adjacent States, large areas of cutover lands that are of poor quality for farming have been set apart for forestry and recreational uses only. In recent years, a growing number of exclusive zoning districts for business only and for industry only have been created. Now agriculture is catching up.

The primary land uses in all exclusive-type farm zoning districts are agricultural. Other permitted land uses are secondary and accessory to farming. Residences are permitted only as accessory uses to the permitted agricultural uses. Usually the need for farmhousing varies with the intensity of farming and with its type. It includes housing for owners, tenants, and others who work on the land.

The various types of farming call for farm sites of appropriate but differing sizes. Intensive types of farming often are conducted on small tracts—for example, nurseries and greenhouses on 1-acre tracts, poultry farms on tracts of 3 to 5 acres, and feedlot dairies of 5 or 10 acres. Zoning regulations reflect these differing needs.

Districts zoned for farming and related uses only have been created to protect general farming areas as well as areas of specialized farming, such as orchards, truck crops, dairying, and poultry farming. Districts range in size from a 35-acre zone used for growing field and greenhouse flowers to a district that contains 175 square miles and is devoted to several types of farming. Whatever the prevailing agriculture or the size of the district, the zoning regulations need to be shaped to serve local needs.

ADDITIONAL INFORMATION on planning and zoning may be obtained from a number of sources. Nearest to home are the planning and zoning agencies in most cities and in many towns, villages, counties, and townships. Some States have State planning boards, development organizations, and similar agencies that may be helpful. Colleges and universities in some States may be sources of information and aid.

A professional organization in the planning and zoning field is the American Society of Planning Officials, 1313 East 60th Street, Chicago 37, Ill.

Among publications that may be helpful are Rural Zoning in the United States, Agricultural Information Bulletin No. 59, January 1952, United States Department of Agriculture, Washington, D. C.; The Ins and Outs of Planning, 1952, State Planning Section, New Jersey Department of Conservation and Economic Development, 520 East State Street, Trenton, N. J.; Your Community and Township Zoning, Circular Bulletin 184, February 1945, Agricultural Experiment Station, Michigan State College, East Lansing, Mich.; How To Make Rural Zoning Ordinances More Effective, Circular 546, April 1957, Extension Service, College of Agriculture, University of Wisconsin, Madison, Wis.; Farm Land Disappears, September 1953, and Agricultural Zoning Makes Sense, September 1954, Agricultural Extension Service, University of California, Berkeley, Calif.; County Zoning in Illinois, Publication 109, April 1952, Illinois Legislative Council, Springfield, Ill.; Zoning in New York State, a Guide to the Preparation of Zoning Ordinances, 1952, Department of Commerce, State of New York, 112 State Street, Albany 7, N. Y.; Principles of Industrial Zoning, August 1951, National Industrial Zoning Committee, 820 Huntington Bank Building, Columbus 15, Ohio; Zoning and Civic Development, January 1950, Chamber of Commerce of the United States, Washington 6, D. C.

Since the last issue of the Democrat, a great excitement has prevailed throughout our town. At 6 o'clock, Saturday evening, many of our prominent citizens seated themselves at the door of the Land Office, that they might secure, in season, the door for the Monday morning following. Before break of day on Sunday morning, some fifty had gathered upon the steps and registered their names in a book. This little band continued to hold its own till afternoon, when many more were added. Evening came, and still larger numbers gathered. During the day, however, the speculators had been laboring to enforce the number system, which gave each man (settlers excepted) an opportunity of registering his chance to enter the Land Office and enter two quarter-sections of land.

Outsiders, finding themselves thwarted on every hand, resolved to make one general rally, and if possible, crowd those at the door up so hard that they would yield their positions. At one time scores would rush up against them in front, then on the sides, then upon the front and side at the same time.

These operations were continued, and were for the most part unsuccessful, from about five till nearly eight A. M., when more harsh means were used. We passed the office at about seven, and saw many who were nearly exhausted from fatigue, having stood upon their feet thirty-six hours. A constant agitation and clamor was kept up by the crowd on the outside, until many were so crushed that they fainted . . . .

Window panes were broken out from a tier of lights above the door, and several buckets of water thrown upon the fainting ones below. The Register, seeing many were likely to be killed, and others badly injured, went upon the roof of the building, and declared that none who pushed or crowded should be served that day. This served to produce the desired effect upon many; others were so much wrought up that they almost felt desperate.

At 9 o'clock the door opened, and many fell prostrate and nearly helpless upon the floor. To sum the matter in brief, we have never seen a more distracted and desperate set of men than were about that office. All were armed, and resolved to defend themselves to the last. Mr. E. M. Downs of this place had a leg broken; a gentleman from Ohio had some two or three of his ribs broken, besides a large number of persons who were badly injured, but were fortunate enough to have no limbs broken.—Dubuque [Iowa] DAILY REPUBLICAN, *June 19, 1857.*

Planning for stability in a great area.

What some persons have come to call the Dust Bowl is a broad empire of good soil and big potentialities. It is also a land of little rain and recurrent drought, when unprotected soil may blow away. It is suited to range and pasture, but people forget that in the occasional years when moisture is barely ample and prices are good. Here are some helpful suggestions. By *Erling D. Solberg*.

THE GREAT PLAINS is one of the great sections where the way land is used demands special attention and caution.

It encompasses the parts of Montana, Wyoming, Colorado, and New Mexico that lie east of the Rocky Mountains; western North Dakota and South Dakota; and Nebraska, Kansas, Oklahoma, and Texas.

It is an area of recurrent drought and crop failures. Duststorms have occurred in all 10 States, but the worst wind erosion has been in the southern part. People called it the Dust Bowl after the severe drought of 1931–1938. Drought struck again in 1950 and lasted until 1957, and there were more duststorms.

The crops are good when moisture is ample. The soils usually are deep and rich in plant nutrients. People therefore are encouraged to expand the acreage in crops when a few successive seasons have fairly good rain and snow. If prices also are good, more virgin sod may be turned under and restored sod replowed. The hot winds come, the crops wither, and the soils blow. That has happened four times since the area was settled in the 1880's. Year after year of low rainfall leads to disaster. A lesson then is relearned: The long-term average precipitation must always be heeded in dry-farming areas.

A precipitation of about 20 inches a year, the longtime average in the area,

is considered the minimum for growing crops without irrigation. A serious error is to regard the rainfall of a series of wet years as permanent.

Soil blowing is so frequent on some of the land or cropping is so hazardous that permanent retirement to pasture is desirable. Other lands are suitable for growing tilled crops under restricted practices, except in severe drought, when they, too, need to be protected by a cover of grass.

The Great Plains Agricultural Council has estimated that almost 14 million acres of land in the Plains used for growing grain and other crops are physically unsuited for crops. Nearly 15 million acres used for crops in 1957 are considered suitable for crop production only part of the time.

The dust falls on land in well-adjusted agriculture and on land in unstable agricultural uses—on the just and the unjust. It damages crops and pastures. The damage may be local or widespread. The soil from one field may settle across the line fence or beyond county and State boundaries. Duststorms are an individual, local, State, and regional problem.

The problem, the recurrent dust, is obvious. The causes seem clear. The remedies have been outlined, but shaping them has proved to be difficult.

A 1956 publication, Program for the Great Plains, Miscellaneous Publication No. 709, Department of Agriculture, outlines a program for improving agriculture in the Dust Bowl:

"The goal to be achieved is a more stable agriculture, more dependable sources of income, and progressively satisfactory livelihood for the people of the region. To achieve this goal, there must be widespread use of good soil management and water conservation practices and adjustments in sizes and types of farms which will enable farmers and ranchers to effectively cope with the climatic hazards of the region."

A necessary first step is to take inventory of soil capabilities—to step up the survey of soils of each farm in critical wind-erosion sections in order to permit land-use adjustments on the basis of facts, rather than guesswork.

Carrying out the program of needed changes in land use and suitable land and water conservation practices requires cooperative efforts of farmers, ranchers, civic and agricultural groups, and local, State, and Federal Governments and agencies. It will involve outlays for establishing conservation practices, making needed improvements, and attaining adjustments in land-ownership and size of operating units. It will take time.

Suitable measures to regulate the use of land can be helpful.

THE MEASURES can shorten the time required to make needed changes in land uses and practices. Their objectives might be to restore wind-damaged lands physically; prevent the plowing up in the future of new areas of potential blow lands; prevent the recurrence of soil blowing after restoration in crop and pasture areas; prevent future wind damage to lands in normally safe farming areas; and encourage the blocking up of economic farming and ranching units.

A final objective would be to protect conservation gains and still allow for future adjustments. The regulations might permit a temporary expansion of the acreages of grains and fiber during periods of national need. A waiver of restrictions, with adequate safeguards, may be desirable under some circumstances.

Existing measures for regulating the use of land could be employed, perhaps with some reshaping, to help attain the objectives.

Available legal materials are the existing types of land-use measures and techniques. Among them are rural zoning, soil conservation district land-use regulations, easements, and protective covenants.

Public ownership of some acreage might have a place, perhaps with limits as to the length of time it can be held, the rights in land, and the total acreage. Questions arise as to the level of government that would administer measures to regulate the use of the land.

Zoned districts have been created in some States to protect specified land uses and prevent the establishment of harmful uses. Harmful uses that were there before zoning are known as nonconforming uses and usually are allowed to remain.

Zoning regulations may differ by districts, but all properties situated alike within a district must be treated alike. The regulations may be used to prohibit new uses that are harmful. They may not be used to compel the doing of specific acts. Zoning usually is on a local basis, but other units of government may pass zoning ordinances.

Of the States in the Dust Bowl, all but counties in Texas and New Mexico and rural counties in Kansas, Nebraska, and Oklahoma had zoning powers in 1958. The powers granted were intended primarily to enable counties to influence suburban development. None of the States in the Dust Bowl, except South Dakota, had expressly empowered their counties to enact zoning ordinances for regulating uses of agricultural land.

Soil conservation districts, organized in most of the counties in the area, are empowered to adopt land-use ordinances if approved by a favorable vote.

District regulations may prohibit and compel. They may prohibit the use of land in specified harmful ways. They may require special methods of cultivation, contour plowing, strip-cropping, rotation of crops, terracing, and shifting any steep or erodible land from cultivation into trees or grass.

Soil conservation district regulations as to use of land do not exempt existing harmful—nonconforming—uses from the regulations, as is done under zoning ordinances. Instead, land-use regulations may be used to compel the discontinuance of harmful land uses and practices that existed before the regulations were passed.

There are other differences. Zoning regulations are generally applied by districts that contain sizable areas. Land-use regulations may be applied by tracts within a district as small as a farm or a part of a farm. One has its roots in land uses; the other in land capabilities. Neither zoning restraints nor land-use regulations involve compensation for alleged or actual damages. Both kinds of regulations are an exercise of public police powers.

A SECOND GROUP of measures involves public acquisition and ownership of such rights in the land as are required to obtain the needed degree of control of land uses. The rights acquired might consist of all rights in lands that are subject to serious wind erosion.

Another plan envisions public ownership of less than the whole bundle of rights. For payments or other consideration, only conservation rights might be acquired. Conservation rights in many areas might consist of cropping rights. All other property rights in blow lands (including the right to pasture and to harvest hay crops) would remain in private ownership.

Publicly acquired conservation rights to restrict future uses of blow lands might be vested under either of two legal devices: By formal conveyance by the owner of a cropping easement or by a contractual promise in writing, called a protective covenant, in which the owner agrees to the restrictions.

An important legal difference exists between the two devices. An easement is an actual conveyance of rights in land. A protective covenant is a contractual promise, which normally is enforceable by an injunction not only against the contracting owner but also against someone taking title with actual or constructive notice.

Easements and protective—restrictive—covenants have been used in urban areas for many years. These legal devices, like early zoning, were shaped to gain urban objectives under urban conditions. Some reshaping might be needed to attain new objectives in rural areas. Certain difficulties that require legislation may arise when control of land use in the Dust Bowl is contemplated by easements or protective covenants.

Easements and protective covenants are flexible. Regulations applied under them result from voluntary contracts, which may vary according to objectives and conditions.

Other programs may be needed to bring a more stable agriculture to the Dust Bowl—those having to do with technical assistance, credit, aids and grants, research, and conservation improvements. Changes in land use and adjustments in landownership and in sizes of farms and ranches will be needed.

How and in what combination could existing regulatory tools, perhaps after some reshaping, be used to help do the tasks at hand in the Dust Bowl? Probably there is no best way. Several combinations of measures might be workable. All likely combinations should be considered.

Under one suggested arrangement, several kinds of regulatory measures could be used at the same time. Zoning regulations could be applied to gain a degree of control over the uses of land in broad areas. Easements or protective covenants could be used to attain more precise control of land uses on specific properties.

Soil conservation district regulations could also be applied to specific properties and used as emergency measures. Possibly, for best results, the administration of some of the measures might be at a level of government higher than the local. Possibly, also, application of land-use regulatory measures in the Dust Bowl should proceed by planning districts of suitable sizes.

Agricultural lands within planning districts might be enclosed in farming zones. Their boundaries might be drawn in broad outline to separate lands that are suited mainly to farming from lands that are suited mainly to grazing. Farming zones might consist largely of land classes I, II, and III and grazing zones largely of land classes IV through VIII. The first three classes are suited for cultivation but with increasing risks of damage, which are slight, moderate, and severe, respectively. Class IV land is suited for occasional cultivation only. Land in classes V, VI, and VII are suited for grazing or forestry. Lands in class VIII are useful for wildlife, watersheds, or recreation.

Both of the proposed kinds of zoning districts, if adopted, would contain lands in stable agricultural uses, as well as lands in actually or potentially unstable agricultural uses. The first category, comprising lands in stable uses, probably would include the lands in classes I, II, and III (suitable for tillage and for growing feed crops) and land in classes VII and VIII (suitable for grazing or other less extensive uses). The second category, lands in unstable uses, would consist of lands in classes IV, V, and VI. These two broad categories would be made a basis for differential treatment.

Lands in the unstable-use category may or may not have been used for crops. They may now be in use for growing cash crops or supplementary feed or for pasture on virgin or restored sod. Past, present, and prospective land uses have long been a basis for regulatory differentials.

In districts to be zoned for farming, four agricultural uses and activities might be permitted, with reservations. Cash crops could be grown without restrictions on lands in classes I, II, and III. They could be grown as permitted nonconforming uses on lands with cropping histories in classes IV through VI. Supplementary feed crops could be grown without restrictions on lands in classes I through VI. All classes of land could be used for pasture.

Land could be used without restriction for farm or ranch headquarters and for such related activities and uses as are necessary or convenient.

In districts that are to be zoned for grazing, five uses and activities might be permitted. Lands of any class could be grazed. Supplementary feed crops could be grown without restriction on lands in classes I through VI. Cash crops could be grown as permitted nonconforming uses on lands with cropping histories in classes I through VI.

Any land could be used without restriction for ranch headquarters and for related activities and uses that are necessary or convenient. Existing farm headquarters could be considered a nonconforming use.

Zoning regulations could be used in the proposed grazing zoning districts to discourage future parceling of ranching units to establish new farms on lands suited primarily for grazing. Such zoning would forestall pressure to grow cash crops and allay tax burdens.

Zoning restrictions might be used in farming and grazing zones to prevent an enlargement of areas that are likely to blow. The regulations might prohibit the breaking of virgin sod on lands in classes IV through VIII and restored sod on the same classes, if the intent to grow future crops has been abandoned legally. In both kinds of zones, land-use regulations might be used to require the carrying out of conservation practices that prevent or minimize soil blowing.

In the zoning plan I presented, traditional rights in nonconforming uses would be fully respected. Other regulatory measures are suggested for obtaining the needed conservation control on land in unstable uses, especially lands that are nonconforming.

Conservation problems and objectives may differ considerably with respect to these lands. The control measures would have to be clear and firm—but also flexible as to time, area, scope, and method of application.

Conservation control of lands in unstable uses, especially nonconforming tracts, might be attained through cropping easements or the right to limit cropping under protective covenants.

The agency selected to administer the regulatory measures might acquire the necessary conservation rights in land in a number of ways and at various times.

It might acquire the needed rights by purchase of fee simple interests (absolute or full ownership), followed by resale of lesser interests, not including conservation rights. It might buy only the needed conservation rights. The expenditure of public funds for restoring grass cover (and possibly for other conservation purposes) might be conditioned on the transfer to the agency of the needed conservation rights.

Both techniques—easements and protective covenants—permit tract-by-tract regulation. Both permit acquisition of conservation rights to proceed at the same pace as the overall conservation program. Under both kinds of legal measures, the scope of the conservation rights acquired might vary with land-capability classes and with conservation needs.

Cropping might be restricted on classes IV, V, and VI lands, whether in large blocks or small tracts. The blocking up of ranch pastures might be aided by prohibiting cropping of isolated tracts in classes I, II, and III.

Either regulatory measure might include provisions, with proper safeguards, for temporary waiving of conservation rights in times of national need on designated classes of land. Permanent waivers might be authorized if restricted land is needed for the growing of feed, irrigation development, or nonfarm purposes or if future technological advances permit cropping without harming the land.

The passing years, since early settlement, have seen regulatory measures shaped and reshaped so they would serve in an ever-changing environment to attain an old and familiar objective: To prevent land uses that cause injury to others and to the community.

Regulatory tools, like farm tools, need to be designed for the tasks they are to do. Old tools, shaped for other jobs in other places, such as cities, could not be expected to work well in the Dust Bowl. New regulatory tools will be needed there. Will new tools be forthcoming? The decision rests with the people of the States concerned, acting through their legislative bodies and regulatory agencies.

The Great Plains

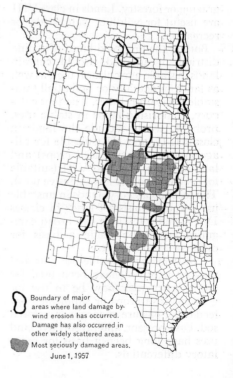

Boundary of major areas where land damage by wind erosion has occurred. Damage has also occurred in other widely scattered areas.

Most seriously damaged areas.

June 1, 1957

Safe, efficient, and attractive highways.

The idea of control and regulation, especially of private property, is objectionable to many in a society based on free enterprise. Accidents, ugliness, inefficiency, exploitation, and needless expense also are objectionable. We are free to choose one set of ideas or the other for the highway systems we are now building. By *Erling D. Solberg.*

ONCE IT WAS a proud, pleasant thoroughfare, and it bore a proud name.

Now you get through it as fast as you can, but that is not fast, for the trucks, the parked cars, the stoplights, and its width, too narrow now for the traffic it handles, slow you down, sometimes to no progress at all.

Every fourth building, once very likely the home of a prosperous family, seems now to have a sign, *Tourists.* Every third house, perhaps with a false front, has a sign: *Beer, Pizza, Groceries, Aunt Minnie's Cafe, Joe's Hotdog Shoppe, Ice Cream, Soft Drinks.* Others offer insurance, real estate, used cars. The rest are stores that seem to have no business, whatever their brave, bright lights and their gaudy pretensions; a few that people live in; a few, falling down and unkempt, adjoin auto graveyards or junkyards. Equally depressing are recurrent blocks of weed-grown vacant lots—vacant except for the billboards clamoring for your attention.

It's name? It may be the Baltimore Pike, which leads from the Nation's Capital to the University of Maryland and the Agricultural Research Center at Beltsville; the route of kings, U. S. 101, south of San Francisco; U. S. 99, the main road south of Seattle; highway 70, the route from Nashville to Memphis and Little Rock. It may be in your own State, for such roads radiate from most large cities.

They are the result of a failure 10 or 20 years ago to plan for an increase in traffic. They also are a lesson for the future. They are ugly, unsafe, and costly.

A study of traffic accidents on about 400 miles of highway in Minnesota disclosed a direct relationship between traffic accidents and the number of access points—the customers' driveways to a business establishment, of which every ribbon-developed highway has many. The sections of highway with the most commercial access points had the most accidents. Advertising signs also seemed to have a connection with the number of accidents—the accident rate was higher on roads and streets that had the most signs.

The empty, weed-grown lots—what will happen to them? Will they be developed for business? Very likely not, for only 2 or 3 percent of the developed area of the average community is used for business. Then for homes? Very likely the lots are overpriced for homes; even at lower prices, they might not be wanted for homesites.

You wonder about the future of the business in such roadside districts, where congestion is bad. Possibly a bypass will soon be built to divert traffic around it. Will a bypass hurt business and lower property values?

Something of an answer is given by the experience of two Indiana towns, Lebanon and Kokomo, where bypasses were opened to divert through traffic around the central business sections. Parking problems and congestion in

537

the downtown areas were eased greatly. Total business increased 3.7 percent in Lebanon but dropped 4.4 percent in Kokomo. In both towns, businesses that catered to local customers increased, while businesses that served through traffic (such as tourist courts, service stations, and eating places) declined. Gains and losses in the two towns varied greatly according to the type of business, of course. Business moved to the bypasses, where a number of new business establishments were opened. They may attract customers away from the central business district—and in time there might have to be bypasses to bypass the bypasses. That has happened elsewhere.

The problems I have mentioned arise from the uses made of the land that borders the roads. They affect the traveling public, taxpayers, farmers, suburban homeowners, and States and counties.

For motorists, who foot the bill for new roads made necessary by congestion, highways should be safe, efficient, and attractive. Homeowners, who live in the suburbs or in the country and work in the city, are troubled about their travel time. Farmers and others who use the highways to move their products to market have higher hauling costs because of slow traffic. Businessmen themselves worry about the prospects for their districts—what will happen to Aunt Minnie's cafe and Joe's hotdog emporium?

Two TYPES of measures are available for controlling the uses of land adjacent to highways.

The first involves the purchase or condemnation of rights essential to roadside development. It entails public ownership of strips of land along the highway, besides the land needed for the roadway.

Private use of the margin of the road and access to the road itself can thereby be prevented. Sometimes, instead of outright purchase of these strips of land on the margin, easements—the

right to control their use—in the strips are acquired.

The second type of measure entails the exercise of zoning and similar police powers.

ZONING has been used to restrict the uses that may be made of land that borders roads, to specify the distance between buildings and the roads, to locate offstreet parking facilities, to provide appropriate access points, and to regulate billboards and signs.

Roadside zoning regulations are applied oftenest as part of a community zoning plan. Some States have created strips along both sides of highways. These long zones are a few hundred feet to 1 thousand yards wide.

The degree of regulation and restriction on roadside development to insure safety, comfort, and orderly growth depends somewhat on the classes of highways and the volume and destination of the traffic.

Highways have been classified in various ways—as Federal, State, county, and local, or as interstate, primary, secondary, and local. Primary and interstate highways link States and the larger cities. They carry the heaviest workload, much of which is through traffic. Secondary highways, less traveled, connect smaller centers, and include farm-to-market roads. Local roads serve mainly local traffic.

Opposition to control also may increase with the volume of traffic, because then the interests of owners of roadside land may conflict with the interests of the traveling public. Many business enterprises have been located on roadsides, although the development has resulted in increased traffic hazards, followed by a reduction in permissible speeds and a decline in traffic-carrying capacities. This conflict of interest has given rise to several control measures.

IN A FEW YEARS much traffic will be diverted from existing roadside business areas.

The Federal-Aid Highway Act of

1956 calls for the construction in 13–15 years of an interstate system of highways. Access to them from abutting land will be fully or partly controlled by a public agency. Access may be denied except at selected public roads, intersections, or interchanges.

Construction of the new system of 41 thousand miles began in 1956. The cost has been estimated at 34 billion dollars. Over these major arteries will flow, at expressway speeds, a large share of the Nation's long-distance, passenger car, bus, and truck traffic. The Congress has provided some safeguards to insure that their safety, efficiency, and appearance will not be jeopardized by commercial exploitation of roadsides, but other safeguards have been suggested as being needed also.

FEDERAL AID up to 90 percent of the total costs has been authorized for the purchase of rights-of-way and construction.

Upon request of a State, the Secretary of Commerce may acquire rights-of-way for it. Title to the lands acquired, including an interest in land needed to control access from adjoining land, may be taken in the name of the United States. (Actually, most States buy in their own names the needed rights-of-way.) The Secretary of Commerce later must convey title to the lands or interests in lands acquired to the respective States.

In States that do not provide control of access, through zoning, easements, or in other ways, however, title to the outside 5 feet of rights-of-way must be retained by the Secretary. Ownership of these 5-foot strips will enable the Federal Government to control access and development on the roadsides. If at a later time the laggard States, if any, make provisions for control of access that are satisfactory to the Secretary of Commerce, then the reserved strips must be conveyed to them.

The Secretary will insist upon effective control measures. Public safety and large public investment are involved. Many States presumably will control access along new interstate highways in the same way as the Federal Government. By purchase or condemnation, they will acquire ownership of strips of land or easements that are essential to roadside development. Federal-aid funds may be used for these purposes. Other States may control access by means of regulations applied under public power known as police power (similar to zoning) without payment of compensation.

When no prior right of access exists, as along new highways, the courts are fairly well agreed that owners of abutting land are not entitled to compensation for denial of direct access. The courts are not in such clear agreement, however, regarding a State's right to limit access without paying compensation when it converts an existing highway into one with controlled access— marginal service roads or access to other convenient roads must then be provided or be available.

THE STATES had in operation 4,600 miles of expressways with full or partial control of access in 1956.

Some people have suggested that new Federal laws will be needed to control billboards along the new highways on the grounds that billboards are hazards when traffic moves at expressway speeds because they distract a driver's attention, obscure official signs, and they spoil the countryside.

Others maintain that billboards will help prevent accidents by making driving less monotonous and keeping drivers from dozing. They say also that motels, restaurants, service stations, hotels, and other businesses depend on roadside advertising to attract customers. Many persons feel that any control of billboards should be left to the States and communities.

The Congress considered several billboard-control bills in 1957. One measure would have authorized the use of matching funds (90 percent Federal and 10 percent State) for buying advertising rights along 500-foot strips adjoining rights-of-way. A second proposal was to increase Federal highway aid in States that control billboards. The State could use the additional funds to buy easements, or they could control roadside signs with zoning laws and use the funds saved for other highway purposes. A third proposal would reduce Federal allotments unless the State passes zoning laws barring billboards within 750 feet of the outer edges of pavements. The zoning laws would be administered by State officials. None of the bills was passed.

Essentially similar bills were introduced in 1958.

Two States passed laws in 1957-1958 to regulate billboards. Vermont prohibits the erection of advertising signs, with certain exceptions, within 750 feet of controlled-access highways. Maryland prohibits billboards within 600 feet of all interstate routes and expressways. Exceptions include signs offering the premises for sale or lease and signs advertising produce grown, products made, and services performed on the premises where the signs are.

LOCAL AND STATE police powers have been exercised to control access. Billboard regulations also have been imposed at both levels.

In the past, however, ordinances for roadside zoning have been adopted only by local governments, including counties and townships. The roadsides of many primary, secondary, and local highways have been zoned by rural units of government as part of a community zoning plan. Suitable districts, embracing roadside properties, have been zoned for farming, homes, business, industry, or other uses. Roadsides zoned in this way exist in most States. County zoning ordinances that apply only to road-bordering lands along specified highways have been adopted, however.

Such zoned districts may be grouped into three classes, based primarily on restrictions placed on business activities.

The first type excludes any and all kinds of business establishments from areas extending a stated distance—for example, 1 thousand feet—on both sides of specified highways.

The second type is the roadside-service district. Business in these zones is restricted primarily to activities needed for servicing through traffic. Among the businesses permitted are motels and auto courts, service stations, restaurants and similar establishments, and certain kinds of retail stores and recreational facilities.

Roadside-service districts are tied to through highways. The zones are long and narrow to serve the traveling public better. Reasonable groupings of a variety of establishments are more convenient than isolated filling stations and other businesses strung along the road for miles. Furthermore, roadside service zones serve better if ways are made for the motorist to stop or to go through, as he desires. This is facilitated by the provision of suitable drive-in parking space. Some ordinances prohibit curb parking in order to keep roads open for traffic.

The third type of roadside zone, the general roadside business district, is designed to serve both travelers and residents. These zones usually permit the conventional kinds of retail stores, service stations, commercial recreation facilities, and light manufacturing.

Regulations that pertain to each of these three types of roadside districts usually include provisions for setbacks and offstreet parking, restrictions on outdoor advertising, and sometimes a measure of control over the design of buildings.

Trends in business areas may foreshadow the decline of roadside business districts, especially ribbon districts that depend on the local people for trade. Shopping centers, which are near rather than on traffic arteries and have convenient offstreet parking space, are winning increasing favor.

Which kinds of regulations, if any, are justified along local roads?

Most frequently applied are regulations that require buildings—farm and nonfarm—to be set back stated distances from the right-of-way. Sometimes deeper setbacks are required along busy highways than along less traveled local roads because heavier traffic increases noise, dust, and fumes. Traffic dangers also are lessened by adequate sight distances, especially at intersections.

Commercial uses, including stores, taverns, and billboards, are often barred from areas that are zoned agricultural or residential. These restrictions are usually applied areawide, rather than along the roadsides only. The exclusion prevents an invasion by activities that may be injurious to the neighborhood and that generates traffic on local roads.

Only a beginning has been made in protecting primary and secondary and local highways with zoning. The total of zoned mileage is small, and regulations often are poorly administered. Fewer than half of the counties in the United States had authority in 1958 to zone.

Merely granting zoning power to counties and townships does not assure adoption or enforcement of adequate controls. The community or its neighbor may have poor regulation or none at all. Local pressures may cause a gradual breakdown of the regulations.

Good roadside zoning often ends at a political boundary—but the road passes through.

Roadside zoning ordinances in the past were mainly local products. The benefits from zoning of this kind accrue in large measure to the general public, however. The State's investments in the arterial roads are protected, and traffic safety is enhanced. Roadside landowners, on the other hand, may receive little or no benefits. In fact, their interests may be served by preventing zoning.

A large job remains to be done. Local action is likely to lag where benefits are largely nonlocal. As has happened in the past, unsolved problems of land use may prompt the shaping of new zoning techniques. The best solution in some States may be to have a State highway agency zone some classes of roads. In other States, cooperative State-county zoning of the roadsides may be most effective. State aids might be paid to counties that provide a designated standard of roadside zoning protection, or a State agency might be empowered to do the zoning job, if a county fails to do it after notice.

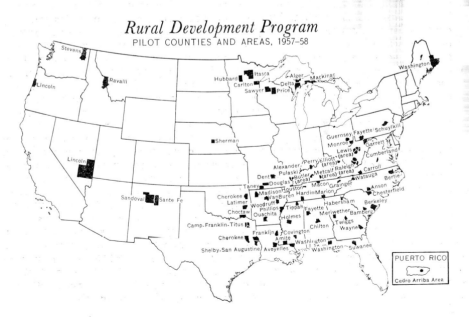

Rural Development Program
PILOT COUNTIES AND AREAS, 1957–58

Public development of resources.

This chapter, which is intended primarily for specialists, officials, and economists, discusses the Nation's policy of public development of land and water projects—an expression of its interest in the use of natural resources. Public programs have had many forms in our history. Many policy issues remain unsettled, however. Some of the activities have been criticized widely. By *William A. Green, Harry A. Steele,* and *Mark M. Regan,* Land and Water Section, Farm Economics Research Division.

PUBLIC PROGRAMS to develop our natural resources embrace many activities and purposes.

Among them are zoning and regulating the use of land and water; forming districts for resource management; collecting basic physical and economic data; conducting research on the use and control of resources; giving technical assistance to private individuals and organizations; making incentive payments to stimulate the development of resources; formulating, designing, and evaluating projects; installing and maintaining projects for development of the resources; and marketing products and services produced by the projects.

The origins of many of the activities and policies can be traced to legislative acts, court decisions, and administrative findings since early in the 19th century. Nine Federal legislative actions have made significant contributions toward moulding existing policy on the development of water resources.

The Rivers and Harbor Act of 1824 authorized the engineers to remove specified sandbars and "sawyers, planters and snags" from the Mississippi and Ohio Rivers as an aid to navigation. The Congress in 1879 established the Mississippi River Commission and instructed it to prepare flood-control plans for the lower Mississippi Valley.

The National Reclamation Act of 1902 authorized the Federal Government to undertake surveys, to design and construct irrigation projects financed from the Reclamation Fund (set up to operate as a revolving fund), and to contract with water users for repayment, without interest, on the capital investment. The act provided also for the installation of powerplants to assist in construction or to pump water.

The first Federal expenditures specifically for flood control on the Mississippi and Sacramento Rivers were authorized in 1917.

The Federal Water Power Act of 1920 established a Federal Power Commission and authorized it to conduct surveys of waterpower potentialities of river basins throughout the United States.

The National Flood Control Act of 1936 authorized a nationwide program of flood control, the major costs to be borne by the Federal Government.

The Flood Control Act of 1938 largely removed the already limited requirements for non-Federal participation called for in the 1936 act.

The Watershed Protection and Flood Prevention Act of 1954 authorized the Department of Agriculture to cooperate with local interests in planning and constructing water-resource projects in small watersheds.

The Water Pollution Act of 1956 authorized the Federal Government to cooperate with State and local governments in the solution of problems of stream pollution.

The authorizing legislation requires an estimate of funds needed for the proposed improvements and in most instances an estimate of financial returns or benefits. Usually the cooperation of local groups is required in the construction of a project. Sometimes they must bear a small portion of the cost. Some legislation requires that a part of the initial cost be repaid to the Federal Treasury.

FROM THE GROWING need for water and the economies inherent in large-scale projects, two concepts have evolved.

The first was that a land and water project should be developed for multiple purposes to achieve fuller utilization of natural resources and better use of materials, labor, technical skills, and other economic resources needed for the project.

The second extended multipurpose planning to an entire river basin. All important relationships between the many parts of the land and water resources of a river basin are taken into account.

The major purposes in planning for river basins and watersheds include flood prevention, erosion control, drainage of agricultural land, generation of electric power, irrigation development, navigation, pollution abatement, development of fish and wildlife values, creation of recreational facilities and values, and care of municipal, industrial, and agricultural water supplies.

Adequate consideration of these purposes and functions requires many kinds of technical knowledge and skill and the close cooperation of Government agencies and public administrators.

The Federal Government has spent twice as much since 1940 on the development of water resources as it did in the previous 150 years. Annual Federal appropriations for this purpose have exceeded 1 billion dollars in recent years.

Public investments are needed in developing resources primarily because private investors are not in a position to take account of all the economic and social values of multiple-purpose projects and lack the means of acquiring the necessary managerial control.

Much of the stimuli and restraints of the market place that guide the use of resources in the private economy are lost in public investment programs. The profit motive of the private economy may not lead to full economic use of natural resources, but it does tend to prevent uneconomic investment of other resources in ill-advised projects and activities.

Individual investors and private firms ask two questions before they invest: Will the contemplated use of resources bring financial returns greater than their cost? Will their contemplated use be more profitable than other available alternative uses? A decision to invest capital ordinarily requires an affirmative answer to both questions.

ECONOMIC ANALYSIS is something of a substitute for the stimuli and restraints of the market place that are sacrificed when economic resources are diverted from the private economy into public projects.

The aims of economic analysis in public-land and water programs are to provide assurance that the total economic returns from projects will equal or exceed the economic cost, facilitate the formulation and design of public projects that will maximize the surplus of benefits over costs, and help us compare projects as to economic efficiency.

These aims are embodied or implied

in Federal legislation providing for the programs and are reflected in policy statements of the Federal agencies that administer them.

Most of the economic analysis of public water-development projects is known generally as benefit-cost analysis. The end results of a benefit-cost analysis are expressed as a benefit-cost ratio. The intent of the ratio is to show the mathematical relationship between net economic gains (benefits) expected from the project and the economic cost.

The project is usually considered to be economically justified if benefits are greater than costs. The economic justification of a project that has a high benefit-cost ratio is rated above a project that has a narrow ratio.

Sometimes we stress too much the benefit-cost ratio as the sole measure of economic justification. The potential value of benefit-cost analysis in project formulation often is more important.

The benefit-cost ratio has meaning as a measure of economic justification or comparative efficiency only when the projects being considered have been formulated properly.

The preparation of a plan that will bring the greatest net benefits may require a benefit-cost analysis of many alternative plans. Involved in the analysis are such factors as the functions to be included in the project, the physical capacity and design of each structure or feature, and the inclusion or exclusion of each structure or feature in the plan.

An adequate test of the full range of possibilities requires a more elaborate series of computations than has yet been attempted. The new high-speed statistical machines and improvements in mathematical techniques should result in more rapid progress in this phase of economic analysis in planning a project.

Benefit-cost analysis is potentially useful also in the selection of projects as parts of a program. For a given amount of investment funds, maxi-

mum benefits can only be obtained by choosing projects yielding the greatest benefit in relation to cost.

Factors other than the benefit-cost ratio also may have to be taken into account in selecting projects. A project with a lower benefit-cost ratio, for example, might be chosen to ease distress in an area of unemployment in preference to a project with a higher benefit-cost ratio in an area of full employment.

The individuals and agencies having to do with benefit-cost analysis decided long ago that the prevailing economic concepts and methods appropriate for private investors were not adequate for a public evaluation.

The Federal Interagency River Basin Committee in 1946 made the first concerted attempt to develop a comprehensive body of evaluation concepts for this purpose. Its Benefit-Cost Subcommittee aimed to "formulate mutually acceptable principles and procedures for determining benefits and costs of the water resources projects." It prepared a series of reports on current practices. A final report, "Proposed Practices for Economic Analysis of River Basin Projects," was published in 1950. The subcommittee and its successor, the Evaluation Standards Subcommittee of the Interagency Committee on Water Resources, have continued to study problems not fully resolved in the report.

The intent of the report was to bring about more uniform standards and procedures among Federal agencies.

It also pointed up the problems of concern to other individuals and organizations.

Contributions in improving the theoretical foundations of benefit-cost analysis outside the Federal Government include those by economists in the University of California, the University of Chicago, Harvard University, the State University of Iowa, and Montana State College.

Research undertaken by Resources for the Future, the program of a water resources seminar at Harvard, research in the University of Chicago, and activities of the Committee on the Economics of Water Resource Development of the West of the Western Agricultural Economics Research Council also have helped to clarify the economic issues involved and stimulate research in benefit-cost analysis.

Benefit-cost analysis also has received attention from several special commissions and study groups created or sponsored by the Federal Government: The Commission on the Organization of the Executive Branch of the Government, 1949 (the first Hoover Commission); a Panel of Consultants on Secondary or Indirect Benefits of Water Use Projects, retained by the Department of the Interior, 1952; the President's Water Resources Policy Commission, 1950; the President's Advisory Committee on Water Resources Policy, 1955; the Commission on Organization of the Executive Branch of the Government, 1955 (the second Hoover Commission); and the Missouri Basin Survey Commission, 1953.

Their reports have recognized the important role of benefit-cost analysis in developing river-basin programs, but most have been critical of benefit-cost analysis as practiced by Federal agencies concerned in the development of water resources.

THE POINTS OF VIEW of private concerns and governments differ, although both attempt to maximize the returns from the use of economic resources.

Private firms are interested mainly in values that will be reflected in their financial statements and returns to the operators and owners of the business.

Governmental bodies are interested in all of the effects of the projects upon the society that they represent. A State government, for example, is concerned mainly with the sum of all beneficial and adverse effects on all citizens of the State; and the Federal Government similarly is concerned with the aggregate effects of a project on the Nation.

From a Federal viewpoint, the major

attributes of a benefit-cost analysis are that it should account for all beneficial and adverse effects (benefits and costs) and that it should evaluate products and services in accordance with anticipated national requirements.

The calculations of a private individual in considering the development of new agricultural land, for example, would include the benefits expected from price-support or subsidy programs. The public viewpoint requires that such values be deleted or that the analysis otherwise account for the offsetting adverse effects that would be borne by others.

The evaluation of a proposed navigation project provides another illustration. From a private viewpoint, the expected transportation service would be valued entirely on the basis of expected freight rates and quality of service. From a public viewpoint, the analysis should take additional account of the adverse effects on other forms of transportation.

In developing a power site on a river, a private utility would center attention on the value of power produced by the plant. It might omit consideration of such functions as control of floods and erosion, the improvement of agricultural land, and beneficial effects on hydroelectric installations owned by others. Consideration would be given all these aspects in formulating and evaluating the effects of a public project.

In another situation, the public viewpoint would demand consideration of effects that would not enter customary trade channels, such as fish and wildlife values. The private firm probably would disregard them.

A BASIC PRECEPT in the Benefit-Cost Subcommittee's report in 1950 was the principle of basing economic costs on "resource productivity in alternative use." When goods and services are utilized for any purpose, a major economic impact of that action is to preclude their employment in alternative uses. The values that would have resulted from alternative uses are the true economic costs of the resources used in the project.

Thus defined, the annual cost of a project is parallel and comparable to its annual benefits, and the resulting comparison of efficiency is between two annual volumes of economic output. If a benefit-cost ratio is greater than unity, the output of goods and services is increased by diverting resources from other uses to construct and operate a project. The resulting benefit-cost ratio is not likely to provide the measure of economic efficiency desired unless costs are evaluated in accordance with this economic concept.

The application of this notion of economic cost to benefit-cost analysis is complicated by the lack of knowledge concerning the specific alternatives to project development.

The expected annual value of output from the use of economic resources in the private economy, however, must be sufficient to cover depreciation of plant and machinery (capital stock); cover the value of all resources used annually in operating the enterprise; pay interest on bonded and similar indebtedness; pay all taxes levied against business firms by Federal, State, and local governments; and compensate the owners of the firm for the use of funds and the bearing of risk. These prospective conditions are required to attract resources into private investments.

Research in the various sectors of the private economy can provide reasonably satisfactory estimates of returns from the use of capital resources as evaluated by the private viewpoint.

Many of the problems, conclusions, and procedural principles outlined in the following sections arise from adhering to the concept of "economic cost." The discussions of commodity prices, interest rates, and tax treatment in project analysis, for example, are closely related to this definition of cost.

THE DEVELOPMENT of product and service prices and their application to the physical products and services expected from a project is an essential element in benefit-cost analysis. Uniform pricing concepts are required in order to use benefit-cost analysis in the justification, formulation, and selection of projects.

If the product from one project function is overvalued in relation to the products of other functions, the project cannot be formulated properly and its economic efficiency cannot be measured accurately. If adequate estimates of the value of so-called intangible project effects are lacking, there is no easy way in which they can be compared with the products from competing project functions.

Because the factors of demand and supply influence the price, the prices applied should reflect conditions in which the factors are in balance. Each factor puts a limit on the price that can be applied appropriately to any given project effect.

The demand restriction is imposed by the relative preference of consumers for an additional amount of a product or service in relation to all other products and services that satisfy consumers' wants. The price attached to a given product must be such that the additional production would clear the market.

The supply restriction is established by the cost of producing additional products or services required to satisfy market demand. If this factor is adequately considered in the development of price estimates, the benefit-cost ratio will measure the relative economic efficiency of producing a given product between project and alternative nonproject means.

Because supply and demand determine prices, each requires careful analysis when one tries to derive estimates of prices. Expected future prices, rather than current or historical prices, should be used in the evaluation of project benefits.

An essential step is to evaluate the

future need, prospective supplies, and technological developments that are expected to influence the efficiency and costs of production.

An equally essential step for products sold on a national market is to translate this analysis into a schedule of projected commodity prices.

Local and regional studies are necessary to derive a schedule of projected prices representative of conditions expected to prevail in the market area of the project. These studies are concerned with expected local and regional markets in relation to the national market for products sold nationally and an analysis of supply-requirement conditions for the products and services that would serve only a local or regional market.

An example of an analysis of future conditions of supply and demand and their conversion into a schedule of projected prices on a national basis is the studies of projected prices and farm costs by men in the Department of Agriculture. Examples of local and regional studies made for benefit-cost analysis are the ones made by the Federal Power Commission in estimating the future power market and power values for different regions.

Inflationary and deflationary trends should be removed from the analysis of commodity and service prices so that a constant dollar may be used in comparing project costs and benefits.

A PROBLEM in the evaluation of benefits arises because there is no readily available price for some products and services—such as fish and wildlife, recreation, and pollution abatement. They often are not included in the economic analysis, although this limits the usefulness of benefit-cost ratios and forces the analyst to rely on physical descriptions.

Even though the establishment of competitive market prices for some of these items is not likely, unit prices that are reasonably comparable to other prices used in evaluation of other project functions can be derived.

Procedures for deriving such values involve estimating a demand schedule for the so-called intangible effects and estimating the cost of providing similar goods and services by alternative means. Studies are needed to develop the type of comprehensive treatment of cost and benefits necessary to make benefit-cost ratios more meaningful.

UNIT PRICES used in establishing costs of projects should represent the value of the required resources in alternative use—the prices that others are willing to pay.

These cost prices may be close to their value, as indicated in the market during periods of full employment. Market-determined prices may not represent the alternative-use value in periods of widespread unemployment or if the project is in an area that has unemployed labor and resources. Special studies are necessary in such periods to estimate a set of prices that take into account the unemployment of resources that could be expected if the project were not undertaken.

Special economic studies are needed in estimating the alternative use and resulting values for resource items that are not priced on a competitive market. Examples in connection with agricultural projects are management and risk-bearing services and family labor, the return for which is seldom separated from the return to other productive factors.

COSTS OF RESOURCES required for a project are determined by their value and expected productivity in alternative uses. Their value is measured by the pricing of the resources at the time of use. The interest charge should represent their annual productivity.

The report of the Benefit-Cost Subcommittee suggested that the Federal borrowing rate would serve as a reasonable approximation of society's time preference for present goods over future goods and also as a measure of the productivity of alternative investments.

But it pointed out that because of

public taxing authority and the resulting security in Government obligations, the Federal borrowing rate did not reflect the risk. The report suggested that predictable risk associated with a project should be taken into account by making conservative estimates of benefits and by assuming a restricted life for the project.

The report also recognized the possible need to include an allowance in the interest rate for residual risks that cannot be considered fully in other ways.

The subcommittee's recommendations on interest rates have been questioned as to their theoretical adequacy and from the standpoint of practical application of risk allowances in planning and evaluating a project.

Some analysts have suggested that the allowance for risk should be included in the interest rate and that the Federal borrowing rate falls short of representing the productivity of private investments.

Questions center on the adequacy of the long-term Federal borrowing rate in benefit-cost analysis as a full measure of the productivity of resources in alternative use.

Additional analysis and review of analysts' conclusions would be needed before they can be accepted as an alternative standard for interest rates in analysis of benefits and costs.

In the meantime, the deficiencies that may result from using the Federal borrowing rate in the economic analysis of projects can be minimized by using the same interest-rate standard in estimates involving cost comparisons of the project and alternative means of production. Current procedural practices generally do not entail this type of comparison or any other appropriate adjustment.

AN EQUALLY IMPORTANT unresolved question in benefit-cost analysis concerns taxes.

The report of the subcommittee said that the major tax problems in benefit-cost analysis are "changes in tax revenue of local governmental units affected by the project, which are not fully balanced by changes in governmental expenses of the same unit" and "the effect of taxes on the value of benefits when calculated on the basis of cost from an alternative source, as in the case of power."

The report also stated: "To the extent that taxes are reflected in the market prices of goods and services, such taxes, whether income or property, will have been considered in estimating the value of goods and services used or produced in water resource development projects. . . .

"When the benefits of a Federal project are evaluated on the basis of the cost of producing similar products from an alternative, private cost should include taxes that would be payable."

In treating costs, the same tax rate would be applied to both the project and the most likely alternative. Such rates would be based on expected increases in the cost of governmental services.

For hydroelectric power projects, an allowance for taxes is included as a cost of the project. For other functions or types of projects, cost estimates generally take no account of taxes—either in the benefit-cost ratio or in comparisons of costs between the project and alternative sources of production.

The treatment of tax costs in an analysis of benefits and costs should be in accord with the principle that it should be comprehensive in its accounting of beneficial and adverse effects. Then the project would be analyzed so as to reflect the real costs and social values for both the project and the alternative sources of similar products and services.

The way in which taxes are considered and the extent to which they are included in the economic analysis can be of controlling significance in justifying and formulating projects.

A method of attaining comparable consideration of taxes is to use the same tax standard for calculating nonproject production costs as that used in computing project costs.

Another method is to include a tax allowance in the cost estimates comparable to the tax component in prices used for computing the benefits of a project. The allowance will vary from project to project, depending on the commodities or services produced.

One of these two procedures is necessary to assure that the analysis permits comparisons of economic efficiency. Comparable treatment is equally important for the formulation of projects.

There appears to be growing recognition now that economic analysis is essential to assure efficient use of the resources required for project development, although benefit-cost analyses as currently made frequently are defective, lack comparability, and so are less useful than they could be.

VARIOUS COMMISSIONS have noted that organizational and administrative arrangements are often an important barrier to satisfactory planning of land and water projects, including benefit-cost analysis.

Among the observations by commissions are:

Except for general evaluation standards prescribed by the Bureau of the Budget and cooperation of the Federal agencies in the development of economic concepts and principles through the Evaluation Standards Subcommittee, there is no effective mechanism for achieving uniform evaluation procedures between agencies. Even within major Federal resource-development agencies, arrangements for review and procedural guidance are not always adequate.

It is not customary to include detailed evaluation data and procedures in project reports. Consequently the present system of interagency review is less effective than it could be in improving benefit-cost analysis.

Time schedules for surveys are often set without adequate time for accurate economic evaluation.

Responsibility for benefit-cost analysis is frequently delegated to agency personnel not trained adequately in economic analysis.

Expert assistance and advice from individuals and groups outside resource development agencies are not fully utilized.

Because the functions of benefit-cost analysis and project formulation frequently are not integrated, adequate application of benefit-cost data in the development of plans is impossible.

SEVERAL SPECIAL COMMISSIONS and study groups have made general suggestions concerning the organization of resource-development programs that would have important influences on benefit-cost analysis.

These groups generally have not centered their attention on benefit-cost analysis, but their recommendations on changes for project planning would affect favorably the economic analysis as well as the overall process of project planning.

A noteworthy example is the report, "Water Resources Policy," issued in 1955, by a Presidential Cabinet Committee made up of the Secretaries of Agriculture, Defense, and Interior.

Among the committee's recommendations were:

That the present program of basic data collection (such as rainfall, streamflows, and hydrology) be accelerated and be programed and carried out on a more consistent and definite basis.

That an organization plan be adopted to provide or establish:

the position of coordinator of water resources to provide Presidential direction to agency coordination and to establish principles, standards, and procedures for planning and development of water resources projects;

an independent board of review to analyze the engineering and economic feasibility of projects and report to the President through the coordinator;

regional or river basin water resources committees, with a permanent nonvoting chairman appointed by the

President and with membership composed of representatives of all Federal departments and States involved; and

a permanent Federal interagency committee, advisory in character, on water resources, to be established under the chairmanship of the coordinator, composed of principal policymakers of the agencies concerned.

That evaluations of water projects by all agencies be on a uniform basis, requiring balanced consideration of all benefits and costs which can reasonably be measured in dollars, as well as consideration of other values not readily expressed in monetary terms.

That each major water resources project be separately authorized by the Congress.

That, as a general policy, all interests participate in the cost of water resources development projects in accordance with the measure of their benefits; that the Federal Government assume the cost of that part of projects where benefits are national and widespread and the beneficiaries are not readily identifiable; that power and municipal and industrial water users pay the full cost of development; that where projects are primarily local, and the beneficiaries are clearly identifiable, the Federal Government's contribution should be limited, with non-Federal interests bearing a substantial portion of the construction costs of the project as well as the replacement, maintenance, and operation costs; and that under certain conditions the Federal Government may bear a higher proportion of the costs.

EVEN WITHIN the general framework of the present organizational structure, relatively minor changes in arrangements and procedures could lead to more adequate and effective benefit-cost analysis. The interagency committee on water resources could ask each functional agency or department to prepare detailed procedural guides and to specify minimum standards on the reporting of the results of the economic analysis in the project reports. Thus,

the agencies that deal with recreation, in cooperation with the Evaluation Standards Subcommittee, might be requested to develop detailed procedural standards and guides for the evaluation of recreational benefits. The subcommittee might also be asked to review the procedural guides thus developed to assure that accepted principles are followed and to assure comparability between functional procedures.

In addition to its inherent advantage of obtaining a degree of comparability within and between resource development agencies, this procedure would enhance the value of interagency review. In addition, the procedural guides of each project function would serve as a basis for critical review by interested individuals and organizations and hence could be used for improvement in procedural techniques.

DESPITE ITS DEFICIENCIES, the need for benefit-cost analysis and its value in the development of land and water projects is clear. It is the only device that sets forth meaningful criteria for decisions on public investment in land and water projects.

Opportunity exists for improving benefit-cost analysis.

Some of the potentially fruitful lines of endeavor for this purpose are to:

enlist the assistance and advice of leading economic analysts outside the Federal Government to help resolve issues of theory and principle;

increase efforts to collect relevant basic data;

develop and improve planning techniques further to facilitate a more complete consideration of alternative water-control methods, scales of development, and combination of project functions;

improve present administrative arrangements and devices for achieving comparability in procedures;

and carry on special research efforts to derive economic values for those project effects now considered as intangible.

Arrangements for our public lands.

This review of the use and management of public lands examines existing policies and cites some proposals people have made to change them in response to our changing national needs. By *Fred A. Clarenbach,* Farm Economics Research Division; *Walter L. Graves* and *Edward W. Schultz,* Division of Operation, Forest Service; and *John B. Bennett,* director, Technical Review Staff, Office of the Secretary, Department of the Interior.

THE EMERGING problems of ownership and control of public lands stem from growing, changing national needs and the competition among those who want to use the lands.

Conflicts over the use, management, and disposition of public lands have made many chapters of American history, but the ways in which needs for public land are changing during the second half of this century differ from those of earlier years.

The need and the demand for most of the diverse services of public lands have multiplied in response to large increases in population and income and related developments. The timber harvest from national forests, for example, is about three times greater than during the wartime peak. The recreational use of national parks and national forests has increased greatly. Exploration for minerals, especially oil and uranium, has intensified. Military needs for land have expanded. The watershed—the water-producing—function of public lands has grown in importance.

Therefore people have begun to reexamine existing arrangements and possible alternatives to facilitate use, development, and protection of Federal lands.

We review some of the proposals for altering present arrangements relating to ownership and control of national lands and give some attention to the much smaller total of State and local public lands.

We approach this task in no doctrinaire spirit. Our touchstone is the best possible multiple use. The common quest is for effective and equitable ways of organizing to administer our public estate for a changing best combination of the diverse uses in response to our changing national needs.

Government agencies hold public lands subject to a variety of interests, claims, and rights of private persons. The Government in a broad sense is a trustee. It holds and manages the public lands for the benefit of the citizens of the country.

Various types of advisory boards and associations of local users have evolved for most Federal lands. These groups cooperate with Federal land-managing agencies in several ways. They may advise and make recommendations as to administration of the Federal grazing lands. Some board members act unofficially as mediators and arbitrators when disagreements arise over distribution of the range among individual operators. Local associations often make substantial contributions in cash and otherwise toward protection and improvement of Federal rangelands.

In short, there is a vast network of

private rights and interests in and responsibilities toward the Federal public lands. Uncle Sam owns the lands, but millions of individuals and groups have legal rights and certain privileges to use and to reap benefits from this national estate, according to established laws and rules and customs. Uncle Sam's ownership does not mean that Federal agencies have complete, exclusive, and absolute control of the land the Government owns.

A PROPOSAL TO DISPOSE of major parts of the Federal lands therefore cannot be a simple solution to the intricate problems of adjusting the manifold rights, privileges, and interests that private persons and public bodies now have in the lands.

State ownership and private ownership have been proposed as alternatives to present Federal holding of the public domain. The proposals raise issues that relate to redistribution of rights and interests in land and to ways in which such changes, if adopted, would affect the use, protection, and development of the land.

In the early days of the development of the United States, large areas of Federal land were granted to the States, usually for such public purposes as common schools, agricultural colleges, and hospitals or in the hope that the States would reclaim swamp or irrigable lands. This policy of disposal to States was intended to encourage the development of vast areas of unsettled land, the establishment of new States, and the creation of schools as areas became settled. As the Nation continued to grow and the population spread to the borders of the country, the need for (and the possibility of) major grants to many States diminished, and the policy of making large grants was abandoned.

A companion measure to grants of Federal land to the States was the disposal to private persons and railroad companies to induce people to leave the settled areas and push westward into unknown territory. To provide this incentive, laws were enacted to make it possible for individuals to obtain Federal land free of charge or by very low payments.

The selection of Federal lands by private persons was left pretty much to the desires of the individual. Although the acreage that could be taken by one person was limited by law, the location of the tract was left to the individual. Ways often were found to circumvent the laws restricting the acreage that could be acquired by one person.

It became apparent in the early 1900's that the land-disposal policies of the Federal Government meant serious abuse of the land. Many frontier farmers tilled their lands until crop production fell off. Then they moved to new areas. Timber was cut without regard for proper management. Grasslands were overgrazed. Fires burned uncontrolled over large areas. The philosophy was that the supply of land was inexhaustible and that there was no need for any type of management.

An aroused public opinion halted the headlong disposal practices, and late in the 19th century began the present era of reservation of Federal lands for the public good.

Generally speaking, the lands reserved in Federal ownership are those least desirable for agricultural purposes—desert or semidesert areas or lands too mountainous to be attractive to early settlers.

Additional lands have been bought by the Federal Government and added to the reserved areas. Other tracts also have been turned over to individuals, States, and local governments by sale or through exchange for other tracts. Usually the areas purchased by the Federal Government have been submarginal or wornout lands or those of such low productivity that a decent living cannot be made from them.

MANY ARGUMENTS have been advanced for and against the retention of lands in Federal ownership: That Federal ownership deprives the States of tax revenues and that private ownership would mean more efficient management and protection—or that the annual payments received by States from the Federal Government as a share of receipts offset the loss of revenue from taxes.

The payments are based on gross receipts received from the sale of products and the use of Federal land. They vary among States and among agencies. Many other contributions in kind benefit States and counties—fire control, reforestation, road construction and maintenance, developments for recreation, and other services that the Federal Government provides on its lands.

If these lands were in State or private ownership, the States, local governments, and individuals would be obliged to bear the costs. The Federal receipt-share payments, plus contributions in kind, often more than offset the taxes that State and local governments would get from the lands.

Advocates of Federal ownership also aver that history has shown that abuse and mismanagement of privately owned lands sometimes has resulted in a reversion of the lands to public ownership.

Although there has been a tendency toward better management of private and public lands, a feeling is strong that most lands presently owned by the Federal Government can be best protected against fire, insects, and other harmful things and managed by national agencies and should be retained for the benefit and enjoyment of the people.

There is an equally strong belief that no major additions to the Federal lands should be made. Disposal or acquisition of small tracts to provide better management or to meet special needs generally is acceptable, but proposals for major acquisitions or disposals have encountered opposition.

Thus Federal public-land policies in the past emphasized disposal, reservation for designated major uses under permanent administration of Federal agencies, limited custodial management of most of the remaining public domain, and limited acquisition of marginal and special-use lands.

Apparently we are now in the early stages of an era of more intensive management for multiple uses, with minor disposals, acquisitions, and exchanges needed for efficient management.

That is a difficult but potentially rewarding course to follow. It makes us face many questions concerning the kinds of governmental and cooperative arrangements most appropriate for implementing the underlying policy.

IT IS IMPORTANT to have good arrangements for pricing the products and services of Federal lands and workable arrangements for investing funds for development. We must also face questions about Government organization to administer the land, the role of cattlemen's associations and similar nongovernmental groups, the place of official advisory boards of land users, and the participation of State and local governments.

Timber sales from Federal lands for commercial purposes are usually made by competitive sealed bids or an oral auction. No bids are accepted that are below a minimum price, established by appraisal. The competitive-bid method is much the same on all types of Federal land, but the appraisal methods vary among agencies. Appraisals of the Forest Service are based on the proposition that timber is worth the selling value of the products manufactured from it, minus the cost of production and a margin for profit and risk to the purchaser. Selling value minus cost of production is the conversion value, which is split into two parts—a margin for profit and risk to the purchaser and a stumpage fee to the Government.

All costs and returns in Forest Service appraisals are based on the concept of an operator of average efficiency in the locality. It is presumed that the stumpage under appraisal will be manufactured into products of the highest value for which it is suited.

The selling value is computed at the stage at which there is first a true market for the product in its particular state of manufacture. Lumber, pulpwood, poles, and posts are the usual products for which selling values are ascertained and used in appraisals. Appraisals for sale to a log market are seldom used except in the Douglas-fir region of Oregon and Washington.

All costs of production of the products for which returns are computed are allowed in the appraisal, except interest on borrowed capital and income taxes. Allowance for them is included as a margin for profit and risk.

Estimates of costs and returns are based on records of industrial experience during a period selected and stated by the appraiser. The period selected should be long enough to form a reasonable basis for the determination of conversion value. A specific base period is necessary to facilitate comparisons with other appraisals.

The two basic reasons for selling Federal timber by competitive bid are to insure that the Federal Government receives a fair value for the timber and to allow all interested persons a chance to bid on the timber.

Oral bidding is used if strong competitive interest may be expected. It is used also when there is an established operator in the area in which the sealed-bid method might mean that the successful bidder would be an outside purchaser who would process the timber at some location remote from the area. Thus a timber-dependent community would be deprived of an opportunity for employment. Oral bidding gives the locally established operator a chance to meet the highest bid.

Timber may be sold without competitive bid when the volume offered does not exceed a certain appraised value, which varies slightly among agencies. The Forest Service may sell timber without bids if the appraised value does not exceed 2 thousand dollars. The maximum for the Bureau of Land Management is 2.5 thousand

dollars. Even if the amounts are below the maximum, however, timber is sold by bid if competitive interest exists.

Except for relatively minor amounts of timber cut under free-use permits, timber on lands administered by the Department of the Interior is sold in the open market at not less than an appraised price. Sale may be by sealed bids or oral auction or both.

Timber is sold by agencies of the Department of the Interior, chiefly from the Oregon and California Revested Lands, Indian reservations, and the unappropriated public domain. Some timber is sold from wildlife refuges when cutting is in accord with the primary purposes of management. Sales are made in national parks only of timber cut along rights-of-way for highways or on sites for buildings, or it may be salvaged and removed to prevent the spread of insects or disease.

THE FEES charged for grazing use on Federal lands generally are not determined by competitive bidding. Grazing fees for national-forest lands are set administratively.

Base grazing fees on the national forests were developed in 1931. They were derived from a study of the rentals paid to private persons, corporations, States, Indian reservations, and Federal Government agencies for use of comparable grazing lands. The study covered several years and areas large enough for fair comparisons.

Base fees thus determined were then correlated with livestock prices. The periods 1921 to 1930 for cattle and 1920 to 1932 for sheep were selected as representing complete price cycles for each industry. The average price received by producers in 11 Western States during these periods was established as the base livestock price.

Grazing fees since 1931 have been raised or lowered from the base as the average price of livestock has varied from the base livestock price. Average livestock prices for the preceding year are obtained each January from the Agricultural Marketing Service. The percentage of increase or decrease over the base livestock price is then applied to the 1931 base fee to determine the grazing fee to be charged for the current year. An example: The base fee for cattle was 14.5 cents a head a month in 1931. The average price for cattle in 1957 was 270 percent of the base livestock price. The grazing fee for cattle in 1958 would then be 39 cents a head a month (14.5 cents times 2.70 equals 39.150 cents).

The number of livestock permitted to graze on a national-forest grazing allotment is based on the number that the unit will support during the regular grazing period over a series of years without injury to soils, forage plants, watershed, or trees. Numbers permitted to graze may be adjusted when necessary to protect the range.

The reason for allocating the grazing use on the national forests and grazing districts to preference permittees, rather than sale through the bidding procedure, stems from the early land policy of the Congress. The idea was to encourage the stability of settlers and small ranchers as part of the western development.

Returns to the Treasury from grazing permits in grazing districts established under the Taylor Grazing Act of 1934 are in the form of grazing fees calculated on the basis of a fixed charge per animal-unit month.

Since fees were instituted in 1935, charges for grazing in grazing districts have been substantially lower than the going rates for grazing privileges on privately owned land or on public land where the privileges have been disposed of in a competitive market.

Several circumstances, including restrictions on disposal of grazing privileges contained in the Taylor Grazing Act, have been responsible for this situation. The basic reason for the low returns has been the fact that for many years before passage of the Taylor Grazing Act the grazing lands of the public domain had been under no regulation and had been open to all stockmen without charge. Such grazing rights to the public lands as had been established by individual stockmen through various means had been capitalized largely into their base properties. They consequently have resisted attempts to raise grazing fees beyond the initial nominal fee of 5 cents an aninal-unit month. The fee was 15 cents in 1958.

LEASABLE MINERALS on public-domain lands that are open to mineral exploitation are disposed of under two separate systems. Leases in unproved areas are made to the first eligible applicant at a flat annual rental per acre plus a fixed royalty of 12.5 percent of the sale value of the minerals removed. This is about equal to the average royalty paid to small holders of privately owned land.

On public lands within the boundaries of geological structures in which there are producing oil and gas fields and on the Continental Shelf beyond the offshore boundaries of the States, mineral leases are sold at public auction. The basis of the auction is the amount of a bonus that a bidder will pay in addition to the fixed rental and the royalty of 12.5 to 25 percent.

The mining laws of 1868 and 1872, under which mining claims for metallic minerals on the public domain still are filed, in effect merely sanctioned the procedures for filing claims and protecting them against trespassers, or claim jumpers, that had been adopted locally during the California gold rush.

The object of the laws was to promote private prospecting and development of the minerals in the public domain by protecting private interests in mining claims established under local customs. There was little thought of compensating the United States for alienation of mineral rights. The returns to the Federal Treasury from mining claims consequently are nominal. There is no Federal charge for establishing a claim and no royalty on the minerals recovered. If the claimant wishes to obtain a patent, or private title, to his claim, he pays both the cost of surveying its boundaries and 2.50 to 5 dollars an acre for the surface area it includes.

Abuse of the outmoded mining laws is indicated by an estimate, based on experience of the Bureau of Land Management, that 9 in 10 mining claims are located for purposes other than mining. Lands otherwise unavailable to individuals have been obtained under mining laws, and frequent conflicts with the broader public interest in recreation, timber harvest, and rights-of-way have arisen.

GOOD WATERSHED management and stabilized streamflow are vital to both local and regional economies. The Federal Government gets little or no direct financial return from its outlays to protect and manage watersheds, but the broad public benefits of these measures are of such importance that in the long run they may outweigh all other values of most Federal lands.

The National Park Service charges admission to most of the areas in the national park system. The amount varies generally with the extent of the area and the services. Except in a few favorably situated units, the charges are not enough to offset the costs of maintaining the services. Meals and lodging are furnished by private concerns under concessions. The concessioners pay fees for the privilege of doing business. They charge commercial rates for their services.

Admission to most wildlife refuges is without charge. In a few refuges that are great recreational attractions, concessioners provide meals and lodging and other services to visitors.

Public-domain lands may be leased for recreational purposes by individuals, States, local governments, or nonprofit associations at rates based on appraised values.

Recreational use of the national forests generally is free. More than 4,700 developed camp and picnic areas exist on these lands. Some 50 heavily used areas that have special features or facilities and are suitable for collection of a charge are operated on a charge basis by concessioners. The Forest Service supervises the concessioner's operation, regulates his fees, and sees that he keeps the area in good condition. The concessioner charges enough to reimburse him for the costs of operating the area and earn a reasonable profit. He pays the Forest Service a percentage of his gross profit. Because most recreational areas on the national forests are small and widely scattered, the cost of collecting fees for using them would exceed the amount collected.

Recreational areas that offer winter sports, swimming, boating, and such special facilities and services as ski lifts, boat rentals, clothes checking, stores, and restaurants are operated by concessioners on a charge basis. The installation of all commercial facilities in these areas normally is financed with private capital.

THE BUREAU OF LAND MANAGEMENT leases or sells public land in tracts not exceeding 5 acres for residence and business sites, usually at an appraised price but sometimes at public auction.

The Bureau of Reclamation also leases land for various purposes, including crop production. Leases may be made by negotiation or by public auction. Several thousand acres of reclaimed cropland in the Klamath irrigation project in California and Oregon are leased for production of small grains and potatoes at auctions where bidding is limited to veterans of the Second World War.

The Bureau of Sport Fisheries and Wildlife leases land for crop production, usually to neighboring farmers on a crop-share basis. The Bureau's share is left on the ground for harvest by wildfowl.

The Department of the Interior sells power generated at powerplants constructed by the Bureau of Reclamation in connection with reclamation and multiple-purpose projects, as well as at powerplants constructed by the Corps of Engineers, Department of the Army. Sales must be at rates sufficient to cover the costs of operation and maintenance and at least 3 percent interest on construction costs allocated to power.

A special-use permit is required for any permanent occupancy of national-forest land. The general policy of the Forest Service is that special uses may be granted if the proposed use is consistent with the broad objective of national-forest management, which is to manage the areas for the greatest public good. In general, a charge is made for all uses of a commercial nature and for uses that involve exclusive occupancy by individuals or private organizations. The fee charged for special uses of a commercial nature must be commensurate with the value of the use authorized by the permit. Uses of a public or semipublic nature may be issued free. Sometimes there is competitive interest in a particular location for a special use of a commercial nature. In instances of this kind, a bid prospectus is issued and announced locally so that all interested persons may apply.

The Forest Service permits commercial special uses only when there is need for the services or accommodations proposed. It is not the policy to allow special-use permits if such action will create competition with similar uses on private lands in the same area.

Returns from Federal lands appear as both monetary and nonmonetary income. Revenues to the United States Treasury include direct cash receipts paid to the Treasury by purchasers or users of the different raw products, facilities, privileges, or services on or from national lands and income taxes paid by individuals and businesses whose enterprises use and depend on national lands.

Other monetary returns go to State and local governments from income and property taxes based on harvesting, processing, and marketing products from national lands.

Nonmonetary returns include the annual value of uses that are free because of policy, economic, or legal reasons and the annual value of water yields and the recreation and wildlife resources of the Federal lands.

Net receipts from products and services provided by the Department of the Interior for the fiscal year 1956 aggregated 457 million dollars. The largest single item, 178 million dollars, included the revenues from oil and gas and other mineral leasing from the public lands and the outer Continental Shelf. Next came revenues from power sales, 111 million dollars. Sales of timber and other products and services from the Oregon and California Revested Lands were almost 21 million dollars. Alaska Railroad revenues totaled 18 million dollars. Sales of hunting stamps, receipts from sales of wildlife refuge products, and sales of Pribilof Islands sealskins amounted to 15 million dollars. Collections from water users on reclamation projects were 12 million dollars. Admission fees and concessions, largely in the national park system, amounted to 4.8 million dollars. Revenues from grazing fees in grazing districts and grazing leases on other public lands totaled 2.4 million dollars.

Although some of the receipts were credited to special funds (for example, the Reclamation Fund to which 91 million dollars were transferred), almost none of the receipts are available for expenditures unless specifically appropriated by the Congress.

Certain percentages of some of the receipts are transferred to the States or counties from which the receipts are derived as payments in lieu of taxes. Thus, 37.5 percent of receipts from mineral leases on public lands (but not from the outer Continental Shelf) are transferred to the States. Twenty-five percent of receipts from wildlife refuges and 75 percent (with deductions for access roads) of receipts from the Oregon and California Revested Lands are transferred to the counties from which the receipts are derived.

The national forests and other public lands administered by the Forest Service in fiscal 1956 took in receipts amounting to 118,517,321 dollars. (The expenditures for these lands, including the current operating and capital investment expenditures, in 1956 amounted to 94,406,237 dollars.)

The Congress has provided that an amount equal to 25 percent of the gross receipts from the national forests be paid each year by the United States Treasury to the States for distribution to counties that contain national-forest lands. These payments are for county school and road funds.

Besides these cash payments to the States, the Congress provided that 10 percent of the national-forest receipts be made available each year for expenditure on forest roads and trails in the States of origin. Direct appropriations are made also for construction and maintenance of forest highways and roads and for protection and management.

The public lands require intensive management and substantial investment for improvements if total returns are to be increased substantially.

INVESTMENTS NEEDED may be divided into two classes.

Immediate investments to meet current levels of demand include investments necessary to continue present levels of protection and management in administrative improvements, recreation facilities, fire equipment, and road construction.

Investments to meet future requirements include investments for reforestation, stand improvement, improvements in wildlife habitats, range revegetation, and watershed rehabilitation.

Federal land investment needs are derived from expected future demands on the resources. The Forest Service estimates that by the year 2000 the national forests should produce 21 billion board-feet of timber—more than twice the present annual harvest—to meet the projected demands. Production at so high a level will require heavy capital investment in reforestation and timber-stand improvement to enhance the productive condition

of virtually all commercial forest areas not now ready for harvest. An investment in timber-access roads will be necessary to protect, manage, and harvest the timber.

Investments are needed also to supply the recreational demands of a growing population.

Operation Outdoors, a 5-year recreational development plan for the national forests, calls for the construction of 2,150 new areas to accommodate the 66 million visits predicted for 1962. As more than a fourth of the recreational visits to the national forests are primarily for hunting and fishing, this demand will require investments in improvements of wildlife habitats, such as planting feed for game, fishing dams, streams, and lake improvements.

Mission 66 is the program of the National Park Service to develop, equip, and staff the National Park System for the 80 million visitors expected in 1966, the 50th anniversary of the Service.

The forage-producing areas of the public lands will need to be developed. This improvement will require intensification of management, aided by investments in fencing, water developments, and reseeding.

To insure high yields of good water, investment is needed for the rehabilitation of the watersheds that have the most seriously eroded and denuded areas. This would involve investment in such measures as seeding, planting, gully plugs, check dams, water diversions, spreaders, and the stabilization of grades.

To protect and utilize forests and other resources, investment is needed for fire protection and construction of roads and trails. Intensification of fire protection means an increased investment for expansion of fire equipment and facilities, fuel reduction by removal of snags, and construction of firebreaks. Access roads are for proper utilization of all resources and are needed currently in advance of timber harvest so that timber stands not yet ready for harvest can be properly managed and protected.

ALL THE NEEDED INVESTMENTS could be made through increased direct appropriations. Some improvements, such as timber-access roads, may be built by timber purchasers as a timber-sale requirement. In this example, however, whether the public or a timber purchaser builds the road, the actual cost is borne by the Federal Government. If the timber purchaser builds it, the anticipated cost is deducted from the amount he can be expected to pay for the timber. If the Government provides the road, a correspondingly higher price for stumpage can be obtained. (If the required State-local payments are taken into account, however, the Federal Government may actually lose.) Either arrangement is only for current road needs; neither provides means for access roads in advance of harvest for protection and management.

An additional arrangement is provided by the Knudson-Vandenberg Act of 1930, which authorized the Secretary of Agriculture to require, in addition to the charges made for timber sold, deposits of funds by purchasers to be used for reforestation and stand improvement in timber-sale areas to keep them growing good timber.

Similar deposits can be required from timber purchasers for reduction of hazards in sale areas. This arrangement, however, does not cover the needs for reforestation, stand improvement, and reduction of hazards in areas not associated with timber-sale cuttings.

Some investment needs are provided through cooperation with private users and with municipal, county, State, and Federal agencies that have a direct interest in Federal lands.

By arrangement with concessioners, investments are made in recreational facilities for winter sport areas, lodges, and other public-service installations. Civic organizations and municipal and county governments often cooperate through work or funds in installing recreational improvements in the national forests.

Water-development groups have provided cooperation in watershed improvements, chiefly for improvements that are necessary to utilize water or protect water-storage and conveyance installations.

The States provide considerable financial cooperation in stream- and lake-improvement projects, construction and maintenance of access roads and trails for hunting and fishing, wildlife-habitat improvement for big and small game species through food and cover planting, and water developments and clearings for game.

Users of forest and range also contribute to needed investments. Holders of grazing permits, for example, are encouraged to spend their own funds in developing Federal rangelands. These arrangements usually involve contributions in labor and materials toward construction of range improvements and for revegetation.

THE PROBLEMS OF INVESTMENT NEEDS and how to meet them are related to questions of charges for the products and services of the Federal lands. Neither set of issues can be treated adequately in broad and simple generalizations.

Several widely recognized problems nevertheless may be indicated.

Are charges for some uses, grazing, for example, too low compared with market-determined rates for comparable land?

Does the practice on some lands of almost routine renewal of grazing privileges practically convert a privilege into a right or quasi-right?

Is the value of a "right" to use public grazing land at substantially less than full market rates typically capitalized into the sales value of a private "home-ranch" property?

Are present and growing needs for heavy investment for protection and improvement of public lands met adequately?

Should existing arrangements respecting user charges and revenue sharing with State and local governments be changed to encourage increased investment in land improvement?

Although these questions are recognized widely, their possible implications are not acceptable to all individuals and groups. Nor are they meant to point to a comprehensive statement of issues in public-land policy and administration. They do, however, suggest some of the kinds of problems to which attention is given by administrators, legislators, and users of the lands.

The central economic difficulty in administration of Federal land is insufficiency of funds for current management and for investment in needed protection and improvement. Remedies for this condition are likely to be achieved, if at all, only as a result of a series of changes in law and policy over a period of years.

Among the kinds of changes often suggested in recent years are: A realinement of bases of sharing revenues (as payments in lieu of taxes) with State and local governments; modifying or eliminating the requirement of large payments, from receipts of public lands, into the Reclamation Fund; increasing fees and charges for some of the uses of public lands—for example, grazing permit fees and grazing lease rates; permitting Federal land-management agencies to retain a major share of their revenues in lieu of increased direct appropriations; and increasing direct appropriations for administration and improvement.

MANY PROPOSALS for changing organizational arrangements have been advanced. They include a relatively minor shifting of responsibilities among existing agencies to major departmental reorganization and the idea of establishing a comprehensive Federal land corporation.

No recommendation for major reorganization, whatever its merits, has received effective support.

One persistent idea has been that of a Department of Conservation, which would include all major land-management agencies of the Federal Government. The creation of such a department was recommended in 1937 by the President's Committee on Administrative Management and in 1949 by the Task Force on Natural Resources of the first Hoover Commission. However, the Hoover Commission's Task Force on Agriculture and a majority of the Commission itself recommended the establishment of an Agricultural Resources Conservation Service in the Department of Agriculture, to which the Bureau of Land Management would be transferred.

A central issue here, as in connection with certain more limited suggestions, was whether the Bureau of Land Management should be moved (wholly or in part) to the Department of Agriculture—or whether the Forest Service should be moved from the Department of Agriculture to the Department of the Interior.

One suggestion would in effect combine a sweeping organizational reform with a grant of rather broad administrative and discretionary authority with respect to land-management policies. It proposed the creation of a Federal Land Corporation, to which would be transferred the management of the lands of the national forests and national parks, the grazing districts and other public domain, reconveyed and revested areas, wildlife refuges, the submerged areas of the outer Continental Shelf, and possibly some additional areas. Within limits determined by legislation, the corporation would have power to buy, sell, and exchange land; exercise eminent domain for certain purposes; determine charges for use of public lands and related facilities; retain certain classes of revenues; and borrow for investments to protect and develop land. It would manage the Federal estate with the flexibility in arrangements needed in enterprises that involve large volumes and many varieties of business transactions.

Whatever the potential advantages of such an innovation, its adoption does not appear to be feasible in the near future. Some of the elements of the proposal, however, may be adaptable within the present organization.

A second suggestion is that a Federal Land Review Board be created. It would have no direct powers in land administration, but would assemble, analyze, and publicize facts about Federal land management. An important tool of analysis would be a comprehensive Federal land fund—actually, an economic account similar in function to the consolidated balance sheets and revenue and expenditure statements of major private corporations. Recommendations by an independent review board of this type, with a small research staff of recognized quality, might provide significant guidelines for detailed improvement of Federal land management over the years.

A FINAL CONSIDERATION of importance in Federal land administration is the role of advisory boards and of State and local governments.

The Bureau of Land Management and the Forest Service have found it helpful to have groups of interested individuals organized into boards or councils to advise as to the management of public-land areas. Groups of this kind may be established to represent a single type of user or use (grazing, for example); or there may be representation from most or all significant groups of users (including, for example, lumbering, mining, and water).

The area served by a board may be small, such as a ranger district; or it may be a large grazing district, a great national forest, or an entire State. Some boards are established under statutory requirements; others are relatively informal groups without legal status.

Members of boards established under statutes are elected by ballot, and the basic requirements are established by law. Members of informal boards may be selected by the Federal agency concerned or by organized groups that represent the various uses on the area served. Advice and recommendations

445509°—58——37

submitted by an advisory board are given consideration before decision is reached on any matter considered by the board, but the Federal administering agencies are responsible for making the decisions.

The proper role of advisory boards has been a moot question. The system of boards associated with the operations of the Bureau of Land Management ordinarily has been more influential than the system associated with the Forest Service. In any event, the Federal administrator, especially at the local level, must somehow get along with the agency clientele. Often the task of reconciling broad agency policies and national public interests with the needs and pressures of local user interests is difficult. Appropriate advisory-board systems may ease this task.

A widely applicable principle is to establish and maintain advisory-board membership to insure balanced representation of all significant interests concerned with the multiple uses of an area of public land. This practice can help to minimize possible undue influence of any one group of users.

Much of the wildlife within a State lives on the national lands all or part of the time. The State is responsible for the management and protection of resident wildlife, and State fish and game laws apply on national forest and other Federal lands. The Federal agencies are responsible under international treaties for the management of migratory wildfowl and for the public land—the soil, water, and vegetation—that produces much of the wildlife. The proper management of wildlife, therefore, requires close cooperation between the responsible State and Federal agencies. They must jointly formulate programs to balance game populations with available forage supplies and to improve wildlife habitat. Development of State and county road programs that involve Federal lands, protection of State, private, and national-forest lands from fire, and many other programs require close cooperation among national, State, and local agencies.

Tenure and the use of farm resources.

We achieve the best use of farm resources when we organize and use them so as to obtain the highest possible net returns consistent with conservation and development: The resources should be channeled into the uses and combined in such a way that they will yield the greatest satisfaction to society. If we are to reach this goal, land-tenure arrangements must be adequate. By *Walter G. Miller, Max M. Tharp,* and *Lawrence A. Jones,* Farm Economics Research Division.

MANY PERSONS hold rights in land— farm operators, either as tenants or owners; landlords, who rent land; creditors, who own mortgages on land; and society, which reserves certain rights in all land.

The terms and conditions of holding or owning, which we call tenure arrangements, are needed to insure that the rights are distributed in the most effective way and to establish proper understanding among the individuals or parties who hold them.

Tenure arrangements have a major part in determining how well we use our farm resources, including land, other capital, and labor.

Tenure arrangements will contribute to a better use of resources if they encourage farming units large enough for the most efficient operations; give security of tenure that will lead to adoption of effective long-range farm plans and improved farming practices; and result in an equitable division of costs and returns between landlords and tenants.

The enlargement of farms has been one of the major adjustments that farmers have made to economic and technological changes. It involves a greater use of the land and other capital assets of a farm. It reflects the desire of farm operators for greater efficiency and higher net incomes.

Many small farms with inadequate land or capital and low incomes still exist. These farmers may be marginal in the sense that they do not operate at the lowest possible cost per unit of output. They are vulnerable to cost squeezes from larger, more efficient units. Their income may be so small that they cannot expand their acreage or adopt and maintain improvements. After living expenses are deducted, little may be left for the savings needed for expansion of operations or other capital investments.

A farmer ordinarily has two ways of enlarging his operations: He may buy, with his own or borrowed funds, all the additional farm assets he needs, or he may rent additional land and buy other farm assets, if he needs them. Some farmers have not taken advantage of either possibility. The tenure arrangements may be a handicap.

Buying additional land continues as a way of enlarging farms in many sections. But some farmers—the ones in the lower income groups who often have the more urgent needs to expand their operations—may find it hard to buy land even though the level of economic activity is high.

Among the reasons for their difficulties are these: Larger farmers frequently can bid more for land because they have more cash or easier access to credit; the farm-mortgage market, on which the smaller farmers depend, is more favorable to the larger farmers who may be producing more efficiently; and farm values have reached an historically high level. Major financial outlays and greater risks are involved in the purchase of land. The price of land, particularly the better grades, is high.

The index of land values (1947–1949 = 100) for the United States increased from 49 to 143 between 1940 and 1956. According to this index, the price of land in 1956 averaged about three times higher than in 1940. With a debt-ratio limit of 50 to 60 percent, the required downpayment on land in 1956 in some instances was greater than the entire sale price of an equivalent tract of land in 1940. Thus major financial outlays often are required, and buyers who have little capital or low equities have found it difficult to obtain credit to buy land.

Furthermore, under the farm real-estate market, mortgage debts often are large. Incurring a large debt to buy additional land involves some risk of losing the property if prices of farm products should fall considerably or if a long drought should occur. Many have bought and paid for land, but not all persons want to expose themselves to the risks involved.

Because of the high demand for land with which to enlarge farms in most areas and the difficulties small farmers have in buying additional land, it is to be expected that enlargement through buying will take place more frequently among the larger farmers. Capital thus will be channeled into areas or farms where its productivity may be less than elsewhere and where its net contributions to agricultural efficiency and social welfare will be smaller. In addition, there will probably be the tendency toward more farms larger than family size, while other farms continue to be inadequate.

Farmers with inadequate land or capital may rent land. Although some farmers prefer to own all the resources they use, they often do so at the sacrifice of greater income possibilities and better use of resources. In general, full owner-operators are more limited as to land and working capital than are full tenants (apart from sharecroppers) and part owners. This is true because, given the same amount of funds, a farmer can control more assets by renting than by buying, for he need not tie up part of his money in land.

More and more farmers have been renting additional land as a means of enlarging their farms. The number of part owners has increased while the number of full owners and full tenants has declined. Part owners who operated commercial farms in 1954 rented 206.5 million acres in addition to the land they owned. Full tenants rented 182.3 million acres.

The 206.5 million acres rented by part owners represented nearly half of the land operated by them. These part-owner farms averaged larger than those of other tenure classes (apart from manager-operator farms).

The growth of part ownership as a method of obtaining control over more resources stems mainly from the prestige and security that one feels from ownership and the greater amount of resources obtainable through renting as opposed to buying. Furthermore, renting land is often safer. In the event of serious losses, a farmer's risk of losing his equity is less than if he had borrowed funds to buy additional land.

Then, too, rental property sometimes is more available than property for sale. Widows, retired farmers, and others may prefer to rent their farms because they depend on them for continuous income.

Part ownership is of signal importance in American agriculture. It facilitates farm enlargement, but associated with it are certain undesirable features. It may involve the operation of scattered tracts, and certain inefficiencies in farming will result. A part owner occasionally may exploit the land he rents in favor of the land he owns.

Regardless of whether land is rented

by full tenants or part owners, the type of lease affects the acreage rented and the way the land is used. A study in Iowa showed that, if given a choice, farmers thought that they would rent more land under a share-rental arrangement than under a fixed-cash rental. One reason for this is that under share rental, the amount of rent payable is automatically reduced when farm income declines. More of the risks (and profits) of farming are thereby divided between a landlord and his tenant. Under a fixed-rental payment, the same amount is due the landlord even when farm income declines. If this occurs, the renter bears more of the risks. As a precautionary measure, he usually adopts less speculative farm practices and concentrates on more stable enterprises.

Cash leases have certain disadvantages, and their use has declined. They still have a place in achieving larger farms, however, and they should not be discarded entirely. Rather, cash rent can be made to vary with farm income and thus the disadvantages of fixed, rigid payments will be overcome. Some landlords and some tenants still prefer to rent on a cash basis.

Inasmuch as renting facilitates adjustments toward larger farms, some landlords object to the renting of additional lands by their tenants. They fear that the tenants will spread their resources too thinly or that conflicts of interest will arise if another landlord is involved. The immediate economic consequences are the relatively low productivity of labor of the tenant and his family and the relatively high costs of machinery inputs. Sooner or later, a tenant who seeks to obtain greater income and fuller use of his labor and other resources must find opportunities elsewhere.

All classes of tenants, except sharecroppers, have shown recent increases in the average size of their farm units. The average size of sharecropper units was 43 acres in 1950 and 37 acres in 1954. The average size of commercial farms increased by about 12 percent.

Under sharecropping arrangements, the landlord makes the management decisions and provides most of the capital and equipment. As a result, increasing mechanization in cotton farming has caused some changes in sharecropping arrangements, but whether the real income positions of many sharecroppers have been improved is doubtful. Most sharecroppers are in the lowest economic classes; in 1954, about 60 percent had less than 2,500 dollars in farm receipts.

The number of sharecroppers and the total acreage they operate as a group have been declining. Their displacement presumably is associated with both increasing mechanization and better employment opportunities elsewhere. These trends, if they continue, probably will reflect improvements in farm-tenure conditions.

SECURITY OF TENURE is related also to the use of farm resources.

A farm operator's tenure is said to be insecure if he is uncertain as to future control of the land or if his occupancy is short—conditions that may discourage him from developing and following sound farm plans.

Arrangements for adequate security of tenure are especially important in such programs as irrigation, drainage, control of erosion, and flood control.

Security of tenure is needed also to encourage the construction and maintenance of proper buildings and the shift to types of farming that require practices from which income accrues only after considerable time has elapsed.

Tenant operators in general have less secure tenure than owner operators, partly because of conflicts of interest between some landlords and their tenants and short-term or oral leases.

A renter ordinarily organizes his farming system according to the limited time that he expects to occupy a particular farm. The time often is too short for such him to adopt farm plans that involve such investments as more adequate buildings, irrigation systems, and soil conservation measures.

Even when provisions are made for the automatic renewal of leases, tenants have no assurance that their leases will continue longer than from one year to the next. Operating a farm under such uncertainty does not permit adequate planning and may result in unwise use of farm resources.

Better use of resources would be possible if the time a tenant expects to occupy a farm were more definite and long enough for effective planning. This objective could also be accomplished if the landlord agrees to pay the tenant for the improvements he makes, in case the lease ends before the productive life of the improvement ends.

IN THE ABSENCE of landlord-tenant agreements that specify otherwise, permanent improvements made in or on land (such as terraces, drainage structures, and fences) belong legally to the landlord. Hence it is unlikely that tenants, particularly those who move frequently, would undertake investments under such circumstances.

It is therefore not surprising that some tenants consider rental arrangements and the lack of cooperation of landlords as major obstacles to the adoption of soil conservation measures and other improvements. To overcome these obstacles, some renters recognize that landlords should do more of the improvements and the length of leases should be extended.

Certain difficulties are likely to arise in either instance, particularly from the landlord's viewpoint. A tenant is not always willing to permit changes in his lease, although changes may be necessary if the landlord makes improvements. Some landlords are also unwilling to make certain improvements, such as buildings, unless they are certain that the improvements will be suitable for succeeding renters.

A question as to who should make the improvements on rented farms also arises.

The decision as to whether the landlord or tenant, or both, will make the improvements will depend on their relative capital positions and ability to obtain credit. Sometimes tenants are unable, even though willing, to obtain necessary credit because of their inability to furnish real estate as collateral or because their length of tenure is too short for the long-term loans that are usually involved. Some landlords find it difficult to undertake large expenditures.

Although some tenants prefer long-term leases, a fairly good case can also be made for short-term leases. Short-term leases permit periodic reviews of the tenant's performance by the landlord, who reserves the right to have the lease discontinued if resources are not used properly. Short-term leases also avoid extended frictions between landlords and tenants.

Because short-term leases have certain acceptable features and may be mutually satisfactory to the persons concerned, other measures to alleviate the effects of tenure insecurity must be sought.

Compensation provisions for the unexhausted portions of improvements made by tenants and penalties for abuses taken of landlords' resources by tenants have been recommended for many years.

But provisions of this kind have been virtually neglected in the United States. Although a few States have incorporated features of compensation and penalties in their legislation, the effectiveness and enforcement of the legislation are questionable.

The adoption and enforcement of the compensation provisions, however, would assure renters the returns from improvements they make if the lease is dissolved before the end of the productive life of the investments. At the same time, penalty provisions are necessary to protect landlords from abuses of their resources by renters. Investments would be encouraged if rental agreements contained both kinds of provisions.

The kinds of enterprises on farms operated under relatively secure tenure can also be expected to differ from those in which the tenure status of the operators is insecure. Insecurity may lead to enterprises that yield quick turnovers, such as hogs and field crops, as opposed to enterprises that require more extended periods of maturity, such as dairy and other livestock enterprises. Occupancy for many years also is necessary to realize full benefits from a sound crop rotation and cropping sequence and application of fertilizers that have long carryover effects.

The relationship between farm and farm enterprises is of particular importance in sections in which farming adjustments are needed to meet changes in the demand for different agricultural products. This problem is more relevant to areas like the Southeast, where some farmers have shifted from cotton to livestock farming. To facilitate these adjustments in the pattern of farm enterprises, changes in tenure arrangements will be needed on some farms. These changes may be accomplished either by changes in the content of traditional leases or changes from one type of lease to another.

SOME OWNER-OPERATORS also have insecurity of tenure—those who have only life estates and those who have high encumbrances through mortgage indebtedness. Insecure owner-operators react in somewhat the same way as insecure tenants.

Owners with only life estates (those who have the use of the land only for their own lifetime) may have little desire to keep land resources intact for their successors. They tend therefore to mine the soil in an effort to gain the greatest current farm income. Thus costs, in terms of lower future productivities of farm resources or expenditures for rebuilding them, fall upon future occupants and society. The situation is worse if the soil deteriorates to the extent that restoration to its former productive capacity is not economically feasible.

Owners who have large mortgage debts with fixed payments of interest and principal due each year may not always be in a position to use their resources in the best way. Fear of foreclosure, and hence uncertainty of tenure, represents an environment in which there is little incentive to invest in land or buildings that yield returns over a long period. The heavy periodic payments may force the owner to strive for the maximum immediate cash income rather than maximum returns in the long run. The pressure of farm debt is greatest during long periods of low income.

Because of the possible effects of a burdensome debt on the security of tenure and on the use of farm resources, prospective borrowers should give careful thought to the amount of debt they incur and the repayment conditions agreed upon. In determining how much debt they can carry safely, farmers should allow a safe margin for risks stemming from crop failures or sharp drops in prices. They should also choose lenders of long-term loans who understand farming and who would not be hasty in resorting to foreclosure in the event of a default.

EQUITABLE DIVISION of costs and returns is an important consideration if the use of resources is to be improved on rented farms.

Under leasing, different parties furnish land, labor, and capital in various proportions. In order to obtain the best use of these resources, each party should receive returns in accordance with his respective contributions. When this is accomplished, both tenant and landlord will have the incentive to use resources for the benefit of both as well as for the personal interests of each.

If a landlord pays none of the expenses of applying fertilizer—labor and equipment, as well as the cost of materials—he is interested in having the maximum amount of fertilizer applied, as he will receive part of the additional income that the fertilizer yields without paying any of its costs.

As the tenant bears all the costs and receives only a part of the returns, he will prefer a lower level of application, or none at all. If the opportunity exists, he may use his resources in some alternative from which he gets the full returns.

The same reasoning applies to the landlord if he must pay for the application of fertilizer but does not receive a proportionate share of the returns from its use. There may be restrictions in the use of fertilizer or any similar factor of production in either instance, although more of it could increase net farm income considerably.

In order to assure that resources will be fully employed, the cost of producing a product should be shared in the same way as the product is shared.

As a practical matter, this solution sometimes may be difficult; but approximations may be made as in the case of the usual 50–50 livestock type of lease, in which all costs and returns are supposedly shared in the same proportions. Even under this type of lease, however, there may still be conflicts between landlords and tenants over the values each places on the quality of the land furnished by the landlord and the labor and management furnished by the renter.

Other conflicts of the interests between landlords and tenants occur when the landlords have limited capital and the tenants have a more adequate amount, or vice versa. Some adjustments will be necessary then in the relative shares of their contributions to the farming operations and, therefore, in the returns each receives. The most adequate share lease will therefore vary with the resources owned and contributed by each party.

Under fixed cash leases, an inequitable division of costs and returns will also arise if the level of rent is out of line with the productivity of the land or the improvements made by the landlord. Whenever the rent is greater than the productivity of the landlord's resources, there is a transfer of income from the tenant to the landlord. It is

likely that the tenant will furnish a disproportionate share of the resources used. Whenever the rent is relatively low, the reverse is likely to occur.

Because of changes in the relationship of prices received and paid by farmers, as well as changes in technology, the tenure arrangements best suited to improve the use of farm resources need to be examined periodically. Hence flexibility in share or cash leases is required in the division of costs and returns. Rigid rental terms and changing conditions over the years can cause a pattern of resource organization that is not in the best interests of either party to the lease, the farm unit, or the economy.

The customary land-tenure arrangements in a community or region may not be the best ones, especially within a changing environment. Land-tenure problems therefore are likely to continue to arise because some of us are not always aware of their implications and because it is difficult to work out arrangements satisfactory to all the individuals concerned.

Because of wide variations among farms, farming areas, and individuals (in terms of their preferences and financial positions), no blanket recommendations on specific tenure arrangements to cover all conceivable situations can be made. Apart from the problems mentioned here are problems that involve the tax structure, inheritance and transfers, manager-operator farms, partnerships, father-son arrangements, and so on.

In general, tenure conditions should not cause undue restrictions in the size of farming units or discourage needed changes. They should not impede adoption of sound, long-range farm plans. They should not give incentives to combine farm resources and products in a way that does not yield the highest net returns along with the maintenance and further development of resources. Sound tenure arrangements can be designed to prevent such situations. They are necessary if better use of farm resources is to be obtained.

Planning for the new land frontier.

Alarm that our cropland will disappear into the urban maw serves the useful purpose of alerting us to the need for planning. Enough thought about the dynamics of areal and regional growth often can reduce waste of resources. Sound plans are instruments for saving productive farm units. By *Hugh A. Johnson*, Farm Economics Research Division.

I RETURNED to the United States recently after a long absence. My absence in itself is of no particular significance or interest. What was noteworthy, though, was that I could not recognize approaches to the university town where I had lived for several years and that when I drove into farming areas to visit friends I could not find their farms.

Villages had become cities. Small, sleepy county seats had taken on an industrial bustle. Regional centers had sprawled far beyond their former boundaries. New suburbs had sprouted from the countryside, and new highways connected them in a metropolitan complex.

During those years my father had retired. The buildings on his farm had been removed. His fields had been added to those of an adjoining farm. An uncle had sold his farm to a partnership of father and son, who needed more land on which to use their equipment and labor. Another relative had sold his farm to a subdivider.

The changes had seemed gradual to my stay-at-home relatives and friends. We began to realize the extent of the shifts as we discussed the old days of really not so long ago: Hundreds of other farms had disappeared from the rural scene, and many more would follow them if the cities and industries I saw across the country and the new highways I drove over were to continue normal, healthy growth.

As we discussed these changes, we knew that our points of view differed, depending on whose ox was being gored. We concluded that many city people do not understand farm problems and that many farmers do not understand city problems—or, to generalize even more broadly, people in one region may not be aware of the dynamics of other regions.

On this we agreed: Everyone has problems. Some problems apply to the management of the home farm business. Some apply to local or community situations. Some are statewide or regional. Some are national and international in scope. We seldom separate our problems into neat categories. Decisions to act in one way often cause unexpected institutional changes harmful to individuals: New roads, airfields, and subdivisions disturb the established patterns of land use, change the lives of those who are on or near them, and add another piece to the regional and national jigsaw picture that is changing day by day, faster and faster.

The fact of change we cannot escape, much as we would like to think that our fathers' farms should always remain for us to go back to, that the scenes of our schooldays will always be as we experienced them, that the new highways and airports will not actually spoil or devour the landscape we love. But we might as well be realistic about it.

568

We have to face the fact that every year thousands of acres of tillable land in the United States are going into such uses as urban subdivisions, industrial sites, defense establishments, highways, railways, and airports, and that since 1940 about 17 million acres of our flattest and most fertile farmlands have been converted to nonagricultural uses. If these withdrawals continue at the present rate for another 15 years, a total of about 100 million acres that once were tilled will have been converted.

A fact that we are apt to ignore is that large sectors never should have been in farms. We only now are squeezing out the surplus and getting our resource base of land more nearly in balance with production needs.

For example, 10 to 20 percent of the tillable land in 13 Northeastern States has been removed from agriculture since 1940.

Lester E. Klimm, in the Geographical Review, estimated that perhaps 85 percent of the empty areas in the Northeastern States was characterized by steep slope, poor drainage, or poor soil and that perhaps 60 percent also has some climatic handicap.

The National Resources Board estimated that nearly half of New Jersey is nonagricultural and mostly suitable for forest.

Some areas are empty because people tried to farm them and failed. Others are empty because people knew better from previous experience. Some areas are losing population because of isolation, severe climatic conditions, and better opportunities elsewhere.

The grasping tentacles of an urban octopus and the specter of a land-starved future are widely publicized fears. We seem to welcome a bogy of soil scarcity and impending starvation, even though we have been in a period of great prosperity. Our attitude toward land resources is almost diametric to the one we held during the drought and depression years of a short time ago. The wide arc that marks the pendulum swing of public knowl-edge and opinion often measures only gross distortions of facts. Let us look at some facts.

Farms have been combined, subdivided, and abandoned, and the type of farming has changed over a long span of years. Adjustments actually began in colonial times. The longtime trend simply has been accentuated. Yet the markets are full, and controls of farm production appear to have become a continuing national problem. The face of our land has changed—and not all the changes are pleasant, desirable, or necessary. Many of these changes are only remotely related to physical growth of urban and industrial communities. Most are related to changes in our national social, economic, and technological growth.

Agriculture, since about 1940, has joined the technological revolution. As a result of improved technology, one farmworker now can feed himself and about 18 other consumers. His productivity has grown 2.5 times during one generation. Efficiency in farming methods has created technological underemployment for millions of farm people and management problems in the economics of size and adjustment of resource inputs for millions of farm operators.

We have continued to produce about 5 percent more agricultural goods than domestic and foreign markets will absorb. Our productive potential lies in a magnitude about 40 percent above our output in 1958. Each improvement in technology increases that potential.

Studies by men in the Department of Agriculture indicate that, even if present rates of alienation of farmlands continue, we could come within about 5 percent of feeding the population of 220 million we will have in 1975 and 300 million in 2000 at its present levels of living. Expected improvements in technology will make the difference.

T. W. Schultz, professor of agricultural economics in the University of Chicago, thinks that, under conditions of changing demand and technology, the farm income in an area in the long run depends primarily on its relative ability to adapt its agriculture to changing conditions.

A. M. Tang, professor of economics in Vanderbilt University, put it this way: "Longtime, increasing disparity in agricultural income [per worker or per farm person] among areas is related to the pattern of local industrial-urban development whose positive income effect is transmitted to local agriculture through its impact upon local factor and product markets."

You and I know that farmers have been unable to reduce appreciably their farm output during periods of low prices. Their fixed costs continue, and their main hope lies in increased efficiency of production, greater volume of production, and smaller unit costs. It follows, then, that periods of prosperity and strong demand are the time to bring farming into adjustment with other segments of our economy.

We shall return to this point later and fill in some of the details.

Let us consider now some of the changes in several parts of the Nation.

Professor Tang and his associates studied the longtime development pattern and income characteristics of 21 counties in the upper part of the Georgia and South Carolina Piedmont, a relatively homogeneous area and one of uniform natural resources. Its agriculture and its people had a long history of low production.

Industry and cities have grown in parts of this region since about 1900. The rates of growth were fast, but highly uneven, during the 1940's. The counties with industrial developments had significantly higher agricultural incomes and labor returns per farm-worker in 1940 than did the undeveloped counties. The correlation between industrial-urban development and farm income per worker was even greater in 1950. Thus the industrially developed counties have continued to move ahead of the underdeveloped counties in productivity of farm labor. Why did this occur during a period of full employment when disadvantaged

farm people had so many alternatives?

An examination of the situation brought out that real reductions in the farm labor force were more important than increases in farm capital, yet changes in output were related primarily to changes in capital and only to a limited extent to changes in labor. Thus the presence of an imbalance in the application of resources came to light. Farms were overcapitalized on labor, and substantial underemployment was widespread. Reductions in farm labor did not appreciably lower output; rather, they increased the effectiveness of the labor that remained on the farms. The movement of 54 thousand persons out of farming in the area, however, still was insufficient to meet the low-income problems of agriculture.

Farmers near industrial-urban developments received benefits not available to their fellows living farther away. They tended to receive higher prices for their products and to pay lower prices for their inputs. Creation of new markets for some farm products, as a result of urban growth and rises in per capita income, and opportunity to market their products in the most favorable form, such as fluid milk, gave them additional opportunities for desirable adjustments in their farm business organization.

The part-time farms of the developed counties were no larger than those of the undeveloped counties in 1950. Yet, with far less labor per farm, these operators received comparable incomes per farm.

Professor Tang drew the conclusions that an increased ratio of capital to labor (primarily through decreases in labor) had been the major type of adjustment on part-time farms and that modern part-time farms represented small subsistence units of the past, which had contained much initially underemployed farm labor. The diversion of a substantial part of this surplus labor to off-farm work did not appreciably affect output per farm.

The availability of any nonfarmwork

within reasonable commuting distance is vitally important in determining the extent to which farm families may work off the farm without actually changing residence. Since this type of adjustment was easy to make in areas where nonfarmwork opportunities are prevalent, it is no surprise that families of part-time farmers responded with alacrity to the changed situation.

Dr. Tang pointed out that off-farm employment of farm persons tends to select those in the most productive age groups. The unfavorable age composition of the remaining labor force (the elderly and otherwise less employable) on part-time farms accounts in part for the apparently low level of income per farmworker.

(I might add, however, that the same general situation applies in commercial farming. The most mobile segments in the labor force gravitate to the better opportunities, and the less mobile make other adjustments in place. This "adverse" age distribution of farmworkers will continue until the time that returns to labor from farming are competitive with other forms of livelihood for the mobile segment of the labor force.)

Thus, agriculture of the Southern Piedmont has benefited from the growth of industry. Absorption of formerly underemployed farm labor has made possible substantial increases in farm income per farmworker without appreciably affecting total farm output. Benefits have accrued first to families relatively near the nonfarmwork opportunities. It follows that continued industrial growth and activity will encourage further transfers of farm labor and, as nearby underemployment disappears, the effects must reach farther afield.

Continued disappearance of disguised unemployment in the developed areas might be accompanied eventually by larger and larger reductions in farm output until a point of equilibrium is reached in demand for farm products, which will justify profitable production by the remaining farm laborers. The underdeveloped areas still faced with unemployment of their labor force will improve their economic position and farm-labor productivity as outmigration and opportunities for off-farm work drain off the surpluses and allow better organization of farm resources.

SEVERAL OTHER STUDIES across the Nation provide variations in the application—but the same tone and theme—of favorable trends in adjustments.

A study by men in the Department of Agriculture and the West Virginia Agricultural Experiment Station disclosed that 96 percent of rural residents in that State were partly or fully nonfarmworkers in 1957. Only 5 percent of the households in the Upper Monongahela Valley depended solely on agriculture. Forty-one percent were part-time operators who also received income from nonfarm sources. Another 40 percent did no farmwork, and 14 percent received income only from such nonfarm sources as rent, royalties, public assistance, retirement funds, or social security. Eighty percent of the workers had industrial or business experience. They had adjusted to regular employment and acquired skills valuable in nonfarmwork.

Harold G. Halcrow, head of the Department of Agricultural Economics in the University of Illinois, made a study of part-time farming—in which the income from work off the farm equals receipts from the sale of farm products—over the Nation.

Items that have influenced the growing trend to part-time farming include improved transportation, farm mechanization, the establishment of industries in or near rural sections, and a desire to live in the country.

In 1954, Professor Halcrow pointed out, 1,334 thousand farm operators (27.9 percent of all farm operators) were working off their farms 100 days or more; in 1929, 700 thousand (11.5 percent) worked off the farm 100 days or more. Between 1929 and 1954, the number of American farm operators declined by nearly one-third.

Off-farm employment has become a notable factor in agriculture in most of the main farming areas of the United States. Such employment used to be largely among farmers who sold less than 1,200 dollars' worth of farm products in a year, but lately the number of operators of larger farms who work off the farm has increased.

L. A. REUSS, of the Agricultural Research Service, reported that recent trends in Florida included a rapidly rising urban population, a moderately increasing rural nonfarm population, and a declining farm population. Projections to 1970 indicated a possible slight increase in the number of farms, a moderate increase in urban areas, and a marked growth in the rural nonfarm population.

Spreading urban and suburban areas intensify problems of providing roads, electricity, sewerage, police and fire protection, schools, and shopping facilities. Tax and zoning problems are multiplied. Premature subdivisions often do not provide for services.

Urbanization has a strong impact on the attitudes and goals of farm people as they are brought into closer contact with nonfarm or part-time farm people, urban employment, and ways of life. This impact is greater in northern and western Florida, where the culture of the rural population is more homogeneous than in the rest of the State. Increased opportunities for nonfarm employment increases interest among rural people in education and training.

The number of noncommercial—part-time and residential—farms has dropped in northern and western Florida and increased in central and southern Florida. In some counties there were decreases or only slight increases in the number of farm operators working off their farms 100 days or more; largest decreases in this group were reported in Duval and Nassau Counties in the Jacksonville area.

A study in Duval County by Daniel Alleger, an economist at the Florida Agricultural Experiment Station, showed that two-thirds of part-time and retirement farmers were gainfully employed, one-fourth were retired, and the others were self-employed.

Two-thirds of the home-farm units had fewer than 6 acres. More than half had fewer than 4 acres. About half of the operators planted one-half acre or less in crops. Nearly 90 percent of the enterprises were gardening types of agriculture. About 80 percent of the operators kept poultry or meat animals. The economic advantages of part-time farming came more from savings than from increased earnings.

As population and economic activity have grown in Florida, there have been tendencies toward a gradual upgrading in the use of land: Subdivisions replace citrus groves, citrus groves replace improved pastures, and pastures replace native rangelands.

The acreage of bearing citrus groves increased about 25 percent (an estimated 567 thousand acres in 1958) and the nonbearing acreage doubled (94,500 in 1957–1958) from 1949 to 1958, according to Mr. Reuss. Some established citrus groves were being cleared for subdivisions, highways, and industrial parks. Some estimates indicate that only 50 thousand to 100 thousand acres suitable for citrus have not been planted, and of these 25 thousand to 50 thousand acres would be taken up for homes. All ridgelands in some places are occupied, and new groves are being set out on flatwoods land after ditching and bedding. Demand for land for citrus in central Florida affects the supply and the cost of land available to producers of other farm products.

The area of improved pasture in Florida was estimated at more than 1.6 million acres. Continued expansion is expected. Florida has perhaps 10 million acres that could be converted from native rangeland into improved pastures. Some loss of acreage of improved pastures occurs when new citrus groves are set out and when residential and commercial subcenters are established in open country.

The acreage of truck crops increased by more than 50 thousand acres between 1949 and 1957 (410 thousand acres for harvest in 1955–1956).

The demand for land for truck crops in 1958 was not in serious conflict with other uses of land. Urbanization encouraged increases in the acreages in truck crops in rural areas such as the Everglades, some expansion in acreage around urban markets, and some outward movement of production areas at the perimeter of expanding urban centers.

The acreage in general field crops has declined slightly. Demand for land by pulp and timber companies affects the economy of general farming in northern and western Florida.

Several examples are at hand of some of the effects of a high demand for land. Dairy farmers near Miami have sold land for subdivisions for 1 thousand dollars or more an acre and moved their operations to cheaper land north of Palm Beach or near Lake Okeechobee. The same type of movement is taking place near towns like Tallahassee. In the process, the dairymen may increase greatly the size of their farms and boost land values at their new locations. Cattlemen are refraining from investing funds to improve pasturelands that may be in demand as sites for citrus groves or subdivisions. In areas where the land market is highly active, especially the coastal and metropolitan areas, investors are permitting much land to remain idle, pending resale or the anticipated change to a higher use. Dwellings in rural areas are in demand as housing for part-time farmers and for nonfarmworkers. Market values of tracts that have dwellings seemed in 1958 to exceed current or prospective values for agricultural purposes.

IN LOUISIANA, according to Robert W. Harrison, of the Agricultural Research Service, the subsistence economy of Acadians is giving way to a suburban economy. Many country people are employed in the expanding oil, sulfur, salt, and related industries on the gulf coast. Extensive ranching enterprises are developing in the great Tensas Basin of Louisiana and Arkansas.

The dominance in economic and community affairs of the traditional sugarcane and cotton plantations, with their distinctive labor organization and social structure, is giving way to newer economic and social patterns.

The migration from the alluvial valley of the Mississippi of thousands of young and capable farmworkers and the movement of many other farmworkers to nearby cities and villages have made it necessary to reconsider the role of labor in the economy. The lack of trained workers for mechanized farming and of workers who have knowledge of livestock and diversified farming is increasingly a factor in shaping the agriculture in the valley.

Harald A. Pedersen, of Mississippi State College, has pointed out the close relationship between the general economic level of the Nation and the availability of farm labor in Mississippi. Between 1940 and 1950, an estimated 400 thousand persons, mostly farmworkers, left the State every year. Many of them were young sharecroppers. As long as the wide margin between industrial wages and the returns to farmers persists, the high mobility of the surplus farm population will continue. Plantations and large farms have adjusted to the reduced supply of workers by mechanization. A business recession would cause a damming up of surplus workers, and possibly a reversal of migration would result in sizable increases in the labor force.

J. R. Bowring, M. C. Purington, and O. B. Durgin, economists at the New Hampshire Agricultural Experiment Station, made comparisons of population changes in New Hampshire in 1940 and 1950. They found a drop in the number of rural farm and urban age groups and a rise in the rural nonfarm residents. The latter can be explained by the movement of city residents to neighboring rural areas and small towns, partly because of industrial development and partly because they preferred to live in the country and commute to jobs in industrial centers. Improved roads and transportation facilities and improved incomes have accentuated this preference for living in small towns.

They discovered facts they believe are of great significance to planners for future balanced agricultural-urban relations: "The decrease in the number of farms has been accompanied by an increase in the level of living of the remaining farm families. The number of farms in New Hampshire declined from 18,786 in 1945 to 10,411 in 1955 (45 percent), but the average size increased from 107 to 140 acres. The major sources of farm income are dairy and poultry. Cow numbers decreased somewhat during the decade from 65,000 to 59,000. At the same time, however, milk production per cow increased at least 25 percent. The movement off farms does not indicate a decline in the economic significance of the industry so much as an economic reallocation of resources to increase the total product of the State."

Economists at the Ohio Agricultural Experiment Station also reported the trend toward fewer and larger farms and more farmers working away from home. Thirty-seven percent of farmers in Ohio worked off the farm more than 100 days in 1954; in 11 counties, mostly in northeastern Ohio, the proportion exceeded 50 percent. About half of the part-time farmers were employed in factories. Others worked only seasonally in industry or sought work with more flexibility.

The increase in the proportion of Ohio farmers who took other jobs was associated more directly with the availability of industrial opportunities than with the quality of land or type of farm. Some operators of farms that were larger than average in northwestern Ohio had taken advantage of industrial developments to hold full-time jobs in industry. Industrial expansion in the Ohio River Valley has encouraged part-time farming by giving many operators a chance to overcome their longstanding problem of low farm incomes.

In Arkansas, William H. Metzler, an economist in the Agricultural Research Service, noted that farming had lost almost 800 thousand persons in 30 years. The net movement was greater for Negroes than for whites. More tenants and sharecroppers moved than farmowners. Net outmigration had been partly to nearby towns and cities, but was even greater to towns and cities in other parts of the country.

Dr. Metzler noted a situation with vastly improved relationships between population and resources in the Ozark area of Arkansas. The farms averaged 50 percent larger in 1957 than in 1939, and the investment per farm was four times greater. A change from intensive row-crop farming to livestock and dairy enterprises has occurred. Lumbering and other industries have developed significantly. Total retail sales ran five times higher in 1954 than in 1939.

The decline in numbers of farms and farm families reflects the movement of thousands of marginal farmers from the Ozark area. This has permitted farm enterprises to grow to a size better adapted to present-day use of capital equipment and labor. Thousands of other underemployed people have moved to other areas where employment and income are more regular. The net result has been better living for farmers and nonfarmers alike in a region historically poor in land resources.

J. Z. Rowe, of the Federal Reserve Bank of Dallas, reported that almost half of the farmers in the five Southwestern States had off-farm work in 1954. Thirty-eight percent of the farm operators had outside income that exceeded agricultural income in 1954.

This rising trend is the result of pressures to supplement family income and the attractiveness of alternative nonagricultural employment.

Dr. Rowe said, however: "On balance, the increase in off-farm work and the smaller farm population probably have resulted in a gain to the southwestern economy as a whole. . . . For persons remaining on part-time farms, supplementation of the family's income through off-farm employment has resulted in a higher and more stable income and has contributed to the growth of the economy."

California has been thought of as a State of burgeoning urban population and dwindling resources. Yet, for the State as a whole, Varden Fuller reported in the February 1955 issue of California Agriculture that between 1930 and 1950 the amount of cropland increased by 2.3 million acres, of which 1.8 million was irrigated, although none of the changes increased the total number of commercial farms. Farms of fewer than 1 thousand acres (except the small units of fewer than 10 acres) actually declined.

Dr. Fuller concluded that agriculture in California does not offer opportunities to new commercial farm operators except as replacements on presently existing units. There also will be less demand for seasonal workers, because skilled and technically trained workers operate and maintain equipment designed to perform the more exacting procedures of technologically advanced agriculture.

California's large-scale commercial farmers, except milk producers, have specialized in production for markets outside the State rather than in it. The growth of population within California, according to Dr. Fuller, would have little effect in itself on what its agriculture produces, other than such commodities as market milk. Future changes are likely to be influenced much more by national and world markets than by the size of the State's markets or the need of an expanding occupational base to absorb its growing population.

DETAILED AREA STUDIES of changes in land use due to urban growth have been made less frequently than have analyses of social changes, employment, taxation, local government, or attitudes. The few studies centered on changes in uses of land complement in many ways the illustrations I have given.

They are unanimous that the rural change would not have occurred without the urban catalyst. Each area apparently has reacted differently under the impact of the various stimuli, however.

Three localities in Michigan, Wisconsin, and Utah illustrate some common adjustments in land uses.

Sociologists and economists in the University of Michigan have studied several suburban areas in Michigan.

J. Allan Beegle and Widick Schroeder described land use on the edge of North Lansing as a blend of densely populated residential areas, large sections of tilled soil, and a sprinkling of commercial and industrial structures concentrated along the main transportation artery. Because there are no zoning regulations, they said, different types of structures are allowed next to one another, and many new dead-end streets and roads are indications of a rapid growth and the lack of coordinated planning.

E. Howard Moore and Raleigh Barlowe studied the effects of suburbanization of land use in two localities between Okemos and Williamston. Both were settled more than a century ago and until recently were used primarily for farming. The impact of suburbanization is causing a gradual change in both. The Okemos area, being closer to Lansing, felt the impact of suburbanization first. A few city workers resided here before the Second World War, but the major influx has been since the war.

Much of the suburban development has resulted from piecemeal sale of lots and highway frontage from farms. Both areas, however, contain subdivided properties. Some of these platted areas are having a high type of development. The subdivisions generally are less built up and concentrated than are subdivisions at the outskirts of Lansing and East Lansing.

Nearly 60 percent of the land in the Williamston area and 35 percent in the Okemos area was owned by full-time farmers in 1951. Part-time farmers held about 25 percent of the land. In the Okemos area, 40 percent of the land was owned or rented by rural residents, as compared to 15 percent of the Williamston acreage. Most of the rural residents held relatively small tracts. A preponderance of their cropland was idle or in relatively extensive use through rental to nearby farmers for pasture, hayland, or grain fields.

Farms occupied by part-time farmers also generally were smaller than those of full-time operators. Much of their cropland was rented out.

Two of three full-time farmers operated units of 100 acres or more. Fields rented from rural residents or part-time farmers often were part of the units. Younger operators tended to operate the larger farms.

Neither the size of farm nor the nearness to suburban developments seemed to have much effect on the use of land for crops and pasture. Part-time farmers, however, tended to use more of their land for crops and less for pasture (probably because they had less need for pasture) than full-time farmers. Part-time farmers and small operators tended to concentrate on one or two crops. Most of the active full-time farmers used a 4-year rotation based on corn, oats, wheat, and hay.

A general air of impermanence seemed to prevail. Many farmers in both areas, but particularly those in the Okemos area, felt that suburbanization has resulted in poorer farming practices. Fewer livestock were kept. Less attention was paid to good cultural and soil conservation practices. Cash cropping, rather than regular fertility-building rotations, were common. Mining the soil generally was related to the relative imminence of platting for nonfarm uses. Under the circumstances, however, this practice is not to be condemned too harshly.

Full-time farmers farthest from Lansing indicated plans to continue their current rotation system of farming. Most had in mind sale or lease for future nonfarm development. Forty percent of the part-time farmers indicated plans to continue present uses of their land; 25 percent planned shifts to beef or other livestock; 20 percent planned more crops; and 15 percent had no plans. Rural residents generally had no well-defined plans for future land use except for gardens and small orchards.

About one-eighth of the total land in these areas was idle or unused. Some idle land was associated with suburbanization and use for rural residences, but much of it was on farms operated by full- and part-time farmers. Some was left idle because of low fertility. Other tracts that could have been used to advantage were idle because of the age or health of the operators or because of alternative work opportunities off the farm.

The findings of Professors Moore and Barlowe coincide with several others over the country that proportions of idle or unused lands tend to be high in areas of rapid suburban development. This practice of nonuse is one of the hidden costs of rural residence and industrial development that can be attributed to lack of unified planning.

These places in Michigan were beyond the zone of most intensive subdivision, and a high proportion of full-time farmers still were trying to farm efficiently. This fact definitely affected the demand for fields that could be rented for cash crops, particularly wheat. Some farmers went several miles to rent fields, but there was little interest in fields smaller than 5 acres. Modern machinery and effective use of labor require larger acreages for full efficiency.

Both of these areas are in a region where dairying used to be regarded as the most profitable farm enterprise. Both have experienced a general shift from dairying to cash crops. Part of the reason for the change is the favorable prices of wheat and corn in recent years. Part is due to the effects of suburbanization.

The rural residents generally kept no livestock. A few had chickens, pigs, riding horses, cows, or calves. Part-time farmers also tended to keep small numbers of livestock. In fact, 60 percent of those in the Williamston area and 75 percent of those in the Okemos area had fewer than 5 animal units per farm. Part-time farmers placed less emphasis on dairy animals and more on beef, considerably less on sheep and hogs, and slightly more on chickens than did the full-time farmers. Thirty-four percent of full-time farmers had fewer than 10 animal units.

Almost all the residents of the two areas felt that suburbanization had caused a rise in property taxes. Practically all of the increase went for school purposes. Assessed values were highest on properties of full-time farmers and lowest on rural residences.

Tracts along the highway or in places that promise a high level of development command the highest prices. Lots within a mile of a main road seem to be preferred, but sometimes hilly land close to developed centers brought as much as good bottom land, and residential buyers were forcing up the prices of both good and fair farmland.

Changing uses of land in the fringe areas near Milwaukee, Wis., were studied by Arthur J. Walrath, of the Agricultural Research Service. Milwaukee County was one of the early leaders in the field of suburban zoning. Of six counties in southeastern Wisconsin surrounding Milwaukee, four have county zoning laws, although the laws did not apply uniformly in all townships within the counties.

Dr. Walrath concluded that zoning had provided relatively little control in development of nonfarm uses: Zoning often was only a slight obstacle to be overcome when the owner decided to subdivide his land.

The trend in numbers of farms has been downward in the six counties—Ozaukee, Kenosha, Racine, Walworth,

Washington, and Waukesha. It began before the depression and continued at a faster rate after the 1930's. The number of farms dropped 14 percent during the 1940's and another 9 percent between 1950 and 1955. The decline is apt to continue for some time if economic forces are allowed to make desirable adjustments in factor inputs between farm and nonfarm enterprises.

Continued subdivision, commercial and industrial developments, scattered housing, and modification and improvement in the highway system no doubt will reduce the number of farms. A further reduction in numbers will occur through the consolidation of uneconomically small units and the adjustment of farm size to modern technology. The retirement of older farmers and transfers of the younger operators to nonfarmwork will make tracts available.

Dr. Walrath found no clearcut pattern in the decreases or increases in the numbers of farms by townships in relation to the distance from cities. The land in farms was less in the counties, and the number of farms declined, but the average size of farm increased through absorption of other units going out of production. Smaller farms tended to disappear.

The remaining cropland is used more intensively. An additional acreage, which was not accounted for in subdivisions and rural homes, has shifted from agriculture to temporary nonuse. There is little prospect that it will return to agriculture. Present owners are holding it in a nonuse status until it can be developed profitably for urban use. Some of it may be available for annual cropping by nearby farmers, but there will be fewer and fewer farmer bidders for it as the area becomes more and more urban.

Relocation of highways can affect the future of individual farms by taking essential acreages of cropland and by cutting a farm in two. A limited-access thruway might make one part of a farm inaccessible and usually would disrupt the farming and marketing.

These six counties have been important in the production of fluid milk and vegetables for city markets.

Unlike the previous example of a dairy area in Michigan that had changed to cash crops and rural residences, the Wisconsin dairymen had maintained their milking herds, increased their corn acreage, reduced their small grain acreage, and were farming more intensively.

Dr. Walrath's data bring out the anomalous conditions that may develop in situations of rapid change. We normally would expect some kind of relationship between the kinds of crops that are grown and urban concentrations (besides the type of soil). Farmers in southeastern Wisconsin evidently do not follow a norm, as land uses in adjoining townships often differ.

The several farming communities vary remarkably in the adjustments to various stages of urbanization. Total production for the six counties, however, has not suffered. The value of all production in 1954, even after adjustment for price levels, was 101.2 percent of what it was in 1949. The composition of the total had changed, however. Sales of whole milk had increased 2 percent; sales of eggs had dropped 3 percent; sales of chickens increased 10 percent; corn harvested for grain increased 39 percent; and small grains dropped about 15 percent.

Changes in acreage of tame hay seem to be associated with new growth of urban areas. The acreage in hay in some sections was expanded because of the acquisition of farmland by persons whose only interest in farming is to keep weeds down by cutting hay or by selling the standing crop. In other sections, with only a slightly different ownership pattern, these acreages would be untended and would be considered to be idle.

The increases in farm production resulted from shifts in enterprises and higher yields. In Waukesha County, for example, yields of corn increased from an average of 49 bushels an acre in 1941–1945 to 58 bushels in 1949–1953; tame hay, from 2 tons to 2.4 tons; canning peas, from 1,872 pounds to 2,109 pounds; and milk per cow, from 6,879 to 7,380 pounds.

Urbanization had little effect on farm acreage before 1940. Fewer than 1 thousand acres were subdivided in 1941–1945, but in the next 5 years more than 3,500 acres were in newly recorded subdivisions. Another 7,400 acres of subdivisions were recorded in 1950–1955, when an additional 44,427 acres disappeared from farming. About 40 percent of this was cropland, which often is held for development or speculative rises in land values.

The six counties and Milwaukee have lacked an overall plan of development. Spasmodic growth into predominantly agricultural sections all too often has been followed by an unorderly urban sprawl. One result is that islands of undeveloped land may remain after a large part of a section is in the new use. More serious results are in heavy public charges for ill-timed and poorly adapted services and facilities. Suburban living loses many of its amenities under these conditions.

MORE THAN 50 PERCENT of the farms in Utah sold less than 2,500 dollars' worth of farm products in 1954. Nearly 65 percent of the farmers worked off the farm for pay. About 45 percent worked more than 100 days off the farm.

Davis, Salt Lake, Utah, and Weber Counties, which include much of the nonfarm population and business activity of the State, contain nearly half of the low-income farmers in Utah. Sixty-eight percent of the farmers in the four counties worked off their farms, and 57 percent worked more than 100 days off the farm, primarily because they had greater opportunities for off-farm work.

Clyde E. Stewart, in Farm and Home Science, published at Utah State University, wrote: "Farm mechanization and large off-farm employment opportunities are strong forces in our economy, and tend to increase the size of farms. At the same time, more off-farm work opportunities and shorter working hours probably have encouraged part-time and residential farms. Many of our farmers operate land in combination with off-farm employment. Frequently this arrangement gives a profitable return."

Dr. Stewart believes that many of the small farms were acquired as a supplementary operation in an effort to develop desirable aspects of a two-income plan in areas where industrial employment is available. Dependence on this kind of small commercial, part-time, and residential farm is growing in Utah, especially in terms of farm numbers, land use, and people.

The population of Davis County, whose county seat is Farmington, nearly doubled between 1940 and 1950. A major reason was the general industrial expansion in Utah and the establishment of military projects and installations in the northern parts of the county. Several large oil refineries were developed, and an increase in all types of business occurred.

Suburban expansion occurred in communities near Salt Lake City.

Small towns grew as young married couples moved in for employment in defense industries or commuted to jobs in Salt Lake City or Ogden.

Farmland, much of it of low-intensity use, near city boundaries was transmuted into new towns.

Settlement had taken mainly the pattern of single-family dwellings, with lawns and backyards. Enough land for building purposes made this type of development possible. Because the platted residential areas were interspersed with farmlands in some communities, an unutilized margin was available for future expansion. Some communities controlled housing developments so as to maintain standards and prevent undesirable uses.

George T. Blanch, of Utah State University, reported that 27,545 acres in the four counties were changed from agriculture to other uses between 1937 and 1952. An estimated 13 thousand acres underwent change between 1952 and 1957.

The 27,545 acres were only 1.5 percent of the total land area of the four counties—but 16,651 acres of it were irrigated and amounted to 7 percent of the total irrigated land. The rest was dry cropland, grazing land, foothill range, and wasteland.

Of the land taken out of agriculture, about one-third had been within the boundaries of incorporated towns or cities but used for farming before 1952. Residential uses account for about 80 percent and industrial and commercial uses for about 20 percent of the land whose use was changed in incorporated areas. All the military and most of the industrial developments were placed outside incorporated areas.

About half of the acres removed from agriculture are in residential uses, although some tracts are large enough to support part-time farms. About a fifth of the area serves industrial and commercial purposes. The third that is in military reservations may return to agriculture if it is needed.

The four counties exemplify regional economic problems at work. The developed agricultural community has invested time, money, and effort into developing a relatively stable economy, based on irrigated small farms and a settled way of life. The readily available water supply was utilized almost wholly to meet needs of the established community.

The new growth of cities and industries and new demands for water upset the balanced economy and introduced some problems. As previously irrigated lands sprouted roofs instead of roots, the irrigation companies began worrying about recovering their outlays for dams, ditches, and laterals to farms that were going out of existence. They also had to raise additional funds for new and probably more expensive projects to irrigate former drylands lying above present ditches or beyond reach of them.

Farmers that were being displaced had the same kinds of problems in sunk costs for leveling, ditching, and developing productivity; problems of water supply; and distance from markets.

But to say that the presently developed farmland is all the land available for use would be misrepresenting the case. More correctly, this acreage was all that was available at the time, the place, and the price.

An investigation of agricultural prospects in the Weber Basin was conducted by the Bureau of Reclamation and the Department of Agriculture. The report said that several thousand acres suitable for irrigation lie on the periphery of lands that have been under irrigation for several decades. The Weber Basin Project, besides providing water for municipal and industrial uses, proposes to provide a full water supply to approximately 50 thousand acres not under irrigation and a supplemental supply to about 24 thousand acres of presently irrigated land. The investigators expressed the belief that an economically and socially satisfactory system of agriculture would result and that, besides supporting the farm families and community institutions at a reasonable level, agriculture can contribute substantially toward the cost of operating and constructing the project.

Granting that bringing these new lands into production would be expensive, it is clear that unutilized land resources several times greater than those already removed by urbanization and other nonfarm uses remain to be developed when the time is ripe—when the food is needed.

Similar situations exist in many parts of the Intermountain region, the Pacific Northwest, the eastern slope of the Rockies, and in the East. The effect of drainage programs in the Mississippi Delta and in parts of the Southeast will contribute additional lands for intensive cultivation. In the final analysis, the cost or availability of water may place a much greater limit on production than will the availability of land.

AMONG THE POINTS brought out in the foregoing examples is that there is no set pattern of desirable growth. Each situation varies with topography, transportation facilities, the type of landownership, and happenstance.

Because urban dispersal into agricultural areas assumes different forms, different kinds of planning and control are required to insure the best use of land.

I list four major forms of dispersal:

Gradual encroachments, in which the metropolis slowly pushes out into its hinterland and which results in a fringe area;

Encirclement, in which urban developments surround agricultural areas by joining prongs of settlement along main arteries of traffic or several communities grow together along isolated points of contact;

Growth through diffusion, which has no particular pattern—single families invade agricultural areas beyond the normal boundaries of urban areas in their search for homesites and some developers leapfrog to pick up tracts wherever they can find them for development; and

Industrial decentralization, which has grown as the space requirements of companies have increased, transportation facilities have been improved, and employees have become more mobile.

Planned dispersals have occurred in communities that acted in time and had development plans available before an influx began.

As for agriculture, unplanned and unregulated growth almost inevitably must result in a decline in producing acreage, uneconomic transitions in land use, inequities in tax burdens, excessive costs for public services, too much speculative development, and general instability.

Advance planning cannot prevent urban and industrial spread into rural areas and it should not attempt to do so, but it can guide, formalize, and make a kind of schedule for growth. Rural communities often can plan a program whereby healthy agriculture, healthy industry, and healthy urban communities can abide happily side by side.

Individuals and businesses have wide choices concerning locations in urban communities. Many factors other than cost of transportation to the urban center influence decisions on where to live and work. Accessibility to a broad region largely has displaced the concept of accessibility to the urban core.

Relative suitability of available lands for the alternative uses is a significant factor in the land market. Land developers like to plan entire communities as units. They buy well-located farms as they become available and take options on adjoining properties if necessary. They need large blocks of land to meet requirements for complete communities.

The economic force of human wants, as expressed by what people are willing to pay for goods or services, is the key to land values. Land is like any other commodity whose use is determined by its value in the market place. Among the values is site or location. Each tract being considered has a variable value for each kind of farming as well as for residential, commercial, industrial, transportation, or other uses. Unfortunately for agriculture, land productivity is a relative thing and weighs less heavily on the site values than do other values. Tracts well located for other uses command a higher price because they are worth more to the buyers than the capitalized value of potential farm products and related other values are to agriculture.

If our national economy is to continue its growth, urbanization must grow with it, and uses other than agriculture will continue to press values and prices of desirable tracts beyond the economic reach of agriculture.

As our population expands, it is inevitable that our residential and industrial areas must expand to accommodate it. It also is inevitable that much of this expansion will cause many social, economic, and institutional problems which can be resolved only by dislocation of vested users, loss of certain improvements, and expense for new facilities.

It is inevitable that families, communities, and regions will have their economic activities turned completely upside down in the maelstrom of our national reconstruction and adjustment to the age of the atom and jet.

It is not inevitable that bad or ill-timed land uses need supersede agricultural uses. There is no need for leapfrogging suburbanization, for ill-planned highway networks, for industries scattered hit or miss over the countryside. There often are adequate satisfactory sites for airfields and military establishments on other than first-class cropland—although factors other than engineering features enter into the considerations that determine their location.

The issue is not agriculture versus nonfarm developments. We need both—in balance. The real problem is to protect the more productive lands of agriculture from ill-planned or unplanned and ill-timed conversions. Directing nonfarm growth along desirable channels is one of the critical problems facing agriculture today.

THERE REMAINS the need for us to put some of these ideas and developments in a larger frame, especially if we are worried that cities and highways are taking all our good farmland.

The maintenance of a healthy economic position of agriculture over the years depends largely on its ability to adapt to changing conditions. Continued depression of an agricultural area or a sector of the agricultural economy indicates that at least some factors of production are badly out of balance in the farm business.

I have heard John D. Black, of Harvard University, state that there is no such thing as marginal land. It is the misuse of resources in relation to the ability of the land to produce that creates marginal and submarginal situations.

Sherman E. Johnson wrote in *Science in Farming*, the 1947 Yearbook of Agriculture: "Scientific progress enables some people to live better, and more people to live. . . . But history affords evidence that technological improvements, which bring profits to the producers who can adopt them and which benefit mankind in general, also bring misery and distress to the individuals who cannot adjust themselves to the new conditions. Such individuals are likely to resist and may be strong enough to delay technological progress. . . ."

Farmers in the United States cannot afford to stop technological progress any more than they can afford to use horses for farm power or grow open-pollinated corn. Farm prosperity depends as much on efficient farm production as it does on a virile market.

A virile market in turn depends on a growing population with high levels of economic activity and employment—high purchasing power.

Carl P. Heisig, director of the Farm Economics Research Division, in testimony prepared for the Joint Economic Committee of the 85th Congress, said:

"Over the longer term, our production problems may continue to be centered around the need for adjusting the pattern of production to changing market outlets, rather than on an all-out effort to raise our production capacity. . . . It is possible that production may continue to press on market outlets for many years, with consequent pressure on farm prices and incomes. . . . The question is not so much whether we can produce food enough, but whether we can obtain the necessary readjustments in agriculture at reasonable cost and with net incomes in agriculture comparable to those in other occupations. . . ."

Agriculture must recognize realities. Too many of us, trained in scarcity economics, are oriented to the past. We are in the midst of a peacetime socioeconomic revolution in which land is of decreasing importance relative to other resources utilized in production of food and fiber.

We tend to forget agriculture's place in our present national economic organization. Whether we like it or not, the fact remains that we can exist only at the call of nonfarm populations. A growing population and a virile economy mean expanding markets for products of the farm. A declining population and a stagnant economy would mean the opposite.

ENGLAND is an urban country and imports much of her foods and feeds. We can learn from actions of the English during an emergency and their plans for the future.

In February 1954, in the Albert Howard Memorial Lecture in London, L. Dudley Stamp pointed out that Britain has been overpopulated "for at least a thousand years, judged by the productive capacity of the time. . . . Now our land [in Britain] is underdeveloped by comparison with its potential."

He estimated that practically the same land surface now in use can be increased by 20 percent in productivity and concluded, "There is much underdeveloped land in Britain: Only man-made barriers stand in the way of its more effective use."

Anthony Hurd, an English farmer and wartime liaison officer in the Ministry of Agriculture, reported that Great Britain had increased her tilled acreage 65 percent during the years of the Second World War. Even under conditions when supplies of material, labor, and money were extremely critical, the total production of calories was increased by 70 percent, primarily by growing more wheat and potatoes for human consumption and replacing imported feedstuffs by homegrown feeds, including grass. The net output of agriculture—the true output of the soil and measure of skill in agriculture—rose, fell, and recovered during the war years as adjustments were made to less imports, but by 1948–1949 had risen to 35 percent above the prewar period. Better methods, better cultivation, better seeds, better use of machinery and fertilizers, and new developments of all kinds were used in this effort.

Even so, W. R. Mead, of University College, London, concluded in late 1956 that: "In many parts of Britain [already improved lands] are not yielding their maximum, and the return from additional investment in them is likely to be greater than from that invested in marginal moorland."

Some of the best planners have worked on Britain's town and country pattern. They recognize that protection of good agricultural lands is essential. Yet the Nuffield College Social Reconstruction Survey noted: "The value of even the best agricultural land is so low in relation to suburban building values that it is to no one's financial interest to save it from building, for which it is often particularly suitable."

THERE WAS a decrease in the number of farms in every State except Florida and in all except 180 of the 3,067 counties in the United States between 1950 and 1954. The number of farmworkers has continued its long-term decline. But the average size of farm has increased from 215 acres to 242 acres and total farm production has continued at high levels.

About 22 million people now live on farms; in 1975 it is estimated only about 15 million in a population of more than 220 million will be on farms. Today about 13 percent of our population provides food for 87 percent of the total; by 1975 it is estimated that less than 7 percent will feed and clothe 93 percent.

Today there are nearly 5 million farms in the United States, but almost 3 million of them are small full-time farms or small part-time operations. This 60 percent of farms produces only 14 percent of our crops and livestock. The small farmer who depends entirely on the income derived from his undersized, uneconomic unit is in real trouble.

The agricultural resources of operators of small units usually are insufficient to produce an adequate volume of crops and livestock or to utilize fully the labor of the farm family, except where highly specialized production is feasible. Production of high-value commodities on small farms is seriously limited by inadequate market outlets or location factors.

The remaining roughly 2 million farms are classified as commercial in that they produce an annual minimum of 2,500 dollars in farm sales. This 40 percent of farm families produces about 90 percent of all farm products sold.

The family farm is stronger today than ever before. It is changing because it is part of a dynamic economy. The family-size commercial farm is larger than ever before because technology has made it possible—and necessary—for operators to use laborsaving equipment, more productive cropping and livestock practices, and better management techniques.

The increased proportion of very large farms, particularly in the drier areas of the country, is of concern to some people. We must recognize, however, that most of these farms are in areas where considerable acreage is needed for a sufficiently large output to be economically feasible. These farms often are on the extensive margin of land use, just as many small farms are on or below the intensive margin.

Urban expansion creates some problems for agriculture and serious problems for some areas, but the degree of severity from the national interest, now and in the foreseeable future, seems to have been exaggerated.

Agriculture should aid continued urban-industrial growth. Continuation of a dynamic national economy requires it, and agriculture cannot be prosperous without it. A healthy urban economy provides agriculture with employment opportunities for its technologically surplus labor and provides wages to augment farm income. Urban growth helps agriculture balance production with the markets, allocate productive resources, and get the use of land in balance with modern needs.

Balanced development of resources.

This summary of our needs and prospects emphasizes that we must keep in mind that the needs of future years must be met with essentially the same land and water resources we now have. We must learn to produce and use more from each acre. This will take balanced use and development of land and water. By *Carl P. Heisig, Hugh H. Wooten,* and *Raymond P. Christensen,* Farm Economics Research Division.

WE HAVE THREE GOALS when we try to achieve the balanced use and development of our land and water.

We should adjust the use of cropland, pastures, and forests continually so that production is in a reasonable balance—commodity by commodity and in total—with market outlets.

We should make progress toward attaining incomes for farmers that are in reasonable balance with the nonfarm incomes.

We should use land in a way that will conserve it and our water so as to meet tomorrow's needs.

One objective at times may not coincide completely with another: Long-time conservation needs may conflict with farmers' need for immediate income. Adjustments of production to market outlets may encourage exploitation of the soil. Some compromise between objectives must be made.

Balanced use at any time, however, must be able to provide adequate benefits to the people who control and use land and water. This responsibility remains the same in all kinds of times, although the times may change the degree of emphasis that is placed on measures in public and private policies and programs designed to achieve balanced use.

Where and when needed adjustments should be made and ways in which the land resources may best be used to meet anticipated needs for agricultural and forest products are therefore of major importance.

The demands upon our land resources will increase constantly because our population—set at 172,997,-142 at 12 m., January 22, 1958—has been growing at the rate of 330 persons every hour.

Looking only as far ahead as 1975, when the population may reach 230 million, we see a need for an estimated 35- to 45-percent increase in the output of farms and forests above 1957 levels to feed and clothe our citizens. We need, therefore, to keep a reasonable reserve of productive capacity.

Emergencies can have tremendous impacts on production. The droughts of 1934 and 1936, for instance, reduced farm output 20 to 25 percent below the normal production level. But farm output was increased by 25 percent in 1940–1948 in order to meet the demands of war and of reconstruction. What is balanced use in one period may be quite different in another. The problem of adjustment to changing needs at times becomes acute.

Even if population expands rapidly, our major problems of getting a balance during the next 5 to 10 years probably will be those of coping with surplus production, with its consequent pressures on farm prices and incomes.

Our farm output in 1956 and 1957 exceeded available market outlets by

6 to 8 percent in total, and our ability to produce such crops as wheat, cotton, rice, and feed grains was considerably greater than that.

Our reserve productive capacity assures us that we can meet the increasing peacetime needs of the next few years with little additional effort. The total farm output in 1958 was almost large enough to meet requirements for the population expected in 1960, although considerable changes in the composition of the output—more livestock products, fruits, and vegetables and less wheat—will be needed.

Farmers continue to increase yields year by year. Our primary concern now is to devise ways and means of putting some of this extra productive capacity into a reserve for future needs, through such programs as the Conservation Reserve part of the Soil Bank. We face both the problem of attaining an approximate balancing of total output with market demands and the problem of balancing individual commodities. The increase in output we indicated as needed by 1975 will have to come more in the second decade than in the first.

By 1975, with a population of about 230 million, livestock production will need to be stepped up 40 to 45 percent and crop production perhaps 30 to 40 percent above 1956 and 1957. Substantial increases in feed grains, hay, and pasture production will be needed to provide for the larger number of livestock. The projected needs for food grains by 1975, however, are below the quantities produced in 1951–1953, before allotment programs were in effect. Unless exports of cotton expand greatly above those of 1957, an increase of about 10 to 15 percent in the output of cotton above production in 1951–1953 may be enough in 1975.

These projected production needs for crops and livestock by 1975 obviously would require large additional acreages of cropland if we could meet them in no other way.

The record of the past and the availability of improved methods not yet adopted by farmers indicate that our chief means of getting the production probably will be through increased yields and improved efficiency in the feeding and care of livestock.

Some increases in acreages of cropland are expected during the next generation to result from irrigation, drainage, and land-clearing developments.

Large additional acreages are available for development if there should be economic justification for such developments.

A reduction in numbers of horses and mules on farms since 1918 has released about 80 million acres of cropland for producing products for human use. Only about 12 million acres of cropland now are used to support draft animals. We shall have to rely in the future mainly on higher acre yields or the use of more land to produce farm products.

Dr. Glen T. Barton and Robert O. Rogers, of the Agricultural Research Service, estimate that the annual expansion in farm output from higher yields and other factors would need to average nearly twice as large from 1951–1953 to 1975 as it did from 1910–1912 to 1951–1953 in order to meet estimated requirements from a crop and pasture acreage about as large as in 1958.

The expansion in output required by 1975 may appear to be high compared with past achievements. Total production and yields, however, have gone up rapidly in the past few years.

We do not question the physical possibilities of expanding the output enough to meet 1975 requirements if farmland is used more intensively.

A more important question is: At what cost can production be expanded? We can be optimistic in this respect, too.

STUDIES OF THE CHANGES a farmer could make in the organization and operation of his farm to improve incomes show in general that it would be possible to expand production by applying more efficient methods, which would involve the use of additional capital goods.

Farmers would need to invest much more in buildings, machinery, and soil improvement and buy more fertilizers, pesticides, motor fuel, and other materials. The production of many farms could thereby be doubled. Total costs would rise, but they would not go up so much as total production, and costs per unit of output might be reduced.

The factors that will get the farm production job done in the next two decades include overall increases in production of as much as 20 percent per acre for crops and 30 percent for pasture and improved efficiency in use of feed by livestock; shifts in acreage from crops in excess supply to those in greater demand, including pasture; and an increase of 5 or 6 percent in the cropland base.

Different rates of increase in demand and trends in agricultural technology will make increases and adjustments in supply more difficult for some farm products than for others.

The 5- to 6-percent increase in the cropland base would supply only about one-sixth of the additional crop and pasture production needed by 1975.

The general conclusion is that most of our increased needs for farm products probably can be met by improved farming and livestock practices rather than by a greatly enlarged acreage of cropland. This will mean greater intensification and sharper economies in use of land, water, and other resources.

Such items as fertilizer, pesticides, machinery, and other equipment, which are not produced on farms, are in effect substitutes for more land in increasing farm output. Much of our greatly increased farm production of the last two decades has come from them.

Existing cropland and pastureland can be greatly improved by drainage, irrigation, and other practices. Production thus can be increased without increasing the acreage of cropland.

Hugh H. Wooten and James R. Anderson estimate that by 1975 there

may be a net increase of about 25 million to 30 million acres, or about 5 to 6 percent, in the total cropland. This increase would include 10 million acres that likely could be converted from permanent pasture to cropland, 6 million acres of undeveloped land could be irrigated, and 10 million to 15 million acres of undeveloped land, on which probably a combination of drainage, flood control, and clearing could be used.

These 25 million to 30 million acres would be in excess of the acreage reverting from cropland to woodland and special uses. We could get the equivalent of about 14 million acres more by supplementary improvement on 42 million acres of existing cropland—by providing water to irrigate dry cropland and additional water for irrigated lands now receiving inadequate supplies, by draining wet fields, and by protecting fertile bottom land from floods.

Thus a continuation of the recent trends in land improvement may raise the total acreage of cropland, including rotation pasture or cropland used for pasture, to about 500 million acres by 1975, compared with 465 million acres in 1954.

The trends indicate a larger acreage of improved pasture by 1975. The total acreage of pasture and grazing land, however, might remain about the same as in 1958, as a considerable acreage of pasture probably would be shifted to rotation pasture in the rotation.

Competition from forestry as a profitable farm enterprise would be likely to discourage large-scale clearing of good commercial timberland for pasture. Other sources of increased acreages of pasture are noncommercial forest land and idle land and wastelands, which often need expensive improvement to fit them for pasture.

The total forest area would not change much with these changes in land used for crops and pasture. We have 648 million acres of forest land, but about half of it is used also for grazing and other purposes.

This projection of cropland and rotation pasture acreages is based on trends since 1940 and land-improvement and reclamation developments that were planned in 1957.

More land would be available for development if it were economically desirable. It is a question of the relative economy of alternative ways of increasing output.

Moderate shifts of suitable areas of grassland pasture and farm woodland to the cropland rotation, however, are physically feasible and may be desirable on many farms, especially those that have suitable unimproved land but too few crop acres and rotation pasture to return reasonable incomes.

More land may be put to special uses. Of the 190 million acres in special and miscellaneous uses in 1958, about 80 million acres were unused tracts in deserts, dunes, bare rock, and marshes. Highways, railroads, and airports accounted for about 43 million acres. The land in urban areas, highways, and reservoirs is estimated to have increased by 831,000 acres a year since 1937. Our estimates of land available for crops, pasture, and forest for 1975 take into account the probable shifts of land from crops, pasture, and forest to take care of the urban and industrial growth.

Balanced use by 1975 thus will involve primary dependence on increased productivity of present cropland and relatively little addition to the 1957 cropland base.

WE CAN BE LESS CERTAIN when we attempt to look ahead as far as 2000. If our population doubles in the next half century as it did in the past 50 years, we will need to expand production of farm and forest products by as much as we are now producing to prevent reduction in levels of consumption. No doubt people will want to improve their diets. With more people, more land will be needed for urban and industrial development, residential and recreational areas, highways, airports, and other purposes.

Can we find ways of doubling farm output from about the same land area again in the next half century? Can we do this without large increases in the use of other resources so that real costs per unit of farm output will not increase?

A continuation of recent gains in the productivity of farmland and labor would contribute greatly to general economic progress and higher levels of living. Much will depend on the extent to which more efficient production methods are developed and supplies of capital goods available for use in farming are increased. Much will depend upon new scientific discoveries.

Some further net addition to the area of cropland is probable as land development and improvement progress. Some unused land and land now used extensively probably will be brought into agricultural use—or more intensive agricultural use—through irrigation.

In appraising the current cropland situation and the longer range potential, probably we should consider as a reserve the 100 million acres or so of improved permanent grassland pasture exclusive of cropland pasture that is suitable for cultivation. It could be put into the cropland rotation if it became necessary or more profitable to use it for cultivated food and feed crops.

Also, 100 million or more acres of privately owned woodland are classified as suitable for development as cropland, if and when it is needed or if it becomes more profitable to devote part of this acreage to food and feed crops instead of trees. This land is now producing forage and forest products. Accordingly, to shift land from pasture and forest to cropland would be substituting one kind of production for another kind. It would not be all net gain, and it should not be done unless it is both necessary and profitable.

The Soil Conservation Service has indicated that 604 million acres would be suitable for crops if necessary attention were given to conservation measures. An additional 132 million acres could be used safely for hay and pasture and occasionally for cultivated crops if care is taken to prevent erosion. This means that the total acreage of cropland could be increased by nearly 60 percent. But, to repeat, to do so would mean large investments for improvement and development, and unless prices for farm products increase greatly over 1957 levels, large-scale development would not be profitable because of higher costs.

We have the suitable lands, the mechanical equipment, and the technical knowledge with which to increase our acreage of cropland materially over the next three or four decades. We would still allow for reasonable absorption of land by other uses, for adjustments needed by the growing population, and for conversion of much poor cropland to grassland or forest. Thus it is obvious that if we maintain and manage it properly, we have a great reserve capacity for future generations.

Projection to 2000 of trends like those of the last half century would not change greatly the general pattern of land use. Some farm and forest land will be converted to urban and other high-value uses.

If expansion of the acreage in special uses increases at the rate of a million acres annually during the next half century, the 50 million acres that might be shifted away from farm and forest uses would be equivalent to about 3 percent of our total acreage in farms and forests.

A major question is: Will productivity of cropland and pastureland increase so that the area of woodland and forests will not be reduced greatly? If gains in productivity of cropland and pasture similar to those of the last half century are not continued, the area of land available for producing forest products might decline greatly.

Partly offsetting the potential shifts of grassland and woodland to cropland are 40 million acres of cropland that the Soil Conservation Service has classified as best suited to grass and forest.

The net potential shifts in use from grassland and forest to cropland that appear to be physically feasible therefore would involve about 175 million acres. Much of the shift from grassland and forest to cropland when it occurs should be to replace necessary conversion of poor cropland to grass, trees, and other uses.

POLICY is involved in the growing needs for land and water, in possible points of conflict, and in how to meet or avoid conflict.

There is need for private and public stocktaking of land and water resources and consideration of all reasonable requirements in planning uses of land and water in specific areas, especially those that involve considerable shifts in use of valuable agricultural, forest, residential, and industrial areas.

A significant question will arise as to whether greater immediate costs should be incurred for public improvements and for urban and industrial developments to avoid using good agricultural and forest areas when other satisfactory areas can be made to serve the purpose. For instance, would the longer term needs of our society be better served by spending more now to locate a new highway on the edge of a valley on poor land, rather than running it straight down the middle and taking good agricultural land out of use for all time to come?

Selection of routes for the new National System of Interstate and Defense Highways will be a major problem in many areas during the next decade. Possibly 1.5 million to 2 million acres of land will be required. About a third of this acreage is likely to be cropland, another third pasture, and the rest forest and land in other uses.

The country as a whole can afford to devote additional land to improve highways, but in choosing highway locations, it is important to appraise the alternative sites available and to recognize the private and public costs and benefits of the alternatives.

A balance sheet of costs and returns for alternative sites doubtless would be helpful in planning public improvements and urban and industrial developments, so that poor rather than good agricultural land will be used when it will serve the development purpose equally well. Some foresighted communities and States are already doing this and are zoning land for particular uses.

In California, Michigan, Maryland, New Jersey, Pennsylvania, Virginia, Wisconsin, and other States, studies have been started of the impacts of urban expansion on the farm economy as reflected in the absorption of farmland, higher land values, higher taxes, and other urban-agricultural conflicts.

An economic analysis of changes in the use of land in Santa Clara County, Calif., for example, disclosed a considerable conversion to residential and commercial uses of the limited areas of land that are well adapted to the growing of high-value nuts and fruits.

Climate and soils often make it difficult or impossible to replace specialized crop areas that are taken up by urban, highway, airport, reservoir, and other developments.

NEAR THE HEAD of the list in guiding and attaining balanced use of our land and water is individual and group action in allocating these resources in particular locations, so as to provide maximum long-term returns to society.

Establishment of appropriate measures of priority in use of land for such purposes as cropland, pasture, forest, water supply, recreation, wildlife, residential, urban, industrial, mining, and transportation uses is essential.

These priority measures will become increasingly important in the next decades. As population increases and industrial development becomes greater, priorities for allocation of water supplies between various claimants will become necessary.

Adjustments in land use that are in the national interest need to be made profitable to the individual farmer or citizen involved, so that individual and public goals will not conflict. At times and in poor locations, these adjustments may need to be in the direction of less intensive use of the land, because of limited market outlets for products best adapted to production in these areas.

The present surplus capacity for producing wheat, for instance, raises serious problems for wheat farmers in the Great Plains. They are faced with the prospect of a limited market for the crop that is best adapted to their growing conditions, but they have the cropland potential to produce more than the market is likely to need for many years.

The next alternative for much of this surplus capacity is grass or feed grains for livestock production. Shifting wheatland to grass is expensive, time consuming, and generally less profitable to individual farmers than the preferred uses for wheat or feed grains. But shifting to feed grains adds to an already large surplus supply in the area. The long-term outlook for wheat markets and the need for conservation of resources, however, suggest that farmers in wheat-producing areas of the Great Plains will have to make major adjustments in land use in the years to come.

Farmers in other areas—for instance, those who are now producing such crops as cotton and rice—are faced with similar problems. A part of these adjustments is likely to be in the direction of fewer but larger farms, operated on a less intensive basis than in 1958.

An important task is to protect our natural resources—our land, water, and forests—for they represent our productive capacity for farm and timber products. In the humid regions, for example, rain-dependent farmers lose a third of the water as runoff. Research is developing cropping systems and tillage practices that get more rain into the soil. Research and group action also can do much to reduce water losses and permit more

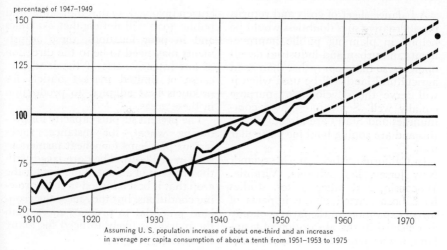

percentage of 1947–1949

Assuming U. S. population increase of about one-third and an increase
in average per capita consumption of about a tenth from 1951–1953 to 1975

Past trends and potential needs of farm output.

effective use of water in our irrigated areas.

Obviously, if we are to have balanced use of our land and water, we must put considerable work and money into efforts that succeed only in reducing losses or in returning productive capacity to its former level.

At the same time, we often get extra dividends that result in more efficient farm production. When conservation and maintenance measures lead to increased productive capacity, we are making progress toward an important objective—that of building for the future.

In all types of land conversions and investments, such as shifts from forest to cropland or from cropland to forest, the available technical means—surveys of soil, slope, forest, land capability, and so on—should be used to guide selection of the best land for cultivation and to discourage use of uneconomic areas for crop production or cultivation of areas that cause serious wastage of soil, water, forests, and other resources. The increase in number of births, the lower mortality in the last decade, and a continually increasing population make the productive use of our land a permanent concern.

Society's lag in dealing more effectively with land and water use, waste, and pollution has brought us to a point at which many areas of the country are suffering shortages of water. Industry, irrigation, and increased domestic consumption, together with drought in several Western States, produced the shortages. But pollution and waste of even ample supplies in the Eastern States can cause a shortage, too. Pollution is responsible for many restrictions on the use of water in industrial sections.

Water can be conserved and pollution reduced in several ways—by prevention of erosion, measures to control transpiration and evaporation, stream regulation, storage reservoirs, diversion from surplus to shortage areas, reuse and water conservation practices, and control of sediment and pollution.

The adequacy and efficiency of our ways of using water are one of the limitations on our ability to increase production and to grow industrially.

Because market prices for land encompass only the demands for its products and services that can be foreseen at a particular time, provision for reserve capacity for various future uses requires public consideration of their

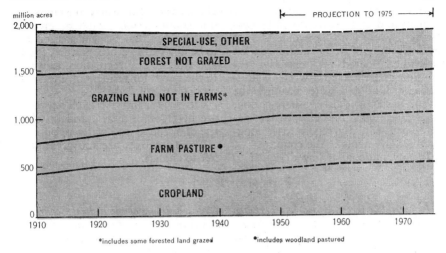

million acres

|◄——— PROJECTION TO 1975 ———►|

SPECIAL-USE, OTHER

FOREST NOT GRAZED

GRAZING LAND NOT IN FARMS*

FARM PASTURE ●

CROPLAND

1910   1920   1930   1940   1950   1960   1970

*includes some forested land grazed   ●includes woodland pastured

Trend in land utilization.

importance and when and how to provide for them. The question of reserve capacity for contingencies such as droughts, war, and harmful atomic-weapon fallout is also involved in the allocation of land among major uses, and in conservation and improvement programs in the different regions of the country.

A LOOK at the land, water, and forest programs operating in 1958 shows that they are not isolated policies, each of which can be effectively carried out separately without regard to the others. The essential need is for greater unification in the development of our national programs.

Activities that partly nullified others have been carried out all too often in the past. An example is reclamation of new land with large public investments during a period when other public programs were spending heavily for storage and disposal of large surplus production.

Furthermore, the reclamation program has been sectional rather than national; sometimes the areas developed have been much more costly and less well adapted to agriculture than others available that were not given public assistance. Public expenditures

have partly counterbalanced natural comparative advantages among areas for production of adapted crops. Thus exploitation of some of our land and water resources has occurred before the resources were actually needed from a public standpoint.

As long as they do not damage the rights of others, however, individuals should be free to develop and improve their farms. They should have technical assistance with land and water problems that cannot be handled alone.

Many small, low-income farms that contain suitable land could be made more efficient and productive if their acreages of cropland and improved pasture were enlarged, thus giving them better layouts for modern farming. Sometime it may again become desirable and profitable to invest considerable public funds in development of crop and pastureland. In the meantime, surveys of resources and studies of comparative costs and returns in alternative uses afford a way to prepare for future needs.

A LONG LOOK forward shows that we are facing an economic era in which competition for the use of land and water resources will be greater than it now is.

More group planning and action by farmers and other citizens will be necessary if waste is to be avoided. Only by such unity of policy and execution can ill-considered and excessive expansion and rapid and wasteful utilization of land and water resources be supplanted by deliberate selection, careful economy, and constructive development with due regard to the longtime requirements of the country.

In any national policy designed to guide land and water development, due consideration should be given to the national and local needs for land to be devoted to crops, pasture, forests, and wildlife and recreation, as well as to the needs for residential, industrial, and commercial uses.

Clearly, the interests of all our people are involved in a wise and beneficial use of our land and water resources.

These interests are too great to be left to chance.

Philadelphia is an appropriate backdrop for some hard questioning and brave dreaming about the environment men create for themselves and their families to live in. Here, nearly 200 years ago, our forefathers committed their lives, their fortunes, and their sacred honor to the democratic idea. And here, today, citizens of diverse means and interests, together with their local government, are joined in a struggle for a new kind of independence—from urban stagnation and decay, and from civic indifference and inertia.

Other parts of the country are confronted with the same problems, and many—not nearly enough—are doing something about them. The United States has changed from a rural to an urban society. The city and city culture are here to stay. And it is up to all of us to make the city the best possible place in which to live and work and upgrade the culture it represents and which is inherent in its peculiar form and structure. . . .

Even those who still live in rural areas are affected by what happens to the metropolitan areas.

Unfortunately, in our attempts to cope with these problems, we are handicapped by woefully inadequate information and research on the specifics of any one of them, and by a lack of well-organized and coordinated efforts to solve them. Only a few organizations or institutions have been developed at the local or regional level to deal with the whole of a metropolitan area. Piecemeal efforts have often created as many problems as they have solved.

Except in few pioneering communities, there is at present no forum short of the State legislature or the Federal Congress for discussing and deciding matters that affect an entire metropolitan area. This lack of such an instrument constitutes a vacuum in American government. And I happen to believe that such problems should be solved locally where government is close to the people and where they themselves can participate in both the plans and the effort. . . .

The needs and aspirations of our cities are not identical. Each area has its own temperament, traditions, and economic, social, and geographic factors that affect the way it must solve its problems. But from efforts already being made by some of our communities, certain conditions for success seem to emerge.

First, the program must have a permanent and representative instrument by which decisions can be made and applied. Second, it must encompass an institutional means for training and research. And third, it must be based on public understanding and approval. All three—leadership, knowledge, and support—are essential; and none of the three is easy to come by. . . .

It is at the grassroots level of government that local officials face the greatest challenge—and the greatest opportunity for leadership, too. The problems that face the units of government you serve figuratively scream out for attention and leadership. Here is a frontier where you, as servants of the people, with ingenuity, vision, and ability, can really pioneer.—From an address by HENRY T. HEALD, president, Ford Foundation, before the American Public Works Association in Philadelphia, September 25, 1957.

Index

594

596